TESTAMENT

TOM DAVIES

BERWYN MOUNTAIN PRESS

First published 2008 by Berwyn Mountain Press

Berwyn Mountain Press,
58 High Street,
Bala,
LL23 7AB

www.berwynmountainpress.com

A catalogue record for this book is available from the British Library

ISBN 978 0 9553539 1 8

Dust jacket designed by Escape to ... Design Limited
Printed and bound in Dubai by Oriental Press

TOM DAVIES, a Welshman born and bred, was a state scholar at University College Cardiff where he graduated with honours in philosophy. He has been a seaman on ships around Australia and Africa, a social worker in the Lower East Side of New York and was the first graduate to be sent to Indonesia by Voluntary Service Overseas.

He later trained as a journalist with the *Western Mail*, the national newspaper of Wales, and went on to work on the *Sunday Times* as Atticus, the *Sunday Telegraph* as a feature writer and the *Observer* where, for three years, he was their diarist Pendennis.

He became a full-time writer in 1983 and has since written sixteen books which include *Merlyn the Magician and the Pacific Coast Highway*, which was short-listed for the Thomas Cook travel prize and recently acclaimed by Bono, the front man of U2, as being the one book that changed his life. *Black Sunlight*, his best-selling novel, was set in the 1984 miners' strike and *Stained Glass Hours*, his pilgrimage narrative, won the Winifred Mary Stanford Prize for the best book with a religious theme.

He has written five books about various pilgrimages including those to Compostela and Rome and his latest novel is *The Tyranny of Ghosts*.

Married with three sons, he lives in Bala in North Wales.

By the same author:

Things fall apart; the centre cannot hold;
Mere anarchy is loosed upon the world,
The blood-dimmed tide is loosed, and everywhere
The ceremony of innocence is drowned;
The best lack conviction, while the worst
Are full of passionate intensity.
Surely some revelation is at hand;
Surely the Second Coming is at hand.

And what rough beast, its hour come round at last,
Slouches towards Bethlehem to be born?

W B YEATS – THE SECOND COMING

PART ONE

MIRROR MAN

ONE

My most abiding memory of myself as a youngster is of standing in short pants in the middle of the terrifying acres of Llandaff Fields in Cardiff, suffering from a sort of sexual 'flu, worrying when I might get a hand down inside a girl's bra or, wonder of wonders, up her skirt.

I was barely fourteen. These were deeply upsetting times, particularly when I was locked in a sexual fantasy like this and had an unwanted hard-on. I had to perform a forward crouch to conceal the unwanted extrusion in my pants in case anyone spotted it, or else sneak off somewhere quiet to let it shrivel up or drain it with a quick knuckle shuffle. Those unexpected hard-ons had become a menace to my youthful sanity: I never knew when they might spring up. On one unfortunate occasion it was during an examination by the school nit nurse, who promptly whacked it with her pencil.

There had been a lot of knuckle shuffling in my bedroom and I had found that, if I pressed my willy in a certain way, it would give off quite a few delicious and entertaining throbs. I was yet to know what these throbs were about: I never connected them with anything other than the wicked bursts of pleasure and relief they gave me.

So there I was, standing in the middle of Llandaff Fields, with yet another hard-on, full of muddy longings and wondering how I'd got into such a mess at such an early age. Was this sickness general or was it just me? Would I really go blind? Why was I so unlike everyone else?

Well it's not an argument that I might advance in a doctorate but, after years of thought, I have decided that rock'n'roll in general and Elvis in particular put me on to what I was suffering from and then made it a good deal worse.

I was making my way to Canton High School along Cowbridge Road in 1956, wearing short flannel trousers, a school cap and a striped blazer. A leather satchel with a few books in it hung on my shoulder and I was admiring myself in the windows of the shops when I was drawn to a mesmeric sound coming out of a music store. I edged closer and had to move my satchel around in front of me and crouch down a bit.

It was Elvis Presley singing *Heartbreak Hotel*, and the song was an angry, pitiless lament; a heavily sexual dirge which I could not quite understand nor would ever forget and, although I didn't know it at the time, Elvis had almost single-handedly hammered out the template of my future emotional life: a life which would have a few ecstatic highs but would mostly consist of rejection and sexual frustration similar to what he was singing about. Elvis had defined my mysterious longings and hard-ons; he had given my vague sexual 'flu a focus and, where once I merely thought I was suffering from a grubby illness, uniquely my own and relieved only with a wank, I now knew it was almost certainly about sex. All my fantasies were sexual and my little hard-ons were merely my dick leaping to attention at their trumpet call. I had never related wanking to sex – just enjoyed the throbbings for what they were – but now I knew what it was all about, I felt more guilty and remorseful than ever. I concluded that everything to do with sex was filthy and dirty and I deeply sympathised with my parents for harbouring such a pervert under their roof.

Other rock'n'rollers got to work on my tiny brain and tinier body: Little Richard, Buddy Holly, Jerry Lee Lewis, Eddie Cochran, Dion and Chuck Berry. We adolescents were flung into a world of hard, pounding sex made all the more mysterious, particularly to our parents, because it was done in code. "Love" was the favourite word of American rock'n'rollers, but all they ever meant was sex.

No matter how decorously they put it, rock'n'roll was about shagging: the need for a good shag, the joy of just having had a good shag, the excitement of being about to get a good shag or the unutterable disaster of just missing out on a good shag. The only thing better than a good shag with one person was a good shag with two – or even three – and it was all that much better if you could somehow manage to string it out all night long.

Not that, at the tender age of fourteen, I was ever close to having sex with a girl, just that Elvis and all his American rock'n'rolling tribe had planted an infection into our young, wild hearts from which it would take many of us a long time to recover – if ever.

Thus it was that sexual images began pattering down on the *tabula rasa* of my young mind; how, in the repeated cries of horny frustration by my favourite singers, I was given a sexual identity; how it was that my main recollection of myself would remain standing in those fields, suffering.

My ideas about sex, stirred up by a few furtive readings of Hank Jansen, seemed to frame my youth and define my world: nothing important seemed to happen outside their scope and, along with my best friend Ray Pryce, and the Jones brothers over the lane, I was set adrift on a sea of boiling hormones as we scurried around our home patch like shoals of starving piranha, galvanised into top speed by the slightest sniff of sex in the waters.

Our first and greatest triumph happened in the darkened corridor of a youth club when Madelyn Maidment, a local trainee trollop, offered us all a quick feel. Ray managed to get his hand up between her legs – or so he claimed later – and three or four of us managed to get our hands inside her bra. This steamy sexual encounter lasted for maybe twenty seconds, then Madelyn got bored and brushed us away like so many irritating flies before storming off grumbling about how one day she was going to meet a real man. We went inside the club and sat next to the ping-pong table staring at our hands which we kept turning over and over as if we were worried they might drop off. So that was what all the fuss was about! But what was it exactly?

We knew this behaviour was deeply sinful and that everyone always paid in full for his sins. Tony Hurford, who was much bigger than us shrimps, if a good deal duller, had a real sexual tryst with Madelyn Maidment up against a garage door down a dark lane one night whereupon he ran home to soak his dick in Dettol. He was hoping to kill off any diseases that Madelyn might have left there but the Dettol inflamed his dick so badly he had to be rushed to hospital in excruciating pain. There, sobbing his eyes out, he confessed all to his mother who slapped him silly in the Outpatients' Department.

If only someone had once – *just once!* – explained it to us properly everything might have been different but all that happened was that we were abandoned in a thickening fog of ignorance and picked up the barest scraps of knowledge wherever we could, usually off the walls of public toilets. Sex education Cardiff-style.

Strange things happened in the barber's, for example, where a lot of whispering might go on between the barber and a customer about "something for the weekend". The barber would take out a key on the end of a long chain attached to his belt to unlock a drawer under the big mirror. With the speed of a pickpocket he would take something out of this drawer and palm it to the customer who would always put it straight into his own pocket without looking at it. All we understood was that it was a packet of three and had something to do with sex. The dirty bastard who bought this packet of three always kept his eyes down and ran straight out through the door before tearing off up the road as if being chased by the cops.

I risked my life in the cause of sex when the funfair arrived over the road from us in Sophia Gardens, as it did every summer. This funfair had a travelling striptease booth and to attract the punters, the proprietor would wield a big sword in the air on the platform outside and then chop a chip in half off a small boy's throat.

This practice would be illegal for any number of reasons today but that's what he did then and, to get into the show free, I was always the first up and, after he'd chopped the chip in half, he gave me a tanner and let me into the show. I could have happily watched that show for ever since it entailed a woman standing motionless behind a muslin screen in a series of poses while the proprietor drew a curtain in between each one. The law required that she be motionless, he explained, and every time he pulled back the curtain she had taken off a few more bits of clothing. When I caught my first full glimpse of a nipple in the final tableau, I nearly collapsed.

The woman in question was a total harpy with hair that had been peroxided so many times it resembled a tangle of hay. She had a shape like Michelin Man and there was something badly wrong with the alignment of her eyes. But none of that mattered: I had beheld a real nipple, a tiny fleshy rosette, and as soon as the final curtain was drawn I was already planning how to be first in the queue of eager kids when the proprietor next wanted to chop a chip off someone's neck.

Apart from the arrival of the funfair, summer was always a joy because lovers would be out on the riverbank hoping for a smooch and a quiet grope in the long grass. We would be concealed there like Vietcong guerrillas, often laughing like drains if we spotted any of them doing anything interesting to one another.

The lovers became narked if they spotted us and would tell us to get lost, but if we saw one of them smiling, we would ask for a tanner to go away and often get it too.

Things didn't always go to plan. One man chased me so determinedly I had to run into the River Taff to get away from him. As I went sobbing and splashing over to the opposite bank the bastard began throwing stones at me – and hitting me too – until, bruised and bleeding, I sat on the other bank and wept.

Thus it was that, with rock'n'roll ringing in my ears, I became a fully-fledged pervert and social menace at fourteen. At this rate I was going to need a white stick and a labrador before the age of sixteen.

I had also discovered that, if I could somehow manage to make myself *look* sixteen, by holding a fag perhaps, I could get into the Globe Cinema where they showed "foreign" films. You were sure of a sight of a nipple or three in those films although getting through the front door was a problem.

"So, how old are you?" the Globe cashier once asked and snorted with derisive laughter when I took a long drag on my fag, blew out a cloud of smoke and told her as gruffly as I could manage: "Seventeen".

"No you're not," she said, "and you're not coming in here."

I did get in occasionally, if she was in a good mood, and it was the most dispiriting experience imaginable. There were usually no more than a dozen of us in the flickering stalls which always smelled of Jeyes Fluid. Most were old men snoozing through some endless foreign rubbish involving a lot of heavy breathing and long meaningful stares.

Than a nipple would hove into sight or a quick, sideways glimpse of some Scandinavian minge, and the whole audience would jerk to attention and sit bolt upright in their seats, the old men frantically fiddling with themselves under their overcoats, until we got back to the heavy breathing and long meaningful stares.

I still blame Elvis and rock'n'roll for triggering this boiling mess which so blighted my youth. I would have been all right and had something like a proper career ahead of me if I had not gone to school that day. I would never have ended up down the end of lonely street if I'd not heard *Heartbreak Hotel*, if I'd been passing the shop when they had been playing something else or even if I'd stuck to something wholesome like traditional jazz or Lonnie Donegan. Ah, all those ifs.

TWO

The first time I watched television was on June 2, 1953: the coronation of Queen Elizabeth II in Westminster Abbey.

We didn't have a television of our own, but were invited upstairs to Mr and Mrs Morton's flat where they served tea and pop during this historic pageant and we had to sit patiently when Mr Morton turned the set off for ten minutes in every hour to "give it a chance to cool down". The curtains had to be drawn and the room completely in the dark to properly enjoy television, Mr Morton further decreed.

When we got a set of our own in 1955, I liked to watch a few of the programmes like *6.5 Special* or *Oh Boy!* but I can't say I absorbed many ideas from any of them, largely because they were bereft of them.

There *were* a few good early programmes like *The Quatermass Experiment*, which frightened the hell out of me, but most of it was bland rubbish like one of the first of the cop shows, *Dixon of Dock Green*, in which Jack "Evening all" Warner stood on the steps of his police station at the end of every programme and delivered a pissy little homily about how good always triumphed over evil and how crime never paid.

It was all like that. The good guys always won in the end and the bad guys got shot or ended up in the clink. The cowboy films were even worse, with Hopalong Cassidy and Gene Autry, The Singing Cowboy, who drove me out of the room screaming in exaggerated despair when he exercised his sickening tenor. There wasn't any sex in the television schedules, of course.

No youth could ever have been corrupted by this stuff although, in one way, the ideas of television did have a negative effect on me. The set, rented from Rediffusion for 2s.6d a week, pretty much shut my father up permanently and destroyed the little that was left of my family life. He loved it from the first hour, an episode of *What's My Line?* He became absorbed in the news, which saved him the trouble of reading his beloved *Daily Mirror*, and even took in *The Brains Trust* since he had long had aspirations to become a bit of a thinker. He liked Cassidy and Autry, claiming that Autry had a fine singing voice and he could not understand my ironic guffaws when PC Dixon began one of his little homilies. David Attenborough and *Zoo Quest* merged with Eamonn Andrews or George Formby or Bennett Cerf. The quiz shows ran into the game shows and that train doing a four-minute ride to Brighton.

It was rubbish without end and, as soon as my father got home from work, he would draw the curtains, take up his place in his armchair, slip off his shoes, stick his stockinged feet up on the mantelpiece, where they wore a big silver patch in the black-leading, and watch the lot. My mother would dutifully put a supper tray on his lap. He smoked an endless series of Players and I pinched the odd one and soon got a taste for them particularly after watching James Dean smoking in *Rebel Without a Cause*. (Anything James Dean did was good enough for us; we all but ate the American films that came our way.)

Whenever my mother, brother Alan or I wanted to watch a television programme, we would take up whatever positions my father would let us see over his sprawled outstretched legs. He remained parked there all evening like an overblown poached egg and the only time he ever moved was either to lift his body to let rip a lengthy fart or when *God Save the Queen* came on at the end of the programmes and he would lunge forward and switch it off before the first note had ended. A Valleys socialist, he had always hated Royalty and the only time he *never* watched television was for the five minutes on Christmas Day every year when the Queen gave her speech from Buckingham Palace. He went and stood in the garden, still with his paper hat on, and communed with the apple trees until she had done.

My father was a strange man of ice and flame. You never knew what mood you were going to catch him in. A bricklayer in the local steelworks, he had moments of cheerfulness and humour but his principal feature was the smallness of his mouth, always pursed in disappointment. Quite what he was disappointed about was a mystery to me. Perhaps he believed he had not fulfilled his destiny as a bricklayer in a steel works; perhaps he loved another woman or was deeply pissed off because his eldest son was a wanker but, whatever the reason for his all-embracing melancholy, he kept it a closely guarded secret.

Early photographs show he was good looking when young – as was my mother, as pretty as a pansy and as delicate as porcelain – but bitterness had tightened up his features and robbed him of his looks. He would go for months without saying a word to me. My mother would sometimes receive this silent treatment although, after a few weeks of it, she would snap, start screaming and flinging things about until, presumably after a good session in bed, he became a happy conversationalist until something else riled him and we'd have to put up with another of his long, storming silences.

The most irritating thing about him was that, particularly after a few drinks, he could be wonderfully funny and entertaining. He could tell marvellous stories and, no matter how many times I heard it, I loved it when he told me how he managed to steal a row-boat from Roath Park Lake and row his way home from work after the River Taff burst its banks and flooded our house. My mother was standing on a chair in the living room and crying when he came rowing down the hallway. "There's no bloody point crying," he had told her. "You'll only make the flood worse."

My father was the star of his club, I was amazed to learn (he never took me in there), and a very good singer. I had never heard him sing a note, not even in his monthly bath, yet he had a fine baritone voice and a small group of dedicated fans, the Memphis Taffia, who followed him around the clubs of South Wales and hid behind the stage curtains from where they would throw tin trays on to the stage whenever he went for the high notes. He was also a big club committee man who knew so much about public entertainment he once turned down Shirley Bassey at an audition saying, with his usual perception, she would only ever make a decent pub singer.

There had once been a rebellious glint in his eye, I was thrilled to learn. My mother explained what he had done in the war – nothing. He had been registered with the Home Guard, it seemed, but somehow managed to avoid turning up for any weapons practice and drills. The War Office caught up with him in the final weeks of the war but he flatly refused to get into his uniform or turn up for anything. An irate official came to the house and warned him about long periods in dirty cells eating porridge if he didn't do his bit so he did go to drill once and once only. He put on his uniform and made my mother stand out in the street to make sure that no one was looking. When she gave the all-clear, he emerged out onto the pavement, jumped on his bicycle and pedalled off to make the world safe for democracy.

A few months after the arrival of television in our flat, something strange happened to my father: it soon became clear that a row was going on between the Dr Jekyll and Mr Hyde within him.

He didn't say what it was about, yet began shoving his food to one side, claiming he wasn't hungry. He was becoming dissatisfied with what was on television and, although he never once admitted it, I guessed he had realised he was a prisoner to television's personality and, unless he did something soon, he was going to stay stuck in that armchair for the rest of his days.

There seemed no point explaining to him the purpose of the Off button so, when his black moods started getting blacker and my mother couldn't stand it any more, she got the man from Rediffusion to take our set away.

Instead of getting better now that he had been released from the bondage of the small screen, my father went into an evil sulk, refusing all food and even cups of tea, denying knowledge of the English language and staring into the yawning space formerly occupied by our set. I was reading the *South Wales Echo* about three days later next to the fire when he exploded and jumped up shouting that he was going to get a big knife and stab us all. He had totally parted from his senses, crying like a baby and throwing his arms around like a mad conductor who had lost his orchestra. I couldn't understand what he was so upset about but my mother knew immediately and told me to get up to the Rediffusion shop and get our television set back *as soon as possible.*

"It might take a week," the Rediffusion manager told me after I had explained that we had to have our television back because my father was threatening to stab us all rather than miss the end of *The Quatermass Experiment.* "There'll be some paperwork to get through."

"It can't take a week," I cried, largely because I didn't want to miss the end of *Quatermass* either. That was the one programme I did watch. "If it's not back there tonight he's threatening to stab us all with a big knife."

"You'd better call the police hadn't you?"

"No, no. He's not turning into Jack the Ripper or anything, he'll be all right if he can have the television back so he can watch the end of *The Quatermass Experiment*."

"Well, as I say, the best we can do is early next week."

"That'll be far too late. We'll all be dead by early next week. It's got to come back today."

The Rediffusion man, to his credit, not only agreed to return the television set that day but was so worried my father was going to stab us all he got the set back to our house before I got home.

That was the end of my father. He was completely crushed by television. He even watched the time-filler slots like *The White Kitten, The Spinning Wheel* or *The Potter's Wheel*. "Oh no, he still hasn't finished that bloody pot," he would cry when the potter got going. "He'd never get a job on our gang."

My father didn't go to his club so much any more and my mother said he had even stopped singing since he started watching television. "I always loved it when he sang," she said, "but now he just sounds like a rope under the door."

He certainly never said much to me – or Alan – except for an "Aaaargh"! or an "Uuuuurgh"! or a "Humph"! or, if he was feeling really chatty, "Why don't you go out?"

He never told me any more of his wonderful stories. Home life had become a permanent wake. I'd come in after school to find the curtains drawn with the sun still on the rooftops, the barely breathing corpse of my father stretched out with the light of the television casting a tubercular glow over his body which moved only to fart or light a fag. As far as he was concerned we might have stopped existing. My mother got on with her life uncomplainingly, finding herself redundant except for cooking his meals and adjusting the aerial outside when the picture got fuzzy. She had to go up a ladder next to the conservatory to which the aerial was fixed and my father, still in his armchair, would shout, "Right a bit, left a bit. No. Back. Right a bit more. That's it."

One night I found him crouched over the set almost as if he was about to climb inside it. He was sweating so heavily he looked like he was suffering a terminal bout of malaria. It turned out that Tony Stompani, one of the first television chefs, was demonstrating how to cook a curry and the mere sight of the cooking pot was making my father break out into rivulets of sweat. "That must be a bloody hot curry," he told me with great seriousness. "I don't know how anyone could eat a curry as hot as that."

My mother did what she could to make a life in the tiny space left between the television and my father. She didn't share his enthusiasm for every programme but, if it made him quiet and happy, that was good enough for her. She was highly strung and his volcanic outbursts and long silences often drove her out to wander the streets at night with all of us out after her, worried she'd been kidnapped or raped.

When the old man was quiet, so was she and she was content to let him get on with his career as Wales's number one television critic, making do with whatever scraps of affection he might throw her. It was pitiful to witness the joy in her face if he acknowledged her presence let alone gave her anything.

16

One afternoon he shocked us all when he came home from the steelworks and handed my mother a few pairs of nylons which he had bought from someone in the pub. "I didn't pay much for them," he admitted somewhat shame-facedly as my mother glowed with pleasure.

She went to her bedroom to try them on but was soon back to explain that they were fine except that the seams came down *the front* of the stockings. My father didn't even look away from the screen before saying, "Ah well, you can always walk around backwards."

My sister Jackie came along about this time, early on New Year's Day, 1957 in St David's Hospital. My mother had a difficult time because, just after midnight, the nurses kept urging her on: there had always been a rivalry between St David's and Glossop Terrace to have the first birth of the New Year in the city, a race which my mother lost by a short head.

At visiting time my father went so far as to give up about an hour of television to take my mother flowers which he carefully wrapped and made *me* carry into the hospital. When the time came to leave he slipped them, still wrapped up, *under* her bed.

And so it was that, corrupted by Elvis Presley and rock'n'roll, disenfranchised by *Dixon of Dock Green* and television, I retreated to my bedroom with my Dansette and the wireless which managed to fill the endless hours of my endless youth. I remained a fan of *The Goon Show, Beyond our Ken, Just William* and *Dick Barton, Special Agent* and I fiddled with the wireless on Sunday nights trying to hear *The Top Twenty* from Radio Luxembourg through various levels of hissing static.

Times were soon to change dramatically with a lot of my rock'n'rolling heroes getting into trouble. Elvis had been flung into the United States Army, which threatened to be the end of his singing career, and Jerry Lee Lewis had been thrown out of Britain after it had been revealed that he'd married a thirteen-year-old. Chuck Berry was facing a charge relating to underage sex and I was grief-stricken when the great Buddy Holly died in an aeroplane crash in 1959.

With such lights going out everywhere it was a miserable time and I only ever got any relief from the tension when I bashed the bishop. But the relief rarely lasted for more than a few seconds before I was engulfed with guilt about indulging in this filthy practice.

I did not know at the time that there was another nasty surprise in my bedroom. The Luftwaffe had regularly bombed Cardiff during the war – they were after the docks – and, one night, a bomb had dropped on our house, gone straight down the chimney and lodged itself behind the mantelpiece in my bedroom. It remained there unexploded for years until builders renovating the house after we had left it, found it and called in the bomb squad.

So even Hitler tried to undermine my life before it got going. There were a lot of things to blame for the mess I was becoming.

THREE

W e have all been fed the greasy chips of romantic love from the first moment of the growth of our consciousness. Along with sexual frustration, it remains the central theme of almost all our pop songs although it is probably at its most influential in the cinema where the hero was always falling for the heroine – usually as soon as he first clapped eyes on her, while one or both were married – whereupon arrangements were immediately made to leave their respective families. A few moments of intense happiness might follow, accompanied by many orchestras, only for them to dive-bomb into a bottomless lake of unutterable misery.

This ageless illusion is pursued in real life as homes are broken, children abandoned and partners shuffled. It was all nonsense, of course, and rendered most of us certifiable but that didn't stop it taking place, even among those who understood it was an illusion. So we plunged on desperately searching for this holy grail. The real flaw in romantic love is its insistence that there is a one-and-only attachment with no possibility that anyone else could *ever* take his/her place. You will retain this exclusive love, deep in your heart, until the day you drop, it says, although the really loopy thing about the lyrics of most love songs is that, while they often sound quite acceptable when sung with some sort of orchestral accompaniment, they sound like the ravings of a psychotic maniac when written down or spoken.

Like so many of my generation I believed in romantic love because everyone else did. But I could not see it happening to me, particularly as, by the age of sixteen, all I had ever managed was occasionally to cop a feel in a dark lane by shoving my hand down a few brassieres. But even that was an erratic business since a lot of girls wore falsies and there was a chance you were just going to get a handful of foam.

Nor did I think I was attractive to girls – certainly not to the girls I wanted to attract. I had fiercely blue eyes, which they liked and often noted, but they were set in an extremely young, round face and even thirteen-year-old girls seemed to need a boy who at least *looked* eighteen or nineteen. Until such time as I grew a few wrinkles or something resembling a beard, it seemed I was going to flounder in a limbo of unattainable dreams, endless yearnings and knuckle shuffles. Like all my mates.

Then, almost out of nowhere, Sandra Bond came rock'n'rolling into my life. If this wasn't romantic love it was something suspiciously like it since she tore my young world apart and it was years before I managed to put it back together again.

She was a fourteen-year-old schoolgirl with dark hair pulled back into a ponytail which she patted incessantly to make sure it was in place. She wore daps and white socks with a short pleated skirt. There were wonderful plump legs and even plumper tits, the very stuff of young boys' dreams. But it was the twinkling devilry in her black eyes which immediately caught me in her thrall: the way they kept quivering with undisguised delight when she spoke to me; the way she would smile and hold her face close to mine; the way those eyes always seemed to be telling me that I could kiss her smiling lips without any effort at all. Just lean your head forward a few inches and get on with it, her eyes always said. You can kiss these lips for as long as you want and at any time. Just lean forward and get on with it. Go on. You'll enjoy it a lot.

We first met at a youth club, playing musical chairs to the Everly Brothers' *Cathy's Clown*. The girls would walk around the seated boys until the music stopped and they would sit on the lap of whoever they found themselves standing in front of, and snog. Sandra never stopped when the music stopped, but kept rushing around and brushing the other girls aside until she jumped on my lap, snogged me and pretty much had to be pulled off when the music started again.

That behaviour told much about her self-confidence with boys even at such a young age. It never crossed her mind to chase a boy. What she wanted she grabbed hold of and hung on to. Somewhat to my surprise I became her latest acquisition and, from the way she was behaving, she was not about to let go.

I walked her home that night and we rained wet, greedy kisses on one another's lips in the dark porch of her house. My whole being was dizzy with delight as we fondled and squeezed the life out of one another. I had a hard-on all the time I was with her until we found ways of curing that with a good rub. But it was those kisses I loved best, particularly the first ones – fiery meetings of lips and tongues which represented the most achingly gorgeous moments that had ever happened to me; peachy brushings so full of fire they would haunt me for years.

We kissed long and lingeringly when we met and kissed long and lingeringly when we parted. Our hours together were built of kisses and I would wake in the middle of the night longing to feel her lips on mine. My mind was always full of her and, even when we were due to meet later that night in Llandaff Fields, we would meet briefly on the way home from school, enjoy a nice long kiss before tea, which we rarely had much appetite for, and rush out to meet in the fields and enjoy another nice long kiss lying together in the kissing grass.

Parting was a pantomime of sweet sorrow too, kissing goodbye in the porch before going out in the street and coming back again for another and another until her father, fed up with all this billing and cooing, would come out and order her indoors. This happened so often we began saying goodnight in the porch next door, but our slurpings were so noisy her father caught us there too.

We carried on like this for maybe eighteen months and got up to almost everything you might expect two young, sex-crazed bodies would get up to – never having full sex since you didn't do that then, particularly with fourteen-year-olds or you might get locked up forever – but almost continually climbing over one another and rubbing our bits against each other's or shoving our eager fingers into warm damp places or pushing our tongues inside one another's ears or down our throats until we got so needy we would lie down together and get one another off within minutes.

Then we might go for a walk or share a fag and I'd tell her how I was going to become the greatest writer in Wales, if not the world, until we found some suitable – or unsuitable – spot deep in the concealing shadows when we'd wriggle around between one another's legs and, with many a strong pelvic thrust, we'd start up the band all over again.

I was permanently knackered when I was with Sandra and never unfaithful to her in thought, word or deed. Some days I had to walk to school bow-legged, hoping that no one would notice this new Hopalong Cassidy style because I was suffering from lover's nuts, a savage ache in the balls which would often last all day and have little hope of clearing up if I was seeing her again that night which I usually did unless it was a Tuesday, when she washed her hair.

Exactly what Sandra and I got out of this masturbatory throbbing and dripping we were never worldly enough to discuss, but, whatever it was, we could never get enough of it, aching for one another when we were apart and flying into one another's arms when we met, always as if it was the first time. Whenever I kissed those lovely lips it was for the first time. It was unimaginable that there would ever come a moment when I would not want to kiss those lips.

Such passionate intensity brought misery and pain. Although our hungry bodies took one another to undreamed-of heights, we were never happy. When we weren't climbing on top of one another, we got bogged down in silly quarrels about trivial issues like whether we should sit upstairs or downstairs on a bus, exactly what time we had agreed to meet that night or why did I always keep my eyes open when we kissed when she always closed hers?

"How would you know my eyes were open if you hadn't had yours open too?"

"I only looked to see if yours were open because mine are always closed."

"But you've got to open your eyes to see this haven't you? I only open my eyes to see what yours are up to."

"You're such a liar. I don't know how I've ended up going steady with someone who lies as much as you."

The worst row came when I declared that I could no longer stand the photographs of Frankie Vaughan which festooned her bedroom walls.

"They make me sick and he's a hopeless singer," I moaned, deep in a jealous paddy. She clearly preferred him to me. It was all over between us. I ran home and cried so much the front of my shirt was wet through when I got there. I stayed miserable for a day or so, then she called at my home to say she had taken all the offending photographs down and burned them. There was no question of her preferring Frankie Vaughan to me. She was mine and mine alone.

This soon led to another continuing source of friction between us. She had proved her love for me by taking down her Frankie Vaughan photographs, so why wouldn't I tell her that I loved her?

Much as I wanted to say I loved her – if only to shut her up since she complained about this almost around the clock – I could never quite get my mouth around those dread words. She had frequently declared her love for me but all I would ever admit to was liking her which, as a small concession, did graduate to really liking her. She wore a silver locket around her neck with two pictures inside it. "Sandra loves Tom," she had written on the back of her picture and "Tom really likes Sandra," on the back of mine.

"What if I got run over by a bus and died? You'd be sorry you'd never told me then, wouldn't you? And I will have spent the whole of my life never having heard it. That's what I call being really selfish."

"I'm not ready to say it. When I say it I want it to mean forever. These are not cheap words. They're meant to mean something."

"My mother and father are always saying they love me. They don't have any trouble with it. Why should you?"

"Well, that's different, isn't it? That's a different sort of love they're talking about. That's the love of a parent for their daughter and we are talking about something else altogether."

"Look, I'll tell you what. You don't even have to mean it. Just say it *once* and I promise I'll never bring the subject up again."

"What's the point of saying it *once*?"

"Because I want to hear it, that's why. I want to hear it once."

"No."

"Well write it down then."

"No."

"All right, then, but those photographs of Frankie Vaughan could end up back on my bedroom wall you know."

"I thought you said you'd burned them."

"Maybe I didn't. Maybe I wasn't telling the truth. Maybe I just wanted to prove my love to you the way you don't want to prove it to me."

The earthquake hadn't yet struck but there were worrying tremors in my life warning me that a very big crack indeed would soon open up and down which I would fall.

I was about to sit my O-levels and Sandra had left school for a job in a city hairdresser's. She became a woman almost overnight. The transformation from schoolgirl to working woman was amazing, frightening and immediate. When I called for her now I was almost in awe of her, often feeling so insecure I would make cutting remarks when we went out together to try and put her in her place, to show her I wasn't completely bowled over by this extraordinary change. It never worked and often provoked another row. I could see I was beginning to get on her nerves and my every remark made matters worse.

I had always got on well with her mother to whom I would often take cooking apples from my garden. Her father, however, was making destructive waves. Why, as a working girl, who could have her pick of any man, was she still bothering with this schoolboy who was only ever good for a few cooking apples?

Well, she loved me, she told her father haughtily, before the rot set in. I was going to become a great writer and we were going to get married and have a hundred kids.

"A hundred kids with him! You're joking, I hope. Tell me you're joking. I don't want to spend the rest of my life surrounded by hundreds of kids like him. Your mother only once happened to mention that she likes apple tart and now she's got enough apples to start her own orchard. It's diamonds you want your men to give you not cooking apples and empty dreams about becoming a great writer. That boy couldn't write a betting slip."

Even though things had become strained between us and although she seemed a year older every time we dated, we still managed to communicate through our randy young bodies. Those moments remained brief and satisfying but there were still spaces to be filled between those pelvic rubs. Where once there had been words, laughter and pointless quarrels there were now ever-lengthening silences. I knew I was losing her but didn't know what to do about it.

I often sat next to the fire in her living room, waiting for her to get ready and making small talk with her mother, my insides squealing with fear. When she did come down, looking more beautiful than any girl had a right to, I didn't fill up with pride – or even longing – but pure dismay. I couldn't cope with this and, to make matters worse, I knew there were already other young men with money and cars sniffing around. She never told me about them, not even when I pressed her about it, but I knew they were there. She had begun looking at me without that twinkling devilry in her black eyes, almost as if she was feeling sorry for me.

We were sitting in the fields, early one evening, with sun-gorged midges quivering in clouds over the paths when, in one last desperate ploy to make things better between us, I told her I had been thinking a lot lately about whether or not I loved her.

"Oh really," she said, flatly as if I'd just told her about some football match I'd seen. She hated football.

"Yes. I've thought a lot about you and the others I've met and how special you are to me and, well, maybe it is love. Maybe I've just not understood it when it's been there all along."

She couldn't have been more underwhelmed. "I can't be out late tonight," she said finally. "I've got a long day tomorrow."

"So would you say you still love me? You haven't told me that for a while."

"Tom, I don't want to go into all that now. I've got to get home. It's been a long day standing in the salon and I need my rest."

That, more or less, was the end of our talk about love and I didn't get many more of our life-replenishing rubs either. The more I tried to re-ignite the divine flame, the wider the gulf became between us. We had grown so far apart we were barely within hailing distance.

She had also become unhappy about me waiting for her outside the hairdressers where she worked and I was aware of a particularly oily jerk called Mike Clee worming around the edge of my consciousness, peering in on me and my girl with eyes I didn't like the look of. Sandra had mentioned his name a few times as being the owner of a garage and I had spotted him sitting in his car outside her workplace combing his hair when I had gone to meet her after work.

A group of us went by train to the beach at Lavernock early that summer. Sandra and I were walking hand in hand down the path from the station when she abruptly pulled her hand away from mine. I looked over the road and saw Mike the Worm sitting in a new car with his arm resting on the driver's side window. She said nothing and looked away. He caught my cold look and turned his head. I felt sick and, although it didn't end between us there and then, I knew that I, a schoolboy with a paper round and limitless access to cooking apples, simply didn't have a prayer of holding on to her.

FOUR

I picked up six O-level passes, enough to enter the Sixth Form, but now Sandra was "washing her hair" seven nights a week. People never seem to say what's on their mind when they fall out of love. When in doubt about love we always lie, lie and lie again.

Everything I had ever cared about seemed lost without Sandra. The wrenching, hurting hole in my belly suggested that romantic love might be the eternal, death-dealing blight it was cracked it up to be. Some nights I thought I would lie down and die of grief: I could not conceive how anyone might ever take Sandra's place; did not believe that I would ever find someone as beautiful as her.

Ray and I might get drunk in some pub in the city if we had enough money, but for most of the time I sat in my bedroom and read any interesting books I could dig out of the local library. Although an aspiring writer – even though I hadn't yet got a clue what I wanted to write about – I had thus far barely read any books and it might have been a good career move if I'd tried to write a few paragraphs of prose too. But I had been too preoccupied with other problems.

John Steinbeck was one of the first authors I took to and I read almost all his work. Ernest Hemingway soothed me in my dejected loneliness since many of his heroes were undone or somehow disfigured by love. F Scott Fitzgerald told me much about the capricious and transitory nature of love which also helped a bit; a real sadness suffused his prose with which I could identify.

We never think we are influenced by books – any more than we ever understand how we are affected by advertisements – but those books began making deep changes in my ideas and world view. Every book I have read – particularly in those dismal, squirty days – affected me in some way. My horizons expanded, I acquired new ideas and was shown there were other people out there wrestling with something far more important and significant than why their girlfriend had run off with Mike the Worm.

One book turned me around: *Martin Eden* by the American socialist writer, Jack London. That novel spoke to me in ways I needed to hear: it went straight to the heart of my badly floundering condition and in no time at all I was up and running in a new direction.

Martin Eden is the story of a sailor who determines to educate himself, become a great writer and have access to upper class society and the hand of the elegant and beautiful Ruth Morse who had earlier rejected him as a failure and a socialist. Using the library as a tool, Martin works on the ship by day and studies at night. He does become a successful writer and wins back Ruth's heart only to reject her when he realises that she is only interested in his new fame and recognition. Martin returns to the sea and a final tragedy in the South China Sea.

Based on parts of Jack London's real life, this book chimed with me on a number of levels, mainly in the single-minded way he became a successful writer and got the girl. If I could become a successful writer maybe Sandra would realise her folly and come crawling back. Maybe I would make a lot of money when I hit the top of the American bestseller list and I could wait for her outside her hairdresser's in my new Ferrari with Frankie Vaughan singing his latest hit on the radio. Maybe I would then have the option of throwing her over because she was interested only in my fame and money, to see how she liked it. Maybe, maybe, maybe ...

Such absurd fantasies have probably motivated far more writers than many of them would care to admit. There can't be any other sensible reason why anyone ever gets caught up in the madness of writing.

Martin Eden also explored the romantic notion of running away to sea and putting your problems behind you. This was now attractive to me so, the day after I had finished reading the book, I went down to the Pier Head in Cardiff. I couldn't find a windjammer going to the South China Sea but I did manage to get a summer berth as an officer steward on the *Britannia*, one of a fleet of six paddle-steamers, owned by P&A Campbell, which plied their trade up and down the Bristol Channel.

For most of the day and much of the night these paddle-steamers criss-crossed the channel tirelessly, packed with passengers on sunny days and almost deserted on wet and stormy ones, their great paddles thrashing the water rhythmically and churning the sea into a huge, foaming wake over which seagulls hovered and called out for food.

The steamers never hung around. They were in and out of the ports and piers within minutes, often reaching speeds of nineteen knots which, for any ship, is fast. The captains were said to recognise only three speeds: full ahead, full astern and stop, and the sight of those ships hurrying across the horizon with black smoke belching out of their distinctive white funnels was a feature of all our seaside summers in South Wales.

The days were incident-packed for us working on board. The rip tides of the Bristol Channel are the second highest and fastest in the world and we always seemed to be getting stuck on mud banks or making a spirited effort to knock down – or at least put a good dent in – an Edwardian pier. Had anyone known how those ships were run they would never have set foot on their decks so eagerly and cheerfully. The absence of radar and the Chief Officer's enthusiasm for alcohol made it a wonder we reached anywhere in one piece. If we weren't smacking into Birnbeck Pier at Weston-Super-Mare we might get our steering jammed and end up broken down and lost in impenetrable fog around Lundy Island. We were forever getting stuck on the mud banks in the River Avon on the way to Bristol, sometimes sitting there half the night waiting for the tide to refloat us.

The crew had to throw their lines to someone on the quay, which was easier said than done. The old duffer at Ilfracombe couldn't catch a cold and whenever he missed we had to steam out in a full circle and come back to try again.

The whole working day was controlled by the speedy ebb and flow of the tides and any delay involved furious, last-minute changes of plan, often meaning that several hundred passengers would be landed for the night in Clevedon and have to be bussed home to Cardiff – all this before the existence of the Severn Bridge.

The weather could turn nasty in a moment and, largely because of the steamers' flat bottoms, we would roll and pitch like drunken butterflies on the confused seas. Instead of cutting through the waves like conventional ships, the flat bottom would ride up over them and come smacking right down on the bows, shaking your belly up into your throat. The steamers would also roll from side to side in stormy conditions with each paddle rising in turn out of the water and whirling around like a giant Catherine wheel.

The seas could get particularly rough off Minehead making the passengers sick. Vomit would slop from side to side over the floors of the snack bar lounge that I was supposed to clean. Even deep-sea sailors would succumb to seasickness off Minehead since there was never any steady rhythm about the ship's movement to get accustomed to. You never knew how the Channel was going to behave. A waterspout appeared off Porthcawl that first summer I was working on the *Britannia* – a seven-hundred-foot spiral whizzing over the waves for about twenty minutes before disappearing. The Captain said he had never seen anything like it except for the start of a typhoon in the Caribbean.

The officers, apart from a few drunks, were a conventional and even boring lot, but the rest of the crew, particularly the cooks and my fellow stewards, were a wild bunch and it was on those paddle-steamers I first learned about feckless, desperate men making their erratic ways in a hostile world.

They turned up from nowhere, worked for a while and disappeared. A lot of them were villains anxious to escape from something. You wouldn't call them fabulous or even interesting characters: they were largely a mumbling collection of near-misses who might tattoo themselves badly with a needle and lead blacking if they had a spare half hour, or would chain-smoke even when they were shaving, or nip their cigarettes half way through so they always had a pocket full of butts and never ran the risk of having to go without a smoke. Every other word was "f..k" or "c..t", sometimes jammed in the middle of longer words as in: "Where the f..k is the f..king marma-f..king-lade?"

Harry the Shithouse Wallah refused to pay maintenance for his many kids, swearing he would die rather than give that cow so much as one penny. So, at regular intervals, the police would turn up and haul him off to Swansea prison to work off his arrears. He always had his bags packed when they came for him at the Pier Head, never uttered one word of complaint about his arrest and, when he'd done his time, came back to us to be re-employed gladly because no one, anywhere, ever kept the lavatories as clean and sparkling as Harry. But he was a disgusting drunk, always finishing off the slops if he was helping to clean up in the bar at the end of the night, and sometimes ending up in a worse state than those who had been seasick.

On my first day on the *Britannia* they had their usual fun at a newcomer's expense, sending me around the ship asking for the key to the fog room locker. Another variation on this game would be to send you looking for the golden rivet or to get a bucket of steam or a jar of elbow grease.

They were long working days, beginning at half-past-six when we would be rousted out of our bunks for the beer carry and had to chain barrels and boxes of beer on to the ship before setting up the tables in the saloon for breakfast, always greasy bacon and eggs. As officer steward I would then clean their cabins and make their beds (a change of linen once a week) before setting up the tables for lunch, always roast beef, and helping out the other stewards with their passengers, who could number several hundred over two or three sittings.

I enjoyed chatting with the passengers who included a sullen Shirley Bassey, the jazzman Acker Bilk and the Penarth actor, Gordon Davies, the radio voice of *Dick Barton, Special Agent*. I also met and chatted a lot with Dr David Erskine, a Harley Street specialist and Dickensian character, who would become a great benefactor to me after I got into several major pickles later in life when I began roaming the world.

Lunch could take all the way to Lundy Island, when we might have half-an-hour's break for a nap or a game of cards and then it was dinner back to Cardiff, plaice and chips or ham salads, which we would keep serving until nine or ten at night.

We usually got back, tides willing, about half an hour before the pubs shut and we would race up the pontoon and catch the last half hour in the Big Windsor pub, often drifting off to the Bay nightclubs for a few more. Those nightclubs were rough, particularly the North Star where, it was often said, they searched you for knives and guns when you went in and, if you didn't have any, they gave you some.

But, after waiting at tables for twelve hours on a rolling ship, continually re-positioning your feet to stabilise yourself, you often found that you were out for the count at the end of the day, your legs so stiff and sore you didn't want to go to some nightclub, not even to fight with knives and guns, but just wanted to fall straight into your bunk.

My aft cabin, next to the anchor chains and constant clanking of the capstan, infringed almost every rule of the modern workplace but I was always far too tired to care about anything as I climbed in to my bunk fully clothed and it was *Goodnight Vienna* until I woke up almost immediately, shaken and shouted at by the Chief Steward, Vic Taylor, to get up and start the day's beer carry again, often before it had even got light. What *did* they do with all that beer?

Two stewards from Bristol, brothers Ted and John, would come and help us out on bank holidays and sunny weekends. They were a sharp and busy pair who would cheat us in our afternoon card schools, largely by covert hand signals. They were always counting out piles of money at the end of each day in the dining saloon, almost three or four times what the rest of us made with our tips.

Vic Taylor caught them up to something one morning and it led to a furious row. The brothers argued that they worked so hard on the ship they were entitled to their fiddles and, when Vic wasn't having that, they rounded on him and told him that, if he didn't shut up, they would tell the management where the Chief Steward got *his* stores.

Most of the stores we were handling on board, it turned out, had been stolen in Bristol. The two brothers were involved and were merely, they said, nipping off their share. In that one row I began to see how P&A Campbell was going broke. It was almost nothing to do with the repeated mantra on bad weather and falling passenger numbers. They were going broke because everyone was robbing them blind.

One night in Penarth, after a long, busy day, there was a panic in the saloon because a woman had turned up at the end of the pier and was loudly threatening to throw herself into the sea. Naturally we all ran up to the main deck to see for ourselves and found this gaunt figure standing in the moths whirling around the sodium lights of the pier, face pinched, hands in pockets, her body stricken and stiff with pain.

This woman, it soon emerged, was one of John's dumped girlfriends. She objected strongly to her new-found status and was pursuing him everywhere he went, threatening to do herself in unless he came home to her where he belonged. Even though John was a part-timer on the ship, she had an uncanny knowledge of his movements – or a simple ability to read a timetable. She bobbed up unexpectedly all along the Bristol Channel.

Somehow you understood the nature of her problem just by looking at John, who was always sharply dressed and had a melodious voice that amused even when he wasn't trying to be funny. He was never short of money, forever producing a wad of notes and letting it be known that he was a four-star shag in bed. With so many dull, sexless and penniless men around you could see why the woman was so upset he had stopped coming home to her. Whatever it was, John had it in spades.

I identified completely with that pained wraith on the pier because I knew *exactly* what she was going through. My own pain even seemed to reach up through that moth-dancing, sodium darkness and embrace hers, as if greeting one another in a comforting fellowship of suffering.

I was still wretched with what Sandra had done to me: the loss of her weighed on me like some great stone and most of the time I didn't feel up to carrying it, didn't think my wounds would ever heal. Rather like the woman on the pier, I feared I would wander the streets of Cardiff for the rest of my life, going half-mad and becoming a menace to everyone in the pubs as I droned on about how I had once been in love with a girl called Sandra Bond who had left me for a prick called Mike the Worm.

There had been no final row or ultimatum. One day it had been too rough for the paddle steamer to sail and I had been given an unexpected day off. We were still speaking so I went down to wait for her outside the hairdresser's, buying her a red rose and hoping to give her a nice surprise. Then I spotted Mike the Worm in a new sports car, also waiting for her.

It was raining hard and I hung back behind some people at the bus stop on the other side of the road. She came out of the hairdresser's, smiled, got in next to him and kissed him. And went on kissing him. I dropped my red rose and just stood there, the rain mingling with my tears, not wholly surprised by what I was seeing but still hardly able to believe the intensity of the pain shooting through every part of me. The wheels of a bus threw water over my discarded rose.

I didn't confront them, didn't rush over and pull off his windscreen wipers or jump on his flash winkle-pickers because I've always hated confrontation. Perhaps I was nursing a lingering hope that, like Martin Eden, I would soon become a successful writer and she would take me back again, weeping and wailing about how we all make mistakes and I should at least forgive her for just this one.

But, in all the messy circumstances, I took the worst possible option and stalked her for weeks, standing around uselessly outside the hairdresser's like that poor woman on Penarth pier, hiding myself but making myself visible too, imprisoned by my outraged feelings yet knowing there was nothing I could do. On days off I hid over the road from her work or got up early in the hope of bumping into her as she went to catch the bus or even waited in the darkness outside her home for her to come back with Mike the Worm, and dying the death of a thousand cuts – oh a million cuts! – as I watched them kiss and fondle one another in his new sports car.

She must have spotted me often enough and the really stupid thing about stalking is that it completely destroys whatever residual affection the loved one might retain. Far from being a young man who loved her and was one day going to become a great writer, I had become a pain in the arse who was following her around like some official in a peaked cap threatening to cut off her electricity.

One of the golden rules of the mating game, I now know, is that to crowd someone is to lose them. True feelings grow freely or not at all and I couldn't have destroyed my relationship with Sandra more completely or more certainly had I sat down with a manual on how to get someone to hate you forever. *Everything* I did, every step I took, made matters worse.

I had to suffer and hope the next day wouldn't be quite so bad as this, except it always was. Surely Jack London couldn't have gone through all this. How could anyone write a word if they were suffering like this?

The hard physical work on the paddle steamers helped assuage my grief and a good skinful of beer or rough cider late at night did wonders for it too. But sometimes, deep in my cups with my shipmates, I would break down and sob uncontrollably.

"Oh don't take any notice of him," Ray, who had joined me on the paddle steamers, would say by way of apology. "He's missing that bloody girl again."

There seemed no way out, no release. She stormed through my dreams and figured in my every desire and fantasy. A quick wank didn't work any more – not even for the few moments before the guilt set in – and there were those days, those long, long, days, when I was convinced I would never laugh or even smile again.

I also fell physically ill because of Sandra's desertion, throwing up all the time and becoming wan, pale and stick-thin. It got so bad I could throw up walking down the street without breaking my step. I'm not even sure how I survived that first year after she left me: my belly seemed permanently seething with acid and all I could ever keep down by way of food was lettuce sandwiches.

"There are plenty of other pebbles on the beach and time heals everything," my mother used to say. But I have often bitterly cursed the moment in that damned youth club when I first clapped eyes on Sandra Bond and I was convinced I would never heal or be free of her pain.

So I was at one with that woman on Penarth pier. We were united in a common grief which would last for eternity and, just for those few cold moments, our tortured spirits rose up into the sea air, intertwined and comforted one another with a bond of warmth. Carry on, move forward, there are other pebbles on the beach. Don't just stand there shivering and crying into indifferent winds. Time heals all the pain there is.

Believe.

FIVE

With the close of the Fifties, postures of rebellion and criminality began springing up everywhere in the cinema and Ray and I were at the front of the queue, watching and absorbing it all. Rebellion had always been at the heart of rock'n'roll but that was mostly about pissing off your parents or making off with your best friend's girl. Just when I was more than ready for it, a new bad-ass social rebellion was breaking through from Hollywood with films like *The Wild One* with Marlon Brando. Such anti-authoritarian films took an immediate hold on our young minds and hearts; they reinforced our concept of ourselves as being outside the rules, daring and free individuals.

In no time at all I would be trying to explain something to my poor mother in a Marlon Brando drawl or standing behind the armchair wherein my immobile father was watching television, pulling up my collar and giggling stupidly like James Dean. These new stars were offering us new identities and, in the inevitable absence of one of our own, we embraced them avidly.

Blackboard Jungle came along and those dysfunctional New York kids, who called Glenn Ford "Teach", were objects of our admiration too, inspirations to bang desk lids and stoke up trouble somewhere. It was vague and low-key but it was there.

Ray and I did little academic work in the Sixth Form and the most generous interpretation of those two years is that we did turn up occasionally, usually when threatened with expulsion for non-attendance. We spent a lot of time in the snooker hall, where they knew everything about nicking stuff, or in the Greyhound, a scrumpo house in the city where you could get a pint of rough cider for eight pence. Drunk after one pint and totally pie-eyed after two, we would sing disgusting parodies of favourite old songs:

A dose of clap first thing in the morning,
A strain of syphilis that won't get better.
Oh how my foreskin stings.
These foolish things remind me of you …

Our little world opened up to a lot of new possibilities when Ray acquired a Morris 8 car which worked wonders for our sex lives. We often managed to pick up two friends out on the town who, for some reason, always came as the "rough one" and the "nice one". I always got the "nice one", who wasn't having any of the old malarkey and went home first. Ray, on the other hand, often managed to shag the "rough one" on the back seat while I sat in the driving seat trying to smoke unconcernedly like Humphrey Bogart and pretending I wasn't looking when I was watching every fumble and thrust in the rear-view mirror. When Ray had finished he always offered her to me but they were never quite *that* rough and strenuously objected to being passed around like a shared cigarette.

While Ray kept picking up gold medals I barely managed the odd bronze. I never really mastered the two popular fashion accessories of the time: suspender belts or, if my luck was really out, the roll-on. Brassieres would come off in a wink but I just couldn't find my way around the roll-on and would often give up at first base and shout at Ray, probably doing battle himself with a roll-on – he didn't *always* strike gold – that I'd had enough and, if we left now, we could catch a pint before the pubs shut.

Ours was a strong friendship, in which we looked out for one another and shared everything, although he was a far better criminal and I merely shuffled along in his wake. I was never sure where he got his ideas from – well, we did like the same films – but nothing was beyond his scope. One afternoon he practically cleared out the record stock in Howell's department store (once they twigged their stock was disappearing too fast they began putting just the record sleeves out on the display racks). Ray would take the records to school and flog them in the breaks.

He was a brilliant card sharp too. Following the lead of the Bristol brothers on the paddle steamers, we began sending one another secret signals in games such as Pontoon, even cleaning out our close friends. Ray never got the blame when we were found out. For some strange reason that always came *my* way.

"I always knew you were up to no good," the father of one of our victims told me after we'd been discovered cheating. "But I always thought Ray was a decent sort of lad."

No he wasn't, but he was a tremendous influence on my youth.

Ray and I had pretty much become a pair of fully-fledged crooks by the time we went on the *Bristol Queen* the next season and re-entered the rotten culture in which everyone was stealing from everyone else.

We made an enormous amount of money although we were introduced to the main scam by a vain Italian, Louis Carpanini, who had bloated pasta cheeks, carefully oiled hair and a small slippery moustache that he kept tweaking with his fingertips. He had been in the catering business for ever but his weakness was that when he made money he would throw it all away on some glamorous tart who would give him the elbow as soon as the money ran out. Then, derelict and heartbroken, Louis would take to the streets, sleeping on park benches and begging, until his friend George found him and set him up in a new job. This season Louis and George were working as stewards in the dining saloon of the *Bristol Queen*.

As soon as Louis came aboard all the menus mysteriously disappeared over the side and the 6s.6d lunch became 7s.6d. The 7s.6d dinner then became 8s.6d and we stewards pocketed the shilling a head. There were many variations on the scam, including, for example, pretending to write on your receipt pad at the end of a meal when, in fact, you wrote nothing at all and pocketed the lot. If an awkward passenger did ask for a receipt you rose to your full height and simply said that it was company policy never to give receipts.

Vic Taylor dozed in his kiosk throughout and was never aware of what was going on although we often had to stand just out of his sight making lightning calculations on what we should give him and what to keep ourselves. If he challenged us we hid behind the defence of imbecility and he never pushed the issue because he was pretty imbecilic himself. Ray and I, in no time, were flush with more money than we had ever seen in our lives, and flashed our wads like Italian mobsters.

The passengers rolled up in their hundreds and we conned them all, even persuading the chef to stop making plaice and chips so we could give them ham salads, which were quicker and easier to serve. We went down the tables with whole armfuls of plates, flung them out like card dealers and hurried the passengers along so that we could pack in another sitting of hungry punters since that meant we raked in another load of money.

There was no way out of the fiddle. With eight stewards working the dining room on busy days, you had to charge the passengers the same rates or else they would talk amongst themselves on the deck afterwards and come back down to complain they had been charged more than someone else.

"You're in the f..king fiddle whether you like it or not," Louis would shout at us. "If you don't go along with it you f..k things up for everyone else."

Even with all our money Ray and I became increasingly competitive and greedy. Where we had once shared everything without question – fags, money and even girls – we now bickered over every last tanner and cigarette. Our greed was boundless and, even at the end of a long, hard day in the saloon, we had so much money we sounded like a delivery from the Royal Mint. We might even make ham sandwiches and carry them around the deck with a pot of coffee and flog them to the passengers who, at that time of night after a day at sea, were often so hungry they would pay a fortune for anything vaguely edible.

No one could match Ray when he got going. One day he realised that Vick Taylor, who was suffering from a bad bout of shingles, barely knew what he was doing and, if you said "6s.6d a pound" thus getting 13s.6d change, he was so befuddled by his ailment that you took the change but didn't give him the pound. Thus you would rob the Chief Steward and, along with what you'd already ripped off the passenger, plus a tip, you could make anything up to £2 a passenger.

The managing director of the fleet at that time was a Mr Smith-Cox, who often boarded us at Clevedon, his portly, balding frame always visible from afar standing alone on the pier as we approached. The very sight of him sent a *frisson* of alarm through the whole ship, with the Chief Steward digging out fresh linen we never knew he had for the Smith-Cox table in front of the Smith-Cox chair of the Smith-Cox corner of the dining saloon. All fiddles were off for the day although I doubt if Smith-Cox would have recognised a fiddle if he had found one in his ham salad.

I always waited on him, which meant I got a fresh, clean jacket, and he was a pleasant enough public school chump, who gave me a shilling tip. Small beer compared with what I was losing that day. But we would often have a good chat about what I was going to do in the future – university perhaps and a career as a writer. He would have made a good uncle, really, managing a department store in Clevedon, always to be relied on for a few quid if times got tough. He certainly didn't have a clue that almost everyone on board was robbing P&A Campbell blind.

Everyone else knew the days of the steamers were numbered and I saw the Chief Engineer, Alec Campbell, one of the last of the family to be associated with the company, lying dead in the engine room just before we left Ilfracombe one Sunday morning. He had died as he had lived in front of his beloved levers and great pistons and I stood in the alleyway outside the engine room and stared through a window for a long time, waiting for him to move. People scurried about and one of the bar ladies was crying inconsolably. His huge girth made him look like a beached whale in oily overalls. There was so much of him the main problem was how they were going to haul him off the ship. He had really tiny feet, now quite still in their highly polished shoes.

SIX

In my Second Year Sixth the scanty furniture in my mind was dramatically and irrevocably rearranged by a single book – *The Outsider* by Colin Wilson. *The Outsider* is a study of the rebel who stands outside society and lives in a hole-in-the-wall. He is disgusted by the chaos of the world in which he lives. Violence or the smell of blood attracts his interest, as do crime, disease and perversion. The moral of *The Outsider* is that the saint and the criminal are brothers.

In a series of brief pen portraits Wilson introduced me to the life and work of Albert Camus, Franz Kafka and Jean-Paul Sartre. Their ideas, which resembled nothing I had heard about or come across, went tumbling straight down into my empty adolescent mind like coal emptied into a cellar. They bounced, exploded and sent up clouds of dust.

You can feel God through sexual orgasm. The real notions are the Ultimate Yes and the Ultimate No. Man is sunk in such delusion he can never know himself. Death is the most important idea. Desire is holy. Sooner kill an infant in a cradle than nurse unsatisfied desires. What is the ultimate reality? Why are we here? What are we doing?

These seemed the only ideas that now mattered and, within the three or four hours that it took me to read *The Outsider*, I was fully radicalised, up and running and wearing the standard black polo-neck sweater favoured by Wilson. I walked the streets of Canton with obscure paperbacks in my pocket, denouncing society and muttering about the "spiritual syphilis" of the age. I also draped myself over the sofa for many long hours, my hair growing long, simmering with existentialist angst.

The Outsider has been dismissed as "intellectual masturbation" but Wilson was blindingly well read and he alone introduced me to the great and dangerous ideas of modern literature.

On the same day *The Outsider* was first warmly reviewed by Philip Toynbee in the *Observer*, Kenneth Tynan went down on his knees before *Look Back in Anger* by John Osborne. Oh right, I was angry too and, largely thanks to Osborne and Wilson, I had been given an identity and set of ideas for which I had long been yearning. The vague and shifting persona conferred on me by the cinema was replaced by the angry outsider, beyond the conventional scheme of things, the god-less rebel who would assert the claims of the imagination over all else and sit alone, in his hole-in-the-wall, seeing too deeply and thinking too much.

After coming across a reference to him in *The Outsider* I was also soon sniffing out everything by Henry Miller and he too became a hero. I loved his anarchism and verbosity and was so fascinated by his claim to have had sex in the middle of a crowded dance floor without anyone noticing that I nursed this ambition myself for many years. Miller penetrated my adolescent mind in a way no other writer yet had; he seemed to speak for my mind – and mine alone – in an alien, bourgeois world. I dipped my hands in these ideas and washed my face in them ferociously, barely understanding how completely they were changing me.

We sat our A-levels the following summer and it was hardly likely that the new adolescent sexual outlaw in a black polo-neck sweater, who knew his Miller from his Mailer, and was heavily into working class existentialism, would do well, and he didn't. He was clearly interested in nothing the examiners hoped to read about – *Might It Be Possible to Have Sexual Relations in the Middle of a Crowded Dance Floor With No one Noticing? – Discuss in 800 words* was unlikely to come up as a subject – and he got Ds in English and History and failed French so badly he didn't even match the O-level which he'd managed two years previously.

Two Ds did not qualify me for university entrance so along with Ray (who predictably got better grades than me, with no work whatsoever) I decided we'd had enough of all this "bourgeois education stuff" and for some bizarre reason, which didn't tally with my new rebellious identity, we both applied for the Civil Service.

The Civil Service was brighter than I'd thought since they turned me down without even offering me an interview but Ray sailed in and was sent away for training to become an executive officer with Customs and Excise.

The new Welsh Outsider really was isolated now, stuck on his own in that lonely hole-in-the-wall.

My resolution to become a writer was firmer than ever but what was I to write about? In my new identity I needed to rub shoulders with violence and perversion; I needed to mix with outlaws working on the margins of society; I needed intensity, colour and extremes and I was soon scouring Tiger Bay, Cardiff's dockland, for material. I had got to know this area from my paddle steamer days and there was much here that I found attractive – the vigour of the pubs, for example, and the remarkable collection of seamen and characters gathered on the street corners. Pubs like the Big Windsor, the Packet and the Frampton throbbed with life, as did the Custom House at the top of Bute Street where prostitutes gathered next to the bridge beyond which the police would never allow them to venture.

One of my favourite watering holes was the North Star which, because of licensing problems, was obliged to serve food with its alcohol. They got around this by giving us Spam sandwiches when we paid to go in, not to eat but to hand back at the door on our way out. After a few days the sandwiches went mouldy and hard with curly corners and only then were they changed, perhaps after some of the more fastidious customers complained.

The New Moon club was another favourite. I grasped the banister going up there one night and found my palm covered with blood. There was never any heat in the winter. We had to wear overcoats and warm up by dancing. Even the bottled beer froze one night and, after I pointed out you couldn't drink frozen beer, they put a few bottles in the pasty warmer until they exploded and nearly cut up the barman.

Most of the prostitutes were so rough you would be taking your life in your hands if you went near them. I was chatting to one in the Adelphi Hotel one night and she asked if I wanted to do any business. I said no but later, as we chatted on, I asked what she charged. "Half a crown up against a wall and five bob on a bed," she said. I wasn't nearly man-of-the-world enough to go with a prostitute no matter how much rough cider I'd sunk. The sight of them filled me with fear and the odd thing was that, despite a lot of fumbling and floundering, I was still a virgin and likely to remain one for a long time yet. Perhaps the chapel boy inside me wouldn't allow me to lose my virginity in a fleabag brothel or up against a dockland wall. Despite reading Henry Miller's thoughts on free love I was certain I wanted to lose my virginity in more salubrious circumstances.

Tiger Bay never let me go and I liked the way that, merely by walking up Bute Street, you could come across so many races at work, play and prayer from the Moslems in their mosques to the Chamari tribesmen in Loudoun Square and the po-faced Chinese with their restaurants and laundries.

It may have been inverted snobbery that made me feel at home in the Bay pubs and so much enjoy the company of seamen but I spent all my free time there. They filled my ears and mind with stories of drinking and fighting in Shanghai and Buenos Aires; there were tempests at sea and men falling over the side and bobbing up again in strange circumstances. Men dressed as beautiful women on some of the big liners, they told me. There was this drunken deck hand in Cape Town who picked up a woman in the port, took her back to his bunk, put his hand up her skirt and grabbed hold of a huge set of bollocks. This "woman" was a docker in drag but the deck-hand was so drunk *and* on heat, he flipped "her" over, had it backwards and enjoyed it so much he never touched another woman ever again.

I also met a man in the Frampton who told me he'd been in prison for shagging a donkey. "What was it like?" I asked after a stupefied silence.

"Well, it was fine," he replied with a smile and a faraway twinkle in his eye. "I used to take my bucket into the field, stand on it and bang away. Trouble was the neighbours didn't like it – and the kid who owned the donkey wasn't mad about it either – so they reported me to the police. I was duly warned but I liked it so much I did it again and got six months for bestiality."

Many of these stories were Merchant Navy myths, I was to learn, highly embellished in the long, empty hours at sea, but I soaked them up. Surely this was the kind of material I would one day use in the great novel I was going to dash off any morning now. What was the point of writing if you couldn't upset or disgust someone or, preferably, everyone? There was a whole world within a world here in the Bay for sure with all of them saying the same thing to me: "Come and write about us. Move down here and become a part of us. Tell the world *our* stories."

But before I could start work on my magnum opus there was real life to deal with. The paddle steamer season was over and, with my studies at an end, I needed to find a job. I would have liked to have said that I became a window cleaner to assert my contempt for middle-class norms but what really happened was that Terry, the local window cleaner, asked me to help him out and I had nothing else to do.

Thus I became the only window cleaner in the city with long hair, a black polo-neck sweater and an obscure paperback in the back pocket of my jeans. To darken the image a bit I rolled my own cigarettes with brown liquorice papers. "Don't mess with me," my look announced. "I am the new Prince of Darkness. Touch me and I'll blow you up."

My poor mother remained puzzled by these changes and my father became ever more appalled but I enjoyed cleaning windows with Terry, a genuine character, sickeningly happy all day long, always singing up his ladder or else constantly re-arranging his spectacles with lenses thick as the bottoms of pop bottles. He put more oil on his immaculately combed hair than they used in the local chip shop.

A bar-room philosopher, who had the ability to pour pints down his throat without troubling his Adam's apple, Terry was always giving me homilies about life and love. The main thrust of these was that everything in life was a load of fanny. When, for example, a housewife asked me what I used in the bucket, I was never, on any account, to tell the truth, that it was merely dirty water rarely changed from one job to the next. I should always say that I would like to tell her but it was a tradesman's secret and, if she really wanted to know, Terry had a still in his backyard and it had been years before he had come up with the right mixture.

The only rule of window cleaning, Terry went on, was to get the windows wet with a sponge. Then give them a quick rub with the scrim. That always did the trick but, if ever there was anyone in the house watching you, you had to give it a lot of fanny and rub like mad. "When in doubt just give it a lot of fanny," was one of his favourite expressions. "You can never fanny a fannier," was another.

Our day began at 7.30am and we worked fairly hard, with plenty of breaks for tea and fags, until Terry judged we had enough money to get drunk. Sometimes we'd end up in hell of a mess after these sessions and Terry would take me home in his battered Morris Minor. I would barely be able to find the front door and my mother would come out and accuse Terry of working me to death.

"Just look at the boy. He's so tired he can hardly stand."

"It's only a bit of hard work, Mrs Davies. Only a bit of hard work. Hard work never killed anyone."

"Well, you seem to be killing the boy with drink too."

"I'm not forcing it down his throat with a funnel, Mrs Davies. He's eighteen now. Old enough to pick up his own beer."

Terry's problem, it emerged, was that he was interested in women sober but danced on the other side of the ballroom when drunk. When he drove me home in his Morris Minor, I'd have to keep picking his hand off my right knee and give it back to him. Even when he handed me over to my mother in a drunken heap on the doorstep he'd give my balls or arse a quick grope if he thought she wasn't looking.

I didn't mind: he was lively company and I never once managed to buy a drink. But one night, just before Christmas, we both got slaughtered on beer with whisky chasers and he drove me home, pulled on the handbrake outside my house, switched off the ignition, flung his arms around my neck and announced that he loved me.

"You don't understand, Tom. I really do."

Instantly soberish I broke his grip and told him I certainly wasn't in love with him. I was in love with Sandra as he well knew, I added, grabbing desperately for the door handle as he continued to declare his love for me with tears rolling down his cheeks.

I finally got the passenger door open and fell out of the car sideways, bashing my head on the pavement. He was out of the car and on me again, down on his knees clutching my arm and insisting I didn't understand. I broke his grip, staggered to my feet and fell over again. He stood up, reached for my hand, fell over and said I must forget about Sandra and *he* would look after me from now on.

"Go and sober up, Terry. I'll talk to you in the morning."

Fortunately my mother came out to find her eldest son and the window cleaner falling all over the pavement and bouncing off his car. Terry backed off when she asked what was going on and took my hand to lead me into the house.

"Look what you've done to him now," she shouted at Terry. "He's only a boy and isn't old enough for all this."

Terry didn't reply. He managed to struggle back into the driving seat, passed out, slumped forward over the steering wheel and set off the horn.

The next morning I awoke with a blinding hangover, a matter of routine while working with Terry, and a bump the size of a duck egg on the side of my head. The front door bell rang at 7.30am sharp as usual – Terry never suffered from any sort of hangover no matter how much he drank – and my mother took it upon herself to answer it but checked with me first.

"Tell him I've got a bad head and won't be going to work today."

A row broke out, my mother's sparrow-like chirps counterpointing Terry's basso booms and the next thing he was sitting on the end of my bed goggling at me through his pop bottle glasses as my angry mother stood in my bedroom doorway with her arms folded.

"Tom, I just want to say I'm sorry and it won't happen again. It was the drink and I got carried away."

"Who got carried away where?" my mother wanted to know.

"Mum, just leave us. It'll be all right. Go."

The bedroom door closed though I was pretty sure she was listening behind it, so I gave Terry the bad news in cracked whispers. "Terry, we can't go on like this and I'm very sorry but I don't want to go cleaning windows with you any more."

"Oh, Tom, you're just saying that because you've got a bad head. Go back to sleep and I'll come back and pick you up at lunchtime. We'll go to the pub and have a few pints and a chat. I really am sorry about what happened. It was the drink."

"No, Terry, it's over. We have cleaned our last window together and you're going to have to find someone else to help you. I'm sorry, but that's it."

I signed on for the dole and my relationship with my father grew more tense because he had never signed on in his life and was heartily ashamed of me. Then my parents went away for Christmas and came home to discover I'd thrown a party in their absence.

The problem was that I had tried to "do" the dole office receptionist in their bed. We were both well lit-up and her prehistoric corset made the whole act farcical. I fiddled with the cord for ages (it didn't help that she wasn't co-operating, merely lying on her back and giggling a lot) but I finally managed to untie an opening big enough to get her knickers off and ease myself down between her legs.

There wasn't any foreplay as such – well, no foreplay at all – and, more by luck than judgement, I managed to locate the hairy crack and rammed my dick into it. I managed perhaps half an inch of penetration then it bounced back out again. Another ram, another bounce. Did she have bed-springs in there or what?

The trouble was I had no clear conception of what I was doing and no yardstick by which to judge my performance. Had I understood foreplay and got a little lubricant going, I might have got it in a further half an inch and, had I known she was a virgin, I might have taken a little more time and eased it in slowly instead of ramming it in with the subtlety of a chimney sweep up a clogged flue. But I knew absolutely *nothing* and returned to the party in despair. Beyond a shadow of doubt I was going to be a virgin for life.

The immediate upshot of this regrettable non-encounter was that the girl from the dole office left her knickers in my parents' bed and my mother found them. By the time they scraped my father off the ceiling I knew I had better leave home fast. It was time to get my act together and sort out my destiny at sea like my hero Martin Eden.

I stayed at Ray's auntie's house that night and took a train to London the next morning, finding digs at Highbury Corner and a job in a Joe Lyons Corner House on Piccadilly Circus.

I found the size and bustle of London oppressive, but I was cheerful enough now that I had some purpose and went to spend the night with Dr Erskine who lived in a fine house in Chislehurst. He had good contacts in the Merchant Navy and gave me a written introduction to the Head of the Pool of London in the capital's dockland.

At last I had made the break and was about to get a berth but after a hard day picking up dishes for Joe Lyons I came back to my lodgings in Highbury late one night and bought a pie and a cup of tea from a stall outside the tube station. Almost immediately I had to race back to the lodging house because said pie and tea were about to explode out of my every orifice. When I got into the lavatory I didn't know whether to sit or put my head down the pan.

The landlady was horrified the following morning when she saw what had happened in her precious lavatory and wasn't best pleased to find me still in bed, whey-faced and confidently awaiting the undertaker so she just flung me out. I'd already paid another week's rent, but she told me to pack my bags and go home to my mother. I was too ill to resist as she rang for a cab to take me to Paddington station and I threw up all the way back to Cardiff.

I had been away three weeks and to my relief even my father was pleased – yes, pleased – to see me. My mother had been up in London, going round relatives and London docks looking for me in the pubs. She'd been a runaway herself when young and, although I never got the details, she used to tell how the Salvation Army had saved her life when she had ended up in the East End.

The next afternoon I wandered into the dole offices in Westgate Street to be met by the giggling receptionist whose blue-eyed innocence clouded into thunder as soon as she clapped eyes on me.

"You have been struck off the dole but you can appeal," she told me so severely I though she was going to reach for her cane.

For one brief, sadistic moment I considered telling the old lags in the dole office what their little girl had got up to on Christmas Eve but, in the event, I merely walked out. There and then in Westgate Street, I decided to go back to school and try for better grades in my A-levels to get me to university.

The headmaster, Harold Davies, agreed to my return, graciously and immediately – not like him at all. "There's something in you which needs to be found," he said. They were always saying that but I could never see it. The next morning I returned to the school to start my Third Year Sixth.

It turned out to be the fastest Third Year Sixth of all time because, two weeks later, I sat an exam for a Craddock Wells Exhibition Scholarship that would take me to Cardiff University as a State Scholar without any of the normal matriculation requirements. To qualify for this scholarship I simply had to write a three-hour essay about The Idea of Society. My essay was vague but I was good at waffle since not only did I write about my own views on society but, again thanks to Colin Wilson, could quote the views of Barbusse, Camus, Kafka, Sartre and Dostoevsky.

I managed to give the impression that I'd read all these writers even though I'd not read one. Almost all the quotations came from *The Outsider*. Be that as it may, it must have rung a few bells with someone because, within a week, I was called for interview by the university Senate. There, when asked what books I had read (they always ask you that question in interviews and you have to have an answer ready) I was able to talk about Colin Wilson all over again. Never has so much bullshit been launched off so flimsy a platform.

I told the Senate I was desperate to study philosophy at their great university and hoped to become a major philosopher myself. This self-confident declaration provoked a big laugh around the table and I knew I'd get the scholarship because you can get anyone to do almost anything for you if you can get them to laugh.

The philosophy professor, Oliver de Selincourt, a man who, I learned later, thought all philosophy ended with Plato, said he didn't think much of Colin Wilson (I doubt if the old buffer had ever read a word of Wilson's) but he was sure that I would enjoy learning what real philosophy was about.

A few days later I heard I had been awarded the scholarship and was a State Scholar – the equivalent of getting three As – and would receive the magnificent and most acceptable sum of £600 a year, not means tested, to attend Cardiff University and study for a bachelor of arts degree.

The scholarship also meant that I need not re-sit my A-levels to go to university because Cardiff University *actually wanted me to be there with them* so there wasn't any point in continuing with my Third Year Sixth either.

With almost nine months before the start of the university term, it was time to go to sea again, properly this time. Armed with my discharge papers from the paddle steamers and still with the letter of introduction from Dr Erskine, I went back to London's Albert Dock where, ever hopeful of becoming the new Ernest Hemingway or Jack London, I was hired on the Pool for £36.10s a month as a steward on a Union Castle liner soon to sail around Africa.

SEVEN

The *Windsor Castle*, one of the giant passenger flagships of the Union Castle line, was on a permanent run around Africa, out through the Suez Canal and back around the Cape. Looking up at her from the quay you wondered how anything so big could float on mere water. Her insides were a buzzing warren of alleyways, saloons and cabins in which you got lost until you worked most of it out after a couple of days.

We weren't allowed to sleep on board yet so a group of us chummed up at the Seaman's Mission and travelled in each morning to work in the tourist passenger saloon from 7am to 4pm. This work involved the meticulous cleaning of the silverware, the frequent hand-scrubbing of the dining saloon deck and making the brass portholes gleam as brilliantly as when they were first cast.

We took it in turns to wait on one another at meal times and I had never eaten food of this quality let alone worked in the kind of saloon that served it. The attention to detail was daunting for someone largely brought up on chips. Dinner was served in six courses and the passengers were allowed to eat as much as they wanted, even three helpings of the same course if that was Sir or Madam's desire.

The trick of working on any ship, I was to learn, is to melt quietly into the background where, with a bit of luck and a fair wind, you will not be noticed or bothered until the voyage is completed. But I didn't know any tricks, often stood around chatting and smoking fags, and soon caught the attention of the Second Steward, a fat git with a foul mouth and the eyes of a young girl. I laughed when he said he had his eyes on me, my first big mistake.

I had cleaned up after the stewards' breakfast one morning and the Second Steward found some dried egg on one of the forks. "Well, it's hardly the end of the world," I pointed out, my second big mistake.

After that he was on my back almost constantly and I made my third big mistake when I mentioned I was a student. I'm not sure what advantage I was trying to work by telling him this – perhaps hoping he might ease up on me – but, whatever I was after, it didn't work and he went from being mildly antagonistic to aggressively hostile. Merchant Navy people below decks, I now know, have always hated students. Perhaps we remind them of the chances they have missed but, from that moment on, he bullied me remorselessly, as if he wanted me to walk off the ship and go back to university where I belonged.

Second stewards have techniques of torture that would have interested Ghengis Khan. When we were finally allowed to sleep on board, I wanted to share a cabin with my mates from the Mission but the Second Steward decreed, possibly in reprisal for misdemeanours I had only yet been thinking about, that I should share a six-berth cabin with five raving queens.

I had already heard about them – the others were always talking about the antics of the "girls" – but hadn't seen any of them until that day, when they fluttered into my cabin like a bunch of deranged peacocks, shrilling about this and squawking about that, hugging and kissing one another like long-lost sisters. When they noticed me, it was with all the horror of finding a turd newly dropped in a swimming pool.

"How'd you get in here, my deah. It's only queens in here. Or are you one of us?"

"Er ... no ... er ..."

"You haven't been put in here by that Second Steward have you, dahling? Oh girls, he's done it again. Anyone he doesn't like the look of he sends to us. The bastard did the same last trip, but that one ended up screwing us girls rotten."

These queens made very efficient stewards and most of them worked in the first class lounge, which meant I didn't see them all day, being in tourist myself but, after dinner, it was bedlam in the cabin as they jammed in together, muttering evilly as they stared into mirrors, constantly preening themselves, putting on lipstick and mascara and loudly arguing over whose turn it was to wear the off-the-shoulder blouse in the crew bar, the Pig and Whistle, that night.

Everyone was called "my deah" or occasionally "dahling" and, if they weren't arguing about whose turn it was to wear various garments, they were talking about sex. I had thought I was sex-obsessed but I was a Plymouth Brethren puritan compared with this lot. They never stopped going on about where to get it, what you might have to pay for it if you were desperate, the size of various deckhands' dicks or who liked to be plated up against a bulkhead. This erotic chatter went on and on and on in much the same casual way as you might discuss the weather, their voices not even registering any particular excitement when they spoke about the unbelievable enormity of the bo'sun's cock. I sat pretending to read a book but absorbing every word.

My main problem sharing a cabin with these queens was that they aroused my own deep sexual confusion and guilt and I couldn't quite work out how I was *supposed* to feel towards them. I had not yet managed to screw a woman properly so didn't quite see how I was going to leap over any number of further psychological barriers to screw a man. I'd had my chances with Terry the window cleaner but my only real sexual skill was wanking and I was reasonably sure I always thought of a woman when I did that.

There was the added complication that, thanks to the relaxation of censorship, a large number of books dealing with what Samuel Beckett called the "cloacic of colonic gratification," had recently been released and had greatly thickened my confusions.

Jean Genet, the French male prostitute and social outcast, was an early favourite of mine, particularly his novel, *Our Lady of the Flowers*, which described the lives of criminals and perverts trapped in their self-destructive circles in Montmartre. James

Baldwin, an American homosexual writer, was busy wrestling with his sexual identity in novels such as *Giovanni's Room*. I loved Baldwin's incandescence and was also impressed by a homosexual scene in Alexander Trocchi's *Cain's Book*. The narrator, a junkie, had met and screwed a seaman in an alley in New York's dockland. It was his first gay encounter and he declared himself happy with it because it had taken him through "a new barrier of experience".

A lot of these ideas were persuasive to my young and certainly immature mind. They created areas of beguiling darknesses which I felt I *should* explore in becoming a writer but, in the circumstances, I developed a sort of amiable, if anxious, ambiguity about my own sexual identity. I didn't really know what I was up to, in other words, and my reading often put me at odds with my true self. What really worried me was that I might get so drunk one night with one of the queens – like that man who unwittingly went to bed with that docker in drag – and end up preferring men. What would happen to me then?

The strange thing was that, after I had come to grips with my early shock and confusion, I settled easily into this group and they accepted me, possibly because they saw I was never judging them or coming the hairy-arsed hetero. They seemed to adopt and mother me, taking me to the Pig and Whistle at night for a drink.

If you got into a one-to-one situation with them they could be intelligent and thoughtful, often happily telling me the most vivid details about their past and how they believed they had become gay which, they all seemed to agree, was a pretty lousy situation to be in. It was against the law and they had been drawn to the Merchant Navy, not for the sex but mostly because it kept them well away from arrest and prosecution. In a sense they were the first *real* outsiders I'd ever met and it wasn't long before I was deciding that I should write about them. But how could I write about them when I hadn't tried it myself?

They always seemed to have plenty of money and threw it about recklessly. Late at night in the Pig, deckhands came over to our group, sure of as much free drink as they could pour down their throats before slipping off somewhere quiet with one of them. These transactions were quite open even if they were never discussed as such.

I caught the Second Steward staring at me hard and hatefully in the Pig one night. He could see that, far from terrifying me, the queens had taken to me.

We were due to sail the following day when the Second Steward told me I wasn't going with them after all but should travel to Liverpool that afternoon to become an engineer steward on the *Canopic*, a cargo boat with the Shaw Savill Line. It was due to sail in a few days out through the Suez Canal to Australia to unload, then load in New Zealand and come back through the Panama Canal.

I was the only one transferred like this so the Second Steward had found a way of getting rid of me. My cabin mates seemed genuinely upset when they found me packing my bags. They had clearly planned all kinds of larks at my expense when we got to sea and said that had I gone to Africa with them I would certainly have come back as gay as a gladioli.

"It's probably just as well I'm not sailing with you, then, isn't it?"

"They've got queers on Shaw Savill too, Taffy deah. I'm telling you now to keep your tin knickers on all day."

A light, grey rain was falling on Liverpool when I first saw the *Canopic*, my home for the next eight months. It was a rusty bucket of a tramp cargo boat with brown gantries on the deck and as different from the *Windsor Castle* as it was possible for a ship to be. Seagulls glided through the drizzling skies and it was difficult to decipher the dockers' Scouse accents.

Voices were shouting up from the hold and down into it from the deck. They had just loaded some large machinery in a box and were discussing how best to jam it behind several beams so that the Aussie dockers wouldn't be able to get it out. This was an elaborate game which had been going on between both sides for years, and, when the Brits did manage to get something well and truly stuck in a hold, they would often write on it in chalk: "Get this out you Aussie bastards".

I found my fellow stewards sitting around their table in the dining room discussing the "ovies" for the trip; the overtime of three hours a day which could add up to a considerable sum after an eight-month trip. They seemed friendly and funny enough when I told them I was the new engineer steward, and it didn't *look* as if there were any overblown queens among them.

There *were* three queens among the stewards, as it turned out, but they were getting on a bit and unlikely to get dolled up in lipstick and glad rags and go roaming around foreign ports loudly searching for men with big dicks. One was fifty-two-year-old Gerald Rockingham-Walsh, who claimed he was a Lord of some kind with royal connections. Peter, an officer steward, a quietly spoken and secretive man, often mentioned his "husband" back home and the Captain's Tiger, Joe, was an amiable and podgy gay, always smiling or laughing gormlessly.

The other engineer stewards were Ted, a young Scouser of about my age with whom I teamed up; Archie, a South African lad with a high forehead and my cabinmate Paddy, an Irishman with a nice line in satirical humour when he wasn't imitating the chirping of a budgie.

We signed articles of employment and, the night before we sailed, a group of deckhands, carpenters and stewards went out for one last piss-up in the dockland pubs. The group was excited because this was a prize trip in Merchant Navy circles, travelling out first to Australia, which wasn't much cop, they said, because it was full of Australians, but then going on to New Zealand, which was God's own little acre largely because it was full of sex-starved New Zealand girls who queued up on the quay as soon as you got in and were all gagging for it.

The girls' problem, Ted told me, stemmed from the fact that New Zealand men drank so much they couldn't get it up or weren't even bothered. In consequence New Zealand girls flocked to the quays in Auckland or Wellington and were so desperate for it you practically couldn't get down the gangway before you were nobbled and dragged off somewhere.

This seemed the perfect place to dump my virginity, which was beginning to weigh me down heavily. I *needed* to get rid of it but became very gloomy in the pub when Ted told me he'd picked up three doses of the clap on his last trip to South

America. You knew you'd got it, he explained, when you tried to take off your sheet after you'd woken up and found your dick stuck to it. There was this sharp, ripping feeling down there.

My new shipmates were always going on about the fifty-seven different varieties of clap and, as most of them claimed to have patronised just about every brothel in the world at some time or other, they probably *had* contracted almost all fifty-seven varieties between them. If you ever got crabs, Paddy liked to say, all you had to do was rub sand and whisky into your pubic hairs whereupon the crabs got drunk and stoned one another to death. Never go out with a girl with big hands, was another of his little tips because it makes your dick look small.

I was apprehensive as the dark outlines of the Liver building slipped away from us into a foggy dawn. I could already see that my shipmates were flawed or deranged in various ways. They were renegades to a man and their mood could turn quickly. You never saw it coming: one minute they would be happy and cracking jokes and the next they would become raving lunatics screaming obscenities, wanting to hurt someone – anyone – with unexpected and unprovoked violence.

My job on the *Canopic* was to look after eight engineers and electricians, cleaning out their cabins, waiting on them at meal times and serving them morning coffee and afternoon tea. It was an easy job, particularly after the arduous eighteen-hour days on the paddle steamers and my charges, no more than glorified garage mechanics, seemed happy enough with me as I was with them.

I could always manage a two-hour nap in the afternoons and spent the rest of my time smoking fags, drinking beer or yarning with the rest of the crew. We were allowed three cans of beer a day from the stores and an unlimited supply of duty-free cigarettes.

Many hours were lost simply leaning on the ship's rail, particularly around sunset, smoking and watching the swelling patterns of the waves. Sometimes you spotted a tree trunk or a bit of rubber and you watched with fascination until it passed from view. There was a memorable moment when an armchair sailed past sideways into the sunset, prompting a long meditation on where it had come from and who might have sat in it.

Thus I fell into a steady routine, getting up, carrying out my tasks and surrendering to the rhythms of the ship until it was time to turn in. Those days slipped quickly into weeks as I became a small cog in the great machine which transported materials from one far-flung part of the world to another.

An interesting feature of life onboard – something, I guess, you also find in prison – was that you got to know your shipmates well. Almost everyone is full of bullshit when you first meet, particularly in the Merchant Navy where bullshit is virtually a way of life, but constant and intimate contact over weeks and months soon stripped that away.

Gerald Rockingham-Walsh's royal connections became increasingly wobbly. He was always leaving letters lying around addressed to some Lord or other. Ted opened one and found the envelope stuffed with lavatory paper. Peter confessed to me one night that he didn't have a husband back home because the faithless bastard had left him long ago for another man. On the other hand, in all the time I shared a cabin with Paddy, he was always an amusing and enjoyable companion but I never learned a single thing about his background and whenever I asked him anything about his past, even something simple like where he had been born, he clammed up, got angry and hard-eyed, asking why I wanted to know these things.

When we made an unscheduled stopover to load cargo at Genoa I went ashore with Ted into the Gut or the Dirty Mile, a narrow, cobbled street of smelly drains and bars jam-packed with sailors and whores. Excitement buzzed in the air and it grew ever louder as the drink went down and fights broke out with one bruiser laying into another with awesome ferocity.

These people lived on the edge, to the accompaniment of loud music, the throwing around of wads of money and unlovely shags with tattooed tarts. It was prudent to sit in a quiet corner of these bars and be fast on your feet. Otherwise you'd get dragged down into a whirlpool of violence, ending up covered in blood and holding up a leg of a chair as the *polizia* steamed through the door.

Ted, who liked to pretend he knew about such things, took me on a guided tour of the Gut, explaining how much the various whores charged and how we were going to drink our way up and down and find a whore to bang within an inch of her life. We wandered from bar to bar, meeting shipmates while Ted tried to establish the going rate and we poured down a fair few of the strong Italian beers. Far from getting drunk, though, I was becoming more and more sober. There was every prospect I was going to lose my unwanted virginity in some fleabag Italian brothel and the thought of it filled me with a curious mixture of horror and despair.

I recalled the way Henry Miller, in *Tropic of Cancer*, lived in an area like this in Montparnasse where "semen ran in the gutters". He was a struggling writer, always hungry, broke and haunting the American Express office daily for a cheque which never arrived. One night he danced with every slut in the joint and tried to do some woman against a lavatory wall but, no matter how hard they tried, he couldn't get it in and ended up spilling his load over her new dress. Later he was strolling along the boulevard Beaumarchais, full of rapacious whores who hardly gave you time to unbutton your flies before it was over. There was no difficulty with them. They spat on your cock and shoved it in for you.

This sort of writing struck me as truthful with insights and observations that went to the heart of things. It seemed to me I simply had to do the things Miller had done if I wanted to get where he'd got. I needed such experiences to become a real writer like him. I simply had to do it. And yet ... and yet ...

Ted seemed in no hurry to strike a deal and I was calming down a little when the whores and sailors thinned out and there were just three people left in this one bar: Ted, me and a monstrous whore with eyes like a pair of tarantulas and tattoos all over her enormous breasts which seemed to foam in every direction. I groaned when Ted asked her: "How much?"

"Short time. Tree tousand lira."

"Too much. One thousand."

"Two tousand. I give you nice time. Best two tousand you ever spend. Your friend, he want?"

"All right. I will give you one thousand and Taffy here will give you one thousand. But you do me first. I can't do seconds with Taffy."

The next ten minutes were the longest of my young life as I flung down beer after beer. "It wasn't bad," Ted announced with a broad, silly smile when they returned. "A bit rubbery but it wasn't bad and she washes herself too. Then she washes you. And those tits!"

"Your friend want go now?"

"No, no," I cried, raising my hand and waggling my fingers in the direction of my nether regions. "Problems down there. Wouldn't get a hard-on. Really. Not tonight."

The whore drew herself up to her full height, threw out her Himalayan tits and asserted with huffy hauteur: "I will get you hard-on my bambino. If you no get hard-on you no pay."

She grabbed me by the wrist and dragged me out of the bar like a bad dog about to get a sound thrashing. Up a rickety staircase we went and into a bedroom where she told me to undress and get on the bed. Not asked, *told*. I caught a whiff of her garlic breath that practically laid me out.

I lay back on the bed looking up at a picture of the Virgin Mary with a neon red heart. Despite all I had drunk I was shaking like a jelly and sure I wouldn't get another hard-on before next Christmas. There might have been a slim chance without the Holy Mother looking down on me but, as it was, none. The whore noisily washed herself between her legs and I gulped as I saw that her arse was bigger than her tits. She beckoned me over to the sink and washed me. Then she marched me back to the bed and laid me down on my back. "Relax bambino," she kept saying. "Relax. Can you relax? So, relax."

When Henry Miller was with Germaine in that Montparnasse knocking shop, she soaped herself and gossiped about this and that. Then, advancing towards him, she began rubbing her bushy twat which became, for Miller, a treasure, a God-given thing. "And it was good, that pussy of hers," he wrote. Afterwards he bought her a drink and they had another shot at it. "For love, this time. And her rose-bush was again fine." He even thought he might be faithful to her.

There was no chance I would ever be faithful to this Italian horror but, amazingly in the circumstances, she did manage to raise a decent erection by a deft mixture of licks and Italian croonings that took about ten minutes. Perhaps she'd found my G-spot. Whatever she'd done, it was a professional job. She straddled it with a low moan of triumph, lowered herself down on my pole and, all but drowning me in the mighty seas of her bosom, she began working her huge bum around in busy, tight circles. This was all right and I was beginning to understand what the fuss was about when the bedroom door burst open to reveal an even bigger whore with a small, comatose sailor in her beefy arms. The two whores began arguing so loudly that the snoozing sailor

49

woke up and I lost the erection which mine had worked so carefully to build.

When the door closed again I indicated I'd had enough and wanted to leave but she pushed me down and got my dick to stand to attention again quite nicely, largely by tonguing my tip. This had never happened to me before and I really liked it too, lying back, closing my eyes, if only to avoid the accusing stare of the Virgin Mary. Then my ears picked up on an odd clicking noise. I realised it was the sound of her false teeth rattling as she worked and with that realisation my erection firmly and finally collapsed and was posted missing, presumed dead.

Henry Miller wouldn't have approved but it was a start, I suppose. I'd gone so far it simply had to be a matter of time before I did it properly *and* left it in to soak. At least now I could talk as good a tale as all my shipmates.

But the truth was my continuing virginity was shaping up into a major personal disaster. Being unable to do it with a nice, attractive girl like the one in the dole office might be comedy but failing to do it with a professional whore in a brothel was getting dangerously close to farce. There was another thing which I picked up from that Genoa night. Not a good dose of clap but a whinnying spasm of garlic-smelling guilt every time I look at a picture of the Virgin Mary.

We continued across the Mediterranean and anchored off Port Said to wait for a pilot to take us through the Suez Canal. We were not allowed ashore in Egypt so all we could do was look at the minarets on the shoreline as the white sails of the dhows fluttered across the sun-burnished sea.

A small black armada of what looked like gondolas began moving off the shore towards us complete with a rising chatter of "Johnny, Johnny, Johnny". The bum-boats of Port Said. "Johnny, Johnny, Johnny." They pulled up next to us loaded with Aladdin's caves of gaudy, twinkling rubbish: carpets, watches, ivory elephants, leather camels, thirty-six-piece tea sets, Spanish Fly, dirty photos – you name it and they had it. They gesticulated and shouted towards us – "Johnny, Johnny, Johnny" – holding up photographs, rubber dolls, coffee pots. "Johnny, Johnny ... you want ... Johnny, Johnny, Johnny ..."

The Captain had given strict orders not to allow them on board under any circumstances because they would steal anything that hadn't been nailed down. Everything went for a walk if this lot came on board and an engineer still spoke admiringly of the time when he had caught two of them walking off the ship shouldering a twenty-foot crankshaft.

There were a dozen of them, holding up items for which we were invited to haggle, passing them up in a basket before we lowered the money. We had more sense than to give them the money first. I bought a "genuine" Rolex watch for thirty shillings, ticking when I got it, but it packed up twelve hours later never to go again unless you gave it a violent shake. Ted bought something equally useless and, when the trader refused to give him his money back, stood up on the ship's rail and tried to piss over him.

The Suez Canal was as hot and stuffy as the inside of a kiln as Egypt slipped past. Palm trees leaned over tiny square houses and children flocked along the banks on their bicycles. I longed to swim in the cool water along with the tiny seahorses.

If the canal was hot, it was the inside of a fridge compared with the Red Sea that followed. The Chief Steward issued lime juice and salt tablets to make up for the sweat which oozed out of us in treacly gouts. Walking around the ship was like wading through warm water and there were moments when we feared we might stop breathing altogether as we lay in our bunks in puddles of sweat. We did almost no work in the Red Sea, lying around near portholes in which we had stuffed squares of cardboard to waylay any stray breezes and divert them in the direction of our labouring lungs.

We docked in the former British protectorate of Aden where we were allowed ashore for a few hours. Some of the men went to the local brothel, no more than a corrugated shed next to a couple of dusty palms and a moulting camel covered with scabs. The heat blasted out of that shed and the men queued up resignedly for the one whore, whom I never did see, before coming out again after about five minutes, buttoning up their flies and looking even gloomier than when they had gone in. There was even less likelihood of my getting a hard-on in that shed than there had been in Genoa. I was resigned to a life of celibacy.

It was unbelievable, when you thought about it. There I was, the sexual and social outlaw who understood completely which end of the pencil Henry Miller had used to write *Tropic of Cancer* and even where Colin Wilson had written *The Outsider* (in a sleeping bag on Hampstead Heath). Yet for all this wild and dangerous knowledge I couldn't lose my cherry, not even when I handed out thousands of lira.

The heat eased after we left Aden but there was a near-mutiny among the crew after we learned our orders had been changed. We were going to continue unloading our cargo around the main ports of Australia but, instead of proceeding to New Zealand to load as originally planned, we were now going to return along the Australian coast to load and go home via Colombo and back through Suez.

There was a lot of quarrelling in the mess rooms and alleyways and I fell out with not one but *all* the engineers I was supposed to be looking after.

Some of the old hands had warned me that stewards should never try to become friendly with the officers they were paid to serve. Yet I had unwittingly crossed all kinds of invisible lines and, if I didn't scrub their cabin floors immaculately, this now meant I was taking advantage of the familiarity that had grown between us. Maybe the engineers were just fed up like everyone else or even more disappointed that we were not going to New Zealand. Whatever the reason, they began trying to kick me around and I was most at loggerheads with the Second Electrician.

This feud escalated so sharply I began serving his food in the dining room long after everyone else: if he came down to the dining saloon declaring he was hungry, that was my cue to go missing in the galley for ten minutes and make him even hungrier. He began coming down to eat long before anyone else so I *had* to serve him but, in truth, the only way he could win this feud was by beating me up and he knew he daren't do that or his career as an officer in the Merchant Navy would have been over.

A few days later, perhaps in an effort to cheer themselves up, the officers and engineers had a riotous party for which they pooled their considerable supplies of beer and spirits. When I came to clean their cabins the next day there were half-empty bottles of spirits on their sideboards and any amount of money scattered around.

It was Ted who had told me that I must never steal a penny in the Merchant Navy. If you were caught, they might put your right hand in one of the big brass portholes and slam it down on your fingers. The Merchant Navy had always hated stealing and if you were punished like this, no one would ever do a thing about it.

This little story made such a big impression on me that I never did steal a penny on the *Canopic* – just as well since it turned out that the officers had left the bottles and money lying about as bait. The Third Engineer had set up mirrors outside their portholes and they were watching us stewards as we worked in their cabins.

Peter, who looked after the senior officers, was caught downing a couple of slugs of brandy from a bottle before topping up the level with water. He lost a month's pay for that and got a DR (Declined to Report) which probably meant his days as a merchant seaman were over. Thereafter his bitterness became implacable.

Our first port of call in Australia was Fremantle and, as soon as we docked, the crew hurried ashore and got roaring drunk. This was the regular pattern in Australia: a sub from our wages and straight into the nearest pub.

We got alternate afternoons off in port but I rarely went beyond the docks. I didn't have much money and couldn't believe that any girl would be impressed by an engineer steward. But, looking so youthful and blue-eyed, I did attract any number of gays and Paddy used to tell everyone it was the best laugh ever watching me walk through the dock followed by an ever-lengthening line of men hopeful of getting into my trousers.

Around this time I began receiving letters from my mother and was surprised at the pleasure and relief they brought me. Her lines were full of domestic trivia but it was unbelievably cheering to hear news from a normal world where normal people did normal things. She was still fretting that I wasn't eating properly and began sending me cakes the size of car wheels, posting them to the Shaw Savill offices in London who, at no extra charge, sent them airmail to me. We always seemed to be eating her cake late at night with a cup of cocoa and my mother almost alone sustained me through that trip. My father never wrote to me, of course, although that didn't stop him complaining to my mother, she said, that I never mentioned him in *my* letters. But it always remained Dear Mam and I never once asked if he was all right. We maintained our feud even at a distance of thousands of miles.

Life got nasty as we continued along the coast particularly in the ports after the pubs had thrown out. There was a considerable amount of violence on board and many of the crew, wildly drunk and as mad as hatters, fought viciously in the crew lounge. Even the funny and relaxed Paddy often ran wild and joined in the fighting although he always regretted it the next morning. *Everyone* got drawn in and there was a particularly bad fight in Melbourne where the violence was exacerbated by "The Five O'Clock Swill". Melbourne pubs closed at six o'clock, so the whole world and his canary crowded into the bars at five and threw as many schooners of strong beer down their throats as they could before closing time. The crew then bought cheap Penfold's sherry to bring back to the ship.

Concerned we had so little to do in the evening in Melbourne, except drink, the Captain ordered a television set to be put in the crew lounge. Australian television was the pits: quiz shows, corn-ball soaps and old films punctuated with any number of ads which always appeared at suffocating length before any dramatic climax. We were sitting there one night, most of us drunk as monkeys and wondering how the programmes could get any worse when one of the greasers said he'd had enough of all this f..king shit, pulled out the plug, picked up the television and dropped it over the side.

At the first sniff of trouble elderly queens like Joe and Gerald made a fast exit, closely followed by me, and that fight lasted for three hours with the crew lounge ending up in a hell of a mess, spattered with blood and most of the furniture broken. I was on deck lurking fearfully in the shadows when I heard the chill cry of "Let's get Taffy" and Paddy screaming at them to f..k off as they tried to break in our cabin door. Satisfied I wasn't there they continued looking for me but I stayed hidden in the shadows.

There was some compensation. Next morning everyone was the picture of sweetness and light. There were cuts, black eyes and even a few broken bones but there was never any question of continuing the ruck or of anyone going to the Captain with any grievance. We were all pals and the deckhand who had been try-ing to knock down my cabin door returned for help with a love-letter.

When I challenged him he claimed he couldn't remember a thing and that he would never, under any circumstances, lift a finger to hurt me. He kept insisting he was telling the truth which made the whole business of violence seem that much more impossible to understand. I had begun keeping a journal in which I spent a dis-proportionate amount of time writing about this violence and its effects. Any sort of violence or perversion had always fascinated me.

Henry Miller wrote wonderfully about the loss of his Mona. Stumbling around Paris alone he would round a corner, see a bench or a few trees and she would be right there: she and all those bitter, jealous scenes.

A thousand times he wondered if she would ever be at his side again. The very buildings and statues were saturated with his anguish. He remarked on a spot where her foot had rested and would remain there for ever even after civilisation had been wiped out. He fed on this grief. "We came together in a dance of death and so quick-ly was I sucked into the vortex that, when I came to the surface again, I could not recognise the world."

This was writing from the heart: words which I could make my own because I was still suffering in much the same way. Miller was articulating my shattered feel-ings, my certainty the intensity of my own loss would last forever.

Sandra's desertion had become a terminal illness. Sometimes I stood on a quiet spot in an Aussie dockland and stiffened to my continuing heartbreak. Like Miller I was feeding only on the bitter ashes of anguish. I wanted desperately to hold her again, to touch her, to have her by my side and look at her. These longings kept tear-ing and lashing me almost constantly from the time I opened my eyes in my bunk in the morning. I learned to live with them until I saw something else beautiful which wrenched at my insides and reminded me of her.

This kept happening to me in Australia. When I saw the black swans of Melbourne or the fantastic French architecture of Brisbane or the waters of Townsville harbour, full of fat, silver fish, I would reach out for Sandra's hand, to share this with her, to make the sight complete, instead of empty, as my very being erupted again into sorrowing requiem.

But she was never there and, when I understood and accepted this, another sword of pain slashed right through me.

The main drawback of life in the Merchant Navy was that you were almost always looking at the back of the postcard. There were the odd enchanting views but mostly it was bloody fights in some dockland bar or endless hours of swelling waves or, for me, a swarm of predatory gays swooping down on me – so much so that I had all but given up going ashore. I only had to step off the gangplank for them to sprout up from nowhere, wondering if I'd like to join them for a drink and not always taking no for an answer.

We weren't seeing Australia and all her wonders; we were the most introverted of visitors, fighting and drinking amongst ourselves, bored stiff most of the time, inflating some minor problem into a major one, if only to give ourselves something to talk about.

Wyndham was a strange, bleak port in the Northern Territories of Australia and we moored at a small wooden jetty that looked in danger of collapsing into the gulf up which we had just sailed.

The heat roasted us as we walked the mile or so to the nearest pub, surrounded by baked scrubland continually swept by clattering flights of budgerigars and parakeets. The pub was a cavernous dance hall with geckos roaming the whirling fans on the ceiling and a long bar counter lined by sundry aboriginals, adventurers and ne'er do wells, who didn't talk to one another, just sat there hunched and unshaven on their stools, getting rat-arsed.

The routine was simple. You came into this bar from wherever, found yourself a free stool, deposited whatever money you might have on the counter in front of you and drank until the money ran out or you collapsed face-down on the counter. If you collapsed face down and your money hadn't run out they left you alone until you regained consciousness, whereupon you sat upright and continued drinking until your money or consciousness were done for. Some drank in this joyless fashion for up to a week or more, then, broke and hungover, shuffled back into the bush presumably to save up enough for the next binge. We boasted we could drink on the *Canopic* but we were rank amateurs compared to this lot. Anyway we knew we couldn't get too sozzled because we always had to walk that mile back to the ship when we'd finished.

I never knew what was going on in the bush at night. It was bedlam, things forever plopping and jumping and whirring as if in some tropical swamp. You had the sense that hundreds of eyes were watching you and, apart from the plops and the jumps and the whirrs, your ears kept teasing out other things like chompings and mutterings and skitterings.

It was one great swelling chorus of noise broken occasionally by a yap or a growl. "Oh f..k me high and low, what was that?" Ted would say. "S..t, just listen to that. And that!"

Gerald and Joe would take one another's hands and increase their speed. "Oh gawd, take a look at that thing wriggling there."

There were moments when the whole of the bush seemed to be alive but we didn't pause to investigate, just skedaddled down the middle of the road as fast as we could go, given what we'd drunk, until we reached the safety of our ship. No matter how much we'd had to drink in Wyndham, we always got back to the ship stone cold sober and ready for more.

It would have been a big mistake to be totally drunk on those nights in the Northern Territories. The night sky was like no other: a huge expanse of black velvet nailed up there by thousands of ferociously glittering stars. Shooting stars fell every few seconds like the silver tears of sorrowing angels. You could never tire of looking at a diamonded sky like this. Such starry magnificence told you, beyond all reasonable doubt, that there was a plan and a planner which your human imagination could never grasp. God wasn't in my mind or life at that time. He had been driven out by more troublesome and pressing urgencies like who was screwing my missing girlfriend, why my father had never treated me as a father should and when was I going to lose my virginity.

All my teens were choked with such worries, doubts and fears and I don't think I enjoyed a single day of them.

The next afternoon we went back to the bar and I began chatting with an Aborigine who told me he shot and stuffed crocodiles. It seemed the crocs gathered in the river near the local abattoir, feeding on the offal and rotten meat that was thrown out. He showed me an example of his work, a real beauty about five feet long with a serrated back, its mouth wide open and sharp teeth ready and willing to bite.

It was love at first fright and, when he learned I didn't have enough money to buy it – he was after about £80, way beyond me – we talked a little more and I agreed to give him the thirty-bob "Rolex" I'd bought off the bum-boats of Port Said, careful not to tell him the watch's real pedigree nor, of course, how much I had paid for it.

I scooted back to the ship to get the watch, giving it the shaking of its life before I went back into the bar and, true to form, it ticked like the real thing when I handed it over to him and he seemed as well-pleased with the deal as I was. Practically the whole crew appeared on deck when I walked down the jetty with this open-jawed monster on my shoulder snarling silently at all and sundry, and even my old adversary the Second Electrician was civil to me long enough to find out where I'd got it.

We were within hours of sailing from Wyndham the next morning when Paddy charged down to the cabin. "Taffy, Taffy, there's a f..king Abo on the quay shouting he wants his f..king crocodile back and, if you don't give it to him, he's going to shove his f..king didgeridoo straight up your f..king arse."

The Rolex clearly needed another good shake but I could hardly explain *that* to him, so I picked up the croc and went and hid with it down in the engine-room until we sailed. If it was hot outside, it was almost at boiling point down there but there I remained, under the hissing crankshafts, until they began pulling me and my croc away to the safety of the Indian Ocean.

The Aborigine remained on the jetty shouting obscenities and waving his fists as we left, but I stayed in the engine-room until we were well out to sea and my engineers, always starving, began screaming for their lunch.

I still have the croc.

Faced with a month or so at sea after we left Australia, the mood of the ship hit a new low. Everyone was at loggerheads with someone over something.

I began falling out with my Scouse mate, Ted. He was getting increasingly bad-tempered with me, particularly with all the "f..king high-falutin' books" I was reading. I was reading these books only to put on some sort of pose, he reckoned.

Joe and Gerald got into a shabby screaming match that went on and on but didn't seem to have any sense to it. The trouble was we had to listen to it all day and Paddy finally went into their cabin and threatened to fill them both in unless they shut up, which they did for about ten minutes.

There had also been a dispute between the First Officer and the cook about what should be left out for his late snack on the bridge and this had got so bitter the cook insisted on knowing which was the First Officer's plate so that he could rub the end of his dick around it before it was taken out to the officers' dining room. The First Officer should have guessed there was something up when smirking faces peered out of the galley door and looked at him as he lifted his knife and fork. There were tales of cooks putting cleaning powder into the food of officers they hated.

The rough weather didn't help our ragged nerves. Most days the seas were so calm you forgot you were on a ship apart from the continual rumbling of the engine but, out here in the Indian Ocean, it could all change in a second with screaming winds ripping the tops off high waves and the whole ship groaning and creaking as if it was about to break in two. When that happened we had to keep tight hold on something – anything at all – to stop being thrown off our feet.

About nine days after we left Australia we had nothing to do except watch the swollen waves and the flying fish who, disturbed by the ship's movements, would leap out of the water around the prow and dance in front of us, sometimes on the water, standing on their tails or flying with small silver wings.

One sweltering afternoon, a nasty and prolonged fight broke out between two deckhands in the crew mess-room. Tony was a particularly gobby tough Scouser who, for most of the trip, had swaggered about the place vaguely threatening everyone he came near. We gave him a wide berth but another deckhand, so quiet and small hardly anyone knew his name or what he did, decided he'd had enough and battered hell out of him. The little feller decked Tony with a few whacking punches and, when he fell on the deck, he sat on his back and abused him for about an hour.

"You don't f..king like it now do you?" the little feller kept shouting. "You can't f..king take it yourself, can you?"

This unexpected battering of the ship's bully may have left a virus of violence in the air. Everyone was edgy the next day and you knew more was to come. Unfortunately it came my way. Ted's hostility towards me over the books I was reading had clearly gone up a few notches and he began pushing me around in the galley as we were waiting for the food to take out to the engineers. I kept backing off – I have always been good at backing off, particularly from fights – but then he threw a punch that hit me on the cheek and said we'd have to have a fight on deck after the meal was over. He continued swearing at me in the lounge as we took the meals out, much to the Second Electrician's delight, and I didn't see how I could get out of it. On a small ship like this there really was no place to run unless you decided to take your chances with the flying fish.

Ted, as he constantly reminded us, knew everything about fighting and was always going on about who he had made mincemeat of. His unlucky opponents were always three times his size and I was sure he was taking his lead from the little feller, who had become a hero of the ship after sorting out gobby Tony.

It was raining when we squared up to one another on the aft deck and I knew I had one chance and one chance only: grab him by the neck, get his head under my arm and punch him in the face a few times before my strength ran out. He might be so surprised by this he might give up there and then. *Might*.

Plan A worked like a dream for maybe twenty seconds. I grabbed him by the neck, got his head down under my arm, punched him a few times straight on the nose and asked him if he'd had enough. But the bastard had clearly had far from enough. He wriggled out of my hold, pushed me down on to the deck, climbed on my back and began raining punches down on the back of my head which I tried to cover with my arms. I had no strength to retaliate so I just lay there in the swirling rain with my face down on the scabbed iron deck as this lunatic kept hitting me and shouting: "You don't f..king like it now do you? You can't f..king take it now can you?"

I caught a glimpse of the Second Electrician smirking at me through one of the portholes as I was pounded by Ted's fists and matters took a turn for the worse when he grabbed me by the hair and bounced my head on the deck.

"We were watching and would have broken it up if Ted had tried to throw you over the side," one of the deckhands said later. "When these fights start they've got to finish in their own way or they'll keep happening."

If I was upset that no one had come to my help I was even more upset when I looked in the mirror afterwards and found my face a mask of cuts and welts, a black eye which was almost completely closed and a row of bleeding bumps all along my forehead.

"Everything all right now, Taffy?" Ted asked cheerily as he stuck his head around the door. "I thought you'd f..king got me at the start. I really thought I was a f..king goner. Good scrap though."

The odd feature of this fight was its aftermath. Even with my bashed-in face or perhaps because of it, I became a sort of hero. Everyone seemed concerned and even the Captain asked what had happened and smiled when I said I'd walked into a door.

"There must have been an awful lot of doors wherever you were walking," was all he said.

Ted brought me a few cans of beer, saying he was glad it was all over and out of the way between us because now we could become good mates again. *What* was all over between us? But that suited me fine because I certainly didn't want to go another ten rounds with him. All he'd got was a tiny cut on the side of his chin and, when I pointed this injury out to him, he claimed he had nicked it shaving.

Even the deckhands gave me a bit of a cheer in the mess-room. I'd had the reputation of a college coward, it seemed, but now I'd gone up against a much tougher kid and stood my ground – well, for twenty seconds anyway – I had proved myself even if that wasn't quite the way I saw it.

These reactions were based on nothing sensible. All I'd done was receive a beating and remained the same chopsy and confused Celt after the fight as I had been before. The cuts and bruises cleared up within a week and it was as if nothing had happened. The beating didn't help me to grow up or anything like that.

Nevertheless the random violence on that ship gave me a lot to think about. Violence was clearly not as it seemed and its outcome never predictable. Some, like the little feller, emerged on top through violence, but there were others, like me, who also emerged on top when we had been losers. Ted complained a few times during the rest of the trip that it was as if I'd actually won that fight and later I learned that a few seemed to believe that I *had* won it.

The ship's mood changed again in our final ten days at sea. We knew the voyage would soon be over, but by now barely anyone was talking to anyone else. It was as if we had withdrawn into our shells with hardly the energy to come out of them, even for a brief argument or fight. None of the engineers or officers was speaking to me, which I didn't mind at all. You could tell by the narrowing of their eyes that they really would have liked to have beaten "that student prick" senseless – and would have if they thought they could have got away with it.

I gave them their food with bad grace, barely cleaned their cabins and, if I didn't like their tone when they asked me for something, went missing and let them find it for themselves. All I wanted to do now was get to university and get on with whatever it was you got on with at university.

So I did a lot of leaning on the ship's rail and chain-smoked as I watched the eternal quarrelling of endless high waves, particularly in the Bay of Biscay which was rougher and wilder than any of the rough, wild seas through which we had so far sailed. I saw some of the formless rhythms of my own life in those waves and kept wondering what hostile shore I might get shipwrecked on next.

Wave-watching like this, I thought about my future and my imagination created various scenarios about what it might be like, say, being a great writer, drifting down to Spain for the bullfights or living in my own penthouse in New York or giving grudging interviews to the BBC or even signing my own books in bookshops where the queues would stretch right around the block. I would be the toast of literary

London, drinking with my mates, John Osborne and Kenneth Tynan, after I'd written my first novel.

This novel would be about a lad who had lost his virginity at the age of ten, turned queer by the age of fifteen and then gone on to discover the mystery of life in a gold-plated Gothic castle in the Sudan. There would be no mention of failure after failure in the knocking-shops of the world. This was where my nineteen-year-old mind was: packed to the gunnels with the ideas and postures of others.

There was no end to these daydreams; they sloshed around my mind before building and swelling like the biggest of waves, only to collapse again and start surging around to form another in which there would be women who would flock to me insisting I take them home to meet my mother who would feed them all with her prize-winning cake while my father, sitting there in his best suit, would tell me that he had never meant to be so nasty to me.

I never knew who I was or what I was about and, if I ever did manage to get hold of a coherent concept of myself, it rarely lasted for more than five minutes before it turned into another mirage. I was like those waves in the Bay of Biscay, continually re-forming and re-shaping but never going anywhere at all. The more threatening reality became, the stronger my protective daydream.

The atmosphere on the ship brightened with what is sometimes called "Channelitis" on our last night at sea: everyone was cheerful our long voyage was coming to an end. The tradition is that the engineers give their stewards a bottle of Scotch or a few quid at the end of a trip, but I didn't get anything from anyone – not even a word of mumbled thanks – which told its own story.

Not that it mattered. All I wanted to do now was take my crocodile home. But we sailed straight into Liverpool and a national seaman's strike. We weren't allowed to sign off and our shipping company wanted us to stay on the ship for a further ten days so we could unload our cargo, some of it perishable, around the ports of Britain. If we didn't do that they would withhold our money for the whole trip until the strike was settled.

Angry union meetings were called in the mess-room and Shaw Savill finally relented but, for some reason, they insisted on stamping all our discharge books with the dread words Voyage Not Completed which, for a merchant seaman, was almost as bad as getting a Declined to Report. Only Peter was happy with this arrangement since he'd already picked up a DR and apparently you couldn't get both.

I didn't give a stuff what they stamped in my discharge book. They could have put Lazy Welsh Prick in it for all I cared. I'd got my money and, after signing off, I hoisted my crocodile on to my shoulder and headed straight for Lime Street Station where I caught the next train to Cardiff.

EIGHT

Cardiff University, in 1960 a loose gathering of old and modern buildings scattered among the towering Edwardian civic edifices in the city centre, was a party waiting to get going. I arrived in Freshers' Week, drank too much, was nervous and permanently sick because, even after three or four years, my whole being was still in tatters after Sandra had dumped me. Did this go on for ever?

Quite soon, though, I was up and running as if I'd been there for ever, loving my brilliant new friends, enjoying raucous debates, fancying intelligent and unattainable girls, writing for the college newspaper and gate-crashing parties. In fact I loved every bit of it except the studies.

For my first year I chose English, History and Philosophy. English was particularly uninteresting: a trudge through Anglo-Saxon and Shakespeare (again) with an unpleasant, self-regarding lecturer, Dr Moelwyn Merchant, who would drone on for two hours about the first two lines of *A Midsummer Night's Dream* without benefit of notes. He thought himself incandescently clever but most of us thought he was a creep and a charlatan and every time I spotted his shiny bald head I had to suppress a strong urge to give it a good slap.

The English department ignored the twentieth century in Part One and the few tutorials I attended made it clear that I could no longer rabbit on about the existentialists but had to read set texts and address the issues in them.

"Every man with a belly full of the classics is an enemy to the human race," Henry Miller had written but the lecturers weren't the slightest bit impressed when I mentioned him in one of my essays.

History was even more of a fog. Not only was I getting nowhere but, except for Dr Henry Loyn, the lecturers were uninspiring.

English and History might be nose-bleedingly dreary, but Philosophy was worse. I had anticipated long discussions about existential angst or the meaning of suffering and all they wanted to talk about was Plato, linguistics or mathematical logic. I never understood one single thing about mathematical logic and linguistics were wholly impenetrable, largely concerned with what we may or may not say. "If it can't be said it can't be said and it can't be whistled either," as one philosophical buffer had it.

My idols Sartre, Kierkegaard, Barbusse and even dear old Henry Miller were all obsolete, according to the tenets of current philosophy. Everything had changed with AJ Ayer and the logical positivists who had emerged in Oxford just before the Second World War. The trend was towards clarity and precision in language.

The tutors quite liked it when a student made a contribution of his own, however silly. But you then had to explain exactly why you thought what you thought. Wild polemics or even simple abuse weren't acceptable: you had to rubbish the rubbish with academic precision. You had to be dry and impenetrable: you certainly couldn't run at it like a bull at a gate so that was me locked out of the philosophical farmyard.

Gilbert Ryle's *Concept of Mind* was about as adventurous as it got. There wasn't the ghost of a mind inside the machine of the body as Descartes proposed, Ryle argued. The mind and the body were one and on this premise he re-interpreted traditional Cartesian thinking on what we might mean by imagination, intelligence or thought. I read this book with glimmerings of understanding but finally met my nemesis in the rotund shape of Professor de Selincourt, one of the Senate members who had awarded me my state scholarship.

He was a cheerful old buffer with a pince-nez always perched perilously on the end of his nose and a most unfortunate stutter in which he started with a completely different letter to the word he was trying to get out. "So we s-s-s-s-s begin today with …" he would splutter. He threw sherry parties for us and drove us home afterwards – even when rolling drunk. We tried to avoid such lifts because he drove with one index finger on the steering wheel and was as short sighted as Mr Magoo. "Tell me, have those d-d-d-d- traffic lights changed yet?"

A classical scholar and expert on Plato, he sat me down with one of my essays one morning and, starting with the first word, asked me what I meant by it. Well, of course, I didn't have a clue. Peering at me through his pince-nez, he asked me what I meant by the next word. He drilled holes into my every word and phrase like a deranged woodpecker at work on a delicious piece of rotten wood. I hated the whole hour – and him. He had humiliated my pretensions and I was in tears when I left. Yet I had probably learned more in that hour than in any other hour of my life. Whether I knew it or not and whether I wanted it or not, my education had finally begun.

It soon became obvious I would never become a philosopher. I liked the world of high ideas well enough and might even have been able to make my way in it but I simply didn't have any aptitude for the dry, technical stuff which, rather like crosswords, you either can or can't do. "It's like chasing a black cat around a darkened room," I wailed in one of the tutorials.

Yet my friends, the intimidatingly bright Pam Stagg for example, seemed able to get hold of it just fine, reeling off their tight, well-argued essays and getting As while my papers came back covered with exclamation marks, red scrawls and even oaths, barely meriting an E for effort.

If I couldn't be a philosopher, I could still be a writer, and I was soon working on a new novel based on my time in the Merchant Navy. I had not been able to write about that at sea, largely because of prying eyes on the ship, but I was now spinning out a Jack Londonish story of the seven seas, with all the characters doing strange, if not incomprehensible acts in exotic places. It never occurred to me that they might do something comprehensible in ordinary places.

The book didn't have much of a story – well, no story at all, I guess, since I was again watching foreign films at the Globe: *Last Year in Marienbad*, for example, in which nothing happens very slowly with lots of shadowy flashbacks and time displacement. The sex scenes were terrific, though, going on and on in a most satisfying way, so there were now going to be lots of them in my books too, with not a trace of coyness anywhere. I was also smitten by slippery concepts like "the long, dark night of the soul", or how you might fulfil yourself through violence, which I spun out on the backs of fanciful phrases stolen from a book I had read recently.

It was rubbish but, in my youthful blindness, I thought it rather good, if not engagingly brilliant, and even after a few months at university I was toying with the idea of dropping out into some garret where I could finish it. I might have done that but for two lecturers who persuaded me otherwise.

I took my manuscript to Terry Hawkes, a much-respected English lecturer who always called a shovel a shovel. He was aghast I was thinking of giving up my studies to work on the manuscript I'd shown him. "Don't go putting all your eggs into this extremely little basket," he said. "It's immature, turgid and derivative from a multiplicity of sources."

The other lecturer, who urged me to stick to my studies, was my philosophy tutor, Lynn Evans, who could see I was floundering badly in this dry linguistic sea which he'd had a lot to do with creating, having written his own fog-ridden books and papers on semiotics and linguistics. "Stay with us and try to last it out," he said. "You are a queer cove like Rousseau. You have lots of ideas spilling out everywhere and, if you stay here, we will give you the discipline to deal with them. It doesn't matter that you don't understand these things. Indeed you will forget almost everything as soon as you graduate – we all do. But you will be left with the discipline. You will be able to argue your corner in a logical manner and say what you mean. I know you want to become a writer but get to grips with the basics of philosophy and you will eventually become a far better writer."

Evans indulged me, never complaining if he didn't see me in his tutorials for months at a time. Had it not been for him I might have been thrown out but, thanks to him, I had the confidence to stay on at university even when it was clear to all that one of their state scholars understood hardly a word he was reading. At least Prof de Selincourt didn't threaten to take my scholarship from me.

I am not sure how I became a Socialist or indeed how anyone becomes political. Political beliefs are always the ideas of other people: at a certain age we take on a core belief like, say, the brotherhood of man, and build on to it ideas that fall within the framework of that belief. These ideas are not then refined or elaborated in any particular way. When it comes to the exercise of pure intelligence, political beliefs don't qualify.

It was inconceivable I should be anything but a Socialist, born as I was in Pontypridd, a small town locked in a permanent traffic jam at the entrance to the coal-mining valleys of South Wales. I had even lost my grandfather in a pit accident in nearby Ynysybwl and my father had worked for a few days down the same pit, beginning on his fourteenth birthday, until he was rescued by an uncle, a mines inspector, who got him fired.

My first view of these resolute class warriors came as a child at the Miners' Gala which, like the funfair, came each year to Sophia Gardens in Cardiff. These were times when the National Union of Miners was a powerful union and the various lodges marched behind their huge banners to the golden ooompah, ooompah of brass bands. There were sheep-dog trials, brass band competitions and marquees full of ruddy faced, blue-scarred miners slopping down gallons of beer. The main attraction was the meeting outside the pavilion where the leaders displayed their brilliant eloquence.

I understood little of what these leaders were saying but they seemed gods massing at the summit of Olympus as they sat on that makeshift stage with their drab suits, fob watches in their waistcoats and Brylcreemed hair, taking it in turns to step up to the microphone, which kept squealing with distortion, as they laid down the left-wing law, interspersed with regular applause. Their words had a rousing effect on the assembled miners who looked up at them with hero worship in their eyes.

It was this thing about words again, the way they could be harnessed to control, move and inspire people. The man with the words had the keys to the kingdom. One man in particular, with a round, boyish face and the sun of the morning touching his silvery hair, was up on that stage each year. Aneurin Bevan, founder of the National Health Service, knew everything about words: despite a stammer and a strong Welsh accent, he captured the men's minds and hearts with short, eloquent hooks and had them cheering heartily.

My father claimed he was a Socialist but wasn't very clear what this meant and it was Cardiff University which first challenged my political ideas, sharpened them up and enabled me to explain positions on issues of the day.

Everyone seemed to be left wing and we met in the Students' Union, the city bars and the late-night restaurants where, over a chicken curry off the bone, we shouted beer-amplified arguments about South African oranges or The Bomb or America at one another.

What had started for me as a few dimly remembered words in the speeches at the miners' galas began coming together into a vague socialism. These political ideas started in ignorance and were nourished by fashion as perhaps are most such beliefs. We were all Socialists then. Such Tories as existed in the university – maybe six of them – were fat, dim bastards.

It was in the Students' Union the following year that I became aware of a ginger-haired mass of noise echoing around the building. You could hear him almost everywhere you turned, haranguing assorted groups, telling tall stories to gales of laughter or inviting us to worship the ground Aneurin Bevan walked on. The air was vigorously stirred when he was around and you didn't have to make any effort when you had a conversation with him because he did most of the talking.

"Who's that?" I asked a girlfriend.

"Oh that's Neil Kinnock, the new big noise in the Socialist Society."

Later I shared a house with Neil and he was a hurricane of energy, always an early riser and often singing a hymn to himself before getting out of bed, a habit, as can be well imagined, which wasn't much appreciated by the rest of us in that small house. He was up and gone before everyone else, organising street demos against South Africa in general and campaigning against their oranges in particular. I never saw him study anything in connection with his subsequent degree in industrial relations and history, but he was a voracious reader of almost anything except books about industrial relations and history and particularly enjoyed the long sentences of Norman Mailer.

He contributed a lot to my nascent socialism and I absorbed much of what he said because I admired the passion and verve of his principles. Freckled, with a strong jaw, he personified the fire of the Welsh coalfields and seemed to have thought hard about everything. He influenced me, I guess, because I wanted to be like him. I wanted to share his political ideas, even if I was naturally far too anarchic to submit to any coherent political beliefs.

Neil was the most humane of men with the great gift of pity, once breaking into tears at a party when a man told him about the injuries he had received in the pits. He never forgot or forgave an insult and would never strip off to the waist – not even when playing football on the beach – since he never liked anyone looking at his body. He was a through-and-through chapel puritan who hated sexual license. As soon as he spotted Glenys Parry in debates there was no other woman. He understood immediately that she was exactly what he needed. Glenys was quiet, thoughtful, loyal and, of course, left wing. They always seemed to be singing from the same hymn sheet and, if you fell out with him, you fell out with her.

Others there included the lantern-jawed Craig Thomas, much fancied by all the girls. He went on to become a successful thriller writer with Clint Eastwood starring in the film of one of his books, *Firefox*. There was Owain Arwel Hughes, our most notable Welsh conductor; Steve Morris, a fine writer and poet who later settled in France; Ian Edwards, star sports reporter on ITN; Keith Ward, now Regius Professor of Philosophy at Magdalen, Oxford and the mighty Vincent Kane, arguably the finest debater of his generation, who had been mainly responsible for lifting the *Observer* Mace several times for Cardiff University in the Inter-University Debating Competition as well as winning the *Sunday Times* best individual actor award.

The forum for all these megalomaniacs was the debating chamber in the Students' Union on Friday nights when, well-refreshed by Hancock's beer in the nearby Alexandra Hotel (there was no bar in the Students' Union then) we gunned down everyone in sight with our reckless assertions. They all got blasted by our youthful and dogmatic certainties on those packed, stormy nights and it never crossed our minds that we might be wrong about anything. If it came out of our mouths it was, by definition, true and that was the end of the matter.

I discovered, to my surprise, that I had a voice that projected well and I made people laugh. This was a mystery to me: I never told dirty jokes, nor did I ever try to be funny. All I ever did was stand there, project my voice and try to be *un homme sérieux* but the result was always the same. I might start with a few stale quips – "I'd like to thank you all for coming here tonight and want to assure you what a great honour it is to have me here …" but the more I attempted to be serious the more the audience corpsed with laughter. Even when I paused and said: "Now I want to be serious for a moment …" it was always the cue for them to start falling off their chairs. I *wanted* to be taken seriously but, every time an invitation came in to take part in a debate at another university and the motion seemed to require humour, they sent me.

There were some real orators in debates. Neil Kinnock, later to be acclaimed the finest platform speaker in British politics, could not get into our top six to enter the annual *Observer* Mace debating competition in his first year. His problem was that he would often get passionate and fearless but then forget what he was being so passionate and fearless about.

Those debating nights also said something about the enduring Welsh love affair with words which I had first heard at the Miners' Galas. It wasn't money but words, we realised, that were the key to everything; words alone would open the doors that we wanted to open; they alone would change the world if only because words were the sole means by which we could express world-changing ideas.

This love of words may also have been at the heart of my growing hatred of modern philosophy, which seemed to me the very enemy of poetry, rhetoric and polemic. Saying what you mean and setting out your stall carefully and clearly was all very well but how did you talk about what was in your heart? How could you talk about how it might be possible to live on a diet of anguish? What was it that made you fall in love or moved you to tears?

My erratic sex life took a real turn for the better when my father, who *was* speaking to me occasionally that year, asked if I fancied a small Morris van which he could pick up for £20. He even offered to pay for it.

This van – FKG 328 – with a mattress in the back soon opened up new vistas of sexual delinquency. It never mattered how drunk I was when I drove it since there was no breathalyser in those days. The passenger seat hadn't been screwed down properly. Given a sudden jerk, it would fall over backwards throwing any passenger up into the air, legs akimbo, neatly landing her flat on her back on the mattress.

I rattled around the city in my passion-wagon, from dance to party and party to dance, almost always getting lucky with my offers of a lift home, particularly if it was raining. Boys with wheels did well with the girls then – as that bleeder, Mike the Worm, would probably have testified – and I always seemed to have a good time on that mattress late at night unless the girl was particularly tight and unwilling to allow access to my marauding fingertips (or else objected to being parachuted backwards onto that mattress – in which case they were invited to get out immediately).

The Part One exams at the end of our first year at university were the most feared of all: if you failed them, it was the big chop. The university let it be known that they would probably fail a third of us and there would be little chance to re-sit. As students we were five per cent of the population, but soon we would be down to three or four. Why they felt the need to threaten us like this I don't know but one lecturer repeatedly suggested that, if we fouled up in any way, we would be intellectually scarred for the rest of our lives. This was our one and only chance: fail now and you were on the scrap heap.

If we passed Part One we would go on to study a Pass Degree in two of our chosen subjects or, if we were good enough in one subject, we could join a group of around twelve strong and study that for an Honours Degree. Get on an Honours course and you were certain of some kind of degree. They never threw you out of an Honours course whatever you did or didn't do, or so they said.

Debates were suspended, as was just about everything else, and we retreated to our various caves to try and pack a year's study into a few weeks. I tried to develop a routine in the Reading Room of the city's Central Library, but no sooner had I arranged my books, set out my carefully sharpened pencils and opened my virginal notebooks, than I was either out on the stairwell, chatting and smoking, or in one of the local cinemas watching any old crap that might be on, or even joining the dossers in the Greyhound getting some scrumpo down my throat and soon too drunk to care.

The Students' Union was all but deserted. A giant cosmic vacuum cleaner had sucked all the fun out of the air. Some bobbed up for a cheap lunch and a lot of the others went down with the runs or spasms of the shakes.

Terror held sway. Most students didn't want to disappoint their parents after raising their hopes by getting there in the first place and many more were frightened stupid by the prospect of having to get up off their arses to find a job.

Those huge lecture halls, with their rising terraces of desks at which we sat in our academic gowns, frowning over unanswerable questions, became sickening assemblies of tension and pain. As the question papers were turned over you could hear muted squeals. Some candidates dashed for the door, never to be seen again. You could feel the concentration and gathering fear in the belly.

The three hours of every paper went soon enough. I always tried to answer every question, usually scribbling anything that came into my head. We held post mortems afterwards about what we'd written or hadn't and by the time all the exams were over I was so convinced I'd failed every subject I didn't wait for the results, but took the next train to London where I was hoping to sign on with the Merchant Navy again.

I knew a little about their ways by now and the first thing I did was to ruthlessly expunge my Bohemian, student image. I had a severe haircut, put away my black polo-neck and donned a suit, collar and tie which I bought in an Oxfam shop.

The 'disguise' worked and the Employment Officer at the Pool of London hired me for the *Rhodesia Castle*, which was about to sail on a three-month voyage through Suez and around Africa. Experience again came to my aid when I hauled my bags on board and didn't tell a soul I'd been to university or that there was a remote chance I might still be at one.

I didn't talk much at all, simply kept smiling at everyone deferentially and the Second Steward didn't throw me in with the raving queens either – there were plenty of them around – but assigned me to a cabin with five others, one of whom may have been a queen but, if he was, certainly wasn't letting on about it by dressing in drag in the evenings in the Pig and Whistle. My other cabin-mates looked pretty normal and gave no indication of having been locked up in the jug for GBH or been caught by the police standing on a bucket shagging a donkey.

I chummed up with Derek Williams, a tall, pleasant lad with oily black hair, who took me under his wing and gave me tips for survival in the silver service saloon. He let me in on such secrets as where to hide your silver so other stewards didn't steal it or how to carry six plates on one arm. If you found yourself serving a particularly delicious steak – or anything else you might fancy – you hid it away in your dumb waiter to heat up later in the crew galley and went back to the passenger galley for another steak. Any steward worth his salt could eat better than any passenger in First Class, Derek taught me. But never nick the passengers' wine. It was half-expected that you would nick their food but *never* their wine.

Meanwhile, everything in the saloon had to be sparkling and spotless because we were due to sail in three days.

I was shaking badly next morning when I rang my friend, Elfryn Lewis, in Cardiff and asked how I'd got on in Part One. My body went numb and I was sick over the kiosk floor – that *bloody* girl had destroyed my belly for ever – when I heard that I had not only passed but been offered an Honours course in either Philosophy or English. English! There had been a lecture in Anglo-Saxon at nine o'clock every Saturday morning but I had never once attended. And I'd had some nasty run-ins with a few of the lecturers over late or silly essays but that's what Elfryn said. Craig Thomas had been offered the same course and I was pretty sure he'd never got up in time for that nine o'clock on Saturday morning either.

The Philosophy department was no less keen for me to join them, Elfryn added, and they knew I was about to sail to Africa but wanted to see me before I went. This sounded ominous, but I knew it was going to be philosophy for me. Being a philosopher had a certain ring to it although, to this day, I've always regretted not choosing English.

So that afternoon my grandmother died again and I had to get to her funeral. The Second Steward gave me a day off and I went back to Cardiff where the Philosophy department had gathered to meet me. They were amused to see me with my short hair and Oxfam suit and wanted to know what I was up to in the Merchant Navy and how long I would be abroad. Then we got down to the purpose of our meeting.

Yes, they wanted me on their Honours course but needed to make it absolutely clear that I had to work this time. I had to submit myself totally to the discipline of philosophy and, if I did, I might even end up with a First. "Submit to it and not only might you make a decent writer but you might even become a decent philosopher. You've got plenty of ideas and all you need to do is bring them under control. Your essays are an alarming mixture of intelligence and ignorance and we'd like to try and get rid of the ignorance." There were also books to be read this summer and we'd all start with a clean sheet in the autumn. "And don't go starting any trouble in Africa – hah, hah – the poor Africans have got enough to worry about."

A First! This was a turn-up in the logical positivist ranks. They had spent all year dismissing my work as crap and no one had ever suggested a First as even a wild possibility. Professor de Selincourt had once publicly wondered if I'd got any O-levels. Yet they now had some faith in me, they said, which they hoped wasn't misplaced. I didn't get it. How could I lift a First in a subject I could barely understand? But I promised to work hard when I returned then went home to see my mother – now in despair at my determination to keep running around the world – took the next train to London and sailed for Africa.

NINE

The *Rhodesia Castle* was a small city, set out on many decks and governed on military lines. The officers were segregated from the crew who, in turn, were segregated from the passengers who were strictly divided between First and Tourist.

You could wander for miles through corridors past huge state rooms on the top deck and down through the bars and the lounges, the concert hall and the dining rooms before confronting the huge iron doors of the crew's quarters where you could again wander for hours. Red fire extinguishers punctuated a giant maze of alleyways feeding into one another or halting at abrupt dead ends. Through open cabin doors you could glimpse a cameo in each as the crew whiled away their free hours reading or arguing or darning socks in between their duties. Then they would scurry about doing tasks which, although often separate, came together for the sole collective purpose of transporting, entertaining and feeding hundreds of passengers on their way to Africa.

Passengers were never allowed to see the crew at work, except for us stewards in their dining saloons where we were encouraged to melt into the background, to try to anticipate the passengers' needs from afar and become a part of the elegant furniture of the place. Five courses were listed on the dinner menus specially printed each day but most of my lot normally settled for soup and a main course.

I was given twenty passengers to look after on two separate sittings: an odd bunch which included one big family bossed by a colonial traffic policeman who had remained working in Nairobi after Kenyan independence; a philosophy lecturer who was going to work at Cairo University – and didn't make the subject any clearer to me – and a bank clerk and his wife, a pair of starched farts who behaved like identical twins and inspected their silverware minutely before every meal.

Most of them were parasitic little racists who had found a soft spot to live on the African belly. They never failed to put in a slight sneer if they were referring to the blacks who did their household chores, looked after their children and generally ran their house for a pittance. These people were being sent by their companies as cheaply as possible and they never quite knew how to behave in the dining saloon. The Nairobi policeman often became unusually gruff and unpleasant about his "rights". Within two or three days of sailing I developed a strange, uncomfortable relationship with him because whenever he made some stupid and trivial complaint about how he'd always hated French mustard and did it have to be on the table, I backed away and became detached. Then he'd become excessively friendly at the next meal.

I had a few ongoing feuds with some of my other passengers too, particularly the snooty banker and his ossified wife who had triumphantly spotted a smudge of lipstick on one of my drinking glasses. "I say," he announced loudly to most of the restaurant, "there's lipstick on this and it's not a colour my wife uses."

You needed a strange combination of talents to deal with neo-colonial twerps like these and I didn't have any of them. Derek got on fine with his passengers and they were always bunging him fat tips so that he could enjoy himself ashore. I guess he knew exactly what barrier to stand behind: when to say something and when to shut up. I never knew when to shut up or back down and we hadn't reached Port Said before I realised I had fallen out with all my passengers except the philosophy lecturer, who was about to disembark anyway. I tried not talking to them, but everything had now gone beyond repair and, not only were those on my tables complaining about me audibly among themselves, but they had also sent a deputation to the Chief Steward asking if there was any way I could be replaced.

The Chief Steward called me to his cabin that night and I knocked on his door expecting a fearsome bollocking. He could not have been nicer as he pulled out a few beers and explained my shaky position to me.

"What you've got to remember, Taffy," he said in a soft east London accent, "is that passengers in the tourist section are all bastards. If I 'ad my way I'd lock them all in the engine room and lower them a bucket of water and a bale of 'ay every few days. But, as they're 'ere and they pay our wages, you've got to be a lot smarter with them than you are. Are you getting me drift so far?"

His drift was that no matter how wrong and unreasonable the passengers might be I must, without fail, act as if they were reasonable and right. I had to learn deference, how to kiss a few strategic arses now and then.

I liked him a lot. When it was time for us to end our little chat, he said he would have a quiet word with my passengers and assure the "bastards" that I was going to turn over a new leaf. Indeed I promised to improve my behaviour for the rest of the voyage but soon realised I'd left it too late.

What I should have done was take a lead from the queens who were remarkably efficient stewards, always clean and immaculately turned out, with a deadly eye for detail and an ability to deflate any awkward situation with a little camp joke that made everyone laugh and forget whatever it was that was upsetting them. They were superwomen and I liked to sit with them in the evenings in the Pig and Whistle where, all glammed up in their powder and paint, they were forever taking the piss out of one another or loudly plotting to get so-and-so out of the engine room and into their bunks. I liked being with them so much that Derek once wondered if I was on the turn myself. I denied it stoutly but my worry about it was real enough – and continuing – and I was afraid that, if I did give in, I might like it and give up women before I'd even got started on them. And would I end up a bender or a stabber?

Being an outsider like James Baldwin or Alexander Trocchi was all very well but I didn't want to get so far out to sea that I might never make it back to the beach. Should I go with the writers I admired or hold back and try not to court new experiences that seemed, well, unnatural? My sympathies were with queers but that didn't mean that I had to sleep with them. Or did it?

They kept trying it on but I pretended I'd gone deaf when any dirty invitations were issued and they gave me up as a lost cause, although they didn't mind me sitting with them. They were funny and generous company and, as the drink flowed, the Pig seemed to stink of sex as the loudspeakers blasted out loud, heart-attack rock'n'roll and we danced around together.

Derek and I walked out of the port of Mombasa and under an archway of giant elephant tusks into the old town full of narrow streets and wooden balconies. This was my first taste of Africa as we looked around an old museum with cells from the days of the slave trade.

I always let Derek go slightly ahead of me because I admired the way he walked and tried to copy it. With his shoulders up, he let his arms dangle straight down his sides and kept his whole body erect. It was not so much walking as gliding. I thought it cool and did my best to reproduce it, to show I was tough and yet relaxed, calm but ready to pounce.

We continued walking until we realised we had walked right through the town and, with the sun blasting down murderously, it was time to get back to the ship. There was real hostility in a lot of the locals' eyes. On the way back to the ship we came across a little drinking joint, the Black Cat, which we decided to check out.

It was a dump with holes in the ceiling and empty buckets standing around to catch the rain. We caught the edge of a lot more hostile stares but they did agree to bring us some cold beers which went down so well on such a hot day we asked for more.

Others drifted in, as did a few of our crew, when a mob of black whores turned up and the forlorn joint turned into a dance party with booming African music, lots of drink and the laughing whores swarming all over us asking what might be our hearts' delight.

The atmosphere degenerated from there because a group of us were swigging large rums. The combination of the drink and African music soon had me well away and I was dancing with a really big, black whore. The only activity I've ever enjoyed more than dancing is drunken dancing and I've scarcely suffered any form of depression which I couldn't drink and dance away in a couple of hours.

Me and the whore were having a great bop when I became vaguely aware that a huge, confused fight had broken out with buckets rattling and bouncing in all directions. I wasn't sure who was fighting who – or about what – but there were plenty of punches being thrown and, instead of buzzing off fast, I stood there trying to figure things out until everything went dark. I learned later from Derek that someone had bashed me on the back of my head with a bucket.

What happened next, again according to Derek, was that the woman I had been dancing with picked me up and carried me off on her shoulders. Derek spotted me floating past and thought it a bit odd because this woman stopped to talk to some of her mates before she left while I hung off her shoulders like a dribbling fox fur stole.

I awoke the next morning feeling like a bucket of arseholes and opened my eyes to behold what might have been the biggest, blackest whore in Africa lying naked and still asleep next to me.

There was a lump on the back of my head and my arm was aching because my yellow fever jab had reacted badly. The pain from the bump and the jab was barely distinguishable from my hangover so, in desperation, I nudged my new girlfriend awake and asked if she had a bottle of beer. She sat up with a groan and walked into her kitchen with her huge buttocks moving like a pair of perfectly synchronised blue-black Indian Ocean waves. When she returned she handed me a bottle and collapsed back into sleep although I had to wake her again to ask if she had a bottle opener. Her hand stretched out, took the bottle off me and she prised the top off with her teeth, the whitest and most perfect set of gnashers I've ever seen.

I sat upright swigging the beer, belching and reviewing my position. My old boy seemed to be quivering with a life at odds with the rest of my body so this was surely my big chance. This *had* to be my big moment. There would be no worries about unwanted pregnancies, no bother about disease – not in those days, anyway – no outraged fathers with shotguns and no silly questions about whether I'd respect her afterwards. She would hardly track me down to Cardiff all the way from Mombasa if she did fall pregnant, so all I had to do, after I'd finished this beer, which was already making me feel slightly better, was lower myself between those two big legs, give her a good rogering and my unwanted virginity could finally be dumped on that distant African shore and I could go home a man.

She must have become aware of my needs – she was a whore after all – as I began clambering over her enormous body. There was certainly some sort of erection getting its act together as I continued my climb and I managed to locate her tiny rosebush, which might have had five pubic hairs around it, trying to guide my dick in as best I could.

As this artful seduction continued she simply lay back with her legs apart and eyes closed, content to let me get on with it as I started what might have been the meanest, driest screw in the whole long and sorry story of human fornication. She neither moved any part of her body nor gave so much as a token wiggle of her bum and I was losing my uncertain and erratic momentum. What kind of whore was this who wasn't even pretending she was engaged in the same act? It was dry as sawdust inside her too and then I became distracted by strange noises which I couldn't quite locate until I realised she was snoring into my left ear.

All my expectations – along with my erection – collapsed and I sat up to finish my beer before getting dressed. I seemed to have quite a bit of money left in my pocket, so she must have been one of the last of the great amateurs. Professional whores, I had been told, always relieved you of all your money so I left her a few quid for her trouble and let myself out. It's a pity I hadn't managed it – she had a great laugh and wonderful teeth – but that's the way it was.

My virginity was a terminal condition.

Stewards were expected to work aboard ship in the mornings, taking every other afternoon off when in port but, after finding my way out of the shanty town in which I had ended up, I decided not to return. I couldn't face anyone while I was still half-drunk and more confused about my sexuality than ever. Perhaps I would *have* to turn queer. I was having no luck on any other front. That bash from the bucket was still throbbing as was my yellow fever jab which had developed into a nasty big black scab.

I took a long walk, strolling under a Mombasa sky of the most uncompromising blue, looking up at the spidery shapes of the coconut palms. Crickets whirred in shimmering heat hazes and every so often multi-coloured birds flew past in streaks of fluttering gorgeousness. This was the Africa I had known from the cinema and I half expected a lion to dash across the road pursued by Stewart Granger with a gun. Those poxy films again!

The oxyacetylene heat was making me dehydrated, if not delirious. The palms were reeling and I knew I was going to have some sort of funny turn, staggering across a parched desert with everything swirling around as my lips cracked and I grew desperate for an oasis. My arm throbbed and I was wondering what to do when I did come across an oasis: a small hotel perched on the edge of a blue lagoon complete with riffling sea, a crescent of the whitest sand and palms leaning over the beach in the postcard manner. I signed in and, after drinking gallons of water, put myself straight to bed where I slept the sleep of the dead.

The penalty for going missing in Mombasa was swift and expensive. As soon as we sailed the next morning, I was hauled up with other miscreants to face the Captain who, in full Captain's regalia and with the ceremonial sword on the desk in front of him, listened to our tales of drunkenness and desertion before deciding on a suitable punishment.

"I had an injection for yellow fever which went septic on me, Captain. I was walking on the outskirts of Mombasa when I came over sick and dizzy so I signed into a hotel."

"That was one night. You went missing for two."

"Well, Captain, that's how long I kept feeling sick and dizzy." I wasn't going to tell him how one of his Union Castle stewards had been desperately trying, but failing, to lose his virginity in a shantytown brothel. "Two nights, Captain sir."

He made no further comment and logged me a week's pay.

The dreaded ship's inspection took place every Thursday morning when the Captain and three or four of his chief officers toured the ship in full uniform and woe betide anyone who caused their white gloves to become soiled. Those gloved hands went everywhere, behind girders and into lockers as you stood next to your bunk togged up in your saloon best: black bow tie, crisp shirt, polished shoes and silver buttons glinting on your white jacket.

After our cabins the inspection party proceeded to the dining saloons and I knew my Merchant Navy game was fully and finally up when I walked in to serve lunch and found that everything on my table had been pulled on to the deck by the Captain. "This is the worst table I've ever seen and I don't care who's looking after it, he's not to come into this saloon again," he shouted.

The Chief Steward was apoplectic. "Taffy, there was bits of dried cabbage all over the f..king silver, tea stains on the f..king tablecloth, rust on the f..king salt cellar and water in the f..king drinking glasses. It was an absolute f..king disgrace so you're now on the f..king chain gang and you've lost another f..king week's pay. Now f..k off out of 'ere."

The f..king chain gang! It sounded as if they were about to start flogging me hourly for the rest of the trip although all it meant was that I was confined to cleaning duties. My financial position was also dire. Unlike the other stewards, I hadn't picked up any tips from my passengers. I had subbed the full amounts allowable on what I'd earned to go ashore and, with the loss of two weeks' pay, it was looking as if I might have to pay *them* something to get off this ship at the end of the voyage.

A further financial penalty was to come because I lost my daily three hours of overtime. Apart from all that, my new job was a doddle. All I had to do was turn up outside the galley at nine o'clock in the morning with the three other delinquents on the chain gang and the Second Steward would point out an alleyway that he wanted scrubbed.

We kicked a few buckets of water around for half an hour or so, but the Second Steward had no interest in us or what we were scrubbing so we were finished by ten o'clock and I spent a lot of time on the deck, reading and sunbathing when we were at sea, or exploring the African ports when we were tied up. It was expected that I return before they sailed although they let it be known that they wouldn't mind much if I didn't and found my own way back to London.

Even though this trip had turned into a holiday cruise I wasn't pleased with myself and kept thinking of the Chief Steward's earlier words that, if I was no good at this job, then I would never be any good at anything. It wasn't a major career setback to have proved I was a hopeless steward but I had meant it when I told the Chief Steward that I was going to buck my ideas up and I'd hoped to take a nice lump of money home when the trip was over.

It was dawning on me with some force that I was a useless person, not physically or mentally equipped to do anything properly. I was studying a subject I didn't understand and was pining for a girl who had left me years ago, still often throwing up twice a day because of her. Blimey! I couldn't even get rid of this virginity I was shouldering around the world like some huge yoke.

What never occurred to me was that I was probably as capable as anyone else at waiting on tables or scrubbing floors. It was my rebel-dog ideas, along with dreams of becoming famous, largely picked up from modern literature and the cinema, which had done for me.

Such thoughts made me all the more determined to become a writer. Then I would be able to work as I pleased without someone standing over my shoulder threatening to stop me a week's pay if I got out of line. Being a writer is the ultimate dream of the true anarchist. Not only does he get to express himself but he also has the freedom to go to hell in his own way.

The main ports of South Africa – Port Elizabeth, Durban and Cape Town – were a severe shock. There was nothing remotely subtle about the way three million whites dominated eighteen million blacks. Wherever you walked, you came across *Whites Only* signs on the park benches, the buses and the drinking fountains. Even more distressingly, the *Non-Europeans Only* signs were always on the unpainted benches or the dirty seats at the back of the buses.

At the docks' exit you saw a notice with an excerpt from the Mixed Marriage Act, clearly directed at randy seamen and warning us that there should be no fornication between blacks and whites. The punishment for this would be a fine, whipping, prison or all three.

They rarely bothered to fine or imprison you I was told, just gave you a sound whipping and sent you straight back to your ship. I'd met a deckhand who'd been whipped for this but he refused to show me his scars and said he didn't even show them on a beach because he was so ashamed of them. "I would have shown them to everyone," I said. "I would have worn them proudly on Barry Island beach like a badge of honour."

This white supremacist society was obscene and, just on short walks around the city or town centres, you couldn't fail to be radicalised; couldn't fail to sympathise with people like Neil Kinnock when he was organising street demos against apartheid. Simply to see it meant you had to lift your voice, no matter how small or weak that voice might be. Only those with hearts of stone could fail to identify with freedom fighters like Nelson Mandela, Oliver Tambo and Walter Sisulu who were trying to organise the African National Congress and sow the seeds of a revolution which would blow this blasphemy apart.

This poison seemed to have spread right through Africa. In almost every port I visited there was evidence of mounting friction between the races even in countries that had been given their independence: Tanganyika, for example, where I got into another fight at a dance hall in Dar es Salaam.

Perhaps it was simply because I was a hopeless dancer but there I was, bopping around with this nice, laughing lady when – as had happened in Mombasa – I became aware of a fight whirling all around me. It wasn't quite the same this time but at one stage I realised a lot of the dancers had formed a corridor and were inviting me to run through it and make for the exit. I'd had quite a lot to drink and thought this might be some new kind of dance like the Gay Gordons until I realised these dancers were protecting me from others who were desperate to fill me in. A few of them were shouting in real anger as if I'd been trying to get off with their mothers. I wasn't trying to get off with anyone: just wanted to enjoy a little bop.

It made no sense. There I was, trying to show them a few steps, and that seemed to be the cue for every African in the room to start fighting. If there had been a career in starting trouble I would have been brilliant at it. Everywhere I went some kind of trouble ensued.

Cape Town, with its grand old buildings, financed by the slave trade, lay at the foot of Table Mountain and was a fine city to walk around, always smothered in warm sunshine. I noticed some extravagantly beautiful white women lounging around the alfresco bars and took a cable car up Table Mountain which was so flat it was as if some deranged god had sliced off its summit. I spent a few hours walking about and looking down at the city or out at the surrounding peaks or in the direction of Robben Island where my hero Nelson Mandela was to spend so many of his sacred years.

I was walking back to the ship late that night when I came across a chain gang digging up the road. This was not at all like the chain gang in which I was languishing on the *Rhodesia Castle*: these were all black, manacled together and singing their tribal songs as they wielded their picks and sledgehammers. One man, the leader I guess, sent up a call which produced a response from the others. The tone was majestic and sorrowful: a people calling on their God in choral prayer as they broke up the road.

There were about twenty of them and I stood transfixed and moved to tears as they continued singing and working in the warm darkness. We all knew how the whites had circumscribed and criminalised the blacks in this godforsaken country and here they were in front of me, chained together and singing in the mournful tones of their homeland tribes.

The large whites of their sad eyes were compelling and their songs powerful, riven with pain. I felt joined with them: me, the useless European in his own chain gang, symbolically manacled with his black brethren in theirs and all of us singing in our frustration that the world was such an unfriendly place. Simply watching them work told you that here was a country that was committing the primary evil of interfering with a people's growth; a country that, one way or other, was heading straight for trouble and bloodshed.

As I stood there, tearfully listening to those picks and sledgehammers smashing into the road and hearing the song of a people to a God who had abandoned them, on this white supremacist night in Cape Town, there were other voices too: the voices of Mandela, Sisulu and Tambo, singing their own songs of the freedom which would eventually be theirs.

I failed to get out of my bunk a few days after we left Cape Town, but no one came looking for me. It was as if I'd ceased to exist and it was clear that, if I didn't bother them, they wouldn't bother me. Others on our chain gang also disappeared into the cavernous belly of the ship. I got my meals from the galley as usual and spent most of the day reading or sunbathing or sloping around looking for someone to talk to. I even began sitting in the First Class lounge but, when I stupidly accepted a drink from one of the passengers, a steward recognised me and flung me out.

Far fewer passengers were around on the return trip to London and fewer still when we hit a fierce storm on the last leg of our voyage in the Bay of Biscay. Large liners are normally so stable you hardly know you are at sea, but everything changed in this storm as we hit waves as high as oak trees, the bulkheads groaning as if wild beasts had been trapped inside them. Every now and then you'd pick up the brittle music of breaking glass or splintering wood.

Trays of cutlery and glasses lifted up and took perilous flight across the dining saloons. Some people found corners of lounges where they sat under blankets looking deathly white, but most stayed in their bunks, not so much because they were seasick but because their bunks were the safest places to be. In such wild conditions you never knew which way you would be pitched next and several shoulders were put out of joint and a few bones broken.

Even the Pig and Whistle was deserted. The crew had got fed up trying to drink out of glasses which kept flying off the tables. We could have been on the *Mary Celeste*. Groaning corridor after groaning corridor was empty with all the cabin doors closed. Such storms are like illness or pregnancy: you are sure they will last forever.

Eventually the storm lifted and we found ourselves approaching the white cliffs of Dover, a weak sun on a flat sea. The Second Steward came looking for me and I was expecting to be put on a fizzer for something or other, but he was all sweetness and light, noting that I'd picked up a nice tan and inquiring, with a light sarcasm, if I'd enjoyed my cruise.

The point of his visit, he went on, was that the crew were expected to complete a declaration stating whether they wanted to sign on for the next trip. Now the Jesuitical catch was that, if I signed such a declaration, they would have to give me a bad discharge. But – a broad smile here – if I said I didn't want to return they would give me a good discharge so that I would then be free to go and cause trouble for another company.

This seemed exceedingly thoughtful of Union Castle and I was more than happy to confirm that I would never darken their gangplanks again.

"Well that's fine then isn't it, Taffy? Everything is now settled between us and the Chief Steward told me to tell you that he hoped you would have some sort of career somewhere as long as it wasn't anywhere near him. There's no real harm in you Taffy. You're just a f..king useless steward."

TEN

Back at Cardiff University I started my second year, once again wrestling with philosophy, a contest I never once looked like winning.

I was really trying this time. I *did* want to understand Kant's ideas on time and human consciousness and I *was* desperate to grasp the nature of syllogisms and I *absolutely* wanted to understand everything there was to understand about mathematical logic but I couldn't get my usually hungover brain around any of them.

Early in the first term I wrote an essay on the Irish philosopher, George Berkeley, who'd had the revolutionary insight that material substance does not exist. What do exist are spirits that perceive ideas – or our perception – and the ideas they perceive. Thus the world is what we perceive and nothing more. Things cease to exist when we stop perceiving them although God continues to perceive them and gives them a regularity.

These ideas have stayed with me but in my essay I asked in what way does this idealistic position differ from the solipsism of a child who, when he leaves the room, has the notion that the room ceases to exist? This was a sensation I had often experienced as a child and I was sure that one day I was going to turn around and see what a dark fraud life was. I would rush into this fraud and see nothing but nothingness. At the end of the day we know almost nothing at all about *anything*; we think we know a lot but the truth is we don't understand ninety-five per cent of anything.

My moral philosophy tutor thought my point was pointless and wrote as much in the margin. You couldn't win. Whenever I did conjure up ideas of my own they were slapped down by some academic smart-arse. Yet they'd said they wanted me there because I was prepared to come up with ideas of my own, so what was going on?

All they really wanted was essays like the ones they'd received the term before. This would prove they were promoting their own theories as successfully as they had the term before that, and we were all coming up with the "right" notions which would get us a B-plus and a transfer to the next course, where we would all think like those poor saps on the last one. Those who opposed the tutors' ideas were laughed at and dismissed. Whatever they might have said to the contrary there was only ever one way to think in philosophy: *their* way.

I did understand Ernest Gellner's *Words and Things* which examined current linguistic philosophy and denounced it as a load of horse feathers. Wittgenstein and his cronies had established an astonishing hold over a generation of philosophers, Gellner said. Wittgenstein had argued that the limits of his language were the limits of his world and thereafter philosophy had become solely preoccupied with questions of language.

Gellner attacked this linguistic sterility with great gusto and his book started a marvellous row. Gilbert Ryle, then editor of *Mind*, the magazine for philosophers, refused to review it, Bertrand Russell attacked Ryle and there was a correspondence in the *Times* and even a leader on the subject.

Modern philosophy had nothing to do with the real world, said Gellner, although his real charge against it was that it was petty and boring. Gellner wanted philosophy to become closer to the social sciences; he hoped it would get back in touch with society.

This was invigorating stuff and I had found myself another hero except that, when I quoted him in an essay, I was firmly told that Gellner was mad and I shouldn't take any notice of him or his work. My disillusion with philosophy was profound.

All my mates seemed suspiciously happy. Neil Kinnock was looking industrious and carrying around loads of impressive books (which we were sure he never opened). Craig Thomas, never a braggart, wandered through the Common Room looking as if he already knew Clint Eastwood would film one of his books.

Despite all my righteous resolutions, I couldn't just go through the motions with philosophy and *pretend* I was getting the hang of it. Pretence wasn't my style so I went back to my bad old habits of staying in bed until noon and driving my van to the Students' Union for lunch. I had lost interest in everything, so bored all I could think of was that another attractive young girl might come along with whom I could play find the sausage on that smelly mattress in the back of my van.

Then I met Pete Hawkins, who was editor of the student newspaper, *Broadsheet*, and I began writing for him under the pseudonym Vinny Roberts. These short articles were more to my liking, done and dusted in a few hours without having to research or work out closely reasoned arguments with footnotes. "I give polemic and abuse therefore I am." My first piece caused a storm and I saw that, if I ever became a journalist, never even a vague ambition until then, I might start a world revolution.

It was a double page spread with the headline THOSE IN THE SHADOWS and a photograph of a man standing in the lamplight of a street. I explained what it was like to be a homosexual leading a life full of isolation and pain. I used everything I had learned from my conversations with the queens in the Merchant Navy and could write with some authority on the way their lives had been cruelly criminalised.

It was a strong piece, written with drive, if a little overcooked: I didn't write it as objective reportage but in the first person. I, Vinny Roberts, was as bent as a butcher's hook. I, Vinny Roberts, a fellow student, was riven with pain because of my growing sense of isolation. I, Vinny Roberts, wanted acceptance and understanding and didn't want to spend the rest of my life in the shadows. There was greater impact if I wrote it in the first person and anyway the pseudonym would protect me. Only three people knew the identity of Vinny Roberts and one was me.

Everyone went crazy, the first person to freak out being the student who had been photographed for the feature. He hadn't been told what the photograph was for and, even though he was but a shadowy blur in a lot of other shadowy blurs, he feared that everyone would finger him.

The college got in touch with the Editor and asked who was the homo in their midst. There was even talk of stopping the grant to the Students' Union if this filth continued. Meetings were held among the academics but never came to anything, particularly as it was common knowledge one of the male French lecturers wore eye shadow. But they did let it be known they didn't want to see anything like this in *Broadsheet* again.

I had miscalculated badly when I thought my pseudonym would give me anonymity. I thought no one would be bothered to seek out Vinny's identity but *everyone* bothered and when it leaked to one it leaked to the whole lot. I knew I was well and truly buggered when I walked into the student refectory and everyone stopped eating and stared at the arse bandit about to have lunch with them.

A staggering farrago of emotions whirled around me — sympathy, anger, derision. I could hardly believe what I'd stirred up and was pathetically grateful not to be queer or there would have been a host of other issues to deal with.

A few students sought me out in private and asked how genuine I'd been in the piece and why I'd written it. I told them about those I'd met in the Merchant Navy and how I believed someone should speak up for them. Although those students never said as much, I knew a few of them were gay and that they had chosen this indirect way to thank me for what I'd written.

I was certainly right about their loneliness and fear and this was the one piece in a lifetime of journalism that I've never had any regrets about. I had managed to take an issue and ram it straight up everyone's nose. It was also the first sign that journalism might be a good career and suit my talents. You communicated to everyone in newspapers, not just the literary few, and I'd certainly communicated my anger and compassion to everyone connected with those Stasi bastards who ran our university.

In the burbling, wintry weeks before Christmas, when everyone gets happier, I was getting really down as Sandra's shadow darkened over me. She continued to haunt my dreams, just standing there with hands on hips and frowning at me, telling me to push off again and again.

But then I was with a few pals late at night in the Cellar, a Cardiff coffee bar, when another pal, Mike Arcos, came in with a girl who he introduced as Kay. She had a lovely, inquisitive manner, asking us all kinds of questions about ourselves when an elephant hair bracelet on my wrist caught her eye. "What's that then?"

"Oh, I've got a girlfriend in Mombasa and she gave it to me as a birthday present."

She turned to question my pals and we were enchanted by her. It helped that she was drowsily beautiful although it was her laughter I warmed to the most, not just in her lovely, full mouth but in the way her whole face lit up, her teeth flashing when she found something funny.

Kay wasn't going out with Mike, I discovered, so I offered her a lift home in my van which, despite a loud chorus of disapproval from the others, she accepted. We parked outside her house in Whitchurch, a twee middle class suburb, and smoked a lot as we chatted about this and that. She wanted to know it all, what I'd done, where I was going, and I was amused to find myself showing off, telling her about my philosophy studies (not *too* much about them) and how I wanted to become a writer about issues that mattered if only I could one day sit down long enough and get on with it. I kept taking up subjects and then abandoning them after a few pages, I said.

"Perhaps you haven't found the right subject."

"Perhaps."

"I'm sure you'll know it when you see it. You'll say 'Ah, now that's exactly what I want to write about'."

I was already smitten by her deadly combination of looks and charm. She was slightly older than me and I didn't understand why there were no boyfriends around.

"No, nothing like that," she said firmly. "Never been interested really."

We must have sat there for hours until we ran out of cigarettes and she said it was time for her to go in. I was going to get nowhere with her on that disgusting mattress of mine and I didn't even try it on. I was mildly disappointed when I leaned across to kiss her only to be offered her cheek. Ah well, early days yet.

She looked at me oddly before she got out of the van and there was something inquisitive yet sad in that look, almost as if she wanted to ask me a question to which she knew I couldn't possibly have the answer. But she did give me her telephone number and we agreed to go out again. I drove home warm with hope and cold with a disappointment I couldn't understand.

We continued going out together for maybe a month, enjoying the pictures and the odd dance. She came alive on the dance floor, particularly after a few drinks, and our favourite haunt was the Casablanca, a converted chapel in the docks where, to the hottest rock, we might bop until daybreak and fall out of the door sweating and exhausted into a seagull dawn rising over the Coal Exchange.

I particularly loved to dance with her in the slow numbers because I could take her in my arms and we could become tenderly intimate. She was a gorgeous armful and I liked to feel the warmth of her breath on the side of my neck. Otherwise there didn't seem to be any emotion – certainly no sexual emotion – in her. She might heat up briefly and offer me her lips, but no sooner was I enjoying their touch and finding parts of me warming up than she would become coldly aloof again and I would begin to feel an inarticulate anger and growling frustration. About the best I could manage was to hold her hand when we were walking down the street. She didn't mind that and I loved the fullness and warmth of her hand.

I kept going out with her because she had so many brilliant qualities. She was always lovely to look at and enjoyably funny. And there was that charm too: even when I was annoyed with her she could get me to do things which I did not want to do. She also managed the almost unprecedented achievement of winning around my father.

If she called and found him sulking and farting in front of the television she would sit down next to him and ask him questions. He would haruumph and splutter but, when she continued her questions, he would open up, even, on one historic moment, turning down the volume of the television so that they could concentrate on their conversation. When my friends had come to see me he had been known to turn the volume *up* so this was a renaissance in our house. My mother and I sat in the background dumbfounded as they continued chatting. He didn't like it when I said we were late for something and had to go.

My mother could never remember him talking to anyone as he did to Kay and it was the more mysterious because he was always completely sober when he got chatty with her. He even invited us both into the sacred inner sanctum of his club one night where we played a few games of bingo.

"You just don't listen to him," Kay said. "Everyone wants to tell someone something and, if you come up with the right questions, you'll always learn something interesting."

Our relationship staggered on but I was becoming increasingly miserable, sometimes ringing Kay and telling her I couldn't make it that night. She never argued, never raised her voice and always said something like, "Oh, well, you know where I am. Ring me when you do want to do something."

The limited physical contact had become a wall between us over which I was finding it difficult to speak let alone reach. Kay was far more beautiful and intelligent than Sandra, but it was the young hairdresser who kept haunting my body, reminding me of how we could barely look at one another for more than a few seconds before dragging each other into some back lane. I had been spoiled by Sandra; I had never come close to meeting anyone as vital and hungry as her.

Everything changed the night Kay and I went to see the film *Breakfast at Tiffany's*. This lovely, sentimental film told of how a high-class call girl, Holly Golightly (played by Audrey Hepburn) meets a struggling but rich writer, Paul Varjak (George Peppard) and how they fall in love in the streets and parties of Manhattan.

Holly enjoys staring through the window of Tiffany's, the New York jewellers, as she eats a hotdog for breakfast. She is liable to suffer from the mean reds: "The mean reds are horrible. Suddenly you are afraid but you're not sure what you're afraid of."

Their affair is chaotic and Paul is almost permanently miserable because of Holly's eccentricities which he can't even start to understand.

Perhaps predictably I identified with the writer all the way through the film, seeing myself and Kay in the relationship on the screen and deciding that Kay might indeed be beautiful and beguiling but all I was ever going to get was misery and bewilderment. Almost before I got Kay home from the cinema I was announcing that I too was suffering from the mean reds and it was time to call it off between us.

"I've got to think about my studies, so we are going to have to give it a long rest," I said as I kissed her lightly on the cheek and opened the passenger door.

"If that's the way you want it."

"That's the way I want it," I affirmed and offered no further explanation. Something in the film had convinced me that it had to be over between Kay and me.

She looked at me with what I *thought* were tears in her eyes before nodding and getting out of the van. The only time I had seen her show any real emotion was when she walked away from me that night with her head bowed and shoulders slumped. That was a shuffle of despair, a sure sign of what was going on inside her. Whatever her problem might be – if indeed there *was* a problem – I was never going to solve it.

About ten days later Kay dropped me a note *begging* me – that's the word she used – to see her again, adding that there were things she hadn't told me about which perhaps she should have. Kay never begged for anything. If it wasn't offered she walked away. I met her in a pub in the city centre where, over a few drinks, and after swearing me to secrecy, she told all.

"The long and short of it is that I got pregnant very young," she said, tears falling silently down her cheeks.

I practically choked on my pint. "What?"

"There's not much more to say, really. I got pregnant when I was sixteen but I lost it."

"And the father?"

"He's still around. You've met him in the house a few times. Joe, my brother's friend. It happened at a party on New Year's Eve. We'd had a lot to drink and I ignored the pregnancy until it was too late and I was sent away to a farm to have the baby. Joe was keen to marry me, even began camping out on the front doorstep and crying all the time. But I didn't want him after that."

She told of the way her father had cried when he learned about the pregnancy. Her time on the farm. The return home. The long tussle with Joe. The rejection of him and other men. The way her emotions had frozen and how she came to believe that, if a man so much as fondled her breasts, he would know that she had been a mother.

So that's why I'd always got precisely nowhere on that front. And she asked so many questions of other people because she didn't want to answer any questions about herself.

She knew that men found her attractive but she drove them all away in the end. I seemed different. She thought that in me she might finally have found someone who could understand her plight and, outside her family and Joe, I was the first person she had told the full story. She could see I was drifting away from her but there didn't seem to be anything she could do about it until I had forced her hand by ditching her. She knew she had to do or say something even if it took a long time to decide what. So she had resolved to tell all and hoped – *really, really hoped* – that she'd done the right thing and I wouldn't think she was some sort of fallen woman.

I tried to be equally frank with her and told her I was sure we could get through it. I was very fond of her too and would never under any circumstances think of her as a fallen woman. Some men might take fright at her story, I could see, but I had never been much of a chapel moralist anyway.

We had a lovely, long smooch in the van that night and, even though my wandering hands never wandered anywhere out of bounds, I drove home blissfully happy. Kay had opened up and that was all I wanted. I would pick up all the pieces and Sellotape them back together. She would become whole again.

Even as I write these words, tears come to my eyes. It had never started to work out for us however hard we tried. The night of the big confession was the only night Kay ever made me happy. All she ever did after that was fill me with sadness. The opening bars of *Moon River* still bring tears. She was one of the loveliest women I've ever met.

ELEVEN

I was now well-established in the Debating Society and learning fast about the way you kicked off a speech with a few jokes and then bashed around four or five simple main points, with a few poetic observations here and there perhaps, before arriving at a passionate conclusion. I was becoming good at convincing people of positions I didn't occupy and the Debating Society sent me around the country to speak at Aberystwyth, Sheffield, Swansea, Bristol and Dublin. I enjoyed these jaunts immensely because I was treated so well, usually with a dinner and a good party afterwards.

Speaking at the Literary and Historical Society in Dublin was the most intimidating experience with several hundred certifiable Irish students packed into the lecture hall baying for your blood. They shouted, screamed and banged the desk lids if they didn't like what you said. Or even if they did.

"Whatever the feck you do, don't stop speaking or these bastards will eat you alive," the President told me.

The night turned into a ferocious battle of words. It was like addressing a thousand drunken soccer hooligans. They shouted obscenities and screamed abuse but I kept haranguing them and they did listen in the end. Some of the Irish debating team spoke like angels force-fed on Guinness and, after several votes, when mysterious motions were passed and others defeated, we all went to a party and caroused until dawn.

My clearest memory of that Dublin visit was going to Mass early the next morning, bottles chinking in the pockets of our dress suits as we made our way down the aisles. No matter how wild it got in Dublin you always ended up down on your knees at Mass early the next morning. It was their way of saying sorry for everything, I guessed. The Irish clearly had similar problems to the Welsh in that respect.

Later I took my communioned hangover on a bus to nearby Blarney Castle. They say that whoever kisses the stone will always be able to charm his way into a woman's bedroom or become a member of parliament and, although this is bollocks, it *was* a moment of pure pleasure when, with no one else on the battlements and the sun beaming down happily, an old Irishman held me as I leaned back to kiss the stone and was duly vested in me the gift of eternal eloquence.

Kay and I were still seeing one another regularly but it was very much one step forwards and two steps back.

We usually went out twice a week, once together for a drink and the other for a dance with friends. When we were alone we would drive out to Wentloog Castle where, no matter how we started the conversation, we always ended up at the same terminus of her "interesting condition," as the Victorians put it. But it was only in these conversations that you understood her private tragedy: how such an event could wreck the life of a young, middle-class, convent-educated girl who would never even smoke in the street.

Working class communities can absorb illegitimacy but the self-regarding, church-going middle classes of Wales looked on it with horror and often drove the poor girl out of their midst.

I was genuinely interested in her story and our discussions provided some therapy for her. Afterwards she could become warm in unexpected ways. I would have done better had I been a trained psychologist though, because she could also become moody and tearful for no reason and ask to be taken home early.

We kept seeing one another but you never knew what was going to happen next. One day she turned up in a foul mood caused, she finally admitted, by a couple who had stayed in her house and who she had heard making love in the next bedroom. She had wanted to pound the wall but just bit the pillow and lay there crying silently until it was over. She had been in this black mood all week.

Then, against all the odds, she would become dreamily sensual and make me unimaginably happy for a while. But such times were short-lived. She would suddenly go cold and accuse herself of being a trollop at heart. No one I've ever met has been less of a trollop at heart but this constant self-criticism must also have been a large part of her problem.

"You'll never know what it means for me to let you touch me there. I enjoy it but it brings everything back and I freeze. Don't waste your life on me."

Our story was a parable of the times – or at least the Welsh times, I thought. It was 1961 but the laissez-faire attitudes of the Sixties had still to reach Wales. What we were trying to do, in our different ways, was make a path through the dark and tangled forests of Cymric guilt and we weren't very good at it. You could never enjoy anything in Wales without feeling guilty. Fun had to be punished and followed by a suitable bout of remorse. These were the golden rules of Welsh chapel culture.

Even as Kay confessed her "awful" past and no matter how much I tried to reassure her, I could feel the guilt trembling warmly inside her. Guilt that she'd dropped her knickers that New Year's Eve. Guilt that she'd allowed Joe in through the holy portal between her legs but, far and away above that, guilt that she had upset her "adorable" father so much that he had, for the first and only time in his life, wept openly.

We would be getting on fine one day when, apropos of nothing, she might say, "What if we did get married? How do I know you wouldn't bring it all up again? You could lose your temper and throw it all back at me?"

I kept insisting that under no circumstances would I do that. We should put it all behind us and only ever talk about it if *she* wanted to talk about it. Some hopes! We could not sit for half an hour together before we began chomping on the same old bone and whenever we managed to develop a little intimacy, the drawbridge would come crashing down.

I still wanted to become a writer, even as my relationships and studies were collapsing around me, and it was about now that my friend Elfryn Lewis told me about a man who had lived in West Wales at the turn of the century.

This man, Evan Roberts, had led the great chapel revival in Wales in 1904. This was the last time the Holy Spirit moved with any great power in Wales – a country which has had more religious revivals than any other in the world – and I was immediately hooked on the story of this man and wanted to learn everything about him.

Evan Roberts sparked this revival after a service in his home chapel of Pigsah on the Burry Inlet. He converted twelve young people that night and, doubtless helped by the trauma of a local train crash and the fact that Wales had just lost at rugby, his movement spread to a larger chapel in nearby Loughor before packing out the chapels of South Wales.

In that turbulent winter of 1904 Roberts changed the mood of Wales. He was not a great speaker, given to long silences and even convulsions in the pulpit but, with the backing of eight female singers, he held huge and emotional meetings where, in between the ladies' sweet singing, came the hymns and the personal confessions. Evan would talk of the coming apocalypse: how Christ was preparing to rout all the gathering forces of evil with the transcendental brilliance of his Second Coming.

Fanned by Press sensationalism the effect of all this on an insecure and imaginative people was overwhelming. Miners and farmers abandoned their work to follow a call to the ministry. Prisons were emptied and magistrates found they had nothing to do as crime in many parts of Wales fell almost to zero. Drinking and rugby clubs were disbanded and bookshops complained of a shortage of Bibles.

Less than a year later, the revival fizzled out almost as quickly as it had begun and Roberts went into seclusion for the rest of his life, first staying in Leicester then, in 1932, moving to Cardiff where, a lonely and solitary figure, he lived on charity until his death in 1951. He was buried at Loughor where a granite statue was erected to him in the graveyard of the Moriah chapel in 1953.

Kay had often said I would recognise the subject of my first novel as soon as I came across it and here it was. I had made barely any progress on my Merchant Navy novel. Perhaps my heart wasn't in it but the story of Evan Roberts had a powerful appeal and I went down to sniff out the area, delighted not only to visit Evan's old home and chapel but also to wander the nearby sands of Penclawdd, still being worked by the local cockle pickers.

When I walked out on to the sands, an area seven miles long and four miles wide, it was unlike anywhere I had ever been. Oystercatchers wheeled overhead and packs of wild horses grazed the distant marshes. Sometimes a horse would run for it, setting off all the others, leaping the gullies and struggling through deep pools until, panic over, they began grazing unconcernedly again. Sunshine broke through the massing clouds in rainy pillars of glory and everything seemed ragged and elemental from the distant low grumbling of the sea to the way the winds whined with dark sorrow over the Burry Inlet as they tossed the dry sand in frantic eddies and whirlpools.

You had to keep a sharp eye on the tides out here, a cockle picker told me: they could sweep in faster than you could walk and unless you knew the sands you could quickly be a goner. Yes, these sands had to be the most beautiful and primitive in the world and even the cockle pickers would admit they sometimes looked up from their backbreaking work and became overwhelmed by the beauty around them.

Cockle picking was one of the oldest jobs in Wales, dating from the time that the cockle women of Penclawdd would take their horses and carts to scratch out a living on the sands after losing their husbands down the mines. This work was one of the first forms of Welsh social security and, wrapped in flannels, their bums sticking up in the air, the women of Penclawdd became an early symbol of human defiance and will to survive.

You had to be tough to survive here, menaced by fast-moving tides and lightning strikes, soaked in storms and lost in sea mists. You could be surrounded by oystercatchers, who can eat more than their own weight in cockles every tide. Every now and then, as you walk across the sands, you come across bright banks of busted cockleshells where these birds have been feeding. They slice open a shell in a flash and the cockle pickers hate them. "Rats on wings," they call them and I was once there when the men from the Ministry of Agriculture and Fisheries tried to net some. They used cannon and nets, worked all day and only caught two birds, which they released.

The cockles can be little bastards too, moving around under the sands so fast you never know where they are.

I saw strange things in these romping spaces. Thunder always seemed louder out on the sands and seagulls stood with their beaks to the wind. The hiss of the incoming tide kept changing, becoming louder and ever more menacing. There was the soft drum of blood beating in my ears and a sorrowful yearning for my two women, still wondering whether, between them, they might yet cause me to die of a broken heart.

Here was the setting for my first novel for sure but it also dawned on me, even at such an early stage, that Kay's story was a story of Wales and that I could weave her fall and struggle for redemption through the larger tapestry of a country convulsed by a mighty religious revival.

There could be a love interest for her provided by a local cockle picker, one of the first of the socialists who were making a showing in the South Wales valleys then. Such a book would have everything from the early collision between socialism and the chapel movement; a revival which was sweeping and changing the country and a love story, the most heartbreaking love story ever, about two people trying, but failing, to make one another whole again. There would be a death or two at the end – out here on the sands.

This actually formed the basis of one of my early novels, *One Winter of the Holy Spirit*. But it was to be another twenty years or so before it was published, after I had accepted that, to write anything at all, you had to develop an iron discipline, clear the decks and work at it every day until it was finished. Then you worked on it again and maybe again as you kept choking on the bitter pills of rejection.

I was merely posturing and daydreaming at that time, the odd page here or scurrilous article for the college newspaper there, but nothing of any significance. I was still in thrall to existentialism and angst and alienation and filth which even I – in the confused, changing state I was in then – didn't see how I could work into a love story set against a chapel revival in 1904. I simply wasn't ready to tackle God yet – unaware that one day soon he was going to tackle me.

And there was the additional problem of Kay's certain wrath. "I do not want you to put my story in any book you might write. All this is between you and me."

It took a long time for me to understand that my life *was* my material. A writer has nothing else to work with. Anyone who gets tangled up with a writer puts themselves at immediate risk. He may look blank or drunk or even uninterested for most of the time but it is all being thrown on the internal compost heap for future reference. Just when you think he's forgotten, out it spews.

Sorry, Kay darling – at least I've changed your name.

My affair with Kay had cooled considerably but we were getting on quite well. She enjoyed and needed a platonic relationship and seemed happy now I wasn't putting any pressure on her body, which she still regarded as holy and untouchable. Maybe I had put too much pressure on her from the start. Maybe I should have let her be herself and worked off my excesses elsewhere. Maybe I was the one who had messed it all up with my unreasonable, needy demands. Maybe …

I was again seriously considering giving up my incomprehensible studies, becoming a rolling stone – "dropping out" as they called it – and repairing to some bed-sit to work on my novel. This seemed a serious option but, after a stormy series of hustings, I was elected President of Debates for the following year. Now I would *have* to come back. I had complained at the hustings that debates had become too trivial with lots of stupid, frivolous motions. I wanted debates to return to the blood-curdling punch-ups they'd been when I'd first got here.

This electoral victory was a good opportunity on all kinds of levels since, not only could I now raise the roof a few more inches on Friday nights with strong motions, but I also got to wear a glittering chain of office and sit on a big wooden throne with a gavel which I could bang loudly and repeatedly on the arm of the throne when I was calling for Order. I could expel anyone who upset me and I could select the *Observer* Mace debating teams with me, of course, in the leading pair with Tim Brooke, the best speaker in the university. I could cherry-pick the invitations that came in to speak at other universities *and* I got a small room, with my own key, and its own sofa, albeit with some springs sticking out of it. It sure as hell beat the mattress in the back of my van and I had high hopes for it – and me – in the autumn term.

Yes, it was going to be a lot of fun and there was a suggestion the Philosophy department wouldn't throw me out – as I still feared – because I was President of Debates. It didn't reflect well on the department to expel high-profile students, I was told, and such an expulsion would cast doubt on their judgment in letting me into their Aristotelian midst in the first place.

About the same time, something extraordinary happened to me, again prompted by a newly released film, *West Side Story*. I went to see it with Kay and it gripped me from the fantastic opening frame as the camera glides in through the clouds and hovers over the skyscrapers of Manhattan before swooping down on gang members running around the slums of the West Side.

The story is a modern re-working of *Romeo and Juliet* and Natalie Wood was completely gorgeous as she began a love affair with Tony Moreno which ends in tragedy and tears. It wasn't so much the love story that caught my imagination as the setting: the vitality and cruelty of this dark world where gangs fought one another to the death over a few yards of turf; the neurotic poetry of the street corners where these tortured kids gathered and sassed one another or the police or the social workers.

I couldn't stop thinking about it when, almost as if it was preordained, I opened the *Observer* the following Sunday morning and caught a few paragraphs which told of a group, the Clayton Volunteers, who were about to take some young people from Britain to become social workers in the Lower East Side of Manhattan. John Winant, the American ambassador to London, had long been organising groups of American students, the Winant Volunteers, to work in the East End of London, so now the Rev Tubby Clayton, co-founder of Toc H, was to send a similar group to America.

Before the morning was over I had written applying to become one of the new Claytons and was invited to London for which I duly got out my Oxfam suit and had a severe haircut. I told the selection panel about the book on Evan Roberts I was "working" on, which went down well with them because they were committed Anglicans, and was accepted to go to America at the end of term for three months.

I met the marvellous Tubby Clayton at a small garden party in London which had been arranged for all of us to meet one another for the first time. He was eighty-odd but full of vim and fight and, at one stage, lifted me an inch off the lawn when he began speaking about beautiful ideals. All my life I have responded to sudden glimpses of greatness in people and tried to learn and build from them and Tubby certainly made a mark on me. Not all influences are pernicious, as I have often been suggesting, any more than all new ideas are bad.

No men or women are inherently bad or good either. They are defined by the quality of their ideas which will then make them bad or good. Everything depends on what has been fed into you from an early age: what one hears, sees and reads will lay down the paving stones of the path of one's future life. With any luck you will meet people like Tubby at a time when you *need* to meet them and they will offer a firm, if not beneficial, correction to your wandering path.

I was feeling pretty damned pleased with myself after coming back from Tubby's party in London and wasn't even dismayed when Kay announced that she was going to give up her job in an accountant's office in Cardiff and train in Bristol to become a nurse. Ah great, I thought, though I kept my thoughts to myself. At least she can torture some other luckless sod in Bristol.

A gang of us went for a barbecue in the sand dunes of Fontygary one warm night just before I left for America. We had a few drinks and a burned sausage or two before creeping off over the side of one of the dunes where, for no reason at all, Kay became sexually alive. I got my tongue half way down her throat, which, for her, was the equivalent of a normal girl jumping into a gang bang, and sent my hands wandering all over the interesting folds of her body.

I rolled off her, looked up at the amused stars and wondered if it had happened to me. Surely this was happening to someone else in a film or book. Kay could not possibly act like this.

I never knew what that little bout of un-Kay-like animalism was about. Her way of saying goodbye, perhaps. But I did know that she got cold and moody again almost as soon as it was over and it never happened again.

She saw me off at Cardiff station and kept waving until the train rounded the curve and, wiping a tear from my eye, I knew that was that. There would almost certainly be a new one in Manhattan – Natalie Wood herself perhaps. My daydream machine was still intact and blasting away.

TWELVE

I was soon back in London's dockland for the third time in three years, this time aboard a chartered liner, the *Aurelia*, as one of sixteen Clayton volunteers on their way to sort out the social problems of Manhattan's Lower East Side.

The week-long voyage was an opportunity for the group to get to know one another and I could see that I was in for a singular summer since I was the only member who was not already an ordinand or hoping to become one. All were training to become Anglican ministers – even Joy, the only female member of the group – and I guess it was on that ship that the idea of God became real to me, not as the words of others or some difficult concept in the Bible but as a living, working faith, a force that you could tend and develop within you.

I was many years and even more nights of debauchery away from becoming a convert but, rather than turn my back on them and run off to have fun with others on the ship, I sat and ate with them, listened to them and studied them in our cabin when they got into their pyjamas and prayed for up to an hour before turning in. They were as different as it was possible to be from all those raving, sex-obsessed queens on the *Windsor Castle*. You wouldn't catch any of this lot arguing about the ideal length of a dick or whose turn it was to wear the off-the-shoulder blouse in the Pig and Whistle that night.

"What do you pray about at night for so long?" I asked Dave.

"I go through the whole day in my mind from the time I wake up," he said. "I review everything I've done and said and consider how I might have done it better. I want my whole life to be a pleasure to God."

This was a new language to me although I had been a regular attender at chapel before Elvis and Co got at me and turned me into an under-age sex maniac. I had received no encouragement from my parents in any matters of faith, not even from my normally supportive mother when I would come home with yet another presentation Bible for regular attendance. "You haven't read the last one yet," she would say, clearly picking up on my father's gift for sarcasm.

I didn't know it at the time (yet again, no one had bothered to tell me) but there had been a child before me who had contracted meningitis as a baby and died. When my grieving parents had been visited by the chapel minister they had both asked him the one question that mattered: "Why had God allowed this to happen?"

"God always likes to pick his best flowers first," this dolt had explained. If that was how he behaved, my parents concluded, they wanted nothing further to do with God or the chapel.

But my childhood chapel had a genius of the spoken word: the Rev Charlie Evans, whose sermons in his little wooden pulpit were always inspirational, chugging along for a while like a bus idling at a stop, but then getting into the *hwyl*. He became more and more fierce, shouting his words with raw passion and pounding his lectern with angry fists as he spoke about the damnation we would suffer, both now and for all eternity, unless we mended our sinful ways.

The chapel was the heart of every mining community and, between them, those sacred pulpits produced a glittering dynasty of great preachers who fashioned the Welsh soul with the hammer and anvil of their fiery words.

Charlie's influence on me remained strong although I was now developing into something of a socialist who saw religion as a reactionary, capitalist force that kept its foot on the neck of the poor. We Lefties agreed with Caradoc Evans, the long-dead Welsh satirist, who had once said that every chapel in the land should be burned down and a good pub erected on the ashes thereof.

Perhaps predictably, being with the Claytons on that ship revived and developed my faith, stimulated by my recent researches into the story of Evan Roberts. The philosophy of religion was much more important than the logical positivists would admit, so I had many a discussion with my new pals and sensed they thought they'd spotted a possible convert. Conversion would be a central part of their future career after all and here was a chance to get in some early practice.

I listened, and they dealt politely with my objections, but a slight depression was already getting hold of me. Within my enormous limitations I was prepared to work hard as a social worker but the prospect of being with this lot all day and having to live with so much prayer at night was filling me with gloom. I had hardly begun to sow my wild oats and my fellow Claytons drank nothing stronger than a thimble of communion wine, none of them smoked and you could see some of them visibly in pain and lowering their Prayer Books if I made some crass remark about a passing girl's figure.

How had I got mixed up with a group like this? Maybe I'd been picked to test their faith.

We didn't know anything about our accommodation in Manhattan, but I simply couldn't see how I would be able to have any fun at all if I was billeted with them. If I so much as thought of having a quiet wank they'd call a full-carpet prayer job imploring the Lord to get me to cut it out – or off – before I went blind.

Almost every detail of my first plunge into Manhattan remains in my memory: the teeming life that swarmed round those streets, bridges and skyscrapers; the yellow cabs, which I had only ever seen in films, making their determined way through the honking traffic which every now and then cleared for a few seconds to reveal a dog in the basket of a cyclist or a roller skater, hands clasped behind his back, performing tricks in the middle of the road. WALK turned to DO NOT WALK. Everything seemed to be moving twice as fast as anything I had ever known and the strangeness of this seething ant hill was reinforced by a sweltering heat, not at all like an English summer but steamily tropical and almost stifling. DO NOT WALK turned to WALK.

We were taken to the Henry Street Settlement House where, a little to our surprise, we were met by several journalists. I received my first introduction to the wild and wonderful ways of journalism in that settlement house when the man from the *New York Times* wrote a bright, witty piece about us that included a few "humorous" quotes from me. A reporter from the *New York Post* also interviewed us but, when he returned to his office and wrote up his version, they told him it wasn't half as interesting as the piece in the *New York Times* and that he should go back and do it again. He returned to the settlement house later that afternoon and accused me of giving the *New York Times* funny quotes but keeping my quotes to him deliberately dull and serious. Why had I got it in for him? He didn't make any sense at all, particularly as the man from the *New York Times* had invented my quotes anyway.

Over dinner that night we were introduced to the staff of the settlement house and scattered to different apartments around the area. I shared an apartment in nearby Delancey Street with two young men who had flown in from London that day: Sam Smith, a tall, cheerful Jamaican with a degree in public and social administration, and David Doubleday, a water board clerk who hoped to become a minister. We also shared with a gang of cockroaches in the bathroom and a bum sleeping in the hallway over whom we had to step at night – which wasn't much fun after a long day especially if he'd shat or pissed himself.

All in all everything looked very promising, particularly as there were lots of American college girls attached to the settlement house for the summer. I had a good feeling that I would soon become attached to a few of them particularly as we were all due to have dinner over the long polished table there every night. I already had my eye on a few candidates to take home to Delancey Street to meet the bum in the hallway and the cockroaches in my bathroom. God could wait.

It was thrilling to be in America at last because so many of my key influences and ideas had been American. America, through books, films and music, had occupied almost every corner of my life. I might be Welsh but could easily argue that, like so many of my contemporaries, I was a child of America who owed as much to Bob Dylan as to the Rev Charlie Evans.

Bob Dylan was a force in the land when I got there. Like most youngsters on the campuses, I identified closely with his embittered antagonism towards authority, the ways we had been lied to and how some day we would be released. We had been betrayed, we were angry and one day we would get our revenge. His Bobness spoke for all of us. He had walked these very streets. Open any café door or a club window and his ragged, whining voice came groaning out. My heart still lifts a few points when I hear the dull thwack of the snare drum and the opening rolling riffs on the organ in *Like a Rolling Stone*.

I sniffed around my area, finding the Lower East Side a random collection of crumbling tenement blocks, abandoned cars, junk-filled shops and murky bars, all bolted together by thousands of fire escapes. Every race in the world seemed to have some sort of ambassador in this bopping banana republic. Orthodox Jews, dressed in black and with long beards, sat on the stoops outside their businesses or homes and nodded at you as you went by. Puerto Rican girls in tight, satin trousers stood on corners patting their carefully lacquered hair and young Africans lounged or chatted in the corridors of pool halls. The Italians had their delis and soda parlours. Kids of every colour would occasionally let off a fire hydrant in the oppressive streets and play in the cooling water.

Policemen twirling sticks swaggered down the sidewalks and the sight of the bums in the nearby Bowery was heartbreaking. Grizzled and defeated, they stretched out next to the rubbish bins, but got up and became aggressively animated if a passing tourist tried to take a photograph of them.

Almost every person you came across wanted to speak to you. *Where are you from? What are you doing? Where are you living?* Word had gone out that you had come to give a helping hand in the community and you always knew there were friendly eyes watching out for you. Shopkeepers would slip you the odd apple and the man in the deli always offered a scoop of ice cream.

I never felt menaced by anyone in all the time I was there nor did I ever so much as clap eyes on a gang anything like the ones in *West Side Story*. There *were* gangs in Manhattan but I never came across any and, far from fighting with chains or blowing one another away with their Saturday Night Specials, all the youngsters of that age I met were busy making money.

It was the younger ones who were getting into trouble, the twelve and thirteen-year-olds who were not kids but not adults either. These had one foot in the play-ground and the other in the street and it was my job to bring together a group of them from a nearby tower block and keep them occupied and out of trouble for the summer when the petty crime rates in Manhattan go through the roof. *Just keep them out of prison until they go back to school and you'll have done a good job, Tawm.*

We had the first planning session of the Pied Piper programme under the super-vision of its leader, Ora Dorsey, in the offices of La Guardia Project. I was introduced to some of the American students I had already met in the settlement house but I perked up at once when I was introduced to Elsa Lingstrom, a twenty-year-old Swedish girl with long, blonde hair, cold blue eyes and legs that went on until next Christmas. She wasn't a classic Swedish beauty but she smiled a lot and looked extremely bright. She had been studying psychology in California and was now doing a stint of social work before returning to Sweden.

Our job, it turned out, was to look after about thirty kids who turned up eager-ly first thing every morning at La Guardia and we would walk them around Chinatown or to the United Nations; take them to Central Park or on the Staten Island ferry or, once or twice a week, on a privately chartered bus to somewhere a little more distant like Orchard Beach, Jones Beach or Wolf Pond Park. These were *our* children in a manner of speaking and we would look after them like concerned parents. Elsa and I also tumbled straight into a joyous and memorable love affair.

It began on the very first night when, after Ora had fully briefed us on our duties, I invited Elsa to spend the night with me in Delancey Street. My sex educa-tion started almost immediately when I undressed and turned off the light before climbing into bed leaving her to make her own way into it after doing whatever it was that she did among the cockroaches in the bathroom. I was then surprised to find a nude woman in my arms.

In Bible-black Wales in the early Sixties it was expected, as a matter of normal sexual routine, that the man work his way through several layers of brassiere, stockings, heavily elasticated drawers or an iron-lined corset and he was not bound to get lucky even then.

But here she was, all feathery long blonde hair and warm, deep breaths, clearly ready for action. I put my hand on her Aunty Mary and felt it was wet and warm almost as soon as I touched it. One inexpert move led to another when – Geronimo! – my long imprisoned virginity escaped inside her in a series of long, heavenly spurts.

After so many near misses and hypothetical hits I had finally managed to do it properly. I rolled over suffused with happiness and relief that I had accomplished all this on a wonderful, warm Manhattan night with cockroaches scratching around in the bathroom and a bum snoring in the hallway. It was as life replenishing as I had hoped and after a while she dried herself and pretty soon we were off again.

But it is not possible to get free from a lifetime of sexual guilt in one night. I woke up with the tawdry old feelings of self-disgust and locked myself in the bathroom for an age trying to deal with them, telling them to go away, fighting not only my self-disgust but another sort of self-disgust for feeling self-disgust.

Elsa made coffee and gazed out of the window until I got to grips with my erratic feelings. She did a lot of gazing out of windows when we were together and never caused a fuss when I got like this, seemingly happy to let me work things out for myself. With her forensic intelligence she soon learned when to speak and when to keep quiet, a necessary strategy for dealing with someone as uncertain and changeable as I was.

The Swedes knew all about sex from an early age, I was to learn, and not from lavatory walls, as we did in Wales, but in the classroom. "Anyway I like sex and have no time for moralisers," Elsa would say. "And you should never worry about me becoming, how you say, up the duff. I always wear a Dutch Cap."

A Dutch Cap! In my Welsh innocence I knew nothing about Dutch Caps. They may even have been something you bought in Amsterdam and wore on your head for all I knew. Despite all my travels around the world I still knew almost nothing.

It was a pretty unedifying story of sexual scholar meeting weeny wanker and, after floundering around in this department for so long, I found myself fast-tracked on an honours course in straight sex, one degree I wasn't going to shirk or flunk out of.

We got down to it all over the city that summer, once under the boardwalk of Coney Island, another time on a golf course on Long Island and once in a back room at a party in Greenwich Village. The old chapel feelings broke through occasionally and sometimes I resented the hold she had over me, but all such worries were soon swept away by this bold and bright force of Scandinavian liberation. She spurned reserve or restraint, once telling me that if she saw a man she liked she just hunted him down with her sex.

But, yes, I *had* thrown off one of my youthful shackles. Now there were only three dozen others left to deal with.

Our working day began at eight o'clock. The Lower East Side, particularly the clothes market in nearby Orchard Street, was already in a brightly humming ferment and these were the best hours of a Manhattan summer. You could breathe the air normally early in the morning, later you had to chew it.

We took breakfast at the settlement house, coffee and toast usually, before going to La Guardia where the children would be waiting for us and we would collect the few cents the families were expected to donate. Ora always insisted on these few cents being collected because it meant the families were taking some responsibility for our work.

The children were a racially mixed group: Africans, Puerto Ricans, Poles and Italian-Americans. They liked to stay close to you for attention or else perched high up some distant tree hoping you would notice them. Caesar Bell, a little West Indian button of a lad, who loved to drum, might saunter over to me on our daily trips and say: "Tawm, I've got a bug in mah ear." I'd examine his ear carefully and say it was fine so he would drift away again happily. Within an hour he'd be back with the same complaint and we'd go through the same little charade again.

It didn't take long to work out that all these kids wanted was love and they had at least a hundred ways of getting it. They crowded around you and shouted. They sobbed shamelessly for no reason at all. They stole things openly or toppled dust-bins over.

Raul Ramos, a Puerto Rican, always had a pair of pliers hanging off his left ear. Maria Gomez wanted to know when her breasts were going to grow. Mandy Westlake would steal anything that wasn't nailed down. Bruce Pasadov only smiled after he'd punched some boy or pulled a girl's hair. Gary Harmon would sit up a tree and wail plaintively until we got him down again and Michael Moncrease was always rattling public telephones to see if he could get any spare coins out of them.

Every belch and fart was forced out for maximum volume and offence. They were forever asking for money or leaping over turnstiles even when you didn't have to pay to go through them. Street vending machines were kicked as a matter of routine and car aerials snapped off in a wink. They were always threatening to push one another under buses or on to train lines.

I would feel the strangest emotions as I watched them scampering around in confused and delicious terror as the high Atlantic waves thundered on to Jones Beach. They were all ragamuffins in trousers too big and dresses too small. They would urge one another to dive into the waves but not one of them ever did because not one of them could swim. Later they might gain a little collective confidence and rush out after the lacy tongues of the receding waves like sandpipers before rushing back up the beach again, screaming and hollering, before the next advancing wave. Someone might be caught by an unusually high wave and would stand there crying as I rushed out to grab him before he was swept away. You had to be on your toes every single second of the day.

On rumbling, sun-kissed afternoons such as this you knew you would never change the world but you came to understand the healing intimacy of love with these children. You knew you could never help them in any material way but it was possible to make them happy for a few hours.

It was there, on Jones Beach, with these children and my Swedish girl, that I had my first insight into – or feeling for – the nature of God as a force of healing love. A God who would reveal himself in the ways we reacted and helped others less fortunate than ourselves. A God who could bring us all together and make us feel secure and wanted. All vague, I know, but those were my first inklings of a force beyond us. Those sweltering hours became my first faltering steps to faith.

Later God would become a mighty avenging force who struck me down so hard I still haven't recovered.

I often spoke with my fellow Claytons about such thoughts and got the impression they were coming to think I might not be the lost cause I so often appeared. There might be something in me yet and they urged me not only to start taking my philosophy studies more seriously but to do an MA, B. Phil, or even a doctorate. Education was everything in religious matters, they kept insisting, and the Anglican Church expected her ministers to be the best-educated people in the parish, able to defend their corner against all comers.

A few of them, however, were unhappy with the education I was receiving between the legs of the Swede. My flatmate, David, was clearly in the right job as clerk to a water board and was forever droning on about how I was turning our apartment into a brothel. "Even the bum in the hallway must be ashamed of what's happening in here," he shouted in one memorable outburst. "Even he's got to have higher moral standards than you."

We led a rip-roaring social life in Manhattan. Invitations to events and parties flooded into the settlement house daily. Everyone wanted to meet the mad Brits who were fighting the even madder gangs of the Lower East Side. They had all seen *West Side Story* and seemed to think we spent all our time dodging bullets while trying to keep the peace.

Elsa and I liked to party in Greenwich Village, the great new kingdom of Bohemia, where we bumped into the wildest characters. There was the man who went everywhere with a python draped around his neck; the great poet working on a parody of *Paradise Lost* and given drink by his friends if he could *prove* he'd just composed a few more satisfactory lines; the man who had written a very long book which no one wanted to read let alone publish. My favourite was a garrulous black man who gloried in the name of Moses and claimed he was a poet, prophet and educator. His mission in life, he said, was to teach all those who had taught him when he was too young to know better. He had never been off the island of Manhattan because everything anyone could ever want was right here. I often got locked in fruitless argument with Moses and always lost because he pressed his points with a careful Jesuitical precision. I was on the right track, he would say patronisingly. When I worked out exactly what I was saying and *why*, I might even get somewhere.

We met young girls dressed in black with thick spectacles and the strangest attitudes. Most of them were comprehensively screwed up, often embarking on sentences so long they forgot how they had started them, or getting worked up about nothing at all. They took any excuse to spew out pointless babble. The boys were poets and chancers, broke and, like Dylan Thomas, looking for some rich woman to live off. They gravitated to the Village to launch their literary careers or get laid or become high on drugs. These were the children of *Howl* and Mailer's *The White Hipster*. The talk was of Corso, Ginsberg, Ferlinghetti and Kerouac.

We talked in those parties – oh how we talked – about everything and nothing but mostly about nothing. Back in Wales there might be a couple of dozen who liked to talk like this but here in Manhattan everyone seemed to be at it, even a messenger boy might spot a book in my apartment and launch into some full-blown speech about whether it was any good or not.

That was the way it was in the Village, everyone locked in an argument about something or other, be it the reality of dreams, the mysticism of the flesh or the perpetual climax of the present. Between them they would have driven my philosophy professor right round the bend.

"The d-d-d-d-d-mysticism of the flesh!"

Therein lay the problem: we all launched into extravagant and wordy discussions about everything under the sun without bothering to work out exactly what we meant, if anything at all. Moses would stand bravely in our midst, challenging us, mocking us, urging us to explain what we meant and we always backed away from him in the end. No one won a verbal joust with Moses.

With all these strange ideas chasing one another around the city it was interesting how we often claimed them as our own. One night I was having a chat with a Rhodes scholar about Mailer's *Advertisements for Myself* and we were both, I realised later, offering one another the views of Kenneth Tynan on the book.

The old was forever masquerading as the new: we posed endlessly with one another's insights because we had none of our own. We fed on any scraps. My problem here, I suppose, was that I'd caught the swing of philosophy without its content. At least I knew what was rubbish. Intellectual rigour never held sway in Greenwich Village.

But hey, we were only just starting to make our way: people need to be a bit mad when they're young. There was plenty of time to get sensible but, no matter how tired we were after a party in the Village, I was never too tired to be thrilled by the long walk back home to Delancey Street with Elsa, down through the great, echoing canyon of Wall Street, where we could just about make out the night sky nailed up there by the tips of the skyscrapers.

Would we ever work it out? I would wonder, looking up at the enormous Manhattan night. Would any of it ever add up to anything sensible?

Then, as a matter of routine, we climbed over the bum in the hallway and fell into bed where we held one another carefully and even tremblingly before making long, slow love and falling into a deep, dreamless sleep.

Our Manhattan affair was far from being a melody. Discords occurred when, say, I received a letter from Kay. They were chatty letters with news about our friends, but Elsa would prowl around me like a lioness in season as I read them. What was I laughing at? Why was she still writing to me when it was supposed to be all over? Was she still in love with me? Perhaps I was still in love with her?

She would glare at me, hard-eyed and angry, but just as quickly, she'd calm down. One morning when I smiled up at her after reading Kay's latest letter Elsa threw an electric fan at me, narrowly missing my head.

I never liked violent moods. I worried about how it might be between us a few years down the line when such moods might last for weeks and even months, like my father's. Intensity always frightened me and I did not want to get into that sullen, inarticulate iciness again. I still shuddered whenever I thought of my father – which wasn't often.

After an unusually long silence one day, Elsa announced it would be best for both of us if I came straight to Sweden to be with her when our summer in New York was over.

"We could find a place together in Lund where you could get on with your writing and I could get on with my studies. You say you hate your philosophy studies, so give them up. Live with me and get on with your writing. You could be a wonderful writer but you won't be a writer unless you start writing properly. You will be like all those other writers in the Village, standing around at parties and talking about writing. Writers who talk about it all the time are not writers."

There was a gloomy logic about what she said. Her praise for my work was most acceptable, of course, even if it was based on nothing more substantial than her reading half a dozen pages of mine, but this talk of living together was a more serious suggestion for which I was unprepared. Flies were appearing in the Manhattan ointment.

One problem was that I had never got into a position where I had been physically longing for her, unlike Sandra and Kay. Elsa had made herself too available, which never really helps in any relationship – particularly if a chapel-haunted Welshman is involved – and I had lost my appetite for all the frequent and available sex. It had become predictable, routine and I wanted it to be more exciting, more feverish, a long struggle with all that bloody underwear in the back of my van.

What I didn't know then was that, sexually, this was as good as it would ever get. You can't spend the rest of your life struggling with underwear in the back of vans after all. Sexuality doesn't work like that: those who crave constant sexual excitement often end up with half a dozen marriages, all of them unhappy. I was often unhappy with Elsa, I know now, because she was actually giving me what I had yearned for from Kay and Sandra.

Nevertheless, I could not end the relationship because that would have led to violence. She had meant to hit my head with that fan and might have better luck next time. Anyway the summer would soon be over with her going back to Lund and me to Cardiff. I would be safe from Swedish wedding bells in Cardiff so I would keep things ticking over peaceably here and make the best of it.

She knew I wasn't responding as she had hoped, but she kept at it doggedly. There would always be an open door for me if I could get over to Lund. I will help you become a writer. You can rely on me.

Elsa kept opening other interesting doors for me, introducing me to the work of her fellow Swede, Ingmar Bergman, who was having a season at an art cinema in Greenwich Village. These were films she liked and which I had never seen before, covering major questions like "Why must we live? Who are we? Is there a God?"

Bergman's world had people at the end of their tether struggling through bleak, wintry landscapes, often in pain and always lonely as they looked for answers which were never forthcoming. Everything was wrong; God had abandoned us. "My whole life has been a meaningless search," said the knight in *The Seventh Seal*.

His films throb with cruelty and despair: everyone is tortured in some way. "Understand despair and you understand Bergman and the Swedes," Elsa said one night after we had seen *Wild Strawberries*. "Without despair we are nothing."

Bergman framed his work in ways that I had begun to understand. He made me see the world in *his* way. I reacted positively to his melancholy. I had found similar preoccupations in the writings of Henry Miller and James Baldwin, but Bergman visualised them in an arresting way. Almost every scene was beautifully framed in black and white and it helped that his favourite actress Liv Ullman didn't mind taking her clothes off.

New armaments were being wheeled on to the battlefield of my mind. Everything was at war with something else.

Those sweet and sour days moved inexorably towards their end. Grief and emptiness threatened everywhere. Elsa and I had been warned by the professional social workers in the settlement house that we should not get too involved with our children because, if we did, we would end up with emotional problems which would affect our ability to do a proper job.

My fellow Claytons were managing well. They remained strong and effective, sustained by their life of disciplined prayer. In prayer they could solve their problems or put them in the hands of God. Such ideas remained new to me and made a strong impact because, while I was becoming emotional and ineffective in my work, the others managed to maintain a sort of detachment and work around the clock if necessary. They were better social workers than I was and this observation became another key for me when I was trying to unlock the Christian faith. The most extraordinary feature of Christianity, I now believe, is that it works. It can make you a better, more capable person and, if you follow its precepts, you are *made* happy.

But I was far from being a Christian in those wild Manhattan days and not much of a social worker either, always letting my feelings get in the way of my better judgment. Bruce and Raoul, for example, had taken to following us home to Delancey Street and we had often let them into the apartment for a while. When we asked them to leave they hung around and annoyed the bum in the hallway or else came back early in the morning to be with us as we walked over to the settlement house for breakfast.

We didn't mind that – even encouraged it – but Ora gave us both a right old bollocking when she found out what had been going on. "You do *not* just favour a few with attention like this," she stormed. "It drives the other children away from you and makes it difficult for them because they would also like to go home with you. You have got to appear to care for them all equally to succeed as a professional social worker."

It was upsetting trying to explain to Bruce and Raoul that they shouldn't hang around us and it would be better if they went home to their families. Such suggestions rang hollow because we knew what their homes were like. Raoul had rats in his cellar; no one would want to live in a rat-infested dump like his.

After our final trip to Jones Beach, several parents came to meet us when we got back to La Guardia project and gave us gifts such as bingo markers and discount stamps. Having said goodbye to them and their children, it was time for Elsa and me to say goodbye to one another.

We had gone through so much together on these sweltering streets and she had dealt so maturely with my Welsh silliness that I had begun thinking there might be some future for us on some far Swedish shore and I might be able to settle down with her and become a writer.

The one great barrier to becoming a writer, I knew even then, was finding the space and time to actually get on with it. Time and space mean everything to a writer, almost more than a little literary talent. And here was an intelligent girl telling me that if I got myself over to Lund she'd provide me with all the space and time I'd need.

"I will feed you and you can have sex any time you want. I will even treat you like that Village poet working on his parody of Milton. You write three good pages and I will give you an extremely good f..k. You write a book of three hundred pages and you will have had a hundred extremely good f..ks."

I still couldn't quite get used to such unblinking candour, but she did make me laugh when she talked like this. The girls in Sweden couldn't all be like this could they? Now, you will do this. Now you will do that. Then, if you do as you are told, you will get fed and f..ked in a very good way. So get on with it or you are going to end up wanking on your own again.

The night before Elsa flew home we repaired to a sordid dimly-lit bar in the Bowery. She had become inconsolable, her pale blue eyes red with tears as we tried to reassure one another we had a future together. But my repeated assurances had no effect. Whenever it seemed she might smile again she got worse, sobbing and muttering in Swedish. What a strange woman: one who could move swiftly from cold rationalism to harrowing despair. Her protestations that it couldn't work out between us, that she had never had any luck in love and that it always went bad for her weren't helped by the low, smelly comedy stumbling all around us in that Bowery bar.

The door kept bursting open to reveal some ragged half-wit shouting incomprehensible oaths before being ordered out. Presumably the burly barman knew which of the bums had money because some of them were allowed to sit at the counter where they were given drinks until their money ran out and *then* told to leave.

"Wadsammaddawidye? Dis ain't de place for love tawk," the barman eventually told us. "You two wanna tawk love tawk dis ain't de place to be. Take da goyle to de Village or somewhere nice."

By the time we left the bar to walk hand in hand down the Bowery we had become so accustomed to the bums we ignored them, just letting go of one another's hands and stepping around them if they did stand directly in front of us. Perhaps it was Elsa's endless legs or long blonde hair but, on hot nights like this, whole platoons of bums materialised out of the gutters asking for a drink or a dollar. They never threatened or laid a finger on us, although they might let rip with a few choice obscenities if we ignored them.

I returned to my theme that we cared too much for one another to let it fall apart but, looking towards the distant United Nations building and listening to the lonely hoots of the passing ships, with a police car cruising past to check we were all right, I suspected everything I was saying was weasel words, pointless lies to calm her down.

Even as I was saying it would work for us in the future another voice inside me insisted it would be a big mistake to try and recapture a summer like this. Oh, we could always meet and *try*. But to reclaim such excitement would surely be beyond any couple. This had to be a one-off affair between ourselves and the children in our care and conducted in the heart of a wondrous and vibrant city. It had worked because of all kinds of unlikely factors but now I was concluding the juice had been fully squeezed out of the orange.

Yet Elsa was already planning our next Christmas together when we would go to the family house by the sea – all Swedes have family houses by the sea, it seems – and maybe go skiing in the mountains, a sport which, it came as no surprise to learn, she was very good at.

"I love the exhaustion when we return from a day on the slopes," she said. "That great tiredness as you drag your body the last few yards home."

The bum in the hallway groaned his usual welcome as we went up to our apartment where we continued smoking and chatting for the rest of the night. But I never hinted that I thought it *was* coming to an end, just kept reassuring her we had a future – hard work because she had an exceptional intelligence that could home in on bullshit.

We made love one more time before falling asleep in each other's arms so soundly that in the morning we had to run into Delancey Street and flag down a yellow cab which took off fast to the airport. I tasted the salt of her tears on my lips as I waved her goodbye.

I left Manhattan the next day with a copy of Jack Kerouac's *On the Road* in my back pocket. I was going to make a tour of the southern states as he had, using a mixture of bus, hitchhiking and my own two feet. All the Claytons were due to meet again in Washington in three weeks' time before taking the ship back home.

On the first part of my journey, I managed to catch a ride to the Black Mountains in North Carolina with two of the settlement workers and was more than happy to curl up under a blanket in the back seat and snooze fitfully. The summer had exhausted me mentally and physically and that Manhattan frenzy lingered. Odd images haunted my mind ... Moses talking at parties, Elsa taking off her clothes, the children screaming at the high waves of Jones Beach ...

But I had also picked up a lot of new ideas in the whirling galaxy of the world's liveliest metropolitan imagination: a ragbag of stuff gleaned from all those parties, the wilder shores of the *Village Voice*, the chat on the street and the stream of new

American writers I had discovered. These ideas seethed in my brain, making me more anarchic and embittered than ever, putting me firmly on the margins of society where I had long wanted to be. My clothes had changed too: cannabis-flowered T-shirts, torn jeans and the mandatory long hair.

Only today do I fully understand why a beatnik turns on and drops out. What I had in my mind then seemed an original defiant pose but I was merely acting out the fantasies of the books I had recently read: the work of the beats in general and Jack Kerouac in particular. I was far from alone, though.

"*On the Road* sold a million Levis and a million espresso coffee machines and also sent countless kids out on the road," William Burroughs was to write many years later.

Jack's hip prose and swirling sentences took my adolescent imagination prisoner. I would study a page, think about the words and project myself into Jack's chill dawns and wild highs. I would have loved to have been like him and all his other real gone cats, chasing along those wide, marvellous roads, getting high on Benzedrine, stealing cars, shoplifting, balling chicks two at a time and following the sundry and diverse paths of our every desire.

There were mystical edges to Jack's prose, a certain stoned quality in his words which enabled you to be spiritual without being stuffy, holy without being straight. I hoped to find freedom out in the wide, open spaces of America: out on the road with all the rest of his children of the rainbow.

We spent our first night at Jo-Jo's father's farm in the Black Mountains and I rode my first horse at a nearby riding school. All ribs and arthritis, this horse was a prime candidate for the knacker's yard, and I managed to get him to go all of twenty yards down a track before he stopped and refused to move another step. When I did turn his head around his ears pricked up and he bolted straight back to the riding school. "This horse only wants to run home," I told the owner, a wonderfully grizzled old bastard who might have been one of Sam Peckinpah's *Wild Bunch*.

"What you gotta to do is beat the bejasus out of the lazy f..ker," he shouted at me. "Just whack the lazy f..ker as hard as you can. Let 'im know who's the f..king boss around here." With that he picked up a thick stick and beat hell out of the horse's rump. The horse whinnied and reared up.

"Go on. Get on the f..ker. He'll run like hot s..t now."

I got back on him and we went clip-clopping happily down the same track until, a little more than ten yards beyond where he'd stopped the last time, he halted under a tree and showed no inclination to start running anywhere. I snapped a branch off the tree and was about to hit him with it when his head turned around and he bit my foot. Had I not had shoes on he would have had my big toe off.

On my next stop I stayed with the family of a Lutheran minister in Atlanta. This minister was keen on prayer, always bobbing up at odd moments to pray about something. You never knew what would set him off but I enjoyed listening to his colourful orations except when we were about to eat, a meal steaming on the table in front of us, and he started praying for the hungry in Africa. "What about the hungry here in Atlanta," I always wanted to shout out. "What about us?"

From there I took a Greyhound bus down into the Deep South, chasing through the great white-speckled cotton fields and the stooped black workers picking the cotton balls, a scene that Jack had evoked so vividly. It had never occurred to me that cotton looked or was harvested like this and, with butterflies bouncing around in the watery heat hazes, I half expected Clark Gable and his army to come storming past in pursuit of Vivien Leigh.

The stench of racism was pretty strong there, even in the Greyhound bus stations and, after seeing it in South Africa the previous year, it was somehow an even bigger shock to find it in America. Blacks had made their way in all walks of life in Manhattan and skin colour had never seemed an issue there. Indeed the races were better integrated in Manhattan than they were in multi-racial Cardiff and I had naively assumed that integration was the American way. But it wasn't, and right here was the proof.

Civil Rights marches had begun in the South with Martin Luther King making his charismatic speeches. The times really were a'changing with the sons and daughters beyond your command and the campuses in an uproar, all instigated by young students like me. Bliss was it to be alive in that revolutionary dawn except that revolution had not got so much as a toehold down here. Nothing seemed to have been changed by the American Civil War although I often ignored the signs and went where I wasn't supposed to in the public lavatories or diners. But, disappointingly, I was never locked up for this or got the National Guard out and was always given what I wanted. Those racist bastards could spot a longhaired trouble maker a mile off.

There was plenty of time to think on the long Greyhound rides through the South, with Manhattan fading from my thoughts. I was missing Elsa badly – not her icy moods but certainly the sex. Yet Sandra and Kay were also making something of a comeback and, as we sped through those simmering cotton fields, I wondered if there was a sense in which we carried the ghosts of all former relationships with us for ever, if we were doomed to be hunted and haunted by them for all time.

When I arrived in New Orleans I telephoned a young couple I had met at a party in New York. They had promised me a mighty fine Southern welcome if ever I found my way down there. The woman was vivacious and good-looking and they'd given me the impression they just couldn't wait for me to get there.

Well, here I was, and the woman told me to get into a cab and over to their home where after a conversation in their lounge that lasted no more than a few minutes, they took me to the outhouse in their garden, where they were sure I would be happy. They didn't offer me so much as a cup of coffee and went out for the night. I had no access to the *locked* main house or kitchen and finally had to go out for a long walk and find a diner where they sold cheap hot dogs. I didn't see my host or hostess for three days until, just before I left, they *did* speak to me again for about five minutes.

American notions of hospitality have always been a mystery to me. They are often all over you for a couple of days and then, just when you're thinking you could live with these wunnerful people for ever, they lose interest or even become actively hostile. This had happened to me several times in New York: a doctor on

Long Island, where Elsa had been staying, all but pressed the keys of his Thunderbird on me on my first visit and barely spoke to me on my second.

But I had the New Orleans streets to wander around and it had been one of my childhood dreams to come here. I still had traditional jazz records by Kid Ory, Bunk Johnson and Louis Armstrong which I'd bought before Elvis colonised my hormones and here I was walking around Basin Street and Bourbon Street in the old French Quarter where they had first performed their wondrous licks. The wrought-iron balconies and old bars like Preservation Hall consumed my eyes and I stood staring into them, hearing the flirtatious, exuberant music of my youth.

I looked in through the doors because I couldn't afford to go in. Most of them were ruinously expensive clip joints and way beyond my almost non-existent budget. I had bought my Greyhound ticket back to Washington and was now almost as broke as the panhandlers on the corners here. All I could afford to eat was hot dogs that didn't so much fill you up as ruin your appetite.

Being broke is not always a disaster since it encourages you to find alternative sources of interest like the local cemeteries, which are free. New Orleans has a fantastic Gothic cemetery, where they filmed the psychedelic passage in *Easy Rider* and I enjoyed wandering around the tombs there, peering in through the rotted holes of the vaults at the coffins lying around like cases in a left luggage office. What I really like about cemeteries is the tension they create, an extreme nervousness, a kind of formless panic that you are about to miss some important bus yet again. This tension is often mirrored by the tangled vegetation, the way the weeds seem to be engaged in some slow-motion battle to throttle one another. Nettles do well in cemeteries because they thrive on the sulphates in human bones.

Mooning around in such places, searching for new insights among the mouldering tombs, is the very best way to spend a day as, like Bergman, you attempt to grapple with the fearful, cold shadow that hangs over us all.

I also managed to take a short ride on a riverboat, marvelling at the huge, brown sweep of the Mississippi.

"On rails we leaned and looked at the great brown father of waters rolling down from mid-America like the torrent of broken souls," wrote Jack, "bearing Montana logs and Dakota muds and Iowa vales and things that had drowned in Three Forks, where the secret began in ice."

The Greyhound bus ride back to Washington was a long nightmare not much helped by my reading Joseph Heller's *Catch-22* in one sitting. They must have thought that they had a lunatic on their hands as I giggled my way through the cotton fields, but what I remember most about that journey is the pillows – or rather the lack of them. You could rent a nice pillow for fifty cents but you didn't get to cuddle it the whole night long because they didn't like their pillows to go out of certain areas. From time to time you had to surrender your pillow and rent a new one.

Money had become a serious problem and I wasn't the least pleased when I did doze off on my pillow and deep in some erotic dream of yearning or rejection, to find it being forcibly pulled from my arms with a bad-mannered tug. I hired another but perhaps I had been completely deranged by *Catch-22* since I didn't sleep at all after that and became paranoid about my pillow which I clutched fiercely and hid under my seat when we pulled into a stop.

"All right, we've got a pillow missing and I want it," one of the Greyhound attendants shouted at one stop but I refused to hand it over, just sat there bolt upright on top of it, staring at him, daring him to come and try and take it.

But, even if he'd spotted it, he didn't think it was that important so I got to keep my pillow for a further few hundred miles until they came looking for it again and I hid it again. Perhaps I had flipped by then because, when I did get to Washington thirty-six hours later, having read *Catch-22* from cover to cover, I was still clutching my pillow to my bosom like a much-loved baby and, when I got off the bus, the station attendant had to wrestle it out of my arms.

The party in Washington that night, where the Claytons met up for the first time in weeks, was a good one. I must have still been stressed since I had an argument with a man about love and ended up in tears. Then I got very drunk and tried to get my hand up the skirt of the hostess who wasn't much amused. She was an Episcopalian minister.

Again almost certainly under Jack's influence I refused all offers of a ride to New York and decided I would hitchhike there along the turnpike. On his travels Jack had met a gallery of strange and wonderful characters but all I met that morning on my way to New York were woofters without end and, in the course of five separate lifts, I had my bollocks fondled, my cheeks kissed and my body hugged times without number. One tried to work his thumb up my bum as I jumped around desperately trying to unlock the passenger door. They weren't even memorable in any way, just rather nasty fags trying to get their kicks from a young British hitchhiker who thought he was Jack Kerouac.

THIRTEEN

Everyone was in a cheerful mood in the first few days of the autumn 1962 term at Cardiff University, flush with new grants and already suffering from a hangover that was going to last for ever. I took Kay to Wentloog Castle, but it was evident the little that had held us together had gone. She would start as a student nurse in Bristol the following week and hinted there was someone else. I told her about Elsa and she suggested that Elsa was probably just the kind of girl I needed.

We went out as we had come in, with a cold kiss on the cheek. She departed my life and yet remained a strangely powerful presence.

I had no girlfriend but didn't mind. The longer you go without sex the less it matters. When you are getting plenty, you always want more. All sex ever says is: "Yes, that was all right but how soon can we do it again?"

But I had plenty of other things to preoccupy me including more scurrilous articles for the college newspaper and, as the president of debates, setting out the agenda for our Friday night meetings which I wanted to be the most noisy and controversial ever.

After homosexuality, "Vinny Roberts" became an "expert" on hard drugs. I wrote about the drugs scene in New York in a double-page spread in the union newspaper under the headline JUNKY ISLAND. After the issue appeared the college authorities made more anxious phone calls to the editor, not so much about what I had written, but about the huge photograph, which illustrated it, of a black man, one arm tied up by a belt, taking a fix of heroin. The photograph was lifted from a poster which I had picked up on the Lower East Side.

I don't think the newspaper had ever carried a photograph of a black man let alone a black man taking a fix and right across its centre pages. Still very much under the influence of Ginsberg and Mailer, I always enjoyed upsetting the college authorities and never missed an opportunity to do so. They didn't like what was happening in debates either. I wanted nothing less than blood on the floor of the debating chamber every time we convened and was always trying to think up motions which would raise the blood pressure.

The first duty of any debating chamber was to scandalise, I believed, and, after an indifferent previous year when a couple of dozen might turn up, we soon became packed out every Friday night, attracting three or four hundred to debates which often went on for hours. I devised motions to make people so angry they felt obliged to come along and defend themselves. Thus the motion, "This House Believes that

Christ Died in Vain" got out all the Christians. "This House Regrets that Columbus Discovered America," got the Yanks out in force, and "This House Believes that Everyone over Sixty should be Thrown out of the National Health Service," brought a busload of nurses from the Valleys and I had a very good time with one of them on the sofa in my room in the Union afterwards.

I really did fear that we'd got a war on our hands when we debated "This House Regrets that the State of Israel was ever Created." Jews turned up to defend their state and every Arab student in South Wales must also have turned up, many standing at the back shouting abuse and almost impossible to control. I had wanted controversy but not quite this much and several times threatened to suspend the debate. In the end I did stop it and we all went to the pub over the road early. We always packed out the pub at the end of a debate to swill Hancock's piss, and it was becoming a cause of much irritation that we didn't have a bar of our own in the union.

Neil Kinnock had become a skilled public speaker, able to develop an argument without consulting a note, and Vincent Kane was never less than brilliant. John Collins would let rip left-wing onslaughts and there were girls like Viv Little and Jenny Morris, a feisty blonde who went on to marry Cardiff MP (and future prime minister) Jim Callaghan's son, Michael. Jenny let it be known that you couldn't browbeat any of them just because they were women.

We had Jim Callaghan himself along for a debate on foreign affairs and he smirked his way through the proceedings without saying much. The best speaker of the year was the Welsh writer Gwyn Thomas, who dazzled us with his comic and deadly turns of phrase. The new editor of the *South Wales Echo*, Geoff Rich, turned up for our annual Press debate and many years later told me that I had destroyed him in it. We took no prisoners in those days and it never occurred to us to let anyone down lightly: if they upset us they got it full blast from both barrels.

I made the occasional guest appearance in the Philosophy department, where staff and students alike greeted me with a loud burst of ironic applause. It was clear to everyone that philosophy was a train that had departed the platform without me. I hated it with venom, particularly logical positivism, which had dismissed all metaphysical thought as unverifiable and therefore meaningless. The study of linguistics was also an impossibly arid task: we spent one long seminar discussing the way language relates to reality and most of that was taken up by an argument on why you could – or couldn't – describe a book as "a red bus".

I did show up for the professor's sherry party and half-expected some sort of stuttering bollocking from the old buffer when he re-filled my glass but perhaps he had already hit that sherry quite hard himself, since he was the very picture of sunny affability and asked how my novel was coming on. "We follow your progress through all the t-t-t-t-t noise you make in the Students' Union," he added.

Despite all the noise I was making in the union I didn't want to become a public speaker or a controversial polemical journalist. Every fibre of me still wanted to write that great novel; my whole life would be mystically and mysteriously justified if only I could write that one book and get it published. Or so I believed.

I guess there must be a couple of dozen would-be writers in any one year in university with further hundreds – maybe thousands – dotted around the cities and towns tapping out their thoughts. Anyone who can frame a sentence seems to believe he or she has a novel in them. Many of them keep tapping away for years, putting together a life of postman pain and rejection slips. Yet still they tap on.

There was another "writer" in my own philosophy class, Brian Evans, who used to piss us all off by saying that he'd had a novel about Dylan Thomas accepted by Methuen. Sometimes he'd go missing for a few days and tell us he'd been up to London talking to Methuen about "a few, small revisions". Over forty years later, we are still waiting for it to be published.

I read everything I could lay my hands on, particularly contemporary American novels, and struggled to write something for myself. My efforts were pretty hopeless largely because they were so derivative. The influence of the books I'd just read swept through my style in eddies, until they were displaced by the next book I read.

I still don't know when an individual style becomes strong enough to survive influences. I suspect many of us are never entirely free of influences no matter how old we may be. We all influence one another, not just in the books we read or the films and plays we see, but through the cultures we are a part of or are affected by. We are influenced by *everything* and we are not just the sum total of our ideas, as Berkeley had it, but creations of the larger culture and its ideas from which we can never break free. Even, perhaps especially, those who attack the larger culture are creatures of it.

The rebel reacts against his culture – or hopes he does – but the culture is too strong and pervasive. He is swallowed up in the end, whether he likes it or not, an unwilling component of the host culture. He desires to shock if only because other writers he admires are doing the same. Perhaps all artists are echoes of one another. Only the very greatest thinkers like Plato have ever shown complete originality.

Around this time another gorgeous woman entered my life and hungry arms. She had fine, chiselled cheekbones, dark eyes and a pair of black spectacles which gave her a fiercely intelligent air. And a trim figure, a full bosom and a broad generous smile. She caught my eye during a spectacularly fierce debate in which John Collins had let off a fire extinguisher to clean up all the "dirty talk" and, when we all went to the Alexandra Hotel afterwards, I noticed she was there again, looking at me with a you-could-get-lucky smile.

That was the smile of a supremely self-confident woman. She simply stank of sex and you could see that all she had to do was give a man a smiling eye and he would come running.

"Her name's Janey something or other," Jeff Cocks told me. Jeff kept a careful eye on all the women around the Union. "Everyone's after her and Ray Guy's been trying for ages but we don't think he's got anywhere."

It was most unlike Ray Guy not to have got anywhere with anything in a skirt. An engineering student, he was one of the smoothies in the Union with shades of Mike the Worm about him, always immaculately dressed, with plenty of money and, what is more, the smiling bastard also cruised around the city in a soft-top MGB for which, he kept telling us, he had worked hard for many years in industry.

If he wasn't getting anywhere with Janey in his MGB, how far might I progress with my Morris 8 van?

Quite far, it turned out. Much to Ray's disgust, before Friday turned to Saturday, I'd had a steamy, all-action clinch with Janey on the mattress and I began seeing her regularly. It was the mattress she went for, I told Ray. If only you'd had a nice work-ing-class mattress in your middle-class MGB you might have got somewhere too.

Nothing is ever as it seems with the unfair sex, though. Lovely as she was to look at and agreeable as she always was to being fondled on the mattress in the back of my van late at night, it quickly emerged that dear Janey had a few problems.

She was unable to speak for two hours after she'd got up – not a word – and she would remain in a fair old daze until lunchtime when food might encourage her to get out a sentence or two. She might withdraw and disappear into a crowd and would look painfully unhappy if there was any sign that anyone might say some-thing to her. She wore no make-up during the day and her eyes were always cast down as if she'd just lost a lot of money down a drain.

As soon as it got dark, though, like Count Dracula, she changed completely. She put on some make-up and a fresh pair of knickers, had a few drinks and, in no time at all, was laughing, joking and ready for whatever larks the night might bring. In fact she really came alive just when we were all ready to go to bed.

When she'd given me that first brazen smile across the crowded bar of the Alexandra Hotel, she'd drunk, or so she confessed later, three pints of HB bitter and her friend was up at the bar to get her fourth. In fact she'd had five pints by the time I'd got her into my van: no wonder I'd got so lucky so quickly on my mattress. It normally took at least a couple of dates before I got them on that.

"He didn't get you on that bloody mattress did he?" my friends would shout, enjoying her deep blushes and shrinking embarrassment.

"Yes, he did get me on that bloody mattress," she would boom after she'd had a few pints. "But he's not much good at it. I'm going to have to teach him a thing or two to help him keep up."

It was like going out with two women and I can't say I enjoyed it. Her alcoholic schizophrenia reminded me too much of my father, the life and soul of his club and the death and funeral march of his home. That was the last thing I wanted.

Janey called for me at my house if we were due to go out somewhere and got nowhere with my father. They sat there like a matching pair of china dogs on oppo-site ends of the mantelpiece, both staring at the fire and sighing, barely acknowledg-ing one another's presence until I itched to slam a bottle of Scotch down between them and say, "Hey, let's have a drink and perhaps we can manage a chat."

I kept going out with her because I couldn't see a way out of it. She was always around – even when I hadn't told her my movements – and, if I ever thought of giv-ing her the elbow, she would have a few drinks and I'd be drawn straight back, enchanted by her figure, looks and sexy pelvic thrusts. Even with her glasses on she was a great kisser and we discovered a few very nice moves together on my mattress, though there was never any straight sex. It would not have been difficult but I knew my chances of breaking up with her would be zero if she'd got in the pudding club. So I did what we all do in such circumstances, just let it drift on.

But her attachment to me had become single-minded and the only way I was going to get out of it was by giving her a lot of pain. How could I do that when I knew so well what it involved? I had suffered so much myself on that front I really didn't want to visit it on someone else.

I was drowning and couldn't work out which way to swim for dry land. When you reach this stage everything they do makes you feel worse. Janey also had strange, ambivalent views on our sex games in the back of my van. She enjoyed them well enough but always gave me a good, open-handed slapping when they were over, saying: "You're sick you are. You need a good doctor, you do."

The blows didn't hurt but they irritated me. Perhaps she was frustrated herself. Who knows?

The debates were coming along nicely but there was a nasty outbreak of trouble in the spring term when I suggested we should invite Sir Oswald Mosley, the leading British Fascist, to speak. Mosley had been interned by the government during the Second World War and his marches through London's East End in the 1930s had ignited lots of riots there. I guess I was hopeful he might even start some riots down here.

My suggestion went down badly with most of the debates committee but I persisted, saying that I had once seen Mosley speak at a public meeting in Hammersmith Town Hall and he was one of the finest platform speakers I had ever heard. (An original judgment of Colin Wilson's as I now recall.) "We should know what his ideas are so we can understand them better and defeat them," I argued.

There was almost a stand-up fight at that committee meeting and the row spilled out into the debating chamber the following Friday when I was faced with a motion of censure. Dai Kippest, the debates treasurer, flung his chain of office across the floor of the chamber and, after a protracted wrangle, I was censured and had to resign and stand for re-election.

About eight stood for the debates presidency and I was persuaded to stand again. If I didn't that would admit I'd been in the wrong trying to invite Mosley in the first place. I got back in with a far bigger majority than I'd first been elected with, largely because the election revolved around the issue of freedom of speech.

The first thing I did was write to Mosley inviting him to speak to us but, after causing all that aggravation, the trouble-making Fascist bastard turned us down.

FOURTEEN

My love life had plummeted into the abyss again and I could not understand why. Each of my girlfriends had been beautiful diamonds with fatal flaws: unfaithful, over-intense, frigid or sleepy. Why were they never normal? Why weren't they beautiful, sexy, sane and faithful? Was there no girl out there who would be approved of by my mother and disapproved of by my father?

Perhaps it was my fault for making wrong choices. Now I was stuck with a girl like James Joyce's Norah Barnacle, who was going to cling to me forever. There seemed no way of escaping her this year, or indeed the next. Then I picked up a leaflet describing the work of Voluntary Service Overseas.

This work fitted well with my nascent socialism. It would be an adventure at a time when I was still enjoying adventures but also, a clinching argument, it would put me beyond the reach of Janey who tracked me down almost every night in any part of the city with such skill it suggested she knew something about radar which would have been of keen interest to the RAF.

VSO had been set up eight years earlier by the visionary, Sir Alec Dixon, and sent thousands of sixth formers to the under-developed countries to help out for a year before they went to university. Apart from his contribution to an under-developed country there was great benefit to the volunteer himself. Volunteers were paid little more than pocket money but the scheme had been so successful it inspired the American President, JF Kennedy, to set up the Peace Corps.

In recent years VSO had managed to retire or fire Dixon and the scheme had been expanded to include graduates who, it was thought, would have more to offer. I wrote to them with a carefully edited account of my qualifications and was invited up to their headquarters at the British Council in Davies Street, London, where, resplendent in a new haircut and my trusty Oxfam suit, I told the selection panel what I had to offer.

You should never say you want to see the world on such interviews even though this is almost the only reason why anyone wants to join VSO, nor that you are hoping to change the world in any way but that you feel you have certain skills which might be useful. A panel of the great and good such as these are always taken in by this kind of talk: it suggests gravitas allied with humility. It also helps if you make a passing reference to your faith, even if you don't have one. I told them about the Evan Roberts novel I was planning to write and again that went down sweet as a nut with the sort of earnest, high-minded people who were interviewing me.

What you must never do, under any circumstances, is admit you are desperate to get away from a woman you hadn't the bottle to dump.

Our final degree exams loomed. A lot of my mates slipped away into the undergrowth for revision but I could hardly care less. I was resigned to whatever the Philosophy department was going to punish me with for my year-long absence and continued lounging around the Union, drinking tea, smoking and putting the world to rights with the rest of the malingering revolutionaries.

I even decided to run for the presidency of the Union because it would give me another year off now that the post had become a paid sabbatical. Presidents never seemed to do much more than chair a few meetings, hold the odd reception and attend conferences where they drank a lot of beer and got laid. I had no ambition to get any sort of regular job and would have happily remained at university playing student politics for a long time yet. My only opponent for the presidency, it turned out, was that smoothie in his MGB, Ray Guy.

Even though I promised them everything – including a bar, night club and contraceptive machines – and Ray promised them nothing - I lost the election heavily but escape from the lot of them came in the form of a letter from VSO. I had been selected as a teacher, the first graduate they had ever sent to Indonesia. I would be assigned to Tjurug Aviation Academy just north of Djakarta where I would teach English to Indonesian pilots. My pay would be £3 a week, in the local currency, and it had been decided I would be so isolated I would need a second-hand scooter which I should buy myself (maximum £50) and ship out there well in advance of my departure. I would leave in July, by train from London to Naples and then by ship to Djakarta.

John Bunting, a member of the panel who had interviewed me, said later that my posting had been one of the most interesting discussions the panel had ever had. What should they do with this little Welsh revolutionary? Where was the best place for me? South East Asia, they finally decided, away from everywhere and everyone. "He won't be able to cause much trouble for himself or anyone else out there but we'll give the poor sod a scooter to get into Djakarta in case it's all too much for him."

We had a huge booze-up in the Alexandra that night and I was especially affectionate with Janey whom I no longer had to dump now that I was about to disappear into the other side of the world. She wasn't too happy but was less tense with me now that I was less tense with her.

The prospect of Java was exciting: the very thought of those shapely Javanese women already driving me mad. Driving my mother mad too: she was already worrying that I would come home with a brown or black wife.

"You wouldn't do that, would you, Tom? You wouldn't marry a *Chinese* woman just to get back at your father would you?"

I'm not sure at what point in that celebratory booze-up the crucial phrase from the VSO letter floated into my mind but it did at some stage: *Providing you complete your studies satisfactorily.*

Oh my god! To become the first graduate to go to Indonesia to teach English with VSO I had to *graduate*. I had to get a degree. Terrified, I studied for a whole month in the Reading Room of the Central Library in Cardiff, claiming my seat under the window as soon as it opened at 10am and breaking only for a fag or sandwich and cup of coffee until it closed at 9pm when I often took the reference books home and got into an almighty row with the librarian when I returned them the following morning.

I looked up past exam papers in philosophy trying to work out what questions might come up and, after checking my answers back with my tutors, learning them by rote even if I didn't quite understand them or, indeed, the questions in the first place.

Janey frequently came to the library at 9pm despite being told not to. She may have been shy but she could be as implacable as a Vietcong guerrilla. But we usually had a coffee together before I went home and worked until my eyes were so sore I could barely see the words in front of me. "You've got to sleep, you know," my mother would say. "You won't be able to do anything if you don't get enough sleep."

I was a bag of nerves when finals arrived and, in our ludicrous academic gowns, we shuffled to our desks to read the bad news. I'd like to be able to say that, after completing a three-year course in a month, I got a First, but it didn't work out like that. I found myself staring at lots of questions I could barely understand let alone answer. Some of them were so alien and impenetrable I found myself checking the subject at the top of the exam paper to make sure it was the right one. But I duly wrote my name on the top of the paper and, not for the first time, flanneled away like some brainless washing machine.

Later there was a viva with Professor Korner, a Kant scholar who spoke like a mid-European spy and couldn't pronounce his "w"s. I didn't have a chance with him because he kept bringing it back to boring, bloody philosophy all the time.

My mate, Pam Stagg, had an even more bizarre viva. "Do you think that Kant is a bit vacky?" he asked her. When she said she didn't understand the question he replied: "Vacky, vacky, vat don't you understand about vacky?"

Pam and I went off to learn our fate. She got a Second, which she wasn't happy with since she'd been told she might be in for a First. I got my Third, although the prof rubbed it in a bit by summoning me and saying: "In case you're thinking of complaining, Tom, I want to w-w-w-w-remind you that, apart from a little final flourish ..."

A little final flourish!

"Apart from a little final flourish when you panicked for five minutes, you did no work whatsoever and you are d-d-d-d- very lucky to get that."

Five minutes! It was more like a month, I thought, but I kept my thoughts to myself. Maybe if I'd done two months I would have got a Second. And who knows what three months' work might have got me? Too late now.

For some reason, he continued, I had shown a very good grasp of Kant and the questions I had answered on the old Teutonic bubble-blower (not his formulation) had almost alone got me my degree. I had also shown some understanding of the ideas of the Empiricists, and after a long discussion, they had decided to award me my Third, but it had been a close-run thing.

So there it was. My month's hard labour had not been in vain. I was a Bachelor of Arts who could proceed to sort out the English language problems of Indonesian pilots.

The night before I was to leave Cardiff for the Far East I was sitting around the television with my father and mother in our usual silent conclave before going to bed.

He'd had a few beers and was farting well but I became uneasy when he turned off the television before we had reached the Epilogue. He had only ever turned down the volume when Kay had been around. Whatever was going to happen next?

"Going off to Indonesia tomorrow, are you?"

That was an oration to the Senate for him so I remained in my armchair, curious to see where it was going. "Well, it's a train to Naples first and then a ship to Indonesia."

"It's a long way to Indonesia. I'd never think of travelling that far. Do you know I've never been abroad?"

"You went on a rugby trip to France," my mother chipped in. "Lost all your money in some can-can club in Paris."

"That was a rugby trip. That doesn't count. And it wasn't a can-can club."

"Paris is still abroad," my mother persisted when, overwhelmed by the folly of contradicting him about anything, she sighed and announced she was going to bed.

"What I don't understand," my father went on after she left the room, "is why you're ready to do all this for a couple of pounds a week. You've got an Honours degree and you're ready to go to all this effort for a couple of pounds a week."

"I'm not doing it for the money, am I? It's an adventure as well as a way of helping people less fortunate than me."

"Helping people! The world is beyond help and you're travelling all that way for nothing to help what can't be helped. Doesn't make any sense to me."

This was dangerously close to the longest conversation we'd ever had and I still couldn't see where it was going. His hands were trembling *and* there were tears in his eyes, which only happened when he was truly angry. I could see he wasn't pleased by what I was doing but he surely couldn't be angry and tearful about it, could he? I said nothing.

"I went down the pit on my fourteenth birthday," he continued, raising his upturned palms. "I reached for the moon and ended up with nothing."

"What's your point, Dad?"

"My point is that with all your education, it looks as if you're going to end up with nothing too."

"What do you mean by nothing?"

"You know. No money."

Money, money, money. The limits of his money were the limits of his world. My father could not see beyond the furnaces of the steelworks he was paid to brick up. A week was good if he'd done a few double shifts and been paid well. A week was bad if he was on bare money with no overtime or doublers. He only left his pay slip in his pockets for my mother to find if he'd had a bad week. She never found his pay slip if he'd done a few doublers.

Dreams of money ensured he did the Football Pools avidly and carefully. "Right, let's see if I have to go to work tomorrow," he would say before checking his coupon as the soccer results were announced on the BBC on Saturdays.

My mother was also locked into the same fantasy, always checking hers at the same time before crumpling up the coupon with a sigh of disappointment and throwing her scrunched-up dreams into the fire. They both believed, as an article of faith, that if only they could win £30,000, their lives would change miraculously and the whole world would be theirs.

I have often thought of my father sitting there with his hands trembling and his face drawn with defeat as he gazed tearfully at the dying embers of the fire that night, the light from the embers catching in the tears in his eyes. Something had happened that he couldn't understand. There had been some kind of conspiracy to make sure he never made any money and here he was sitting with his eldest son who, with all his education, wasn't going to make a shilling either. It didn't make any sense to him. None of it.

"Ah well," I sighed, making as if to go off to bed, not wanting another pointless quarrel the night before I left home. We'd done our full share of that over the years.

"No, no. Don't go to bed. Just sit here and talk to me. I've never had any education. Help me to understand what's going on here because I can't. For the life of me I can't."

His hands were still trembling and tears ran down his cheeks.

I could see he needed to reach out to me so we kept talking for a further hour, a family record that would stand for all time. I explained that my generation was prepared to help others for nothing and this was just the way we were. He still couldn't see it, couldn't understand how we could do anything at all except for money and the more money the better.

We didn't reach any conclusions but for the first time I had connected with him: not to the man but to the chaos inside him. His lifelong shortage of money and his disappointment that he'd never achieved any kind of status; his bitterness that no one had ever recognised his talents and frustration that he'd never had any kind of education. And here I was "with all my education" and I wasn't going to do anything with it. I wasn't going to grab all the money I could lay my hands on; all the money that he'd only ever been able to dream about.

"But you don't have an education just to get money, Dad. Education is freedom."

"Freedom from what?" he snorted.

Well, freedom from being like you, I might have said in other circumstances. Freedom from being trapped by *your* unrealised ambitions and longings.

"You seem to think that this job is for ever but it's only a year with an option on two. You know I only want to be a writer and doing jobs like this will certainly one day give me something to write about."

Ah, a writer. That was another subject that upset him. Writers didn't make money. Teachers and architects made money, but never writers. He'd read that in the *South Wales Echo* so it must be true.

"The problem is I haven't studied architecture," I pointed out when he, yet again, told me about all the big money that architects made. "I studied philosophy and, if you really want to know, you don't make any money out of being a philosopher either."

I saw then how completely my education had changed me and put me at odds with my Welsh working-class background. I had been liberated, not by my studies as such – although getting near certain first class minds had helped – but by brilliant students like Vincent Kane, Keith Ward, Pam Stagg, Craig Thomas, Neil Kinnock and so many others with whom I had drunk and mingled over the past three years. It was people like them who had offered me new ideas, releasing me from sterile working-class worries about money and given me a political identity and the confidence to go around the world picking up experiences which might one day make me a writer.

Even rich people couldn't necessarily do what I was about to do. Anyway I had always *felt* rich even as a poor child and there can't have been a student in Cardiff who had more money than me, who drank as much and drove a van around the city offering all kinds of sexual excitements to young girls for nothing. Perhaps wealth really is just a matter of attitude, but what I did realise, in that unique, last-minute conversation with my father, was that I had already developed much further than he had; that I had liberated myself from many of the ideas that had kept him cocooned for so long in a disappointment from which he would never emerge. Might he, one day? No, never. Not even if he won the Pools because the money would never be enough and his ideas and prejudices were ingrained. Education might have helped him – *might* – but he wasn't likely to get anything remotely resembling an education now.

I was almost appalled to find that, within this conversation, my hatred of him was falling away into a form of understanding. As he struggled with his confusion I could see, from his shakes and tears, that this hadn't been a pose to goad me but a deeply felt position. Perhaps I had been too harsh on this strange, over-emotional man, trapped by his hard-won and long-held prejudices? Education – or at least the experience of going to university – had released me from many of mine; he was doomed to remain imprisoned in his.

New insights into those close to you are often disturbing because they can involve difficult implications for yourself and are probably best avoided. I was left with plenty to think about as I packed for South East Asia. That we need to keep evaluating our ideas and be ready to change them, otherwise we end up trapped in the ignorance of other people's ideas or imprisoned in sterile longings like my father.

It wasn't him who was shrinking but me who was growing. Now I saw why Kay insisted I had never known what was going on inside him because "with all my education" I had never bothered to sit down with him long enough to find out.

FIFTEEN

I pleaded with Janey not to come to London to see me off but she came anyway, making me as miserable as she was by continually bursting into tears.

I kissed her goodbye on the platform at Liverpool Street Station and promised to write often. I *was* surprised to find myself thinking about her a lot as the train sped through France, but I was brought down to earth with a bump when I couldn't find my ticket and the ticket collector insisted that I pay for the journey to Naples, about £20. This was an enormous sum and minutes after he'd left the carriage, I found the missing ticket, but he wouldn't give me the money back. I would have to claim it from his head office.

My annoyance soon dissipated as we bowled through the European night. I've always been happy on the move; always known that something interesting would arrive in the coming hour if not the next. Journeys into the unknown have an almost sexual frisson about them as you curl up in the corner of a crowded carriage, gazing out at the towns and cities as they stream past. You catch sight of a figure silhouetted in a lit window, someone you have never seen before and will certainly never see again. You realise we share this planet with billions of people we will never see at all. You become the alienated outsider travelling from nothingness to nothingness through a hostile universe, as Samuel Beckett had it.

I saw almost nothing of Naples and quickly settled down aboard the ship, where noisy Italians served good food and I became friendly with Sue, an attractive English girl sailing out to be with her husband in the RAF in Singapore. It might have developed into a shipboard romance but didn't, perhaps due to the shadow of the waiting husband, and we merely chatted a lot, mostly about the difficulty of relationships. She told me about her past loves and I told her about mine.

For the third time in four years I encountered the bumboats of Port Said. For someone whose income had barely exceeded a student grant for three years I was doing a hell of a lot of travelling. But I soon found myself growling with a familiar kind of frustration, perhaps stirred by a re-reading of Henry Miller's *Tropic of Cancer*, since as soon as we berthed at Bombay I went ashore looking for sex.

Bombay was a shock to my system, perhaps the most shocking of all the cities I had visited, even New York, since here the pavements swarmed with hurrying life and the badly made roads were packed with honking traffic. Wild, bearded men with huge bollocks hanging out of their skimpy trousers stormed through the crowds as if on holy, urgent missions as did limbless beggars on body carts. Sacred white cows with bells wandered unmolested to wherever they thought there might be some food. The smells, baked together by the sweltering heat, almost knocked you unconscious.

I asked a trishaw driver on the dock to take me to a brothel and, after threading his way through the most jammed traffic jam in the world, he dropped me in a narrow street full of cages with a woman sitting on a bed inside each one. The deal, the trishaw driver told me, was that when you came to an agreement with one of them, she would draw the curtain and you got on with it. I knew I wouldn't be able to perform in a cage like that, barely screened from the traffic outside. Anyone could have reached out through their driving window and given me a good slap on the arse, probably what I deserved, so I asked the trishaw driver to take me somewhere a bit more upmarket.

A few more traffic jams later I was taken to a large house where the Madam rang a hand bell whereupon dozens of whores came flocking down the stairs, all with big, black eyes, red spots on their foreheads and orange saris. Not one of them looked more than twelve years of age.

Child whores are common in the East but this lot seemed an open invitation to paedophilia and I was certain I had no inclinations towards that, no matter what books I had read lately. These girls did their best to sparkle my fancy, pinching me or rubbing their bodies up against mine but, disgusted and sweating profusely, I ran down into the street, wondering if Janey had been right all along and I really *should* get some medical attention.

Being a sexual outlaw with an inquisitive dick was all very well but who knows what kind of diseases I might have picked up had I gone ahead? For all my experience I still tackled all sexual adventures bareback, always just got on with it and hoped for the best. But hey, I was young and immortal and if I did cop an early death from some dreadful disease like syphilis that was entirely consistent with the writerly path I had chosen to totter down.

Djakarta, the capital of Java, looked like the boondocks after being hit by a bomb. Dusty palm trees bent apologetically over a quay where little brown, half-naked men carried big and small loads around the huddles of *atap* huts which, presumably, were the port buildings. You looked for significant structures but there were none higher than one storey. Items of cargo flew up out of the holds like panicked birds and I swallowed nervously as I tried to take it all in. You can cope with places like this when you know you may be leaving within a few weeks but I might have to spend two years here. I had signed for one year but VSO let it be known they preferred you to do two.

I knew this was a place apart when a customs officer, finding my one and only carton of cigarettes, ripped it into two and kept half for himself. I had re-packed my rifled suitcase and was carrying it out when another customs officer ran after me demanding the other half.

Fortunately the Second Secretary of the British Embassy turned up and began a big slanging match in Indonesian with the customs official who finally backed off without getting hold of the rest of my cigarettes.

"You've just got to shout at the bastards," the Second Secretary said as we got into the embassy jeep. "There's nothing in their heads. All they understand is abuse."

My tensions developed into something like hard fear as we drove into the centre of Djakarta. We stopped at a level crossing and a train steamed past overflowing with people. I caught my first glimpse of the canals in which the whole of the city appeared to be doing its business. People washed themselves and their clothes in the brown water, cleaning their teeth, shaving or having a crap or a piss off the end of a plank. They just crouched down on the end of the plank and got on with it. Some of the women were disconcertingly beautiful but they didn't like you looking at them, waving their arms around furiously indicating you should push off. Apparently, they threw stones at you if you tried to photograph them.

The Second Secretary told me I was to stay in Djakarta for a few days in a small hotel near the centre to settle in. Tomorrow was Independence Day and I would be taken to a rally being addressed by President Sukarno in the Asian Games Stadium. I was left to my own devices that night and lay on my hotel bed, under the dank suffocation of a mosquito net, wondering how I was going to cope.

I couldn't get those canals out of my mind. I devoutly hoped I wouldn't have to crap off the end of a plank wherever I ended up. VSO liked their volunteers to live like the natives and a good crap early in the morning always set me up for the rest of the day but, if I tried to do it off the end of a plank with half the neighbourhood watching, I was reasonably sure I would never have a decent bowel movement ever again.

The next morning I sat about ten feet away from President Sukarno as he addressed a crowded Asian Games Stadium. This was my first sight of The Bung and it was a long one because his speech lasted nearly three hours. The crowd cheered him to the echo as he spoke, mostly in Indonesian, but with bursts of English, in long, colourful sentences, largely about the neo-colonialist plot of Malaysia set up by the British.

He was a portly, handsome man with a tremendous enthusiasm for sex I was to learn. He only had to spot a woman he liked and he had her. His family had milked the country of its spare wealth but he was quite fond of his people, spending much of his time travelling around the impoverished and starving *kampongs*, often urging them to get to love outer space.

I met the local British Council man that night – Alex, a rangy, intelligent man who took me to his place in the suburbs for dinner. He certainly made a strong impression on me. When I asked him what he'd achieved in his career with the Council he thought for a few moments and said there had been only one thing. He'd been in Burma when three young men called and said they wanted to go to Oxford University. They had walked barefoot through the jungle for days to see him so he made them study and two of them did go to Oxford.

"I was a bit naughty in working them so hard," he added. "One of them had a nervous breakdown. The other two got good degrees, though. That's all I've ever achieved really."

There was no sign of my scooter so an Indonesian Air Force jeep took me to the Tjurug Aviation Academy twelve miles north of Djakarta. The volcanic range of Krakatoa loomed as we drove through glittering parallelograms of paddy fields and I still couldn't get used to the way everyone used the canals as washhouses and lavatories. Chickens foraged in the villages where adults sat happily on the steps of their thatched, stilted houses and swarms of children chased one another. They would often flash you brilliant, gleaming smiles: only the very old seemed to have bad teeth.

The Aviation Academy comprised three or four small buildings next to an airstrip on which I never once saw an aeroplane. My home was a small one-room hut with a concrete floor and an adjoining bog with a hole in the ground – at least it wasn't a plank – in which a big praying mantis had taken up residence. My first meal was a plate of boiled rice with a blackened fish head perched on top that I got rid of quietly in the ditch outside, and, as the sun went down in a storming blaze of colour over the croaking paddy fields, I sat down and wept because I did not see how I was going to survive.

As I lay on my bed inside my net with mosquitoes whining around trying to find a way in, I was desperate to be home again watching television while my dear father farted away in his armchair. VSO had warned us about the misery and loneliness we would certainly encounter before we settled down to our postings but I had never imagined it would be as bad as this. Apart from the few buildings where the aviation students lived and learned how to fly their non-existent aeroplanes, there was nothing for miles in any direction except paddy fields. All my loneliness would do here was to get worse. I longed to see my mother again or Janey or even my old philosophy professor – anyone at all who might reassure me that it was safe to take a piss in that bog with that praying mantis on the window sill, its huge, multi-prism eyes following my every move as it tried to decide which part of my dick to bite.

I managed to settle down after a week or so, determined to see things through, no matter how unhappy I might be. I drew up a tough schedule of work for my pilots understanding that if I failed to keep myself occupied it really was going to be one long bout of misery and boredom. Had one of my pilots knocked on my door and said he wanted to go to Oxford he would have started work there and then. That story about those Burmese students remains one of the most inspiring I've ever been told.

For the fourth or fifth time I started work on a novel, making notes about the characters and the countryside in which I found myself. What I should have done was work out the plot first but I didn't understand the primacy of story then. I was content to sit down with my characters each day and see what they got up to.

My novel was set in Indonesia because everything was so vivid here it demanded to be described. Characters were beginning to take shape amidst this lurid exoticism. Keep working on them and they would bloom into life. They did indeed develop and I could see they might create some company that would help me in my loneliness. Whenever I got bored with them I could kill them off, a trick which beat the hell out of real life.

The time had come for me to grow up, I kept telling myself and, if that meant I had to work here for two years that's what it meant. I would be able to slip down to Djakarta at weekends when my scooter turned up and make new friends there. I must calm down and grow up.

I never really settled at Tjurug. My best intentions kept being undermined by various niggles about why I was out here teaching English to what turned out to be *military* pilots. Teaching the poor to help build their community was one thing but educating pilots so that they could bomb their enemies more effectively was an entirely different matter. What made it all the more pointless was they didn't seem to have any aircraft. They kept talking about new aeroplanes but they never reached the runway.

Then trouble started in Djakarta. Students had been demonstrating outside the British Embassy against the neo-colonialist plot that was Malaysia when some dolt started playing the bagpipes inside the grounds. This so enraged the students they burned down the embassy. These students had a sound insight into what would most upset the English because, after firing the embassy, they went on to dig up the cricket pitch in the English Box Club.

Word came from Djakarta that I must pack my bags at once. I was to be taken to the Hotel Indonesia and evacuated from the country immediately. There would not even be time to say goodbye to anyone. (This seemed an excessive response to a student demo, particularly in Indonesia, where everyone I met seemed to be so smiling and gentle, but in a few years, in this very area, the paddy fields ran red with blood when millions died in a mass slaughter of the Communists.)

Army men were stationed on every corner as we were herded together into the foyer of the Hotel Indonesia, where, directly over the road, we could see the still-smouldering ruins of the British Embassy with passports scattered everywhere. The students had razed it to the ground and I would never have believed there had been a large embassy there had I not previously seen it with my own eyes. That was something I'd have to tell my left-wing pals about when I got home.

Yet the last thing I wanted was to go home now. I had decided to take this job seriously and do the best I could, so I asked my old pal, the Second Secretary, if I could stay on to help in some way but he insisted I board the next plane. With the women and children, if you please.

A reporter from Reuters interviewed me and a piece about my evacuation subsequently appeared on the front page of the *South Wales Echo* along with a picture of me wearing my gown and mortarboard. My mother's work for sure. She had been so overjoyed I'd got a degree she wanted the whole world to know. No one – least of all me – had explained to her the insignificance of my Third and how I'd been lucky to get even that.

A wailing bedlam surged around the potted plants and along the marbled corridors of the Hotel Indonesia as more and more evacuees turned up clutching whatever prized possessions they had managed to grab. All non-essential ex-pats had to go, it had been decreed, although that wasn't as frightening as it might sound because the cream of the Indonesian army was guarding us day and night. The burning of the embassy had taken the Indonesian government by surprise. They often turned a blind eye to student demos if it suited their agenda, but they hadn't wanted the embassy burned down or indeed the cricket pitch dug up.

The most upset were the servants, the ageing *amahs* who had been with their English families for years looking after the kids and cleaning while the English ladies drank gin and played bridge down the Box Club. I had been told that some of these *amahs* put a little opium under their fingernails for fractious babies to suck on until they fell asleep while Virginia was getting wrecked with her mates in the Box.

I sat on the bus taking us to the airport with everything bleeding and crumbling inside me. I had always been aware of the limits of idealism but my whole journey had been pointless. I had made no impact on anything: no sooner here than thrown out again like some unwanted refugee. Two women in front of me were talking about Singapore where the RAF was about to fly us in a Hercules.

A lone trishaw driver had somehow evaded the army cordon and was sitting on his vehicle near our bus watching the proceedings with quiet interest. His skin had been baked black by the sun and he didn't have an ounce of fat on his stringy, mus-cled body. Shortage of proper food and the energy needed to pedal a trishaw around these exhausting streets meant that the life expectancy of these drivers was seven years at the most. He began hand-rolling a cigarette and the tiniest of smiles flick-ered on his thin lips as he watched this refugee drama unfolding around him.

The trishaw driver studied his cigarette, lit it and took a deep pull. The smoke curled around his face as more desperate, frightened people were herded on to the bus, clutching their treasures. "They got everything else but they didn't get my pot," one man cried to no one in particular.

The trishaw driver saw me staring at him and lifted his palm to give me a small wave, as if telling me that I shouldn't worry and that everything would be all right. I responded, acknowledging his concern and offering my own. It was a real moment in which we came together. Despite all this madness we cared about one another, we were saying. We were sorry. It shouldn't have come to this. Maybe another day.

Tears welled up in my eyes. Seven years he had to live. Seven years.

After the crumbling, dusty anarchy of Djakarta the clean and bracing vitality of Singapore came as a surprise. Here were skyscrapers and tramways and telephones that worked when you picked them up. Men in trousers with ambitious creases went about their business carrying briefcases and shapely women in cheongsams slit right up their thighs took your breath away as they undulated past. These women were immaculate and you knew, as soon as you looked at them, that one of them might be yours if you had enough money.

I was met by the British Council man, Paul Hardwick, who put me in a flat over-looking the sea, which had been left empty by an academic on vacation, and gave me a generous allowance while it was decided what to do with me. I'd probably end up at a school in Malaya, he thought. Meanwhile, take it easy and have a good time in Singapore. Everyone in Asia kept telling me to have a good time; it was almost as if no one actually expected me to do any work.

It was easy to take it easy and have a good time in Singapore. I spent many a happy hour exploring the back streets with their fascinating novelties. There was Death Alley, where you could study ornate Chinese coffins, spread out as if in some haphazard morticians' supermarket. *Kyatai* – transvestites – gathered at night in Bugis Street, fussing over their make-up, chatting to one another or constantly tugging at their panties. Some of them were intriguingly beautiful.

There were fish-fights in back alleys with Siamese fighting fish flaring up like unfolding orchids and tearing at one another as the Chinese gambled heatedly around the tank. The Chinese love gambling: money is their life-blood. Certain sections of the Chinese community were entrenched in magic, mystery, monkey gods, moon cakes and hungry ghosts who could only ever be placated with ghost money. Fire-walking festivals in honour of the goddess Droba-Devi were staged in parks.

I also liked to spend time in Change Alley where currencies from all over the world were changed by calculator-brained men who would always take off a nice slice for themselves.

Here I was the alienated outsider again, thinking nothing, feeling nothing, wanting nothing as straw-hatted coolies pushed large bags of this and that on their small handcarts behind me. Singapore was good for literary fantasies like that: the Conradian loner making his way through an exotic, hostile world with only despair in his bags.

The convivial Hardwicks kept me going and I showed Paul an article I had written about my stay in Indonesia which I thought I might offer to the *Observer*. He read it and made a number of perceptive points. He liked a lot of the descriptions, he said, but what had vexed him was when I wrote that when I had first arrived in Djakarta I had "idealism dripping out of my eyes". There was other evidence of this kind of flip jokiness and he wondered why I needed to apologise for my idealism? Why did I see it as some kind of joke? Wasn't I serious about my work? Isn't dying of starvation a serious business?

These were all pertinent questions and he went on to say that he had come to despise modern England, a chrysalis of artificiality where nothing was taken seriously. Why couldn't we be serious? I appreciated these British Council men more and more, exiled in foreign cities with their little libraries and decided that, if my literary ambitions went unrealised, I could do no better than become one of them, running the library, giving alcoholic receptions for visiting poets and bollocking would-be writers for not being sufficiently serious. It wasn't a proper job and it certainly didn't involve anything like real work. But it did look a lot of fun and would suit me fine.

Yet again I had met someone who had enriched my life. As at university, I was still greedily absorbing the ideas of those who impressed me. I never seemed to have a single idea of my own, just fastened on to those of others, worked them around a bit and presented them as mine. I was the donkey who determinedly followed the dangling carrots of everyone else's thoughts.

Then Paul told me I was to take a train to the small town of Alor Star in Kedah state, North Malaya, near the Thai border, where I would become an English teacher at the Sultan Abdul Hamid College. "Best of luck, Tom."

SIXTEEN

I had the strangest feeling of coming home as I got off the train at Alor Star and the trishaw driver pedalled me to the school. We trundled down a main street lined with colourful shops, including something reassuringly called a Milk Bar next to the crowded bus station where a blind man sang lines from the Koran in the vibrant sunshine.

A hi-fi stall stood next to a tailoring shop and there were many Chinese restaurants with skinned carcasses of ducks dangling in lines over flaming woks and barely enough room for six people. Over there, an ironmonger's and a ladies' dress shop. Religious icons were on offer in another. Huge faces stared at me from cinema posters. Deep storm gutters ran down either side of the street and a man with no legs rolled cigarettes from dibby ends scavenged from the pavements.

Everywhere seemed to hold the promise of some kind of amusement. For the first time in months I relaxed: on almost no evidence, I was certain I was going to have fun here. I was overjoyed when I saw the playing fields and the impressive, pillared, neo-colonial frontage of the Sultan Abdul Hamid College, as different from the Tjurug Aviation Academy as it was possible to get. The headmaster greeted me politely on the steps of his grand school and I was shown my new home: a room built on to the Sixth Form dormitory. The boys spoke excellent English because it was the sole medium of instruction. They even had a flushing lavatory, although no toilet paper. You were supposed to use your left hand and soap to wash yourself after you'd finished and it was surprising how quickly you got to grips with it. It left you much cleaner than paper, particularly in the tropical heat.

After the ramshackle, haphazard atmosphere of Indonesia, where a nation conducted a lot of its private business in murky canals and which the Dutch had plundered remorselessly but put nothing back – it came as a surprise to my young anti-colonialist eyes to see how much the Brits had done for their colonies like Malaya; how they had put down good roads, installed a decent telephone system, set up a civil service and, instead of letting the various races like Chinese, Malays and Tamils quarrel amongst themselves, insisted they came together in the one language in a school system closely modelled on the English public school. A surprising number of teachers at the school regretted the passing of British rule; many of them wished we were back in charge.

They all spoke English in the teachers' Common Room where I met those who liked to chat and those who didn't. There were around thirty teachers, many of whom had done their training in England, a practice that had been stopped because the Malay teachers were becoming increasingly reluctant to return after finishing their course. Their accents and odd choices of words like "bounder" or "rascal" made them sound more English than the English.

The Thai female teachers were ravishingly beautiful – as were the Malay women – but you soon understood that you would never get anywhere with them. All relationships in the Common Room were strictly professional and there was no inter-breeding, particularly with randy volunteer teachers on a couple of pounds a week. Marriages were mostly arranged and one Malay teacher I became friendly with said he was getting married in two weeks' time and he had not yet exchanged one word with his bride or even looked at her properly. His only worry seemed to be whether she had been "fired" before.

Teaching here was a pleasure, particularly the younger children who stood up as I entered the classroom, always called me "Sir" – even when I tried to stop them – listened raptly to my every word and laughed heartily at all my jokes. Whatever homework I set was diligently completed. If I asked them to do four hours' home-work that's what came back the next morning.

I was also given the English Sixth Form where I could talk, without pause or patronisation, in whatever way I chose and they took it all in. The Chinese, in par-ticular, were bright as pins, ever ready to pick me up if I got anything wrong and, as we embarked on the A-level syllabus, I again realised I should have taken English at Cardiff, that I had a flair for it and that I could have done a lot better for them if I'd taken my degree in it.

I also began learning about my new hometown, often going for a long walk early in the evenings and rummaging around in the dusty nooks and crannies of the back streets. There was a large cinema with the irritating habit of showing up to an hour of ads before the main feature which had everyone speaking in poorly dubbed Malay. Huge puppet shows were set up on the riverbank and we could sit around for hours watching nothing very much happen in Mandarin.

Each race had its own festivals and one night the Hindus put on fire-walking with men walking the length of a flaming pit, occasionally pausing to pick up a glowing coal and put it in their mouths. A few walkers fainted in the heat and were caught by colleagues and their feet plunged into a trough of cow's milk at the end of the pit. Minutes later none of them seemed any the worse for wear.

The Chinese staged many festivals to their many gods. One night I was sitting in the Milk Bar eating noodles when a whole gang of them came running down the main road following a huge chair carried on poles by six men. The chair lunged this way and that, blessing some homes and ignoring others. Later they gathered on the riverbank and fireworks flashed and exploded as a large ship was pushed out on to the water, set alight and sunk. The Festival of the Nine Gods.

The town was surrounded by hundreds of acres of paddy fields worked by men with buffaloes. You could walk for hours through those still fields, followed only by your reflection in the sun-glazed water, and one day I came across a huge hill with a cave where men were hauling out bat *guano* that Malaya exported as fertiliser for growing orchids. The men worked deep in the cave where thousands of bats screeched and fluttered on the roof until twilight when they went out hunting.

Everywhere I looked there was something to stimulate my writing. I managed to put in some serious time on the novel that had begun taking shape in Indonesia. Several clear characters emerged from my chattering Olivetti, aided by many inspirational cigarettes. After messing about and dreaming about it for so long, my first *magnum opus* was finally up and running.

Alexander Hawkins stepped out into the light and cool of the morning, his mind still dull with sleep. He stood briefly on his porch before walking down through the overgrown garden. A tangle of red bougainvillea was choking a rotten tree and the purple and gold dots of many flowers stood out against the dark jungle which had already swallowed the fence.

He followed a narrow path around the edge of the jungle until he reached the top of a hill overlooking the tin mine. His black eyes could detect trouble at a glance and his thick eyebrows knitted into a frown when he saw there was indeed trouble. His coolies had gone missing.

He walked down to the mine's open face where three Europeans were working in a crater with a high-powered water gun which blasted the rocks, making the earth dance before it eddied down to the huge sieves where the ore was collected. He stooped under the bamboo scaffolding wondering what had happened to the coolies but except for one fast asleep in the cab of his lorry, there were none. A rising babble of excitement sounded from the work hut and his lips tightened when he realised what was going on in there.

It was the second time that month. Some of the female coolies were so anxious not to lose a day's pay they even gave birth on the job. Such births, however, interrupted the working of the mine since the other coolies would watch the event for up to half an hour before the baby emerged.

They were so engrossed they didn't even notice Hawkins' presence in the hut doorway. The woman set about the job with a ferocious energy. During each contraction her face rumpled with pain but, as it passed, her face softened, her eyes opened in a sort of smile and she began humping her buttocks up and down into the mess that was already on the blanket. Another contraction returned along with more pain. She was about to start bumping again when she fell backwards, arms flailing and a tiny body inched forward out of her damp bush, limbs bunched and looking wet and without life until a coolie scooped it up and cut the umbilical cord with a pair of scissors.

The baby was lifted into the air and slapped. Blood dripped from his head, the eyes screwed up in anger, the hand tightened in a ruddy rage and the baby opened his mouth and screamed.

Hawkins felt some sympathy for this baby which would be fed minimally, educated not at all and, when his muscles were slightly developed, pushed into a job loading tin ore into an endless stream of lorries. He told his foreman to send the woman home for two days. "Yes, yes. With pay." Then he ordered the others back to work or he'd stop a day's pay all round. An old woman wrapped the baby in a kimono and took him away to be washed.

I liked Hawkins as soon as he emerged: a sharply drawn character who would become a powerful protagonist and antagonist to the other characters. Here was the archetypal outsider, the Nietzschean superman who had withdrawn from the world to live as a primitive in the jungle. He would become a spirit of lawlessness, bound only by his own eccentric rules in a world which he despised. He would be a homosexual who, when provoked, could react with awesome violence.

An intense Cardiff student called Eric, with whom I was still corresponding, had provided his physical presence but, otherwise, Hawkins had been put together from any number of books ranging from those by Joseph Conrad to Colin Wilson and films featuring lawless loners like Tarzan or James Bond. You would find the spirit of Hawkins living, breathing and scripting solo dreams of revenge in all of these creations. He was an anti-hero for our time.

The rains came to Alor Star with an unflagging ferocity, sometimes keeping at it for a week at a time, when no one went anywhere. They lashed the main street, their huge drops raging against shuttered shops, bolted doors and Chinese billboards. Brigitte Bardot on the poster in front of the cinema looked like a boiled cabbage: her nipples dripping rivulets of red paint and eyes big black smudges as she gazed through tears of rain across the street at empty mobile food stalls stuck in mud.

Unable to go anywhere, I returned to my novel as soon as my schoolwork was over and began shaping a new character: Gabriel Domengo. Shades of Joseph Conrad and Grahame Greene in this creation and a little of the mad despair of Ingmar Bergman films. More than a little Dylan Thomas is also showing up in the picturesque scenes but that's the inescapable affliction of almost every Welsh writer who has put pen to paper. Once you've put your head inside all those lovely, whirling words it takes a long time to get it out again – if ever.

Gabriel is an old, weak, alcoholic mess, lost to himself and the world, barely sane and suffused with suffering and despair.

Gabriel Domengo was pacing from one side of his rectangular living room to the other. It took him ten steps to get from one wall to the other and six steps to get from his bedroom door to his front window. If he crossed the room from one corner to the opposite corner it took twelve steps. Now, with the aid of pencil and paper, he was trying to work out the square footage of the living room for no other reason than that he had little else to do when the rains began.

Sheets of rain mingled with the thunder and iridescent forks of lightning slashed through the sky in angry crackles.

The simple sums defeated him and he stood at his front window, took out a pocket watch and checked the time before putting it back into his pocket. He turned and measured the distance to the centre of the room – four steps – stood still and fumbled for a cigarette butt which he put in his mouth and lit with a match. The flare of the sulphur flickered in his eyes and highlighted his wrinkled face. He sucked on the cigarette as his foot edged the dead match into a crack between the floorboards.

He sat at his table, opened a book and noticed a mosquito, puffed with blood, lying near his reading lamp. He turned it on its side with a trembling finger and its wings quivered. He played with the body with a matchstick for a while before paring off a wing. As the insect floundered he brought his face close to it and blew out a cloud of cigarette smoke. A crippled man struggling in fog. He lifted his finger and crushed the ailing insect into a black and red smudge. That would teach it. Gabriel hated mosquitoes almost as much as he hated the rains.

The rains eased into a fine drizzle but no sooner had the townsfolk put their heads out of doors, held up their hands nervously and scanned the skies than black frothy clouds bundled in over the horizon again for another massed gathering and deluge.

Gabriel stalked into the kitchen, brushed grumpily up against his woman, a Thai in an Army helmet, as she washed up, and took a bottle of beer out of the fridge. He returned to slump in his armchair and curse as the foaming beer half emptied itself over his trousers. Even the workers in the Tiger brewery had it in for him now.

His woman was getting on his nerves. He had sent her packing a few times only to take her back. She cooked for him, looked after him when he was ill, cleaned the house, washed his clothes and, if he was feeling very lazy, shaved him. He took another swig from his bottle and watched a runnel of sweat roll down between the hairs of his chest on to the folds of his belly. She came into the living room and began dusting the sideboard. Hadn't he always told her to ask if she wanted to clean the living room when he was there?

He put down his bottle, crept up behind her, grabbed her round the waist and brought his knee sharply up against the back of her leg. She neither struggled nor protested when he did it again, swinging her from side to side as a dog might shake an old doormat. He carried her back out into the kitchen, put her down and then, slightly out of breath, returned to his beer.

Afterwards remorse struck him. He was a solitary man forced back on himself and should live alone. It was not fair for any woman to have to put up with someone like him. All he needed were his memories. They were enough. He yawned.

The rains did stop for a while and he stood at his window watching the clouds. Newly hatched butterflies were rising and falling on the path outside. Then the whip of lightning cracked again and another clap of thunder shook the earth. It sounded as if a giant was sitting up there on the corrugated iron roof tearing up calico sheets.

He eyed a thick black rhinoceros beetle whiskering its way across the living room floor. He moved his foot slightly. When the beetle was close enough he stepped on it; not hard, just enough to feel it press against the ball of his sandalled foot. The insect squealed: a high-pitched squeal which he enjoyed. Then he stamped down hard on it and the squealing stopped. "Serves you right," he told it. He had warned them often enough. Insects forfeited all rights when they came into his house, even during the rains.

There would be no prizes for guessing where the inspiration for the third main character for my novel, David Roberts, came from. He would complete the trio of displaced Europeans who would engage in a long and bloody dance of death. But he was not menaced yet: he had only arrived in the town that day and was sitting on a trolley at the railway station together with a suitcase tied with rope and a huge yellow guitar.

His long, blonde hair nestled in piles on his shoulders with a pink scarf tied around his neck whose brightness was at odds with the drabness of his cannabis-flowered T-shirt and torn, much-scrubbed jeans. On each hand were several rings and a massive pair of sunglasses effectively covered the top half of his face. Not a rock singer who had missed the last bus to his next gig but a young Welsh idealist and inveterate shagmeister who had arrived to teach English in the town's one and only school. He had been sitting in the noonday heat for half an hour now and was disappointed by the non-appearance of a band and some dancing girls. Flowers and a ceremony of welcome were the least he had hoped for after travelling half way around the world to be here. But there was nothing at all.

He was playing with his sideboards with his be-ringed fingers as he gazed out at a man standing on the bank of a stream next to the railway line. The man was ramming a stick into holes to flush out crabs that he caught and dropped into a bucket.

In an effort to boost his morale David whistled Reeling and Rocking, his head bobbing from side to side, his sandals tapping the beat. The fans shook their heads and screamed as they reached out to touch him. Thousands of girls were transmitting urgent invitations to him from between their legs and the band was managing to keep it tight and funky. His roadies wrestled with the crowd and, as the strobe lights flashed, they all screamed for more, more, more.

This explosion of rocking joy was invaded by a Malay woman who walked to the end of a plank overhanging the stream near the man who was crabbing. She lifted her sarong and pissed long and loudly into the water. David's rounded lips continued to blow but no whistling came out. He lifted his sunglasses slightly to take a better look. Wraiths of steam billowed around the bubbles where her piss hit the water, but she maintained all the unconcerned elegance of a society lady taking cocktails at a diplomatic reception. He stopped whistling completely and, when their eyes met, hastily lowered his sunglasses and turned his head away but took sneaky glances out of the corners of his eyes. That's what he liked about sunglasses. Your head could be pointing in one direction and your eyes could ogle in the other without giving offence. She finished her business and backed down the plank smoothing her sarong down around her wonderfully curving hips.

"Wow," he thought. "What a scene!" That's one bit he would have to work into the great novel.

Darkness came and found him still sitting on the platform so he concluded he could forget that dancing reception – or any other kind. He picked up his guitar and suitcase and walked slowly into the lamp-lit town looking for someone to report to.

SEVENTEEN

Anthony Burgess, who wrote his Malayan quartet while with the British Council in a nearby town, noted how words seemed to pour out of you in the tropics and that was happening to me in Alor Star.

The school day began at seven o'clock in the morning with Boon Let, the Thai gym teacher, ringing his hand-bell, and classes continued until noon. A few of us teachers might lunch together in the town, but then it would be a short siesta through the worst of the afternoon heat leaving me refreshed and with the rest of the day to do whatever I wanted.

I had a lot of reading to do for my Sixth Form work, trying, not always successfully, to keep one step ahead of them. We were working through Aldous Huxley's *Brave New World*, in which people were hatched and controlled with the drug soma, but soon it would be TS Eliot's *Collected Poems* and I knew I would have to be well prepared for that.

Otherwise I sat at my desk at night, hunched over my Olivetti, allowing my characters to take me wherever they wanted. As soon as you put the characters together they will write the story for you, I believed. A writer doesn't have much control over them: he hangs on to their coat-tails as best he can and tries to keep up.

Hawkins had an on and off relationship with Domengo, who occasionally came into the town to play chess with him at the Milk Bar in the main street. Meanwhile David had met Domengo and they occasionally got drunk together and patronised the local brothel.

I wanted to introduce an element of perverted ambiguity into the developing relationships between my three main characters and Nazeem emerged from my subconscious, a combination of the *kyatai* in Bugis Street in Singapore and those who gathered late at night here in Alor Star. The local *kyatai* were truly horrible, forever preening themselves and cackling suggestively as you passed by.

There was a lot of whistling as Nazeem approached the other kyatai, his hands holding a white orchid. The exquisite structure of his jaw was enhanced by his yellow, cat-like eyes, but there was a scar on his forehead so deep that not even his face-powder could conceal it.

Nazeem was the unofficial leader of the town's kyatai, someone to whom the others looked for advice. Sometimes he became so bored with them he would walk away, his hands still holding his white orchid as he ghosted through the darkness of the town's back streets.

The townsfolk didn't like the kyatai to move around after dark. They were tolerated if they remained in the same place near the school, well out of the way, but Nazeem had always been a law unto himself, taking up his usual position in the long, dark doorway of a tailoring shop where he sometimes stepped forward as the revolving glow of a car's headlights broke up the night, beckoning and pouting at the car before moving back into the doorway like a retreating night spider.

The ramshackle personality of the town changed yet again when everyone was asleep. The strolling musicians and puppeteers had long gone home as had Ahmad, the fagmaker, and the blind man who sang lines from the Koran. The restaurants were shut and the fortune-tellers with their boxes of birds had decamped. Long black shadows hung thickly over the empty streets, making the town almost magical; a nowhere place, lit by a full moon, existing precariously on the edge of memory.

David and Gabriel came staggering down the deserted main street, arms around one another and David singing Jesus Wants Me For A Sunbeam. They were near the school when David slumped down on his behind and refused to budge. He had walked too long, he reasoned out loud with slurred words, and was going to spend the rest of the night right there. Gabriel took a swig from his bottle of rice wine and fell in a heap next to him.

After a while David announced that if you looked at the moon through your legs it got bigger.

"Oh what bollocks," said Gabriel.

"That's a fact that is," David insisted. "Here, let me show you."

David pulled himself shakily erect and bent forward to get his head between his legs but somehow missed the opening between his legs and keeled over sideways striking his soft head on the hard street. "Oh Gabby, I'm bleeding. Look at this now. There's bleeding blood everywhere."

Suddenly David became aware of the local kyatai, their lips thick, red gashes across the lower half of their faces.

"This is serious," said Gabriel spotting the sequinned shadows. "We're in trouble."

"What kind of trouble?"

"Caught by the kyatai. They may not look it, but they're men."

David saw that the kyatai were circling them at a distance of about ten feet, some smiling and others cackling like aggrieved magpies.

"They won't hurt us but they'll probably play with us for a bit," Gabriel said.

"Play with us?"

"That's what I said. They'll have a little sport with us, but we've got to make a run for it. They'll leave us alone if we get back to the main street. They won't do it in the open. Let's go."

Gabriel was up and off with David after him wondering what the fuss was all about. After about five yards, he understood. The pursuing kyatai ran lightly around him and kept grabbing his testicles and brushing up against his body. Highly perfumed hands fluttered against his cheeks and body like light veils, smoothing his bum. One pinched his nipples and another mussed his hair.

David took a swing at one but missed by a mile. Another reached between his legs and butterflied his trousers. Gabriel had reached the main street and was standing in the sanc-

tuary of a pool of lamplight at the beginning of the main street. "Run kid," he shouted.
"Don't bother trying to hit the bastards, run for it."

David's lungs fought for air and he felt as if his head was about to burst as the per-
fumed group swarmed over him like a collapsing wave. It would have been less sinister if
they had made some sort of sound, but they remained silent and he felt he was running
along the corridors of a mad house being pursued by all its inmates. It was only when he
flung himself into Gabriel's arms that they raced silently back into the shadows whence
they had come.

Over the months my manuscript had swollen to several hundred pages. Thus far
there was very little heterosexuality in it, apart from a few brothel scenes for comic
effect. Everyone who knew me said I was obsessed with sex. It was true: I had never
been much interested in anything else from the time that Elvis Presley had done a
number on me in the street when I was fourteen.

It may well have been because I was writing a first novel but I was creating a fantasy which owed more to the books and films I admired than the real world in which
I found myself. Perhaps all novels and films are fantasies inspired by the ideas of
others. Many are only too predictable; others merely echo previous publications.
Seldom does any film or novel break the mould. Is there anything new or true in
what we create or do we merely *regurgitate* other people's themes and ideas?

The imaginary world I had entered into with my novel seemed real enough to
me: the four of us had become a close family and I thought, at one stage, we were
all engaged in a mysterious square-dance whose outcome was uncertain and might
even be bloody. Yet whatever the flaws in my characters, and whether or not they
had come alive, not through my own creativity and experience, but from the books
and films of others, I did love the atmosphere of my novel. Original details kept
constantly dropping from nowhere and into my notebook.

One of the teachers told me that frogs had been seen fighting at the foot of nearby Kedah peak. The locals said that was a sign of war. The black frogs came down
from the mountain to fight the green ones below. Thousands of them were fighting
on the roads and in the outlying paddy fields. Was Indonesia about to invade?

While teaching the Third Form one morning I heard beautiful birdsong outside.
"That's a mynah bird," one of my Malay pupils told me. Later he brought me a
young one. It was a delightful little creature and would fly on to my shoulder as soon
as I came home or sit on the windowsill and sing to me while I worked at my typewriter. The only snag was I had to go out early every morning into the long grass
with a jam jar and a tennis racket to catch grasshoppers. These grasshoppers had to
be at least slightly alive before His Birdness deigned to eat them. If a grasshopper
was dead, it turned up its beak haughtily.

Speech day was bearing down on us. I offered to write and put on a giant puppet
show for the event, a sort of Asian *Under Milk Wood* with all religions fairly represented. There were verses for Tamil ghosts, choruses for Mandarin fairies and long
elaborate speeches for the giant *hantu*. As a finale it was announced that President
Sukarno had decided this new Malaysian happiness and integration should come to an

end and was sending in his special new commandos to disrupt this new country.

"Take cover! They've just been parachuted in and nothing is ever going to be the same again."

A thundering drum-roll followed and puppets of the four Beatles came drifting down from the roof of the school's Assembly Hall, all jerking around and singing *She Loves You*.

The show was such a success we toured it around the neighbouring schools, but my abiding memory of that time is the way this new music of the Beatles seemed to connect with everyone everywhere immediately. *She Loves You* starts with a bright drum riff and there's that repeated chorus of "Yeah, yeah, yeah" which always lifts your heart as if you've just been invited to a great party.

The exuberant sound of the Fab Four took over North Malaya within weeks of our show being put on and, after that, I only had to walk down the loneliest path, in the deepest and darkest jungle, for some little smiling kid to jump out shouting, "Yeah, yeah, yeah" as soon as he saw me. Those cries took over from "Hiya" in the paddy fields and you marvelled at how the Beatles' sense of melody and their simple lyrics captured hearts even in the most distant parts of the world.

The success of the show put a smile on my face for a while but it was wiped off when a passing Peace Corps volunteer told me that President Kennedy had been killed in Dallas, Texas.

I felt hardly able to connect with the brutal senselessness of this tragedy. JFK had appealed strongly to young people like me: we admired his nobility, glamour and ideals. He would take us somewhere other politicians wouldn't. Now he was dead. It seemed to get dark for all of us after that and soon it became very dark indeed for me.

My novel was cracking along. Gabriel was threatened by the local religious fanatics with the *kapak gang* (axe head on rattan stick) for having a Malay mistress. Gabriel begged David to come and live with him both for company and protection. David was unhappy with this suggestion although he was spending a lot of time with the old man. They attended a Hindu fire-walk where things went wrong and many of the walkers were badly burned. Gabriel, caught up in the spirit of the occasion, walked on the fiery coals himself, and was severely burned before David managed to pull him off. Hawkins, watching from the crowd, drove Gabriel and David to hospital in his jeep.

David's relationship with Hawkins developed quickly after that. They travelled around Malaya in the jeep at weekends. Hawkins enjoyed telling David what he knew about the land: the myths, the ghosts, the deeply supernatural atmosphere of these former stamping grounds of Conrad and Maugham. David began staying with the tin miner in his jungle home where they often chatted in the hissing, yellow incandescence of the gas lamp in the living room. Nazeem would occasionally stand deep in the darkness outside, his fingers playing with his white orchid, watching them.

One day the pair walked out into the jungle and Hawkins took David to a cave where they were digging guano. Hawkins made his way swiftly up the slope, sure-footed as a mountain goat. David stumbled behind him. They sat on a large rock at the entrance to the cave. Warm air blew out in soft gusts. Bats and shadows clung to the cave's walls and roof which had the soaring proportions of a cathedral.

"This cave exercises a curious compulsion over me," Hawkins said as he took out a torch whose golden beam lanced its darkness. "I often come here to think. The coolies have become accustomed to my presence — most of them are too exhausted to care anyway. The prophet Mohammed saw his visions in a cave which is the durable image of death in life. This particular cave is full of legends and stories."

A coolie, naked except for a strip of cloth around his waist, came stamping past them and then came another and another. Their arms hung loosely at their sides; the full sacks were fastened by headbands, which pulled their sweating head and bodies cruelly backwards.

"One story has it that a labourer found a woman deep down in this cave. She was attractive and had sprained her ankle. The coolie agreed to carry the woman out of the cave on his back, but her weight grew heavier and more intolerable and he found that he could not put her down. He discovered he was carrying a tombstone but could not dislodge it until he fell right there." Hawkins shone his torch on an oblong rock lying next to the cave's entrance. "The coolie was crushed by the tombstone and there he died."

David sprang forward and ran back down the mountain path, foliage snatching at his ankles. He entered a clearing suffused with the buttercup gold of the late afternoon sun where monkeys were chattering and scrambling in the vines. Hawkins caught up with him. "It was just a story," he said. "I did not mean to frighten you."

"You terrified me. Can we go back home now?"

Hawkins put his fingertips under David's chin and lifted up his face to get him to look into his own black-lidded eyes. The world shrank to inches between their lips and the monkeys chattered excitedly as they kissed, tentatively at first, then more urgently. Hawkins' face was bristly and smelled of mahogany.

"Don't hurt me," David begged. "I don't know what I've got myself into, but don't hurt me will you?"

Unable to sleep I was lying on my bed watching the geckos race around my ceiling in pursuit of unwary insects. My fan spun like a giant moth trapped in a cage but brought little cooling relief to the warm soup of the night. A half-typed page protruded from my Olivetti and the mynah bird slept on its perch.

Next to the typewriter was the rapidly swelling pile of my manuscript, its lines attached to my brain as if by invisible gossamer threads. My imagination seemed to be creating a prison from which there was no escape. Is it possible to become a prisoner of one's imagination? "The powers of the imagination are but the simple exercise of mental powers," wrote the philosopher Gilbert Ryle. So it *would* be possible, it would seem.

What I needed were a few friends I could talk and laugh with. But all I had were the old broken reed, Gabriel Domengo, and the queer tin miner, Alexander Hawkins, about to do something really nasty to the rest of us prisoners in the cell of one mind, *my mind*. The thrust of the novel had become irresistible, the act of typing an obsession.

Gabriel, by the light of the full moon, had been picking his way along a path through the bright paddy fields outside the town when he was attacked by a man wielding an axe head on rattan stick, the kapak gang, cold courier of ritual revenge.

His attacker, no more than a shadowy silhouette, brought the axe down on Gabriel's shoulder and warm blood ran all over him as he fled, the man chopping at his head, neck and back. In desperation Gabriel leaped directly into the paddy, making painfully slow progress as the mud sucked at his shoes and his attacker panted along behind.

Gabriel lost his balance and was chopped again and again, the blows raining down on his body as he spun around and fell into the water. The moon, the night and the rice shoots confused his frightened eyes as his fingers searched frantically for something solid to hold on to. His attacker moved in again, raining yet more blows on the old man. Leeches were already fastening on to his bleeding, flailing body. A thin green snake slid over the bank and swam across the water, its head up.

This scene, standard slasher movie stuff, could have been suggested to me by any number of films or books. I had also worked on a number of other violent scenes for this novel including one in which Hawkins, in flashback, had killed a railway clerk after raping him in an allotment.

Where was all this mayhem coming from? The only violence I ever used was breaking up a poppadom with the side of my hand in a late-night curry house and I don't think I had lived in a less violent society than that of Malaya. The Malays were a very sensitive, loving race who cringed and even cried if you raised your voice to them. I had yet to witness a fight or even a skirmish between them.

This novel of mine, however, reeked of violence – or threats of violence – and of perversions that had no relationship with the reality around me. A moment of reality is also a moment of truth yet there wasn't any truth at all in this work where almost everyone was screwing or attacking someone.

The remorseless advance of the jungle into Hawkins' garden was being reversed. Two coolies were cutting back the vines, chopping through the intrusive bamboo and myriad plants which clung together in a dense bank of swelling vegetation. Their machetes chopped one way and swept another, blades catching the sun and sending flashes of light swirling around the garden. Occasionally they stopped and stepped back as something rustled near their feet.

At the far end of the garden Nazeem, half-hidden in the jungle, watched the proceedings. His face was rigid with worry. Sometimes he moved out of sight altogether.

More coolies were carrying yet more bricks and planks into the garden as Hawkins' jeep pulled up by the house. He stepped out and shaded his eyes with his hand as he saw the materials piling up. He took out a rolled-up sheet of paper which he spread over the bonnet of his jeep and studied for a while. It was going to be a strong structure but he had not yet decided where the windows were to be located. He studied the design for a few minutes and then put some crosses on the walls. There would be no windows.

EIGHTEEN

I took a five-week Christmas break in Thailand with Tony Jones, another VSO teacher who worked in nearby Penang. It turned out to be a thrilling journey which began with us crossing the Gulf of Siam out of Songkla in a tiny junk which took three days and cost about five shillings including meals. We had no bed and were expected to sleep on the deck under a tarpaulin.

The food was no more than all right but I never had much of an appetite because of the crew's foul habit of spitting all the time. Spitting is a popular pastime throughout Asia: there were notices everywhere in Singapore and Penang telling you that spitting was a disgusting habit liable to attract a heavy fine. Malaysians weren't too bad but these Thai seamen never stopped, often standing next to you, usually when you were about to start your lunch, clearing their throats, stirring the mucus in their chests for up to ten minutes, then firing off a whole cannonball of gob over the side. Just when you were sure they couldn't have any more gob left in them and were half-looking at your lunch again, someone else would come and stand next to you and re-start the whole process.

We also found we could stay at Buddhist temples in Bangkok free of charge and not only did the monks feed us but were offended if we offered money. At dawn you would awake in your sleeping bag and lie listening to the sound of gongs hanging fatly in the air. You would sit up and look around you at the intricate golden work in the gutterings of all those orange roofs and the ornate spires reaching up into yet another blue dawn. Everywhere you looked a statue of a tubby Buddha gazed down at you with a warm smile. No bleeding and bloody agony on the cross for this lot, just bright, broad smiles all round.

Many of the shaven-headed, saffron-robed monks had already got up and were collecting their food from nearby houses while others sat under trees in the huge, paved courtyards, chanting or meditating. A few would be tidying the garden, sweeping up small piles of rubbish and leaves. They would give you rice, if you wanted it, but I was happy with a quiet fag and a cup of their warm, sugary tea. A good cough and a few gongs. No better way to greet a new dawn.

We bumped into other British volunteers or, more usually, Americans from the Peace Corps who were much more professionally set up than we were, having had a long training programme in Honolulu. They were also paid more although they had to do at least two years. Neither Tony nor I had yet decided how long we were going to stay out here but as my novel was going well, I was thinking of two years.

There was nothing I particularly wanted to get back to in Wales and this might be my only chance to finally discover if I had a book in me.

I particularly enjoyed Thailand's relaxed attitude towards sex. Almost all the local young boys went to massage parlours, but this didn't stop them being spiritual: they saw no contradiction between lighting a joss stick and praying in a temple and then whizzing down to the massage parlour. Even the Buddhist monks smoked dope and gave young girls practical lessons in how to please their men. Buddhism, it seemed, was a religion that didn't suppress anything, a go-as-you-please faith where you could pick up what you liked and discard what you didn't. Coming from Wales, where religion suppressed everything that might be enjoyable and promoted almost everything that was a pain in the arse, I wholeheartedly approved of this.

The bus north to Chiang Mai looked like a collision between a clapped-out lorry and an overblown Thai temple and rattled along at terrifying speeds on hairpin bends along the sides of steep mountains while the driver chatted and laughed unconcernedly with the passengers around him.

An Australian backpacker told us about a hill tribe in the mountains where they grew the opium poppy. We could reach them in a walk of about four or five hours, he said, and they always invited you to stay the night. But they were high up in the mountains, so we should take some warm clothing with us as well as our sleeping bags.

Tony was strong, not having dissipated his energy on drink, fags and massage parlours, but I was feeling weak these days and found the hike into those mountains hard going. Real exercise like this didn't appeal to me. Tony kept me going by continually insisting we were nearly there when we were still miles away and always tut-tutted when I said I had to sit down and have a fag. The journey itself took us through wilder and yet wilder terrain, alongside forested mountains where we looked down into rivers tumbling brightly through dark gorges. "We're lost," I kept moaning. "We're never going to find our way back."

We located the valley. A dozen or so huts looked suspiciously deserted. No one moved. We were aware of five children watching us. They emerged slowly from behind rocks and bushes, dressed Tibetan-style, with chains around their necks and short pleated skirts. When Tony took out his camera they scrambled for cover.

We parked our bums on a rock and attempted to look unthreatening. When the children reappeared we did our little comic double act that had always worked well on children throughout Thailand. But it didn't work here and they slipped away again. A woman walked up and gave a cracked smile of such stunning ugliness it made me jump. Her face was thin and pasty and almost all her teeth were blackened stumps. A man joined her. He could only have been her husband since he also looked like someone who had managed to stagger here straight from the set of a Dracula film. He was filthy dirty, wore a battered trilby and his unbuttoned shirt revealed a chest which had collapsed years ago. They began coughing in unison and their yellow and purple tongues flickered out like snakes.

Dracula gave us another blackened smile and indicated we should follow him which, after a few worried looks at one another, we did. He took us to a large hut on the side of the valley where a woman sat on the veranda working a sewing machine.

We nodded at her and Dracula ushered us inside, telling us we should take off our shoes. It was a huge, dark room with a fire in the middle of the earth floor and walls covered with blackened banana leaves. At first glance it looked deserted, but then we noticed a figure stretched out on a huge plinth, his mouth clamped on a bamboo pipe. He had well-groomed hair and lots of chains and trinkets on his muscled body, exuding a malevolent happiness like a flickering vision out of Thomas De Quincey. He was clearly the chief and seemed pleased to see us when he worked out we were not one of his opium hallucinations. He held out his pipe, offering us a toke.

This was a moment when I could push down another wall of experience and come close to another author who had long captured my imagination.

Confessions of an English Opium Eater by Thomas De Quincey, a seminal text for us in the early Sixties, was said not only to have had an extensive influence over his contemporaries such as Wordsworth, Southey and Coleridge, but also to have had far-reaching consequences for poets such as Baudelaire and even such Outsider *enfants terribles* as Alexander Trocchi and the beats. The book was also almost certainly instrumental in the growth of the drug culture in the USA, inspiring such writers as Timothy Leary with his mantra to tune in, turn on and drop out. Opium released the imagination and gave it wings. Fill yourself up with drugs and fly.

I had tried to get into *Confessions of an English Opium Eater* several times without success. It is a mélange of episodes from De Quincey's life and catalogues the agonies and ecstasies of the drug. He took opium in the hope of increasing his rationality and sense of harmony but I found his style irrational and downright unharmonious. "What an apocalypse of the world in me," he wrote after taking a few hits. "What had opened before me – an abyss of divine enjoyment suddenly revealed."

Possibly for financial reasons I had not yet got my hands on any decent drugs but I was keen to give them a try. I wanted to be up there with my literary idols, anxious, as ever, to become another real gone cat, exploring the secrets and mysteries of life in stoned prose.

So here, at last, was my chance: I could break free from my earthly shackles and open up an abyss of divine enjoyment within myself by taking the chief's opium pipe. I reached out to take the holy pipe, only to spot several unattractive globules of his spittle hanging off the mouthpiece as I brought it up to my lips. What should I do? Wipe them off? Ignore them and get on with it?

As it turned out, the Great Existentialist Druggie Adventurer was so sickened by the dangling phlegm he meekly handed the chief his pipe back with an apologetic smile. Maybe it was simply that I had never thought much of his prose or maybe it was something else again but I didn't *always* go down the roads writers and artists opened up to me.

Very soon I was going to learn, with a concussive force, that I shouldn't have gone down any of those literary roads at all.

The chief wasn't offended by this apparent rejection of his opium, clapping his hands and shouting out to his sewing wife to bring us some tea and telling us we could stay in one of the surrounding huts for as long as we liked. His wife did bring us some tea but she looked mightily pissed off with her old man for getting stoned in the afternoon and inviting the boys around again. After putting the tea tray down in front of us she quickly withdrew without acknowledging our presence.

He was trying to tell us something, in between puffs on his pipe, when he suddenly clammed up in mid-sentence and stared at us vacantly with his mouth open. We decided we had better withdraw if he'd found nirvana. Mr and Mrs Dracula were outside. Follow us, they indicated, and took us to a spare hut to spend the night. I was grateful for the room: I certainly hadn't the strength to walk back to Chiang Mai.

The two of us sat on the veranda of our new home for a long time, drinking tea brought by Mrs Dracula with me smoking legal fags as we watched the darkness settling down over the valley. I was pleased to have someone with me on that veranda since, had I been on my own, I would not have believed what was going on around us as strangely dressed men and women returned from work on their opium plots. Some wore top hats and, with their long hair and frequent cackles of laughter, they looked like a particularly insane bunch of traditional jazz fans.

We were in the Golden Triangle between Thailand and Burma. Some of the people smiled and nodded or gave a thumbs-up sign as they wheezed past. None were unfriendly and, when the women did start cooking, the men took their pipes out on to their door steps where they turned on mirthlessly, lighting their pipes with glowing embers from their fires. The children were the first to be fed, their food put on large banana leaves and we were sent two plastic plates of stew which we ate hungrily.

The mountain cold drove us back into the hut where, fully dressed, we climbed into our sleeping bags but still felt its nip.

"You know what day it is today do you?" I asked Tony.

"No, what?"

"Christmas. It's Christmas Day."

"Oh hell," he groaned pitifully. "I do wish you hadn't told me that."

I wished I hadn't, too.

NINETEEN

Once back in Malaya I was lying on my bed early one morning staring at my growing manuscript when the pages seemed to crackle slightly as if electrified. There was a sense of aggression in that manuscript as if someone was squaring up for a fight. I dismissed it as fantasy, showered, dressed and went to teach my Sixth Form.

After doing battle with *Brave New World* we were wrestling with TS Eliot's poetic masterpiece, *The Waste Land*. I had known nothing about Eliot's work before I had come here but made it my business to find out and was enthralled by the way his mind worked. Here was a scholar of great erudition who not only wrote with passion but with economy and discipline. He could express extraordinary anguish in a few words and his faith interested me too, not based on formless romanticism but classical learning. You could only come to faith through prayer and learning, he said. Ignorance subverted you and took you in the wrong direction. Trust your feelings and you are putting your faith in wrong things. You could never imagine the stodgy old Anglican in a brothel – or even getting drunk. He was as far from my regular heroes, like Miller, Mailer or Baldwin, as it was possible to be.

My heroes wrote with colour, feeling and blood, whereas Eliot had the controlled precision of a crossword puzzle. The odd thing was that, despite what I was writing, I now wanted to be more like Eliot. I wanted to be closer to reason and learning. Just reading the great man's words made the ground move beneath my work and even began undermining my positions. My real trouble, I suspect, was that I had been educated too well for what I was doing and not well enough for what I wanted to accomplish.

It was in preparation for these lessons on Eliot that I had learned a little about the long-standing Romantic/Classical divide. I still wasn't sure what the word Romantic meant.

That morning I asked my Sixth Form class to write an essay explaining Romanticism. They would do it well: some of them were bright enough to ransack every library in the state to come up with whatever angles they could on the subject.

Gabriel had returned from hospital, after treatment for extensive wounds, only to discover that David had been missing from school for more than a week. No one knew where he was. The old man made inquiries around the town until Nazeem told him that Hawkins had built an almost fortified hut in the grounds of his jungle home and that David had probably been imprisoned in it.

When Hawkins was spotted in the town Gabriel went out to the tin-miner's house and located the new hut in the garden. The door was bolted but he managed to wrench the lock off with a claw hammer. He found David shielding his eyes from the light and wearing a black lurex dress with torn women's stockings hanging off his bruised legs. His face had been bruised and lipstick smeared around his lips.

The shadow of Hawkins fell over Gabriel and a hand gripped him by the back of his neck. Gabriel managed to create enough space to turn and fell Hawkins with one mighty blow of his hammer. Hawkins went straight down and, as he lay unconscious, David and Gabriel made their escape through the jungle. Hawkins regained consciousness, ran into his house to get a gun and set off to track them down.

The door of Gabriel's house gave way with the second kick and Hawkins rampaged from room to room gun in hand, toppling furniture and ready to loose off a bullet at anything that moved.

Finally Hawkins drove back to the town's main street where he just sat, gun stuffed down his belt, arms straight and gripping the steering wheel, his breath coming in short, swift gasps like a dog's after a long run. They were bound to turn up sooner or later. The night rumbled with the beginnings of a tropical storm.

After half an hour Hawkins spotted them helping one another down the main road. He accelerated, blinding them with a wall of bright headlights.

Gabriel threw his hammer at the windscreen which shattered as the jeep swerved and crashed into a storm gutter. "Run David, run," Gabriel shouted. "Run as you've never run before."

David pulled his dress up around his waist and attempted to run but it was as if he was moving across mattresses. He kept looking around, hoping for help. A silent flash of lightning silhouetted the burly shape of Hawkins, standing in the middle of the road, legs apart, holding out his gun with both hands. There was a sharp report and Gabriel took a bullet in the back of the neck which tore out just beneath his nose. He held both hands over a fountain of blood gushing out of his disintegrating face but was still managing to move forward when another bullet smashed into his shoulder bone.

Lightning flickered silently as Nazeem ran from behind the bus station and stabbed Hawkins in the back with a long knife. The tin-miner's eyes bulged wide with shock, his cheeks puffed out as if he was holding back a lot of vomit and the kyatai stabbed him again. Hawkins barely knew what he was doing as Nazeem attempted to stab him again but, as he staggered to one side, he managed to kill his attacker with a single shot that took out his spleen.

It was a long, hot day. I'd had a nap in the afternoon after school, but awoke feeling uneasy about everything. I tried to read a book but, after finishing one sentence, forgot how it had begun. Reading one paragraph seemed to require as much effort as reading a whole book.

I lit a cigarette and noticed that my bird was making a lot of hunger noises, jumping up and down on its perch in a state of agitation. I fed it a grasshopper but my hand was shaking so much I could barely hold it up to its beak. The bird snatched at the insect eagerly, jerking its head up and swallowing the body whole, slowing a little to gather up the grasshopper's spindly legs which had got stuck to the sides of its beak. That grasshopper had barely disappeared before the bird began jumping up and down demanding another. *Duw!* I don't know where he put them all.

I usually spent a few hours on my novel in the early evening but today I didn't want to. I was becoming convinced I should put it in a drawer and take a rest from the characters who seemed to have taken over my mind.

A long walk might help me relax so I wandered down by the river where they were setting up the Mandarin puppet show, with a troupe of about twelve busy fiddling with microphones and setting out the puppets. Out in the paddy, where the night was gathering on the still water, there were the guttural croakings of frogs and the electric whirrings of cicadas.

Little moved in the main street. Some of the trishaw drivers were asleep in their vehicles. Rats moved silently down the storm gutters and the chemistry teacher shouted a greeting at me as he bicycled past.

I ate noodles and fried duck at the Tamil restaurant and when I had finished the waiter brought me a cup of coffee too hot to drink. Hawkins walked in and sat at a table near the door. He opened the buttons of his khaki jungle jacket and his belly butted against the edge of the table as he stared at the water jug. His hands rested on either side of the spoon and fork while his head did not move at all – although his black eyes darted slightly – as he asked the waiter for curried chicken and rice.

I studied Hawkins with a mounting feeling of alarm but said nothing as his food was put in front of him – a plate of boiled rice with a bowl of curry in which a chicken leg had capsized. Hawkins tucked a paper napkin into a buttonhole in his shirt, lifted the curry bowl and poured it over the rice. He began shovelling the food into his mouth. His jaw chewed thoughtfully as he stared at the water jug and, each time his chewing was done, in went another mouthful. Grains of rice gathered at the corners of his mouth. He picked up the chicken leg and ripped at it. He put it down half-eaten and drank a glass of water before finishing the rice. The attack on the chicken resumed, and when the bone was stripped clean, he dropped it on his plate. He continued staring at the water jug as he worked his teeth over with a toothpick. He dropped four Malay dollars on the table, took a further sip of water and walked out of the restaurant.

I was intensely worried as I walked back down the main street. People were at prayer in the Buddhist temple and around the glittering altar. Gongs resonated distantly and the humid darkness was fluttering with laughter. I picked up the throaty roar of a jeep close behind me. I stiffened but kept walking. It was Hawkins' jeep, I knew, but dared not look around.

The noise of the engine was almost deafening and I was sweating profusely. My body braced itself for the inevitable impact. The jeep vanished. I went home with a splitting headache. I needed to get drunk. I could have done with several bottles of whisky, but on my VSO finances I could barely afford one beer.

I was lying on my bed, covered only by a sheet and sleeping fitfully when the sound of rain woke me in the middle of the night. For a second I thought I'd seen the over-painted face of Nazeem looking in at me through my open window. It must have been a trick of the light because, as soon as I sat up, there was no one.

Something heavy lay next to my leg and when I lifted the sheet I was horrified to find Gabriel's teeth eating into it. His face was blistering and puffing with fury as he bit into me, the veins on his neck bulging and his mouth slopping blood. I screamed and woke from the nightmare.

The next morning, somewhat to my surprise, was clear and calm. There were no threatening presences and everyone was cheerful and pleasant in the staff room. Martin had brought me his newspaper and Boon Let, planning the school's annual sports day, wondered what role I saw for myself in this great event.

"It won't be a big one," I said and he laughed.

I had a breakfast of coffee and pineapple chunks before teaching one of the lower forms. We enjoyed the lesson, which had a lot of laughter in it. I liked normality and laughter a lot, I decided, and would leave my novel alone for a long time. Put it away and perhaps look at it again when I got home. I had decided not to stay for a second year. The teaching was fine but it was humiliating and even boring to be so broke all the time. I had to feed myself and, with the little I was paid, sometimes could not afford to do even that.

My double English lesson with the Sixth Form also went well. We wrestled with half a dozen lines from *The Wasteland* and it was surprising how many subjects TS Eliot managed to raise in so few lines. You kept hitting new levels of meaning.

At the end of the lesson, I picked up their essays on romanticism and took them home. I was looking forward to reading them: as a teacher, I was learning a lot too. I had enjoyed some of the set books so much I was wondering if I might be able to go back to university and study English. After taking a stroll for an hour or so I returned to my room and gave each of the essays a quick scan to see what they had come up with.

I read the eighteen essays at one sitting and found them learned, well researched and, unusually, almost wholly different from one another. They hadn't all dug their material out of the same book, as you might have expected, but had ransacked various libraries and gone to considerable lengths to explain every aspect of the subject. They always made a big effort for me: they valued my approval.

I hadn't absorbed everything they'd written but, as I worked my way through their essays, I saw that, in an odd but definite way, they all seemed to be writing about me. Certain key phrases made an emotional and intellectual impact.

"A Romantic is one who goes in persistent search of the violent, the perverted, the melancholy and the cruel … His natural home is misery and despair."

"The medium of the Romantic is poetic emotion and he always eschews cold reason …"

"A Romantic always revels in sexual inconstancy and perversion …"

"Always immoral in his ethics the Romantic insists on the primacy and sanctity of the individual …"

"The Romantic deals in dreams, in the supernatural, in morbidity, in exotic places,

in cannibalism and incest … his first love is for mysticism and Grand Guignol … he loves to shock …"

"He likes to deal in horror and in the picturesque and such as Gothic castles …"
"He is in so many ways lost in a complete fog …"

"A Romantic often finds it difficult to distinguish between dream and reality …"

I felt like a crook comprehensively exposed in a newspaper. Almost every essay seemed to have gone straight to the heart of me – the persistent pursuit of violence, the revelling in sexual inconstancy, the attraction of perversion – those clear words uncovering the working of my thoughts and laying bare my private dreams. I was face to face with my own nature. I looked over at my manuscript and lit a cigarette. Not one of my pupils had read one word of my novel, but they had all uncannily described its content. I realised that my novel was a wholly Romantic work written by a wholly Romantic young writer. The rebel had been called to the door and shown himself in a mirror.

Well, if that's the way I was, that's the way I was. I might grow out of it but, until that great day, I might as well just get on with whatever I was getting on with. There were plenty of other artists who persistently pursued violence. Violence pretty much defined the work of the modern cinema, even the "news" services. We couldn't all be erudite and balanced – it takes a special kind of writer to be a TS Eliot.

It was even something of a relief to find myself nailed down like this. I had heard the word "Romantic" only recently from a passing missionary who, when I asked him why a personal knowledge of God was so difficult, had told me it was because I was a Romantic. He was uncomfortable when I tried to push him on what he meant by that and quickly backed off. But now I knew. There it was.

It was Friday afternoon. With a long free weekend ahead, I decided to work on these essays and learn a little more about myself. There was a lot to think about and already my mind was making further unfamiliar connections between my novel, other novels, films and television programmes that had featured perversion and violence. I realised I might have stumbled across a contemporary plague which had not only infected everyone but done for me too.

I went off for another long walk around the paddy fields to decide how best to come to terms with this dilemma. Should I ignore it or try to find some kind of resolution? A Chinese funeral parade crossed a distant horizon like a line of cartoon characters. Some of the mourners were playing bugles and even those shouldering the coffin were happy. Mirth at a funeral challenges our most fundamental notions about grief and death. Almost everything I had come across that year in Asia had challenged my long-held ideas about almost everything. In some ways it was almost as if the very land was ganging up on me.

I could still feel the characters of my novel in and around me, reaching out to me and often making small electric buzzings in my brain like bare live wires shorting one another. Insanely, despite all my earlier resolutions, I decided to press on with my novel, *complete it and be done with it*.

It would have a Romantic ending. Not a happy-ever-after ending – but an extremely bloody ending with knives flailing and bullets flying everywhere.

I was acutely tense when I returned home. But it was not one of my characters who died. My mynah bird was sitting on his perch near my typewriter and I noticed a blue film had formed over his eyes. His body was listing slightly and his wings shivering. Just when he looked as though he was going to topple off his perch, his claws grasped it again and he righted himself, his eyes jerking open to reveal the extent of that sinister blue film. I offered him a grasshopper, but he jerked his head away and soon began listing dangerously again. Those glazed blue eyes of death opened wide and the bird plummeted forward, landing with a loud thud on the floor. His claws were clenched and his legs pointed up into the air.

The thudding sound made my heart jump. A wave of grief broke over me as I bent down on one knee in front of him. The breeze of the fan was ruffling his feathers and I was sure I could hear the pitter-patter of the geckos racing madly around the ceiling in their eternal hunt for insects. One slipped down the wall and raced back up again. The moths fluttering around the light sounded like bats.

I lit a cigarette and attempted to blow smoke-rings, but the fan dissipated them before they got going.

I was stretched to breaking point and very scared. A rustling sound in the typescript of my novel made me jump sideways and I knocked over my chair with a resounding crack. Something was happening. My mind slipped and shifted as if shattering to smithereens. High walls were hemming me in, and I couldn't see how I was ever going to be able to climb them.

I sat on my bed feeling very tired. A huge, luminous fungal growth was rising out of my typescript. I lit another cigarette and sighed as the ball swelled and swelled. It glowed, and brightly coloured veins writhed in and out. Ideas wriggled along these veins like tadpoles. Sometimes an idea would shoot to the surface and then dive back into its heart, causing it to quiver violently. Faces moved inside its translucence, unrecognisable faces, smiling faces, mocking faces.

I took a long pull on my cigarette and slowly exhaled. My hands shook so badly I could barely get it into my mouth. I had understood completely what the fungus signified – the poisoned and poisoning growth of my Romanticism.

My thoughts were disjointed as I watched and a new face drifted into view. Even in this state of shock I understood how faithfully it mirrored my internal life. It symbolised the corruption of my thoughts by violence and perversion.

Books, films and plays had introduced that poison into my system, the *Romantic* books, films and plays that had shaped me. They were all there, from the opium fantasies of Thomas De Quincey to the sexist brothel ravings of Henry Miller; from the obsession with violence of Norman Mailer to the brooding melancholy and despair of Ingmar Bergman; from the crime-worship of Colin Wilson to the rebellion of John Osborne. *All there.*

I tried to stand up, but my body wouldn't let me. I couldn't smoke my cigarette because my shaking hands had frozen. I was transfixed for maybe five minutes, maybe three hours – who knows? Then, as slowly as it had grown, the fungal growth began shrinking until, in a blast of warm air, my body was released.

I *thought* it was all over, but I was wrong. I sat up and looked in the mirror. I felt as if I'd smashed my face into it and different parts of my face were reflected in different shards of the smashed-up glass. When I stood up I felt something hot and quick dart through me. I turned around once, the roof fell in, and I went spinning into a world where nothing made sense.

The ideas in my manuscript were sweeping through my mind like a swarm of bees. I was staring down a well with a cyclone blowing out of it and had to hold the top of my head tightly with both my hands for fear the roof of my skull would blow off. The ideas leaked out of every pore, through my fingers, eyes and ears, pouring down my cheeks and swarming over my chest. I tried to punch my splitting skull back into place but struck only a sparkling jumble of nonsensical ideas.

I finally managed to escape my room and walk into town. For the following few days I was seldom aware of myself as an individual. I stumbled around the area getting lost and seeing fearful visions. Occasionally one of my pupils would find me and take me home only for me to go walkabout again.

Later that night – or it could have been the following night – I had a vision of the world. I saw a silvery plain with matchstick people milling around on it. Tiny ideas flitted between their heads in looping arcs and lightning dashes. A cliff overhung this plain, and all along the cliff-edge, dark and demonic bands of artists were loosing off volleys of wild ideas upon the people below. As the volleys became more intense the movements of the matchstick people became more agitated. They rioted, jumped on one another, rolled around and fought.

I saw that the world was but a jungle of ideas in which artists were corrupt and the people corrupted.

My pupils found me out in the paddy fields, staring at the sky. When they took me back, my room was a mess of crumpled papers with the corpse of my mynah bird still lying among the dust-balls on the floor.

My brain was pierced again and again by a giant metaphysical force. My body was a spinning top and I kept punching the sides of my head, begging God to call off the dogs.

I was back on that same cliff edge looking over a wide silvery plain. This time I was tormenting the people below. My ideas, like yo-yos on vast lengths of string, whirled out of my mind and back in again. I was as corrupt as the rest. I, too, was happy enough to destroy those people with my Romantic ideas.

I do not know how I got through those fearful times. I continued brainstorming, choking on myself and getting lost. One afternoon I found myself walking along the town's main street, trying to get home, but unable to do so because no sooner had I decided where it was and begun stumbling towards it, than I saw another part of my past or a book I'd read or a film I'd seen. I saw why I had gone into so many brothels – not because I particularly wanted to but because this behaviour had been suggested to me by the *Romantic* works of the various batty *Romantic* writers I had allowed into my mind and heart.

Pondering on these matters I would stumble past my home and end up in a completely different part of the town. I decided to go to Penang to see if Malcolm Dalziel, the British Council man there, could help me. But I could not get to the bus station. No sooner had I set off from my home than I forgot where I was going.

A Sikh tried to speak to me about his son's progress in school but I mumbled something irrelevant and my legs walked me back into the paddy where I just stood, hands clamped to my head, waiting for someone to rescue me.

I did get on the bus to Penang eventually and became considerably calmer after the two-hour ride. Penang is a heavily templed island surrounded by a glittering sea. I was happy to be wandering along its cheerful sidewalks, lined with steaming food-stalls. Then I was stopped short by another searing vision. The sky was its usual clear blue but something was ripping it apart. Luminous cylinders began forming in the ripped patch. These cylinders were interconnected and revolved slowly at first but then accelerated in speed. Black marks appeared on the cylinders before disappearing and a trickle of fat black drops fell slowly from the clear blue sky, just a few at first but then a quickening torrent. The black rain.

I recalled a line from the Bible: "I cried to God in the hour of my destruction" as I sat weeping in the British Council library in Penang. Malcolm had been out but fortunately soon returned and took me to his home where he and his wife fed me, listened to my ravings and put me to bed with a few stiff drinks. I have no idea what would have happened to me that day had it not been for Malcolm and his wife. The kindness of strangers again. More than a few of us would have been lost but for that.

I returned to Alor Star three days later, feeling as if my brain had been shredded. I cleaned up my room and burned most of my books but not my manuscript. I had a haircut, got measured for a new pair of trousers and became a model of conventionality for the rest of my stay. The other teachers marvelled at the change.

I managed to get hold of some sleeping pills from the local hospital and they helped a little, but I was still feeling ripped apart. My characters continued to haunt stray parts of my mind at odd moments in the night. I wondered what had befallen me. It was as if God had finally beaten the crap out of me. Tired of my derivative nonsense, he had struck me down mercilessly. But why? Why me?

Was it a Call such as many heard in Wales in 1904? Had God given me a shaking down and called me to his Church?

My concentration was gone. I read one book and one book only now: *The Critique of Pure Reason*. I had lost faith in the printed word, could trust only the tightly structured arguments of the supreme rationalist.

Logic teaches us, Kant wrote, nothing regarding the content of knowledge but lays down the formal conditions of the agreement with the understanding.

I hoped my shattered brain might convalesce in the bath of pure reason. I needed sound thought after riding the wobbling sledge of feelings for so long.

Whatever happened to me next I knew my former personality and ideas were but a distant rain cloud. Not only had I been shown that all my ideas were chaotically wrong, but it had been forcibly demonstrated that such ideas were destroying the world. I, and artists like me, who dealt in cruelty, perversion and violence, were a menace. We purported to take the people somewhere beyond themselves but made their lives perilous. We ensured that this sacred world of ours was made a prey to criminality and violence. Those who set out to save us were precisely the ones who were making us so sick. Oh Christ, how was I *ever* going to come to terms with that?

With the help of some money given to me by Malcolm, I could buy some whisky and have a few hours off, but I would wake up in the middle of the night feeling more thoughtful and worse than ever.

"From the fact that the existence of outer things is required for the possibility of a determinate consciousness of the self," wrote the masterful and *unromantic* Kant. "It does not follow that every intuitive representation of outer things involves the existence of things, for their representation can very well be the product merely of the imagination (as in dreams and delusions)."

I somehow saw out my remaining weeks at Alor Star. The night before I was due to leave, I was lying in bed waiting for a sleeping pill to put me away when I felt a warm presence within and all around me. This presence moved closer and, deeply comforted, I abandoned myself to it unafraid. Tears streamed from my closed eyes and I opened my arms wide to welcome this presence, understanding it would not hurt me. My breathing became softer and warmer. A tender hand smoothed my wounded brain.

A consoling thought was vouchsafed. "You have suffered much but you will not suffer so again. Time will bring healing.

TWENTY

Almost half the school turned up to see me off at the railway station. I had been so preoccupied with my personal psychodrama and had so little self-esteem I could hardly believe the presents and the tears when the train pulled out.

"Yeah, yeah, yeah," I shouted at them, in tears myself, leaning out of my carriage window and defiantly waving my clenched fist.

The effect was immediate. Three hundred school kids began jumping up and down on the platform, smiling their brilliant smiles and shouting back, "Yeah, yeah, yeah. Yeah, yeah, yeah." Then they sang the Beatles' *She Loves You* with further repeated choruses of "Yeah, yeah, yeah, *yeah*!" They might not have learned much English from me but they all knew how to shout "Yeah, yeah, yeah" and sing Beatles' songs.

I knew they would always remember me just as I would always remember them. They might not have got much out of having me around, but I had got an awful lot out of knowing them.

Their singing continued to ring in my ears, but it was a defeated and broken young man who sat on that aeroplane as it soared out of Kuala Lumpur. I looked down on the palm trees and *atap* huts of Malaya and had never felt so broken. I had left almost all of myself down there: every dream and hope had been dumped in those paddy fields. What had I now to look forward to?

An Indian in the aisle seat asked me if I had been on holiday but I gazed ahead blankly and pulled my blanket up over my chest. Had I been in Malaya, working, perhaps? He was just making conversation, but I wasn't interested. I pulled my blanket over my mouth and looked directly ahead, unwilling to listen to any questions or give any replies. A stewardess served a gin and tonic and became concerned when she saw I was crying into it. Was there something wrong with the drink? "No. It's fine."

My main worry remained that God had beaten me almost senseless and sent me a Call. Or had I merely had a nervous breakdown? Aspects of my visions made terrifying sense to me – the black rain, for one. The more I thought about that the more sense it made. We were all living in a time of black rain although it would take me years and years to work out its full implications.

And if I did enter the Church how would I manage without girls or drink? I was no Elmer Gantry and accepted unreservedly that I would have to cut all that out. Evan Roberts had problems with some of his women. First and last he was a human too. I asked the stewardess for another gin and tonic.

We landed in Bonn and I was shocked to see so many white faces which I studied with absorbed interest. When you live in Asia you soon come to believe that the world is exclusively populated by small brown faces. Once back on the plane I was disappointed to find myself giving the selfsame stewardess the eye. It came to nothing but the familiar urge was still there in my ever-burning loins. As her fingertips brushed the top of my hand when she served me another gin and tonic I wondered if I had changed at all.

Heathrow was a screeching bedlam. My unlocked luggage had been rifled somewhere *en route* and some new shirts were missing – *Welcome Home!* I made my way to the bus station worried that someone might speak to me or even *touch* me.

The bus drive into central London was overwhelming. I'd rarely seen a building higher than one storey in Asia; here they loomed and intimidated. I would never be able to explain the fungus and the black rain to this lot. They would be looking for a straitjacket straight away and perhaps they would be right. Perhaps it had been a common-or-garden nervous breakdown?

It was true nevertheless. The black rain was an accurate metaphor for what was going on in the world as I saw immediately when I got to Paddington station. I had an hour to kill before the train left for Cardiff and I trailed around horrified by the film posters advertising fantasies of eroticism, perversion and violence. My addled brain started seething again. I took out a hairbrush and brushed my head vigorously. This, I had found, often calmed my bubbling brain.

The Killers, Godzilla versus The Thing, The Castle of Blood, The Evil of Frankenstein, Séance on a Wet Afternoon, Black Tarantula Spider... all the insidious evil that had been pointed out in me was there, vividly and overwhelmingly, in all those posters. The persistent search for violence ... the Gothic castles ... the bloody and perverted sex ... the morbid and the supernatural ... even the very symbols were the same, a black flood waiting to burst through the echoing and bustling Underground corridors in which I had found them. Far from residing solely in me this Romantic poison was nationwide, universal. We were all drowning in this season of black rain.

I walked into the station bookshop and my brain began buzzing so loudly I had to get out my hairbrush again. Almost all the books and magazines were devoted to sex and violence. Maybe that wasn't how it was but that's how they seemed at that moment. I quickly reversed out of the shop, still brushing my hair and picking up a few puzzled looks.

I couldn't believe I hadn't noticed this before: that I had grown up with this and hadn't spotted this *affront* before. It wasn't just me: we were *all* living through this global storm and had stopped seeing it. We had stopped seeing it because, like the air we breathe, it was there all the time and we had come to take it for granted.

By now I was in a worse mess than ever. How was I to live with all these new perceptions? When you mess around in the counter-culture there are others messing around with you. But now I was completely on my own. No one was on my side since I no longer had a side. The Christians *might* welcome me but I had only ever got on with a few of them. I had sometimes liked their ideas but I could never come to terms with their constant moralising about non-issues.

I sat next to the window in the train and a porter began shouting at me for not putting my suitcase in the corridor. A lady wanted to put her shopping bags in the rack above me. "You're not the only person in the world you know," the porter raved on. "There are others who use trains too."

I couldn't remember the last time anyone had shouted at me like this – it had never happened in Asia – and I looked up at the porter with tears in my eyes, my mouth opening and closing, trying, but failing, to protest my innocent ignorance. Then the lady started on me too.

My suitcase was duly moved out to the corridor and I sat back again, taking out my hairbrush and giving my head a good going over. The lady with the shopping bags sat opposite, glaring at me angrily. A young girl in a polka dot dress came into the carriage with an old man who started quietly filling his pipe from his pouch, packing the tobacco down carefully with his thumb before lighting it with a flaring match and blowing clouds of sweet smelling Balkan Sobranie over us.

I began worrying about my visions again and put away my brush before clamping my hands on top of my head like a prisoner-of-war. Everyone in the carriage stared at me with renewed distrust. What was the black rain all about? The revolving celestial drums had looked so real, as had the fat, black drops of rain in that clear blue sky. What could I do? Why me? Why had he picked on me? There were no answers to my repeated questions although I was already presuming God had shown me the world as he sees the world and that one day I might be able to explain his sorrow for his dead and dying people struggling home through the charred and smoking fields of a dead harvest.

Yet I didn't want to be a damned prophet. The very last thing I wanted to be was a damned prophet. I knew about the Biblical prophets, strange, mad people who lived with prostitutes or in caves; who suffered much because people never listened to them, but laughed at them and even threw rocks at them when they tried to explain the devious and often wild words of God. No one took any notice of a prophet.

I took my hands off my head and resumed brushing my hair while looking out at the fields and towns of England racing past. Remembered Asian scenes mingled with English ones. I might have come from another time or planet with no identity but a new understanding which was going to put me at odds with everything for ever.

When I got off the train in Cardiff I didn't go straight home but walked to Dyfrig House on the Taff Embankment where a minister I had become friendly with at university, the Rev Bruce Davies, was looking after Dyfrig Church. "I've got into a lot of trouble," I told him. "I think I've had a call from God to go into the Church and I don't know what to do about it. I'm worried stiff."

Bruce, a smiling, avuncular sort, who went around the city like a modern Father Brown, became instantly stern: "What you must understand – even if you understand nothing else," he said, "is that there is absolutely nothing for you to worry about. If you accept God you let God do your worrying for you. Hand your problems over to him and remember also that, if God wants you in the Church, that's where you will go whether you want to or not. Meanwhile, take a long rest and do nothing. Just be. Things will get better in their own way and their own time."

I felt better after I left him and despite my heavy suitcase, decided to walk home along the bank of the River Taff. The afternoon was sputtering lightly with rain, but it was comforting to be back in the city I have loved unreservedly all my life.

I looked down on the coal-black waters of the river and heard again the shrieks of childish laughter as we blasted along its banks through those golden summers, taunting the lovers, asking for a tanner to go away. I saw myself running across the river as that bastard hurled stones at me. Then there were those blazing, passionate moments of young love with Sandra whose sweet kisses still haunted my body. I remembered my father's story of the day the river burst its banks and sent a black tide through our house just over the road. There was my mother standing on a chair in the living room, crying, as my father rowed a boat down the hallway.

There was nothing Romantic about this river. It was one of the dirtiest rivers that had ever flowed anywhere, silted with the coal-dust from eighteen colliery washeries in the Valleys whence it sprang. It was also fouled by sewage from the Valleys' homes and industrial effluent. Silt blackened the river stones, clogged the gills of the fish, shut out the light, killed plants and insects. Only roach or eels survived but there were days when even the roach floated on the surface belly-up.

And yet this river of death was still here as I had always known it, still hurrying to keep its urgent appointment with the tidal surges of the Bristol Channel. I would always return to it, looking for it to give me the will to continue when all else had fallen apart. I had been happy on these banks and wanted to be so again. "Welcome home," my black river said. "Return to my banks, lay down your broken heart and spirit and I will make them new again."

I was twenty-three although I felt three. I would have to pick up the shattered pieces of the mirror in which I had grown and start all over again with so much that was new and troublesome sloshing around inside me. Everything was too much for me now and nothing was possible. Even my brain wasn't functioning properly.

For a few warm moments, everything seemed possible when my smiling, tearful, beautiful mother answered the door and put her arms around me. Even my father was unusually friendly, not saying much but offering me a cigarette which, for him, was the equivalent of offering a pipe of peace. My sister, Jackie, now seven, was chirping with pleasure although Alan, then fifteen, was out as usual. You never knew where he was or what he was getting up to in those days.

I settled into the armchair in front of the fire and, apart from going to bed, hardly moved out of it for days, enjoying being made a fuss of, having my clothes washed and ironed, eating the cooked ham and cockles from the market on Saturday. *Do nothing. Just be.* Occasionally I took out my hairbrush and worked on my head while watching television. My mother noticed this but said nothing. When she found a Prayer Book by my bed she must have been convinced I'd flipped and hid it. Any manifestation of religion was a certain sign of insanity to her.

My first visitor was Neil Kinnock who arrived only to be told by my father that I was in the bath. "He must have picked up some awful dirty habits in Malaya," said Neil.

My father made him a cup of tea while I got out of the bath and I told Neil that I wasn't coming out for a while. I'd had quite a hard time out there, I said, and just wanted to lie low for a bit. "We'll meet up soon."

"Janey's around too," Neil said. "I think you might have some trouble getting rid of her. She's been seeing Glenys a lot while you've been away and keeps bursting into tears all the time. Glenys is saying that you're going to have to marry her and that's it."

About half an hour later Janey, perhaps tipped off by Neil, did turn up, but somehow I managed to end it all there quite cleanly and efficiently. I found it hard to believe that such words could come out of my normally cowardly mouth, but the truth was I was feeling far too sorry for myself to feel too sorry for her. With my hands and tone badly miming the usual ritual moves of sadness and regret, I said I'd been ill; I had a lot to work out for myself and that I was very, very sorry but it was all over between us.

My fears about the way she would react had been groundless. Far from bursting into tears and advising me to see a doctor, she stood up and said, "Well, if that's the way you want it," and walked out of my home and life forever.

A week later I felt sufficiently restored to go out for the first time and met my friend, Jeff Cocks, in the Kardomah Coffee Bar in the centre of Cardiff. "What are you going to do now?" Jeff asked.

"Well I suppose I'll have to get some sort of job because I'm flat broke. I'll probably have to become a teacher. I don't *want* to become a teacher, but that's all I know."

As it happened, George Thomas, the local MP who was later to become Secretary of State for Wales and Speaker of the House of Commons, was sitting a few tables away from us, holding court with some friends. His thin, smiling features and great conk gave George one of the most distinctive profiles in Cardiff. His infectious optimism and odd sense of style always put me in mind of a square-dancing fiddler, hammering away on the stage and smiling, always smiling, at his own stunning virtuosity.

We were going to become very friendly over the years, and George even asked me to write his biography but, in those days, I knew him only by sight. Jeff, who knew him slightly, approached him and told him that I had just come back from Malaya with VSO and needed some sort of teaching job. Was there anything George could do?

George spoke to me for a few minutes about VSO and promised that he would do something right away. In fact he went straight to the Education Offices at the City Hall and asked the Director of Education to employ me immediately. That very afternoon I had a note from the director telling me to start work as a supply teacher next morning in Ninian Park, the secondary modern school for the docks. So I was back in the Bay again. No matter how far I wandered I always seemed to end up back in the Bay.

I didn't enjoy teaching there after Malaya. The kids, all rejects from the grammar schools, having failed their eleven-plus, were convinced they were failures and grabbed every opportunity to start trouble. The teachers responded by caning every troublesome hand they got near, which brought a measure of control to the school, but not much. "What you've got to do is beat them like animals," the teacher in the next class, a former champion boxer, told me. "Otherwise you're done for. It's you or them."

This wasn't what I wanted to do and I became so depressed I started drinking heavily, which I found lightened me up and stopped my raddled brain from throbbing so thunderously. For some reason those throbbings didn't interfere with my sleep, but, as soon as I woke up, I could feel their percussion in my hangover. I had a lot of hangovers in those days and only felt normal after about five pints. Then I didn't need my faithful hairbrush. Perhaps I should report to the mental asylum to see what, if anything, they could do for me.

I went to a party with a couple of my student pals and met a bright, dark-eyed girl with an enchanting smile and a lovely figure. Her name was Liz Evans. Her accent suggested she was a Scouser, but she was from that village with the long name in Anglesey, North Wales, she said, which is close to Liverpool and hence the nasal twang. Glenys Parry had lived up the road from her in Holyhead.

She was nineteen, studying English and Psychology, especially promising given my present condition and, more significantly, she didn't seem to have any psychological problems of her own. She was completely normal. We danced to the sound of the Rolling Stones that night and have danced to it pretty much ever since. I have always believed that sometimes you get what you desperately need even if you don't know what it is. I didn't know it at the time but, when I needed it most, I met the love of my life.

PART TWO

INK MAN

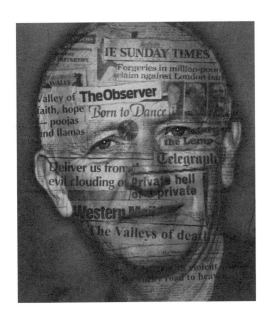

TWENTY ONE

In the autumn of 1966 I became a trainee journalist in Cardiff on the *Western Mail*, the national newspaper of Wales. This move surprised even me: I had never thought of becoming a journalist and had already accepted a job teaching English in Kenya with the Ministry of Overseas Development.

I was going to start a new life out there with Liz who, after two years together, was about to become my wife – if only I could persuade her father what a major catch his only daughter had in me. But he was an evasive North Walian who didn't see me as any kind of catch, major or minor, and every time I did manage to corner him in some pub and put a few relaxing pints down his throat before asking for his daughter's hand, he would jump up and steam straight out of the bar door.

"Jesus is with you in everything you do," proclaimed a poster outside the sour-faced chapel in Menai Bridge when we left the pub after his latest charge for the door. Rain swirled around the street as we peered around the parked cars for him but he had disappeared like a ghost at dawn.

"He'll never say yes, you know," Liz sighed. "He's as stubborn as a mule. Maybe we'll just have to go ahead and do it. He'll come round in the end."

We were already living together in the comparative isolation of Cardiff and were going to have to get married before going to Kenya – although we might well have to do it sooner than that. Birth control then was a form of Russian Roulette, infinitely more dangerous after you'd had a few drinks. You never *cared* after a few drinks although you cared a lot when you woke in that cold hangover which is the mother of all regrets.

But, as we waited to sort everything out before leaving for Kenya, the deputy careers officer at Cardiff University, where I had been awarded a teaching certificate despite having failed a Diploma of Education, called me into his office. Had I had ever thought of becoming a journalist, he asked me.

"No," I said. "All I want to do now is take this job in Kenya and start trying to become a writer." My life would only be complete, I believed, when I could hold a novel I had written in my hands.

"Journalism could be good for your writing," he went on. "The *Western Mail* is looking for graduate trainees. It could suit you down to the ground."

"I don't think so. Anyway, journalism would probably ruin my style. I'd only ever write in short, chopped sentences."

It was some wonder I still wanted to be a writer after my first novel – my *roman-*

tic novel – had turned on me so destructively in Malaya. But my literary ambitions had remained intact while so much else in me had changed. I was in a steady relationship and wanted to get married. The long-term ambition was a home and children. Nothing could have been further removed from the kind of wild, young rebel I'd been. I had new ways of seeing and thinking about things: I regretted almost everything about my feckless youth.

I still suffered from headaches and periodic throbbings in my brain after God had beaten me up with a series of visions in those infernal paddy fields but Liz had a wonderfully calming effect on me and, if she didn't manage it, there was always the drink to wipe out my anxieties and cranial pains. We sank a lot in those early days together. Not that the visions had turned me into a normal, practising Christian. I did go to church occasionally but the closeness of God in a holy space tended to crank up my anxiety rather than diminish it. I was always too scared of him to love and trust him as you were supposed to; always worried that he might beat the hell out of me again. That was the last thing I wanted so, while I deliberately tried not to get too close to him, I didn't reject him either. God and I were reluctant partners in a shotgun wedding.

"I tell you what," said the careers officer. "I'll telephone the *Western Mail* and inform them you're interested. Go in and have a chat with them. Journalism *would* suit you."

I don't think I ever took one positive step towards becoming a journalist. Indeed I didn't even show up when the news editor, John Humphries, sent a note to my home asking me to come and see him. But then, as if I had passed that "interview" with flying colours, I was sent another note asking me to go and see the editor, John Giddings. A somewhat colourless figure, polished and precise as a city accountant, he didn't ask me one single question, merely explained what a marvellous job it was: "You'll always be meeting people in the news which you yourself will make."

I was passed to the features editor, Duncan Gardiner, who took me to the local pub, where I got pretty drunk. Duncan never got drunk himself – beer seemed to disappear into his portly, smiling frame with no effect at all – and, after chatting about this and that, he told me I'd got the job and to report the following Sunday in the newsroom at 2.30pm.

I was to learn this was precisely the eccentric, ramshackle way in which journalism worked. You met someone in the pub and got chatting. He suggested you might meet someone else. This someone else would recommend you to someone else again, who might well suppose you were someone else altogether and before Tuesday became Wednesday you were on the payroll and no one was ever sure how you'd got there.

No one asked me if I'd got a degree and it turned out they rarely bothered to sack you even if you were hopeless. If you were no good at news reporting you could move on from one department to another until you did find something you were good at. If you turned out to be totally useless at everything, you could worm your way around the office until you became the agricultural or gardening correspondent, writing boring stuff which might well suit your boring personality. If you were slightly interested in foreign affairs, say, you might get to write leaders, which no one read anyway, or, if you were really lucky, you could be sent off on some long-term project which might involve a lot of research in the local library and never be heard of – or seen – again.

That's how I became a journalist, not because I wanted to but because I was pushed into it by a series of vague mishaps and misunderstandings. The following Sunday at 2.30pm, I climbed the stairs of Thomson House in Cardiff to look down through a huge window on to the giant printing presses before entering the stinking newsroom which was scattered with papers and empty plastic cups. The whole building stank of the oil of the printing presses and looked so jerry-built, with partitions everywhere, you felt you could demolish the whole building with a screwdriver in half an hour flat. Ashtrays overflowed with cigarette butts, unanswered phones rang sporadically. The old typewriters looked like something William Caxton might have used to set the Bible and you would never in a hundred years believe that a smart, clean newspaper could emerge from a rubbish-strewn mess like this.

I sat drinking coffee and reading a newspaper for about an hour before anyone noticed I was there. Russell Lyne, the deputy news editor, came over and asked me to ring Buckingham Palace for a comment on a forthcoming royal tour. It had never occurred to me that you could simply ring up Buckingham Palace and ask them about anything. Did the Queen pick up the phone and tell you what she was hoping to achieve on her forthcoming tour of Wales?

There was, as it turned out, a Press Office in the Palace that was *supposed* to answer all your queries – although you would generally learn more from interviewing one of the local seagulls than you would from them.

Within a few days I had come to know the others on the graduate trainee scheme and, even though the selection process was ramshackle, it was clear they had somehow managed to round up some impressive young people though I have never, to this day, worked out how.

The newcomers included the languid and polished Geraint Talfan Davies, later Controller of BBC Wales and chairman of the Wales Arts Council; Meic Stephens, the future boss of the literature department at the Wales Arts Council; the smiling Ian Edwards, who was to take control of television contracts for the All England Lawn Tennis and Croquet Club (otherwise known as Wimbledon) and the precise and academic Rhys David, a future senior editor of the *Financial Times*.

On the other side of the newsroom, in the same scheme but working for the *South Wales Echo*, was the elegant Michael Buerk, who went on to inspire Live Aid with his news reports on the starving of Africa; the hard-working Alun Michael, who briefly became the First Minister of Wales, and Sue Lawley who left to become a champion of consumer rights on television and later the presenter of *Desert Island Discs* on BBC Radio Four. Sue had the best legs in journalism; the newsroom went almost completely silent when those marvellous limbs went marching through it.

We were all newcomers to journalism at a time when the Thomson Organisation was trying to brighten up its provincial and national titles which included the *Times* and the *Sunday Times*. Do a good job here for two or three years, it was understood, and you might be fast-tracked through to the *Sunday Times*. Many wanted to go to that hallowed newspaper; one of the great newspapers of the world, it was said.

The old guard in the newsroom, many of whom had come up through the ranks from copy boy, didn't much welcome all these "graduate bastards and poofs". But the old 'uns did have a bright seriousness about them; a cynical knowingness and sharpness that comes from years of gathering news from people busy bullshitting them all the time. You couldn't tell the old guard anything they didn't already know, so the scene was set for a bloody clash between woolly graduates with lah-di-dah accents and the old guard who swore like dockers, could slice the most complex issue down to a few straight paragraphs and were fully paid-up cynics to a man.

One real treasure was Bert Michelle, a short, pugnacious man with a giant mole in the middle of his forehead which gave him the look of an ageing, angry unicorn who had lost his horn in suspicious circumstances. He covered the City Hall and, in between shuffling from dull committee meeting to dull committee meeting, sat in the newsroom hunched over his typewriter, loudly cussing everyone, particularly all us "trendy graduate bastards" who had clearly been hired to make Bert's life even more miserable than it already was.

The main circus master was the news editor, John Humphries, a tall, gangling man who looked like he might have been a high-flyer in the Gestapo. All waving arms and abrupt angles, he would burst into the room at the beginning of his shift, scribbling down lists of ideas or shouting orders at whoever was unfortunate enough to be within earshot. He never had a conversation because he never listened to anyone; he shouted and we jumped to it. Intimidation was the name of his game. He bullied us remorselessly, often sending us out into the city where we were expected to dig up a story. If we returned empty-handed he drove us out again. We were obsessed by him and imitated his hard accent in the pubs.

Any thoughts of preserving my literary style were rendered laughable by Humphries. He took his Biro and slashed at everything we wrote until he stripped our carefully wrought sentences down to the bare bones. He didn't want fancy phrases or literary flourishes in the news pages of the *Western Mail*. No one ever "commented" or "opined" or "guessed" in this newspaper, he ordered. They always "said". You could have the occasional "added" if you had too many "saids" but they almost always "said".

All my literary pretentiousness was bashed straight out of me from day one. We learned to create our news stories like pyramids, putting the most important point at the top and building downwards. There was only one acceptable prose style for news: "straight", without any form of comment. Forget similes, metaphors and adjectives and, under no circumstances, try putting in a joke. Humphries' Biro could spot a joke at a hundred yards, and slash it out without even reading the story in which it was embedded. "You can keep your jokes for the pub," he would say, giving a loud groan as he slashed at another comic gem. Sometimes he cut out our little jokes and puny metaphors so hard he left holes in the copy paper and we had to re-type the lot.

I longed to spread my wings in the features department where they were allowed to *write*. They even had a real novelist, Peter Tinniswood, a Northerner, who worked there so he could pay his gas bills while finishing his first novel. With his Beatle haircut, beard and pipe clamped eternally in his mouth, Peter was precisely where I wanted to be, flinging out words and phrases like a drunken poet.

But this news style did improve my writing immeasurably, I now see. Humphries took language down to its most basic and I did later manage to give this language a slightly painterly veneer, building on the cold insight and hard grammar of news gathering. The first rule of any writer is to be simple and comprehensible, Humphries taught. Every word must count. All the rest is bullshit.

The principles of writing news stories couldn't have been simpler but the stories themselves were difficult for me to get hold of in those early days. The first I went on was with Patrick Hannan, a seasoned hack, to the local College of Music and Drama where the management committee was meeting to discuss the parlous state of their rehearsal rooms. I wanted to open with a description of the state of these rooms. That might have been appropriate for a feature, Patrick told me. But it wasn't the main point of the news story. The *point* was the duller but "newsier" information that they intended to apply for a grant from the council to fix these rooms up. Humphries agreed and practically threw up when he read my "colourful, commenty" version before slapping it on the spike, a long, fearsome metal nail on which all rejected news copy was impaled.

Then he again drummed the art of news writing into my fat head. "Keep it simple. Keep it topical." It was always good to have a "yesterday" in the first paragraph and even better if you could manage a "tomorrow" in the second. News always lived in the moment: if it was more than twenty-four hours old, it was dead.

The key was to work in a Welsh angle. Anyone – no matter how famous or unknown – should have a Welsh angle somewhere. He might have an aunt in Llandudno or a grandfather born in Cwmbran before emigrating to Australia. A famous English singer might have had a father who liked taking holidays in Aberystwyth or be visiting Cardiff to pay tribute to his Welsh roots, or once went through Swansea on the back of a motorbike. Anyone, anywhere, *had* to have a connection with the Land of My Fathers or else *wanted* one. If that were so, it should be right up there near the top of the story.

After I had been shepherded around like this for a couple of weeks, Humphries ordered me out into the city on my own and I landed a major scoop with my first solo news story when I went to an exhibition and found a model taking a bath in a waterproof cardboard box.

"A South Wales model, Miss Sindy Francis, took her first bubble bath in a cardboard box yesterday," I wrote. "'I've never bathed in public before,' she giggled as she buried herself in foam in front of a crowd at an industrial exhibition."

The piece had a photograph of the gorgeous Sindy in the bubble box and Humphries gave me my first by-line for it. As proud as a father with his first baby, I took an early edition home to show to Liz. I liked the seriousness of news but liked its silliness even more. You never knew what the next phone call was going to bring. That teaching job in Kenya was slapped firmly on the spike.

I had been working in the newsroom for little over five weeks when, on 21 October 1966, I drove into the city in my Mini. It was one of those grey, moisty mornings when nothing much happens and I got myself a cup of coffee from the machine at the end of the newsroom before checking the diary to see what I was down for that day. A dog show.

"You've got a car haven't you, Tom?" asked Michael Lloyd-Williams who was in charge of the news desk that morning. "Drive Giles Varrall up to Aberfan. Something's happened to the school there, we're not sure what."

Giles was a senior reporter and it was clear all they expected me to do was act as his chauffeur. Others in the newsroom were making calls to the police and fire services. *Something* had happened in Aberfan, no one was sure what, but it might be big and all senior reporters were being called in.

What I remember most about that drive up through the valleys was the stillness of the morning. Doleful mists moved across the black geometry of abandoned mine workings and deserted, boarded-up chapels. The old order had broken down: King Coal was falling into irreversible decline.

Occasionally the mists parted and we caught long views of the valleys with their horizontal towns and rows of terraces. Rooks flapped on damp rooftops. Giles fiddled with my car radio, trying but failing to pick up news from Aberfan. We passed my birthplace, Pontypridd, straddling an engorged River Taff and I gave its huddled terraces and dreaming spires an affectionate salute.

"It'll all be over by the time we get there, I expect," I said.

"I'm not so sure," Giles replied. "I picked up something about the school roof falling in and all the children trapped in there."

We drove past the village of Mount Pleasant where police were directing the traffic. "Press," I shouted and we were waved on. The policeman's eyes were dripping with tears. I had never seen a policeman cry before.

Aberfan, a village which contained all the perfection of the ordinary, sat at the bottom of a brambled slope in a long, twisting valley. Mists made it difficult to work out what was going on but it was obviously something major since emergency service trucks and ambulances were lined up waiting to get through. A helicopter went whump-whumping overhead and my insides knotted.

I parked in a side street and we made our way down Moy Road on foot. A tiny woman was standing on a garden wall, her hands deep in the pockets of her brown mackintosh. With her small frame and tight brown curls she looked like my mother and I asked her what was going on. Her eyes were red with tears. "The coal tip that was up there has gone down on to Pantglas School," she whispered, pointing directly ahead of her.

"I don't see any school," I said.

"It's been covered by the tip," she replied. "You can't see it because it's been covered by coal. All the children have been covered by coal."

Unable to take in what she was telling me I took out my pen and notebook. "Could I have your name please?" I asked.

She shook her head and tears flew out of her eyes.

"Of course," I said sheepishly, putting my pen and notebook away. "Sorry."

I wandered on towards the broken school. About three hundred miners were digging down through the black, wet slurry, others chaining the foul stuff away in buckets. Their warm breath plumed in the cold air. Sometimes they had to struggle to free their boots which had got bogged down in the mess and, all around, villagers gathered in tearful, anxious vigil, waiting for their children to be dug out.

Every half-minute a whistle blew and the miners stopped working for ten seconds. This was a standard mining rescue technique, someone told me, as everyone could then listen for the sounds of survivors. Those ten-second silences were like great communal prayers that life might return to this valley of death. Sweet Jesus! Miners expect trouble but never this. Never the death of their babies in their own classrooms, dead before their lives had even begun. Here was another bill that had to be paid, another rise in the terrible price of this bastard coal.

More and more people turned up to help, but what could they do? The tip was practically heaving with men digging or chaining away the slurry. We were hearing sketchy reports that a big lake had been building up inside the tip and had finally exploded after a night of heavy rain, sending thousands of tons of slurry hurtling a mile or so down on the school where more than a hundred children had been sitting down to start their first lesson of the day.

It was almost impossible to work out where the tip once was: a slight dip sat at the top of the mountain where everything had spewed out into a long, black ski-slope with trees, parts of stone walls and the roof of a cottage sticking out of it. It hadn't stopped at the school but swept over the road and down into another wide gully. You couldn't have started to guess how it all might have been before the start of the spill. The school had been erased.

The odds against something like this happening were unimaginable. There seemed no way mere words could convey the depth of this horror and, as it turned out, I didn't write one word about the disaster, merely wandered around uselessly looking at it all with disbelief. They had already dug the first of the bodies out of the school, shielding them from view with blankets before taking them away on stretchers.

Another helicopter brought in more members of the national media who began buying up the few telephones in the village. Many were gathering in the local shop with one, Hector Lloyd-Jones of the *South Wales Echo*, dictating his first copy. He stood there next to rows of sweet jars dictating into the phone as other *Echo* reporters dropped further bits of information into his ear. He couldn't have been there long enough to find out anything for himself, but he didn't stop dictating for more than an hour while others jumped around squealing with frustration because they wanted to get hold of that phone. Most journalism – even some of the best – was done on the hoof like this. Experienced reporters reacted instantly, conveying the atmosphere rather than the facts of an event which, in this case, would take a long and expensive tribunal to uncover.

Word finally came through from John Humphries that I should try to pick up some photographs of the children. A colleague, Joy Barden, and I knocked on doors along the terraces, sometimes saying we needed photographs for police identification – which was later to get us into trouble – but, after a short while, I packed it in.

164

I couldn't do this for a living. There wasn't enough money in the world to keep me doing this. Already I had begun lying to people who had just lost their children.

By early afternoon the rafters of the smashed school were becoming visible and tiny blackened bodies were still being dug out behind a screen of blankets. One teacher was found with three children in his arms clearly trying to take shelter behind a blackboard when the tip swept in. The bodies were taken over the road and laid out on the pews of Bethania Chapel which became known as the Chapel of Death. As they were brought out women came fearfully forward to see if they were their own sons or daughters.

I bumped into George Thomas, the Secretary of State for Wales, in Moy Road, accompanied by a grim-faced Lord Snowdon. Reporters gathered around him clamouring for a quote. "I am just too sick to speak," he said, "but I will say this." He condemned the Coal Board, promised a full inquiry and added that the guilty would be named and heads would roll. Even in all this confusion George, as befitted a future Speaker of the House of Commons, remained fluent, his voice bristling with fury. Harold Wilson, the Prime Minister, turned up later.

Such visitors were well meaning but all they managed to do was hamper the rescue operation. Politicians are hopeless in an emergency: they only ever turn up to have their photos taken. And what the hell did Lord Snowdon think he could do there? Pick up a shovel?

There were now too many people swarming through Aberfan and the police set up roadblocks around the village which meant I had to stay inside or leave for good. The landlord of the local pub let it be known we could sleep on the floor of the residents' lounge if we wanted so I continued moving through this nightmare wondering how soon I *could* get out. The reporters, who were still arriving from London and elsewhere, looked alien to us provincial hacks, particularly the hard-faced women in mini-skirts and thigh-high boots. The national male reporters had a frightening quality about them, rushing in with their reckless, insensitive questions.

As night fell I climbed the high slope above Aberfan. Arc lights had been set up over the school and the miners continued digging the slurry. They had given up their ten-second silences and were going at it as hard as they could. A car horn kept blaring deep within the slurry. A man came and stood next to me but neither of us spoke. More bodies were being dug out and the final death toll was twenty-eight adults and one hundred and sixteen children.

No one seemed to be talking to anyone else. There was nothing to say. People stood around the streets, in groups or as individuals, silent, grim and stricken with pain. Even the sightseers who would later be castigated as ghouls were quiet and thoughtful, standing on distant ledges with their torches, surveying the death of a village.

In that cold, dark night, with more rain forecast, it was impossible to get back in touch with the real world. I kept thinking of that teacher who had taken those three children in his arms before they had died together; of how he had taken the register and begun preparing himself for a day's teaching when the classroom was smashed by a towering black tide and, screaming together, they drowned together, their terrified cries stifled until they could breathe no more and their racing hearts were still.

My own parents had never forgiven God for the loss of their first child in infancy. What were these parents going to make of this outrage? Where had God – who knew everything and was everywhere – been when this happened?

Parents waited tearfully outside Bethania Chapel before being allowed in to identify their young ones. They were allowed inside one couple at a time and some would queue right through this savage night waiting for the body of their own child to be brought in. For most it would not just be the death of their child but their death too. What killed the children broke the parents. Every parent who walked into that chapel was broken for ever and every single one of them would gladly have gone to die in that school that morning if, by some bleak transaction, they could thus have spared their children.

God would have a big problem explaining this outrage to those parents, even if he were so inclined. I never felt close to God in Aberfan, only to his detachment and his cruel Old Testament ways. That was the problem with God: he was a complex personality given to bouts of fantastic anger and destruction yet, in the most supreme act of love, he gave the world his only son. You never knew what he was going to do next: build you up or strike you down, as he had done now, with these poor pit people and their children.

By now the international media, those agents of the lost and godless, were turning up in force. A photographer from *Paris Match* broke a rear window in Bethania Chapel to get a shot of the dead on the pews. Crosses made of miners' helmets on shovels were set up on the tip to fake yet more dubious photographs. They were trying to work up sensational angles when nothing could be more sensational than what lay before them.

The Cardiff newsroom was a frenzy of activity when I returned the next morning. Everyone except us trainees had been hauled in to work on this story. Aberfan was the defining news story of the twentieth century in Wales: a sudden glimpse of a Welsh hell full of children slaughtered in their classrooms and the old hated Tory coal barons, long thought dead, but who still seemed very much alive and kicking.

Telephones shrilled, seasoned reporters bustled around in ways we never thought them capable of, typewriters clattered in metallic bursts as Humphries finally achieved his apotheosis, orchestrating this bedlam with rolled-up sleeves and a grim smile. *Where's the angle? Ring the Coal Board. Get back to him now. Tell him that's not good enough.* He picked up phones, barked orders into them and slammed them down again. *What's the Welsh Office saying about this? Look, get around there and kick in the door if you have to.* You could see he was supremely fulfilled when he was handling two calls and his other phone rang. He was the champion surfer on a soaring tide of hard news and he wasn't about to topple off the foaming crest.

One immediate new angle was that no one wanted a coal tip for a neighbour. Everyone was taking a second look at the hundreds of tips which littered the face of

Wales, ringing in about cracks in them, how they were constantly on the move, how they were going to come crashing down any day now.

It is difficult to believe that one small Welsh village could start a fuss that became global. But most of that was down to the media which picked up every heated word and argument and broadcast them throughout the world. From the beginning the media took a whip to the story, galloping it at full speed and *never once letting go*. In a sense the media became the story, with everyone feeding their own agenda into the un-spooling Aberfan narrative as the desolate village was kept reeling by other problems including the Aberfan Disaster Appeal and the terminally stupid Princess Margaret Toy Appeal.

The media left nobody in peace at Aberfan. For years they raked over the ashes of a now-cold disaster on the flimsiest pretexts, an anniversary or some pointless scare, to find a new angle, a new row, any excuse to gaze once more at the face of this huge tragedy and revive it in our minds.

The *Western Mail* went on to win awards for its coverage and subsequent campaign on tip disposal. But I was relieved to get back to news about dog shows or models taking baths in a cardboard box. There was little point in giving up journalism because of Aberfan, a "one-off", they kept assuring me, a "once in a lifetime story" the likes of which we would never see again.

The tragedy defied all logic, all decency, any sense of fair play and, with the best will in the world and a wavering faith in a God I had come to be afraid of, I knew I would never get close to the real and mature faith of the Rev Kenneth Hayes, a Baptist minister who had lost a son to the killer tip. "Let us thank God that things are not worse," were his first words in a sermon from his pulpit in Aberfan the following Sunday. "We must not be bitter, but we must approach it with a spirit of love. Let us be thankful for miracles and thank God for those who survived."

TWENTY TWO

A provincial newspaper suffers its first birth pangs early each morning with several cups of coffee, a fag and a good cough and the start of a ceaseless scrabbling for news in a process as uncertain and unpredictable as foraging blindfolded under a bed of dead leaves for something which you will only recognise when you actually grab hold of it – and maybe not even then.

Most reporters on the *Western Mail* would drift in during the morning and sit at their desks, staring into space for a while or filling in their expense forms or thinking about lunch while waiting for some divine inspiration. The *South Wales Echo*, on the other side of the newsroom, being an evening newspaper, would already have been at it for a few hours with everyone beavering away in a hullabaloo of ringing phones and clacking typewriters.

Some of us had clearly defined tasks first thing like telephoning the fire stations or police headquarters to ask if anything had happened during the night. As often as not, they wouldn't tell us anything, but we had to keep asking anyway.

There was always a huge pile of mail waiting to be opened on the news desk, almost all pointless press releases from organisations like the Gas Board about various new appointments complete with mug shots of the appointees. You could safely have dropped most of this mail into the bin and never missed a thing but everything had to be opened "just in case". You might even spot a real story tucked away in the last paragraph of the Gas Board press release which they clearly thought unimportant. This was why you were in the newsroom and they were in the Gas Board. You only became a press officer with the Gas Board because they paid you more money than you got in the newsroom, because you didn't know what news was anyway, or had long forgotten or simply didn't care. The public relations industry is riddled with reporters who gave up and just went for the money, as most of them will readily admit over a drink.

What you looked for in the mail were handwritten letters as they often contained something more than PR puffery: spiteful tip-offs by neighbours or complaints that local kids were vandalising some public monument. They've gone and put another traffic cone on Nye Bevan's head!

Even when you recognised a story, its success or failure often depended on how you visualised it. Some could find a good news lead and never make it interesting. Even so, there was general agreement among the elder statesmen of the newsroom when you did find a good story: they all recognised what you recognised even if they didn't know quite what it was.

Good news stories gave experienced reporters a quickening of the blood and a twinkle in the bollocks. This quickening and twinkling didn't go away until the story had been written and the consequent post-orgasmic release called for a few pints in the Queen's Vaults pub over the road. The old guard also knew by instinct when they'd written the story to its "proper length". No story ever had a prescribed "proper length" but you always knew when you got there. Most knew when you should type ENDS but there were some trainees who went on and on and on, writing short treatises which Humphries slashed mercilessly. The best reporters are not always the brightest or most academic souls.

Someone had to sit down in the newsroom at the start of the day and read all the national newspapers, cutting out any stories with references to Wales that we could develop in our own way. Most of the London nationals had reporters based in Wales but they rarely came up with anything that they hadn't lifted from us in the first place or from the local television news services. They did originate something occasionally, if only because they had the bigger cheque books, which is why we had to keep cutting the nationals. When we poked around inside these stories, however, they almost always fell apart in our hands with "facts" hotly disputed and "quotes" later denied. National reporters from London, in particular, never seemed to worry about accuracy and we were left to clear up the mess they left.

If you hadn't found something to work on in the newsroom after messing about for an hour or so you could always do your expenses. Expenses were a very slippery part of the culture of the newsroom, having little or no relationship to what you had actually spent. Senior reporters seemed to know what they could get away with, often when they hadn't even moved out of the office, and others guessed. If you didn't judge your level correctly Humphries cut them and, generally, you got away with an amount that was directly proportional to how much or how little your work had been pleasing him lately. Some didn't bother to claim anything but I usually put in for around £3 a week made up of entirely imaginary journeys criss-crossing the city and the odd lunch or "entertainment", as drinks with other reporters were known. If I'd had a couple of strong stories that week I bumped it up a pound or two as a reward and Humphries seemed happy to sign the official yellow expenses slip I submitted.

In fact we reporters spent almost nothing – largely because most things were provided free by people who wanted generous mention in our copy – although I did sometimes spend a shilling or two. Some didn't even spend that. If you were phoning in your copy from, say, City Hall, it was expected you should reverse the charges. But you might have to hang on for ten minutes before the switchboard operator in Thomson House answered. To save this time I would often pay for my local call to the office, unlike Michael Buerk, then the *Echo's* City Hall correspondent, who would hang on all afternoon rather than pay for a call.

"I don't care if I have to stand here all day," he said. "I will never pay for a call to my own office."

"Press!" I would shout if anyone ever asked me for money and they would, without fail, usher you through with a pat on your back and a free drink in your hand.

Sometimes you got so drunk you were incapable of writing anything at all: one company rang the news desk claiming a reporter was so drunk they wondered if we could send someone else.

By 12 o'clock whoever was in charge of the news desk that morning would, after consulting the district reporters, draw up his list of "probable and possible" stories, which he would take into a conference with the editor and other department chiefs. This list was far from definitive so early in the day but you could usually tell what stories were going to lead what inside pages, with most of the late-breaking news reserved for page one. But nothing was set in stone and, if a shotgun appeared around some Welsh farmhouse door or the Free Wales Army threatened to blow up the Welsh Office, almost any page could be torn apart in thirty seconds flat. Everything made way for murder and terrorism. If you want a page one headline to yourself, get a bomb.

That much was clear then and it is almost an article of faith today. Violence is the lifeblood of news and, the more violent the content, the more prominent the story. If it bleeds, it leads.

If I was on the early shift and wasn't working on anything by the afternoon, I might suggest to Humphries when he stormed into the newsroom at around 2.30pm, that I go and have a look around Tiger Bay which I had got to know quite well from my days working on the paddle steamers. He knew that down there I would dig out some sort of story which would make a good news feature with a picture, and almost always agreed. This didn't make him any nicer to me: he seemed to be devoid of even the simplest understanding of niceness but I did notice he often seemed to get far nastier to some of the others for no apparent reason and this left him with less time to get nasty with me. But I always worked hard for him anyway, if only because he scared the life out of me.

I always felt a certain lightening when I walked across The Hayes and over to the top of Bute Street, the main artery of the city down through Butetown. The Bay began, just under the railway bridge, with the Custom House hotel, where the prostitutes hung out and, from there, the main road charged headlong down to the sea at Pier Head with a railway line on the one side and crumbling tenements, pubs and cafés on the other. This road took you through the whole world, from the small community of Greeks who lived around their Greek Orthodox Church at the top, taking in the Chinese block where they lived around their laundry, then down to the West Indian community scattered around Loudoun Square, the two small mosques which met the spiritual needs of the sizeable Muslim communities and finally the small Spanish community based around Pier Head.

Standing under the bridge, being studied by the patrolling whores, you could watch the ebb and flow of these ceaseless tides sweeping up and down into the city, going out to shop or conduct business in the centre or coming in to drink in the Bay and play with the whores. One medical report revealed that the growth of venereal disease went up by some forty per cent in the Valleys after rugby fans had been down in Butetown celebrating a Welsh win in the city's Arms Park.

Men in turbans sat in trams which screeched up the metal lines in the road, others in ratting caps pushed wheelbarrows or came down here to sell fat-bellied fish door to door. A small group of West Indians chattered as they made their way home after a game of dominoes in the Kayak Club or else a commodities broker, complete with waistcoat, fob watch and bowler would come marching up the pavement from the Coal Exchange, as splendid as a Sultan examining his harem. He might have just made a bundle selling a cargo which he hadn't even seen because it was still in the middle of the Indian Ocean.

The area was beginning to be redeveloped and I quickly found that, merely by knocking on a door and having a chat with whoever opened it, you could find a story. Single occupied houses in a line of others that had fallen derelict always turned up a lively story and I did well with Mrs Stella Reffell, who was living with her seven children in a converted butcher's shop in Stuart Street. The council was refusing to re-house her from this slum with no bath, so what could she do, she asked me, banging her fist on the table. What could she do against them all?

"Well," I said, taking out my notebook, "you could always threaten to go into the council offices and break all their windows. That's what you might do isn't it? Break all the windows?"

She bit her lip, frowned and said well, yes, she *could* do that.

"No, Mrs Reffell, you *will* go in there and break all their windows because that's what I'm going to put down in my notebook and what will appear in the newspaper, which the council always reads, Mrs Reffell."

"All right then. Tomorrow?"

"No hurry. We'll just say you're going to do it and you are going to haunt the council forever aren't you Mrs Reffell?

"As long as you like."

"You might even tell me that you're going to take all your kids in there and leave them in the offices."

"Do I have to say that? I couldn't do that."

"Well you don't really have to mean it, Mrs Reffell. Just say it. Threaten them and they might do something for you. Everyone responds to threats. A little smell of violence always gets everyone going."

Thus I got a lively story with Mrs Reffell photographed sitting with her arms loaded with kids.

"No, Mrs Reffell, you must not smile for the photographer, you must look *glum* because you have to live in this dump, Mrs Reffell, and you are about to smash all the council windows."

The story appeared and, as Mrs Refell and her children were re-housed before the week was out, I felt fully justified in doing a bit of quiet speechwriting for her.

I also befriended Phillip Dunleavy, a well-known and much-admired councillor in the area, and we made common cause – he got publicity for helping his constituents and I got my stories. Dunleavy's one great attribute was that he would say almost anything to get his name in the paper, even inviting me to make up quotes for him if his weren't strong enough. We would often discuss what makes news and I might say, "I don't think the story is quite there."

"Well, we'd better have a petition," he would say since he was learning fast. "I'll go down the street and we'll draw up a petition which we can take to the council. I'll get a jazz band to go with us. That'll make a good picture won't it?"

Brilliant. Petitions were always better than the views of one person and a jazz band would give the story life. With a petition you can make a story sound as if there's some mass movement about to descend on the City Hall and play hell there. Some departments only responded if they thought there was going to be trouble. The meek will never inherit a place on the housing waiting list.

If the threat of a petition and some anarchic jazz was not alarming enough you could ring up the local MP and get him to ask a question in the House of Commons. Members of Parliament were always, without fail, prepared to do that since MPs are little more than two-legged self-publicity machines who will ask any question if it gives them a good plug in the paper (which, in its turn, tells their constituents that they are busy on their behalf). Questions in the House always made for a strong story and Leo Abse MP, who understood the wicked ways of journalism far better than many wicked journalists, would tell you that you didn't just want a question in the House of Commons, but a story which would begin like this: and he would begin dictating your intro to you.

Loudoun Square, riven with tuberculosis and sundry diseases, was about to be demolished with many residents being swept up into new high-rise flats. All of them had something to say about this. They didn't want to leave the area but neither did they want to live in the dreaded high-rise flats. Despite its many problems, everyone loved living in Butetown.

Thus, with my trusty notebook and faithful councillor or tame MP, I managed to become something of a voice for the area and began discovering what journalism can do for a community. Sometimes you could hit a story hard and make a real difference. But mostly people, particularly council bureaucrats, ignored our stories, knowing that they would soon peter out and be forgotten in the wake of the next contrived campaign.

Only stories like Aberfan live for ever.

Not that it was all hard-hitting campaigns in Butetown. There were some wonderful characters living there such as Mrs Sophie Salaman who owned the Cairo Café in Bute Street where the Arabs gathered to eat in the main living room and pray in the small mosque which had been built in the backyard. Sophie became a true friend and I would often call into her café on my rounds for a cup of tea or a curry that all but stripped the skin off my tonsils.

"And I went and made it milder for you today," she would say as my watering eyeballs bulged and I pleaded for cold water. "That wasn't hot at all. You should have seen what I served up last night."

Muslim communities are difficult to penetrate – although not as difficult as the Chinese – but Sophie introduced me to most of the main characters in hers, enabling me to get to know them, if not well then at least by name. She was Welsh and had been a sixteen-year-old nurse in the Valleys when she came down to Cardiff for a day out. While looking for the railway station to return home she took a wrong turn and wandered down Bute Street where she bumped into Ali Salaman, who had just fetched up there from the Yemen. They got chatting.

They married and had twelve children – six boys and six girls, in sequence – so it came as no surprise when Ali decided to set up the Cairo Café, if only to feed them. One of their girls, Selma, married an English boy; Assia married a Maltese; Rashed a half-Maltese and half-English; Hinda an Arab and Leila a Welsh lad. That's about as integrated as it gets and the Salaman family became an icon in this famous multi-racial community where the only ethnic constituent they were short of in the local Kayak Club was Eskimo.

Sophie, who had clearly retained her Welsh Valley penchant for gossip, provided me with lots of the stories I wrote up for the *Western Mail*. The Muslims in the gorgeous white birthday cake that was the Peel Street mosque could no longer leave their shoes outside while praying, she once told me, because the local kids kept throwing them over a fence and into the park. In no time at all, the Imam of the mosque, shoulder to shoulder with Councillor Phillip Dunleavy, was threatening to draw up a petition and march on the council offices to break all their windows, together with a jazz band if they didn't watch out, unless someone could guarantee the safety and security of their best shoes while they were praying. But, after we'd discussed it a bit, we decided it might be better if they just took their best shoes inside instead.

The Muslims were lovely, warm people, with whom it would be a delight to share a foxhole, but they were a voluble bunch prone to arguments with the authorities and among themselves. One of the stormiest came when they began slaughtering sheep in the street at the end of Ramadan with blood and guts running over the pavement. The magazine *Animal World* started a fuss over this, protesting that the practice was upsetting the children, not to mention the sheep. These heated words were fanned by – ahem – so much press publicity that even the city's health committee let out a few bellicose squawks and the Muslims were forced to use the local abattoir, albeit with their own licensed slaughter men.

Another row erupted about post-mortems. They said that dissection was contrary to their law. And there was another really good stink when the city cemetery people could not – or would not – dig their graves to face Mecca. You had to go in the same line as everyone else, the cemetery people said, and the row was only finally resolved when the Moslems got their own plot.

All the Muslims in the Bay had once worshipped at the mosque in Peel Street. Then the worshippers had broken into two factions, complicated by homeland politics, with the younger faction complaining that they could no longer worship in the Peel Street mosque because it did not face Mecca. Finally, Ali Salaman led a rebel group away from the main mosque which was how he came to build a new mosque in the backyard of his Cairo Café.

There were few moments as purely enjoyable for me as just standing over the road next to the offices of Metro Cars and hearing a loud elongated wail from the mosque rise up into the Bute Street dawn. Inside the men were on their knees on one side, the women on the other, beneath a copper dome with shafts of light breaking through the stained glass. Two flies buzzed around in frantic triangles in the intensity of the coloured light. One Arabic inscription on a window said: "There is no God but Allah and Mohammed is his messenger." Some of the worshippers wore traditional tunics or saris and all were wearing hats of one kind or another.

It was in these battered and broken streets that I first learned the art of becoming a reporter: not by actually making anything up – although I admit to cooking a few quotes – but by standing there with a fag in my mouth, looking at what was going on around me and scribbling down words and phrases which I would later try to bash into some kind of order.

We weren't supposed to analyse or interpret anything, just stand there and *record* that Eid was being celebrated at the end of Ramadan, bringing a month of fasting from sunrise to sunset to an end. The good news had come courtesy of the BBC after it had been reported that two men in Mecca had seen the new moon with their own eyes. Soon everyone was hugging everyone else and they would be off to parties and feasting all over the city while I trudged back to the office to try and tame my wild phrases into some form of measured narrative.

"It's a pity they don't have some sort of fight in these celebrations," Humphries might say as his Biro chipped and chiselled at my final masterpiece. "A good fight would have livened this story up no end." But he was quite appreciative and gave me another by-line instead of the ubiquitous *Western Mail Reporter* tag under which most of our stories appeared. We loved seeing our names in print; it made everything seem worthwhile.

Fights. Violence. I was already beginning to understand what made news; how the real preoccupations of news were almost totally alien to the lives of real people in an ordinary world. Fortunately, I was showing no aptitude for hard news, with its grisly moments of terror and violence – I was already seen as a "colour" writer, someone who could be sent somewhere and describe a situation or invoke an atmosphere in an interesting and lively way.

The editor, John Giddings, had encouraged Humphries to let me develop like this although Giddings told me many years later that he had also ordered everyone to keep one foot firmly on my neck. They liked what I did but they really didn't want me to do it; they wanted what I did in the paper but they were scared of it at the same time. I showed a definite tendency to go too far. Humphries would look at my copy and, almost as a reflex action, begin chopping and cutting it before he had even started to read it properly. I was going to be the first "colour" writer in the history of journalism to write without any "colour", the first descriptive writer to write without the aid of adjectives and absolutely the first humorous writer to conduct his trade without the use of jokes.

Yet this did start banging severe discipline into my style where there'd been none. In a few months Humphries had given me a far greater sense of control and precision in my words than they'd managed in three years in the philosophy department of Cardiff University.

I did ask for it sometimes. I was sent to yet another dog show and got a bit carried away with descriptions of turds everywhere, the owners pampering their pooches and my all-time great line of bad description: the way the sun lanced down through the window of the school hall and glinted in the various pools of dog piss.

Humphries went berserk when he read this and slashed my ten paragraphs down to about three (but even these, which appeared the next day, managed to upset almost every dog owner in Wales). I had got the name of one of the breeds wrong and the phones didn't stop ringing in the newsroom all day. If you want to upset half of Wales, insult dogs or the Welsh language and, if you can find a Welsh-speaking dog pissing on your lawn *and* get a snap of him, you are really in business.

On the *Western Mail* anyway.

The newsroom built into a frenzy at around six o'clock with a dozen reporters all furiously bashing out copy – with two carbons – in the hope of getting out of the office at a reasonable hour. The trick was, after you'd finished your story, to wait until Humphries went off to see the editor – or was otherwise engaged – then drop your copy surreptitiously on to his desk and take off fast. But he had ways of tracking you down, often hauling you back from the pub to check this or get some more quotes on that. If he was in his normal bolshie mood he might make you re-write the whole thing and, if that wasn't to his satisfaction, he would get you to do it again and again. He was a totally driven man and when I once told him I wanted to get away to meet some friends he exploded as if I'd just offered to give him the pox and shouted: "Friends! I haven't got any friends so why should you have any?"

After about seven o'clock in the evening, little happened in the newsroom apart from the odd telephone call, usually about nothing much. The sub-editors were busy enough on their large curved table at the far end of the newsroom and pages were being busily drawn up by the night editor, John Coslett, but, apart from a few reporters trying to look busy, most of us had disappeared into the pubs.

The one characteristic of news, particularly local news, is that, apart from the odd fire or crash, it doesn't happen in its own right but has to be sought out or created. With news nothing is ever as it seems. People don't suddenly threaten the council with a petition. They are generally encouraged to do so by reporters like me. MPs rarely ask questions in the House because they want to know the answers but because they want their constituents to know they have asked the question. Exhibitions or promotions are staged in the city centre when they are convenient for reporters' deadlines and, if you can't get your political demonstration on the news, it has been a failure.

Instead of reflecting the culture of a community, as TS Eliot once said a newspaper should, we were pretty much in charge of it. We could close plays early and, if not finish careers, then put a mighty dent in them. A few careless words could undermine the confidence of rugby or football players. Concerts would attract huge audiences if we had enjoyed them and we were given our own private screenings of films early in the morning. Whatever happened, even if it went against us for a while, we always had the last word and laugh. No one ever put one over on us. Some did occasionally try but they soon learned that they needed us more than we needed them. With these few insights I was sensing an enormous power, but it was only later that I began understanding its real force.

News services shadowed and controlled not only the community but also one another and we kept our eyes on the local television news and other newspapers to see what they'd got. If we liked what they'd got we would give the story a new "nose" or some fresh quotes and present it on our news pages as our own. Thus news was also cannibalistic and even criminal in the sense that it was often openly stolen from elsewhere, an activity into which the workings of ethics or morality never entered.

This was a strange, new world, redolent of invisible power and thick with cynicism. It specialised in smoke and mirrors and, come seven o'clock, it all went on hold as we flitted from pub to pub in the city. For this reason there was hardly any news on Saturday nights or Sunday mornings: not because the world wasn't revolving on its axis as usual but because people like me, paid to report the news, had something more important or amusing to do on Saturday nights or Sunday mornings.

TWENTY THREE

Detective Chief Superintendent Morris, who was in charge of law 'n' order in Cardiff, was a fearsome character, built like a rugby prop forward, with a strange, misshapen nose which had clearly seen many fights, and an even stranger voice since much of his throat had been shot away by a bullet in one of his tussles with the gangsters in the Bay.

On the eve of my wedding he sent word to the newsroom that he wanted to talk to me about a story on drugs I had written in which I had described how I bought a pile of amphetamines in city pubs. These had been duly photographed in the palm of my hand and featured on page one. I had bought twenty-one single grain Dexedrine tablets at a shilling each, I had reported. "They are freely available in most pubs although the kids mostly like double Dexedrine which have become difficult to obtain." I then added unctuously and falsely that later on I had destroyed the drugs I had been sold.

I wasn't keen on discussing my story with Superintendent Morris since, apart from the fact that I wanted to get to North Wales to get married, I could also barely understand a word he said in his strange, vacuum cleaner voice and, perhaps most crucially for me, the story wasn't entirely true.

I *had* bought the Dexedrine in the Cardiff pubs, but had neglected to mention they had been supplied by my brother, Alan, then eighteen. Alan had long been an expert on all kinds of drugs and my mother had once found, in the lining of his Beatle jacket, a secret stash of pills which turned out to be Black Bombers or Speed as they were more commonly known. "I'm keeping hold of a few of them in case he falls ill," she said. But there was never any sign of Alan falling ill even if you could sometimes shake him and get him to rattle like a castanet. Now I was going to have to face Chief Superintendent Morris and try to hide behind the confidentiality of my sources – difficult, particularly as it was well-known that suspects were regularly beaten up in Cardiff police station in those days. Some appeared in the dock covered in bloody bandages and claimed police brutality only to be shown scorn by the magistrate who might then add a bit more to his sentence for making "outrageous" allegations against our "hard-working and honest" police. I didn't think Superintendent Morris would beat a confession out of me but wasn't absolutely certain.

And I did want to get married to Liz, who was working in the tele-ad department of the *Western Mail*, and was equally keen to get married to me since she was three months pregnant.

Rather than risk shopping my brother or being battered senseless in the police cells I sent along my best man, Ray, to tell Superintendent Morris I was sorry I couldn't come in person but I was getting married and going away on a long honeymoon abroad. But the grizzled old bastard was affable enough, Ray reported later, adding that he could barely understand a word he said. The main relief was that he didn't want me to report back to Cardiff police station when the honeymoon was over.

The wedding went ahead on a chilly Anglesey morning in March 1967 and, after a bad-tempered honeymoon in damp, cold bed and breakfasts around the Llyn peninsula in North Wales, we returned to a small, new semi-detached house in Rhiwbina, a smart suburb in north Cardiff, and a staggering £28-a-month mortgage to begin married life.

I was surprised how quickly I embraced conventionality and a mortgage after my wild youth running around the world and was not too happy about it either. I was no longer writing the great novel, but up to my armpits in debt and about to become a father. My main problem was that I was drinking too much and those searing moments in Malaya continued to haunt me daily, almost hourly – the exploding novel, the artists' attack on the world and the black rain.

This war around my visions raged on inside me. What, if anything, had they meant? Had it been nervous breakdown? Quite clearly I wasn't ever going to know and the few people I did talk to about it couldn't offer any explanation either. Neil Kinnock, with whom I'd shared a house at university, often said he was sure he could talk me out of it if only I'd explain it all to him, but I never did.

My problem was that I was convinced that God had indeed spoken to me; that, in those spectacular visions, he had shown me the world as *he* saw the world, under attack by people who should have known better. I *might* have been able to put it all aside as some sort of nervous breakdown except for that one moment when, long after all the other visions had stopped, I saw those interlocking celestial drums forming in that clear blue sky in Penang and the black rain pouring down out of them.

The difficulty with the black rain was that it looked like a metaphor for a real and universal truth. I kept looking around me with my grinding new insight and could see it pouring out of almost all sections of the media in its relentless search for violence. In that context I could also understand how we had become so godless and prone to thuggery, how and why we were all struggling home, unhappy and tormented, through the fields of a dead harvest.

But all that was now behind me, I had to keep telling myself. It had no relevance whatsoever to the work I was now doing. My new family responsibilities were more important. I was going to have to brush myself down and become a journalist with no place for visions or jokes but underpinned only by hard facts.

After a year or so Humphries made me Arts Correspondent which mainly, if not exclusively, involved going to the New Theatre on Monday nights and delivering my verdict on whatever they had chosen to stage that week. But you had to be careful what you wrote – even if the play was absolute rubbish – since you could pretty much empty the theatre that week if you gave it a truly damning review. Mostly I tried to err on the side of generosity, largely helped by the drinks with which the anxious manager plied me during the interval.

"You can miss the next act because it's terrible," he told me one week. "Stay here and we'll have a few more drinks instead."

After the final curtain I went to the Llanrumney coffee stall nearby, full of tarts and long-distance lorry drivers, and wrote the review with the help of a cup of coffee and a greasy bacon sandwich. I never really knew what I was writing about although, perhaps encouraged by the theatre manager's warming whisky, I always tried to be helpful even when the production stank. You should always give an artist credit for trying, I believed. No one sets out to produce rubbish: no matter what their limitations, they always try their best.

One week the Royal Ballet pitched up at the New Theatre with *Swan Lake*, Dame Margot Fonteyn in the lead. I told Humphries I couldn't review it since I had never seen a ballet in my life. He muttered to himself for a bit and rang a few freelancers who also couldn't – or wouldn't – do it before ordering me to go. "Just do what you can. You don't have to say if it's good or bad. Just flannel. You're good at flannel, I've noticed."

I sat through the first act of *Swan Lake* with my guts turning to acid, unable to think of a single useful thing to say about what was happening on the stage. When the interval came I was on my way to the manager's office for some much-needed drink when I bumped into an old college pal, Jack Young. I was a bit suspicious of Jack, if only because he wore a flowery dicky bow, and became even more wary when he told me that he was a hard-line balletomane. So what was the performance like?

"Well, Dame Margot is doing quite well, but I must say her finger work is slightly untidy," Jack replied.

"Really," I said reaching for my notebook." Tell me more. I'm floundering a bit here."

"I'll make you some notes and give them to you at the end."

This he did and I must say it was a particularly fine piece of criticism that I penned among the tarts and lorry drivers of the Llanrumney coffee stall late that night.

Next morning I was on an early shift in the newsroom when I took a call from a woman who described herself as a ballet teacher in Penarth. "I have been a reader of the *Western Mail* for years," she said, "and have long despaired of seeing anything sensible about ballet in your newspaper."

Oh hell, I thought, now I'm for the high jump.

"But your review of *Swan Lake* was first-class. You have made a great contribution to the art and totally revived my flagging faith in your newspaper. That was just about the best ballet review I've ever read."

That call was a turning point in my life and dispelled any lingering doubts I might have had about becoming a journalist. As I put down the receiver I realised that you can go anywhere and do anything in this job. This work will give you a complete education and, if you don't know anything about a subject, you can always dig up someone who does.

So it was that I scuttled about the city: attending first nights; sitting in on committee meetings at the City Hall, unearthing an eclectic collection of stories by, for example, knocking on doors around a bakery which had provoked complaints about excessive noise at night to encourage the residents to draw up a petition; revealing that some silver cutlery which had once belonged to the poet, Shelley, was going to be auctioned tomorrow because the owners found it too difficult to clean and how ultra violet light was soon going to hot up the war on stamp forgers.

The improbable diversity of it all soon became humdrum. There were hardly any sensational events such as a murder and, if there were, such matters were always assigned to the senior reporters, who could deal with anything coolly and efficiently because they had dealt with such matters hundreds of times before. They were impossible to shock, gazed on the most horrifying accidents with unblinking calm before taking out a notebook to write down the name and address of a victim and returning to the office to write up their stories in time-honoured clichés.

There was nothing new in news, you came to realise. Those who featured in the news thought it was unique – if only because they were in the middle of it – but it had always happened to someone else, somewhere else, at least a thousand times before.

As for us trainees we tried to be everywhere when key decisions were made, announcing the events that were coming up over the next few weeks, attending exhibitions and picking out their key features, interviewing uninteresting people who had been given "gongs" and trying to find something interesting to say about them. You became an instant expert in everything. You were on first name terms with the council leaders: you had meetings held up until you got there. And so you became a part of the city, a small but key cog in its vast and complex mechanism, a faceless recorder of its inner workings.

The work, by its very nature, was never calm which is another reason why most reporters drank so much. You were always worrying, usually about missing something which someone else had picked up. Then, when you felt you didn't really want to be doing this work any more, the phone would ring, there would be a voice telling you something that had been a long-held secret and there was that familiar quickening of the blood and twinkle in your bollocks which told you that a good story was surfacing which would get you a by-line.

As part of the Thomson training scheme I was finally transferred to the features department – not to write features but leaders. This was disappointing since not only did I never read leaders but research had found that most of our readers didn't either. Leaders – or editorial comment as they are perhaps better known – offered the long-considered Aristotelian view of the newspaper on the great issues of the day. It was expected these views would fall within Tory parameters: we were on the side of the monarchy, inherited wealth, law and order and a bit puzzled by the Common Market, while we were against council waste, dog mess and litter in the streets and Welsh language activists who were tearing up English road signs.

Pages of news were devoted to their activities and whole leaders to their denunciation. All this, of course, did them a great service by giving them such attention and publicity. Like the Irish Republican Army, they well knew that misbehaviour is the key to publicity and the greater the misbehaviour, the greater the publicity. When a few of them started burning down homes we went into overdrive and, had they used bombs to press their point, the whole of Wales might be Welsh-speaking and have its own full parliament today.

As leader writers we met at the morning conference when the department heads reviewed their running list of stories so far. Leaders were always pegged to the news and we duly presented our latest view on the American presence in Vietnam or why it was now time to build our own national theatre or crack down hard on the "thoughtless few" who dropped litter in our streets.

I would spend the rest of the day researching my subject – looking up cuttings from the library, making phone calls to experts, reading reference books – before coming up with six hundred words which I would type up and put before the editor. He would read it through first, before staring at you with his coal-black eyes, pushing the tip of his tongue against the side of his cheek and, without making any comment, reaching for his fountain pen and interfering with almost every line, phrase and comma while I sat there looking at my hands wondering why I hadn't taken that teaching post in Africa.

My main ambition during the six months I wrote leaders was to write one so bland and inoffensive he wouldn't alter it, but I never came close. After agonising over my every word, he would have another look and start changing it all over again. One of the main features of the perfect *Western Mail* leader was that it didn't upset anyone. The editor hated receiving letters of complaint and, if I did compose a few lines of fiery opinion that managed to call a spade a spade, his fountain pen always got them before they got into print.

Thus I might be charged to write about the strike at the steelworks in Llanwern which, unusually, I knew something about since my father worked there. Some of the men had struck over the lack of showers and so, in the way of such matters, the management had dug in and the strike was spreading. I would begin my leader by deploring this strike and pointing out that no good could come out of it for anyone. This initial position could not upset anyone, so I moved smoothly on to consider who might be to blame.

The truth was that there were several unruly unions in the plant busily competing for control. The management had failed to manage these unions and were scared of them. The workforce, long disillusioned by the way the place was run, had given up putting in a day's work for a day's pay in favour of sitting in the local pub. Some days, my father rode his bicycle home sideways and had difficulty getting in through the front door, particularly if he'd been on the two-to-ten shift.

I could hardly put that in a leader in the *Western Mail*, especially as it was true, so I would write that the men's demands for proper showers was not the cause of the strike but a symptom of a long-standing malaise in the works which had built up over the years and had its roots in the politics of Welsh steel and an under-performing, erratic market. Fine. Nothing controversial there and we certainly didn't want any of those Commie bastards outside Thomson House picketing us.

Then I would consider the character of the management, a bunch of useless, out-of-touch jerks who barely knew their dicks from their elbows and had messed up the

181

plant because they had become afraid of upsetting the unions when the orders were coming in and were now too afraid to deal with them when they weren't.

It wasn't possible to say any of that, of course – we're talking about the *management* for God's sake – so I continued by blaming both sides for the breakdown in communication. The unions should come together as one union to represent all the men in the plant, I wrote – some hope! – while the management should call for a public inquiry into the issues involved. This was a standard cliché for a leader: when in doubt call for a public inquiry.

That's how we wrote the typical *Western Mail* leader. A bland rumination on barely understood events: non-thoughts put together by ill-informed minds and coming up with nothing. I could just see my father and his mates falling over one another with laughter in the pub when he read out what his son had been writing in the *Western Mail*. Not that I ever owned up to what I was writing. "Leaders are just some crap written by idiots," I told him. "Nothing to do with me at all."

When I finished my stint as a leader writer I was moved to the sub-editors' desk where the news pages were planned and we wrestled the stories into their allotted spaces complete with a headline of a specified size. This activity, which began at six in the evening and went on until two in the morning, had an interesting precision: the continual process of condensing made every word work for a living and there was a sloppiness about a lot of the material which came in from our stringers throughout Wales and even the foreign news agencies.

You were forced to become ruthless, slashing two-thousand-word foreign agency features down to fill a three-inch single news column, digging out the important news point and writing it in bare, skeletal prose.

It was often hard finding any news at all in some of the pieces, particularly with a story by Goronwy Powell, our somewhat elderly stringer in North Wales, who would set off on what could only be described as a Joycean stream of consciousness for five or six pages. You had to work hard on such ramblings to find a few vaguely readable paragraphs. Most of his stuff should have been thrown away but we had to carry *something* from North Wales, if only to justify using the title of the National Newspaper of Wales. Most Welsh news came from the South because, mundanely enough, that was where we were based.

News was divided into different areas of Wales and the local page was changed constantly throughout the evening with a lot of trash included if only because it had the name of a certain place in it. But you didn't have time to work on them for long: if a story was hopeless when it was first written you could rarely turn it into a good one. You could often improve it by making it presentable and intelligible although, more often than not – as most reporters would testify – you would mess around with it so much you would take out whatever worth it had in the first place. There can't have been one district reporter who believed we improved his copy while Goronwy Powell was convinced that we destroyed everything he wrote. I did feel sorry for him insofar as he had now so completely lost his confidence he barely made any effort, just spewed out everything he could think of on the subject and let us sub-editors do our dastardly worst.

I enjoyed sub-editing: it had none of the neuroticism of news gathering, you could only deal with what was in front of you and I liked working with Walter Greenman, in charge of the local page. As a former proof-reader he was a nit-picker par excellence and knew everything about accuracy and grammar, flinging my copy back to me again and again if I'd missed something like a semi-colon in the flower-show results. There was a style for the flower-show results and it had to be followed meticulously. You tighten up working under such constraints. Similarly the chief sub, Brian Radford, would also fling your headlines back at you again and again, always insisting they had a good zip.

For about four hours the whole desk hummed with calm concentration until the first edition for North Wales was printed at ten o'clock, when we had a chance to take a good look at it before the next run went out, to West Wales. Mostly we fine-tuned it and kept changing the local page after that, but there was the occasional late big, breaking story as when the Russians invaded Czechoslovakia at about two o'clock in the morning and only Brian Radford and I were there, playing table tennis in the canteen.

Such late-breaking stories were meat and drink to the *Western Mail* since they gave us the drop over Fleet Street which, for reasons of geography and deadlines, couldn't get anything to Wales unless it happened before ten o'clock at night. Brian broke up the front page – RUSSIANS INVADE CZECHS – and, with copy streaming in over the wires from the Press Association and Reuters, I put together the lead. We were like little boys running up and down the stairs to the stone where the stories were typed out in hot metal on big, clanking linotype machines before being hammered down into a page frame. Then an impression was taken on a special mould to be put on one of the cylinders of the giant printing presses.

When the head printer shouted that our time was up, that there couldn't possibly be any more corrections, Brian and I waved to him to calm down and give us another minute or two as we hovered over the galley proofs, chopping a sentence here and crossing out a paragraph there until, with no more time for anything, we managed to get one final revision underneath a photograph of a Russian tank. The presses began to roll with the pure white newsprint feeding in through an elaborate series of revolving drums until, folded and re-folded, it finally came out as a line of clean, printed newspapers on a conveyor belt below.

Brian and I stood at the window looking down on these presses printing our work. You couldn't help being choked up on such occasions. This was a job with instant gratification. You worked on the news one minute and the next it was dropping through letterboxes all over Wales, telling everyone what those Russian bastards had got up to. We had become a small part of a world-wide web of communication, telling the world what was going on in it even if, unfortunately, it was yet another story of violence. Only violence on such a massive scale would have got us tearing up our front page like that and so late. I still had much to think about.

With so much of my day now free before starting work at six at night, I was able to get down to my own work, giving the best of my creative energy to myself and going in to give whatever was left to the *Western Mail*. There had to be a novel in me somewhere.

Perhaps predictably, in the light of my recent experience with Voluntary Service Overseas, I began working on a novel, *Squaredance*, in which four characters struggle with one another looking for meaning in the Malayan jungle. It all eventually goes wrong when three of the characters are revealed to be the creation of the fourth. There were flashes and visions.

I was now twenty-seven but all my thoughts kept coming back to my Malayan visions. All my mental roads kept leading straight to them and I couldn't see how I could ever get away from them: how to understand them, to unravel their meaning and, somehow, try and tell the world what it was that I believe I had been told. As it is, I have never got away from them. All my books grew out of my visions and I have never tackled another theme. This theme was big enough for any one writer: I had been given the message and the onus was on me to deliver it.

So, as my manuscript grew in the afternoons, I tried to enjoy my fledgling family and neighbours in our small, suburban close, floundering hopefully in an untidy geometry of half-dug gardens, nappies and worrying bills.

Julian arrived on September 13, 1967 and I became one of the first fathers in South Wales to be present at the birth. "See you again next year," said the doctor who delivered him. "No chance," Liz replied. "I'm not going through that again." But twelve months later, Steffan arrived.

None of us seemed to have quite enough money – babies are ruinously expensive – although, of course, we managed to scrape along, doing whatever was necessary to get by. Everyone always manages to scrape along with what they've got, no matter how small: that's life. On Saturday nights most of us went to the local pub where we talked about black-fly in the beans or how the car wouldn't start in the rain before getting a takeaway curry which we ate on our laps with a few more beers watching *Match of the Day* on television.

TWENTY FOUR

After nearly three years on the *Western Mail* it was time to move and I wrote to the *Sunday Times*, the *Guardian* and the *Daily Express* in London asking for a job and enclosing six of my best cuttings. I had an immediate bite from the *Daily Express* and went up with Liz to their huge Art Deco offices – the black Lubianka – in Fleet Street where I was interviewed by the managing editor, Eric Price, in what may have been the shortest interview ever.

"Get this man's first class expenses with meals and train fares from Cardiff ready for when he comes out," he told his secretary on his intercom before looking up at me and asking when would I like to start.

"As soon as you want but I'll have to give the *Western Mail* some notice," I replied, a bit taken aback.

"Right. Well write and tell me when you can start and you can start."

He gave me a brief wave of his hand, indicating the interview was over, before returning to what he had been reading.

"Don't you want to ask me anything?"

"Nah," he said without looking up. "I like to see if someone's got two arms and a head, but that's all."

End of interview. Clutching a bundle of new fivers, which the secretary had put in my hand when I walked out of his office (and which was way beyond what I had spent), I went downstairs to tell Liz I was now working in Fleet Street and off we went, courtesy of a pair of tickets we had won in a raffle, to see Rod Laver demolish John Newcombe in the Wimbledon final.

That was the way of Fleet Street. Everything seemed to work on gut instinct although having some good cuttings probably helped your cause a bit.

Several days later I had a letter from Harold Evans, the legendary editor of the *Sunday Times*, asking me to go and see him. A small man with sharp, bird-like movements and mischievous blue eyes, he also asked me only a few questions before hiring me. Frank Giles, his deputy, was called in to approve and Harry asked me what were my politics.

"Oh, vaguely left of centre," I said, not wanting to give the impression of being any sort of fanatic.

"Ah, another f..king Commie on the *Sunday Times*," Harry beamed brightly.

I was hired as a reporter-sub, a new concept that Harry was trying out. I would work as a reporter for three or four days in the newsroom and then a double shift as a sub-editor on Saturdays. They had been hiring sub-editors just for the Saturday from periodicals like *Butterfly Weekly* and Harry had decided it would be better if they had their own sub-editors who knew what the *Sunday Times* was trying to do.

Harry took me to meet Mike Randall, the managing editor (news) and former editor of the *Daily Mail*, who began raving about the cuttings I'd sent in with my application. This sort of praise was a new language to me. I had almost never heard it on the *Western Mail* but it turned out to be one of the major differences between the cultures of a national and provincial newspaper. If you wrote a good piece on a national, everyone queued up at your desk to tell you so. This had never happened on the *Western Mail*, perhaps because they were worried you might ask for a rise or something equally loathsome. On a provincial paper you were expected to do your job. This was what you were paid for.

I was introduced to some of the reporters in the newsroom. It was extraordinary. I had come up in the lift at their Gray's Inn Road offices wondering if I'd get the job and, within an hour, was being treated like an established member of staff. They all seemed so confident and secure, as befitted those who worked on a great newspaper, and I was totally in awe of Hunter Davies who walked past having just made a pile from his biography of the Beatles.

Before leaving the building I got off at the third floor, where the *Guardian* was based, and called in to see John Cole, the news editor. After about five minutes he came out holding my letter of application and still in the process of reading my cuttings which, he said, in his thick Belfast accent, he found attractive. I explained I thought I'd got a job on the *Sunday Times* but I'd just popped in to say hello as I was in the building. Without further ado he said that, if it didn't work out with the *Sunday Times*, he could certainly give me a job on the *Guardian* and I should stay in touch.

These men were a new breed to me, all so confident in their judgements which were based on the quick reading of a few cuttings. There was no question of interview after interview by committee after committee. There was no suggestion of a trial run or even a probation period. If you could do it you were in.

I started work at the *Sunday Times* on Tuesday, January 1, 1970, sitting on my own in the newsroom at ten o'clock, the only reporter to turn up on time. Michael Hamlyn, the news editor, gave me a pile of newspapers to read and I continued to sit there until the others drifted in around mid-day, suffering from hangovers after Ron Hall's traditional New Year's Eve party. Some muttered evilly through their hangovers as they filled in pink slips – with which, amazingly, you could draw a cash advance on *future* expenses – and then organised a long lunch where they could pick over what had happened at the party while the hangovers were lifted slightly by a lot more of what had produced them in the first place.

This was the pattern of most Tuesdays and a group of us went to Anemos, a Greek restaurant in Charlotte Street, where we took the next table to Michael Parkinson, our football columnist who was surrounded by ten rather lovely women and smiling his face off. His smile was the sweetest, the most beatific and permanent smile I had ever seen and I decided there and then that this was the life for me.

Our Tuesday lunch group included one of the most raucous women I have ever come across, the flame-haired Anne Robinson, who would, in time, become our national Queen of Mean as a television quiz hostess. Anne was later to say of that drunken period in her life, which climaxed in her hiding bottles of vodka in the cistern of the newsroom lavatory and once having to be hauled off unconscious to hospital to have her stomach pumped, that it was down to us lot but, as I remember it, she never needed any encouragement from us to put down another drink.

Fleet Street girls were more laddish than the boys; always going on about how they could out-write and out-drink us. Fleet Street girls never flinched when it was their round and Anne, purse in hand, all but fought her way to the bar to get in hers.

Apart from Anne, the reporters were a gentle, amusing lot and those long Tuesday lunches were like great dinner parties with stimulating chatter. If you told them a good story they always responded with a better one. They had met the most famous people in the land (at least twice) and were almost certainly on Christian name terms with them. The more famous they were, the ruder the chatter about them.

Peter Pringle casually remarked that George Harrison was the only Beatle who had any interest in the financial affairs of the group and liked to ring him about it from time to time. I had once caught a brief, somewhat begrudged, interview with Mick Jagger on the stairs of the Capitol cinema in Cardiff after a Rolling Stones concert but it had never crossed my mind that Mick might ever pick up the phone and discuss his money problems with me. And he didn't.

We would stagger back to the office at around five o'clock, when a few might make some desultory calls before going home after a hard day in the restaurant, hoping to start from scratch the following morning.

On Wednesday mornings the newsroom began moving at a slightly more determined pace with a news conference, chaired by the news editor, which decided on the early running list of news stories and who was going to be sent where on what.

Our travel arrangements were organised by Ruth, the news desk secretary, who booked our taxis, trains or flights (all first class), always insisted on the best room in the hotel and gave us a nice big wodge of cash, courtesy of those pink slips. There seemed to be no stinting on expense. Whatever you felt you needed, you got. We couldn't have been in a more different world to that of the *Western Mail.* .

By Wednesday afternoon much of the newsroom had cleared off to distant parts of the land. For my first story I was asked to investigate a train pile-up on the London to Brighton line where, yet again, Southern Region had managed to make the black life of Sussex commuters considerably blacker by jamming them all together in about a dozen trains in an iced-up tunnel and on the track behind. Mike Randall was keen on this story since he used the same line to commute to work. When news executives were affected in this way it usually meant the story would get a good show. It was their way of getting revenge against whoever had been upsetting them.

This snarl-up didn't seem that much of a story at first but, in the way of such things, it got more interesting the more I got into it and indeed turned out to be one of the liveliest stories I had yet written.

I was up early the next morning in my Brighton hotel to get to the station and work my way through the passengers who had got stuck in that Wednesday morning pile-up. When I'd got through them, I got off wherever and waited for the next train-load to pick up what they had to say. One of the things I noticed was the way my interviewees came to immediate attention when I said I was with the *Sunday Times*. The name opened every conceivable door in the way no newspaper had done before – or has since – and they happily told me about their nightmare morning the day before.

The gist of what had happened was that it took most of the four thousand passengers on the Brighton line some five hours to get to their offices in the City while many of them called it a day about half way through the ride, either getting off the train or getting drunk or both. Singing had started in the restaurant car and it was like the Blitz all over again. Men who had been sitting silently for years began talking to one another.

"I was in the buffet car when it ran out of food, coffee and cigarettes," said one. "Two of the passengers went straight on to the hard stuff and soon a big party was under way."

At Haywards Heath station railwaymen's eyebrows had disappeared into their hairlines in amazement when they saw a procession of freezing commuters – some in bowlers and others in mini-skirts – trooping down the track. The order went out to cut the 650-volt power in case someone decided to step on the conductor rail and end their misery on the spot. By 10.30am, with the power off, there was no heat or light in the trains. There was no coffee to be had anywhere and not even a bit of toast to munch. The City gents who had taken off their coats in the sweltering heat of the crowded carriages put them back on again.

In the square outside the station of the normally sedate town of Haywards Heath there had been a carnival atmosphere. Many of the commuters had already given themselves a day off and were filling up the bars. In one pub the regulars turned up to find that all their normal places had been taken. Fifty-yard queues formed outside the public telephone kiosks. The small taxi office was jammed with people clamouring for cabs. There wasn't one available for five hours and the receptionist couldn't even find time to make a cup of tea. A notice said, "If you can keep your head in all this confusion you don't understand the situation."

By one o'clock the railway communications had not improved. It was more than six hours since the first train stopped, but passengers stuck in Prestbury Park, the first stop out of Brighton, still didn't know what was happening. British Rail did finally communicate with the evening newspapers and blamed the yo-yo weather.

By Thursday there was a definite sense of imminent production on the fifth floor with the art department working out designs for the early feature pages.

All along the corridors the reporters for Insight or Spectrum would gather in small, secretive huddles, hatching something which should stay secret for some time yet or else trying to think of another department where they could dump a piece they didn't want on their pages. Secretive decisions in the corridors were part of the culture of the paper, largely because they didn't want to upset anyone's feelings.

You would never catch anyone telling the writer that his story was total crap as you might on a tabloid. Here they would put their arms around you and insist it was a wonderful piece but, with pressure of space and unexpected advertisement drops on their pages, they were hopeful they could find a home for it somewhere else. "But it *is* a terrific piece."

You could eavesdrop on such discussions in the corridors but they were rarely decisive. Several people might review their options, balancing the strength of one story against another, say, or wonder whether the writer was completely reliable or did he have enough evidence and then slope back the way they had come with everything still more or less up in the air.

In the newsroom odd questions might be asked loudly. "What's the house style for Biro?" Or someone would start cursing because the new copy of *Burke's Peerage* had gone missing yet again or the office lawyer would be back with the news editor telling him that we'd got three more writs that morning. Harry Evans welcomed writs, describing them as people's protection against lazy journalism, and I couldn't help thinking of John Giddings of the *Western Mail* who lived in permanent fear of receiving *one*.

Harry was a whirling dervish who ran everywhere in the office only ever stopping for an occasional pee so, when he ran into the newsroom lavatory, others would run in after him, knowing that he would have to stand still long enough to answer a question or two. He had his nose in almost every area of the paper: you might be sitting at your desk tapping away at a typewriter and, next thing, you would notice him at your shoulder and before you could get to the next paragraph he would have elbowed you out of your seat and started typing the story himself, saying, "It should start like this. And *then* you can get into that."

He would often ask you where you'd bought your jacket or suit before running off to redesign a page, rework a headline and run back to his office pursued by more executives anxious to share his thinking on some issue or other.

By Friday morning the news editor would have reviewed his news list for the tenth time that week, constantly changing the running order while the reporters began drifting back to fine-tune and type up their stories which they had been working on in different parts of the country. We were given plenty of time to write our stories and the brief was to go into them in some depth. The daily newspapers reported what had happened and on the Sundays we were expected to explain why.

Friday was the day of the most intense activity since the bulk of the inside pages had to be finished and sheets of paper being ripped out of typewriters and crumpled into rejected balls. You had the impression of a host of creative, intelligent people all furiously pouring their creative, intelligent energies into that one strange and improbable process of producing a newspaper.

I spent most of the morning trying to track down the press officer of Southern Region, who had promised to tell me the exact logistics of how they had managed their most recent pile-up, and his account turned out to be revealing. They had thirteen de-icing trains standing by every night, he said, but, unfortunately, they hadn't sent one through the tunnel before the night in question.

When one got stuck in the tunnel, they sent in another train, full of commuters, to push out the first. This can sometimes work, but not with an inch of ice on the track. Soon there were two trains stuck. Communications had also become frozen so that, eventually, there were eleven trains stuck on the line all the way back to Brighton. The trouble was there had been a sudden thaw followed by a sudden freeze. But let's remember that all trains travelled trouble-free in adjacent areas.

So could it be, I wondered, that, somehow, the weather had been particularly bad between Balcombe Tunnel and Haywards Heath. "Yes," said the press officer, "yes it could."

With my new "facts" from British Rail and the quotes from the commuters I could pretty much reconstruct the events of that frozen morning, spinning it out breezily from the first breakdown in the tunnel to its final resolution when British Rail told the evening newspapers that it was all down to the weather.

You should never put your story in too quickly on Fridays, I had been warned, or you might get given another, so I wrote and rewrote it, even ringing back British Rail and checking their own quotes back with them. Many journalists frown on this practice, but I didn't; once you had read back what they were supposed to be saying they never had any opportunity for a comeback in a way they might have thought of after reading it in bed on Sunday morning or after an angry boss had rung them.

"But I checked it all back with you," was always a golden get-out when anyone complained about what you had written. "You had a clear chance to correct any mistakes or misquotes."

Also in newspapers, as in life, first impressions are everything and if you get branded as sloppy or inaccurate from the beginning, it is difficult to recover. Harry Evans was particularly guilty in this regard: if he once spotted you wrote too much or had bad grammar or were fast and loose with the facts that was a cross you carried in his mind for ever. Once he had made a judgement on someone he would never change it, no matter how hard you worked to remedy whatever it was that had annoyed him in the first place. Even years later Harry would say of some reporter that he always wrote too much when he might have done so only *once*.

My own story went down well with the news desk and they commissioned a cartoon by Heath to accompany it and, with the news editor's praise for it still ringing in my ears, we all went over the road to the Blue Lion pub where, yet again, we all got soundly drunk as we discussed what we had been up to that week. We reporters kept a close eye on what our colleagues were up to: there was a real rivalry even though it was all friendly enough.

Early on Saturday morning, with our reporting duties finished, we reporter subs drifted in to drink coffee and wait for the deluge of copy which began at around 9.15am. We hardly stopped all morning, first a few foreign stories, later the page leads for the home pages.

Despite all his years in top-level journalism, Mike Randall said, he always got excited at this moment, tasting stories, designing pages and discussing what photographs might go where with his chief sub, Don Berry. Mike wrote brilliant headlines that were short, mad poems in their own right.

People I hadn't seen before, George Gardiner for example, later to become Tory

MP for Reigate and a cabinet minister, came in to sub and re-write the political lead, while a tall man with dark, hooded eyes hung around the picture desk for most of Saturday morning. He turned out to be the cartoonist Gerald Scarfe, always quiet, shy and nattily dressed and very much at odds with the savagery and biting contempt of his cartoons. He would stare around unceasingly and I can't remember him saying a word to anyone about anything. Even when he was hanging out with the photographers in the pub he just sat there and got up to leave when they did.

The pages were designed by another dandy, Robert Harling, who had been a mate of Ian Fleming and, it was alleged, ironed his money before putting it in his pocket so that it wouldn't spoil the careful line of his tight, drainpipe trousers.

The subs' desk gave you a real insight into the quality of the reporters' writing since you saw the copy as it had been written. There were some surprising revelations. I had to tackle a piece by Hunter Davies on the bust-up of the Beatles. It rambled around the houses and took ages to bash into shape. A few other reporters took you on a long road to anywhere but the point, often meaning they had to be re-written from beginning to end. You wondered how some of them had got there in the first place when there had to be any number of real reporters who were desperate to work for the *Sunday Times*.

Perhaps the problem was that Harry hired people too quickly, a situation which was made worse by the fact that he had never, he boasted, fired anyone. Once you were in you were in and hardly anyone ever left. Eric Jacobs, our labour correspondent, once said to me, with his usual tinny laugh: "The *Sunday Times* is a fat milk cow on which you can live almost for ever while doing almost nothing at all."

Despite all these strange and often famous characters wandering in and out and even with the comments, enigmatic judgements and often incomprehensible newspeak of the subs' desk, you noticed that page after page was being cleared away efficiently; that beneath all this humming frenzy, the tight deadlines demanded by the print room were being met.

Sometimes John Barry, the editor of Insight, would throw the system by dropping a big story on us just before Saturday lunchtime but, because they had dealt with such problems a hundred times before, the front bench would quickly redesign a page with a story spiked here or a photograph reduced there and, within a minute, it was as if we'd had the new Insight story all week. Reporters constantly circled the front bench like watchful sharks until they spotted where their story had been placed.

The subs had a reverence for the work of Insight, the six-strong team which had so clearly defined the role of the newspaper with its investigations into scandals such as the way the mighty Distillers organisation had marketed thalidomide to mothers as a cure for morning sickness and had caused hundreds of deformed babies. The main problem with their work was that they always left it so late the lawyer didn't get a proper look at it and, as we marked it up for the printer, we might have a lawyer reading over our shoulder and sighing unhappily. The lawyers' brief was to watch out for libel but lawyers were always seen as the enemy by Insight, a law unto themselves.

Around two o'clock on Saturday afternoon everyone relaxed: the form and content of the first edition had been committed. A few drifted over to the pub for a sandwich and a pint but then we would fine-tune the pages either by tearing them up, redesigning them or making room for late-breaking stories. But such stories were rare since most journalists had probably gone away for the weekend and, as I had noted on the *Western Mail*, news seemed to happen only when journalists were around to fasten on to it. When journalists packed their bags, so did most of the news.

I couldn't have been more pleased on my first Saturday there since, when the first edition arrived, my Brighton line story was a back-page lead over five columns with the headline: *The Train now Standing in the Tunnel of Hate* with the cartoon showing a train packed with commuters, some of whom were half-pissed and climbing down on to the line to stagger back home. And I'd got a bold 14-point by-line too. All stories carried our own names on the *Sunday Times*; this was another Harry Evans' innovation since he believed we would take more care with our work if our names were on it.

I came to believe this practice made us more self-serving. We reporters always wanted to see our name in lights and never worked well as a team. One of the great strengths of Insight was the team's anonymity.

At nine on Saturday night Harry would invariably take a call from our proprietor, Lord Thomson, about the paper or, more specifically, about the size of the ads. Harry would often try to mention a particularly strong story or feature we were running but Lord T was never interested in editorial and simply wanted to know about the advertisements and how they fell on what pages. Lord T's concerns were only ever budgetary and his only toy a slide-rule. Yet this was a blessing to us since, as long as the paper made money, he never interfered.

By eleven o'clock those of us who were left repaired to the local Greek restaurant where we would consume houmous, kebab and copious quantities of red wine led by Mike Randall, who seemed able to drink gallons of the stuff without it affecting him in any way. Hardly had a couple of inches disappeared from the neck of a bottle before he had his finger corkscrewing in the air calling the waiter to bring another.

No one ever had a bad word about Mike, a man who didn't have a mean-minded fibre in his body and was constantly generous in his judgements and praise. If you'd done a good job on a story he always told you so – sometimes went out of his way to search for you to do this – and those few words of encouragement meant a lot to us.

Later, well-fed and well-drunk, we returned to the office to ring for cabs which, on the *Sunday Times* account, took us home. The newsroom would be deserted, with encrusted polystyrene coffee cups standing around silent typewriters. Here and there were huge spikes with paper impaled on them, the fatal casualties of stories and press releases destined never to see breaking daylight.

I caught a cab to Paddington where, clutching my *Sunday Times* to my chest, I dozed on the milk train to Cardiff, waking up now and then to re-read my Brighton line story which I was anxious to show Liz. I had made it at last: I was a true man of ink.

I had to catch that milk train on Saturday nights for almost four months: it took that long to sell our small semi-detached house in Cardiff. It was still quite new, we were only asking £4,600 for it having paid £4,250 three years earlier, and we had sorted out the garden and decorated it. House prices never went anywhere in those days – if you could make a couple of hundred, you were doing well.

Liz had been up to London a few times looking for our next house but we couldn't afford anywhere in such as Islington, Canonbury or Camden, where we wanted to be, and were forced to cast our net further north in Muswell Hill or Hornsey. During the week, I shared a flat in Belsize Park with Peter Pringle whose marriage had collapsed after barely a few months. I have never quite worked out what it is about journalism and marriage, but they're oil and water.

But Liz and I were anxious to be together again so, every time I came home at the weekend, I instructed another Cardiff estate agent. Our front lawn soon had a small forest of For Sale signs that attracted little interest and no offers. On the seventh weekend, out of desperation as much as anything else, I did something which was going to have profound and far-reaching repercussions for us. This ploy would provide us with small fortunes, which we often frittered uselessly on mad adventures, but which also meant we had lots of fun and lived in grand houses. I composed my own advertisement which I phoned into the *Western Mail* and the *South Wales Echo*.

A wonderful modern house in romantic Rhiwbina goes up for sale this weekend. This house, which has the eye of the sun, comes with a Welsh-speaking milkman and a real-live football manager who lives next door but one. It has masses of roses in the garden and is an unbelievable bargain at £4,600. The first genuine offer secures.

The morning the ad first appeared was like open day at Longleat with around twenty cars screaming into our close, including a new Jaguar, all to admire the half dozen or so spindly roses crawling with greenfly in my postage-stamp front lawn and anxious to learn the identity of the football manager (Bobby Ferguson at Newport). Almost everyone said they liked the phrase, "the eye of the sun", and, as it turned out, the sale went to the first young couple who turned up and called back almost every day for the next four weeks to make sure we hadn't sold the house to anyone else.

This ploy was inspired by the famous Roy Brooks ads in London at the time, in which he would go on about a thirty-foot crack in the gable wall or the huge bulge in the roof, but the most interesting thing about my ad was that it had almost nothing to do with the reality of what I was trying to sell, without telling lies. It didn't even mention that the house had three bedrooms or give any of those meaningless measurements of the living room or the colour of the bathroom that are so beloved of estate agents.

What I'd done was to describe someone's dream while trying to make it appear the bargain of a lifetime. I was to try this trick time and time again in the future with marvellous and enriching results. I even sold houses for vast profits during slumps in the property market, and all because I offered an attractive idea that masqueraded as a great bargain. I don't think one of my prospective purchasers ever pointed out that my ads weren't exactly true. They read my little prose poems in the paper, they wanted my house and they rolled up by the hundred.

Had I not been stupid enough to want to become a writer, making almost no money from one year to the next, I reckon I could have made a fortune as an estate agent. I made only a tiny profit on that first house but I had at least sold it when nothing was selling and now we were on our way to a large terraced house in Muswell Hill for which we had forked out the colossal sum of £7,600. I was already thinking up ads to sell the place the day we moved in.

Muswell Hill, with its wide, leafy avenues and sudden, surprising views over the crouching rooftops of North London, was an undistinguished suburb with lots of odd, displaced neighbours who didn't particularly want to be there either. Most of us were young professionals with small families who had come to work in the capital and this was about as close to the action as we could afford. Muswell Hill had crap pubs, no tube station and it was almost impossible to coax a cabbie to take you home late at night because they usually couldn't pick up a fare back into town again.

Our two were soon in a play-school – where Liz picked up a part-time job – and I settled down into my reporting duties which, in those days, were generally serious and socially hard-edged: chasing Iraqi diplomats who claimed diplomatic immunity after crashing into other drivers' cars, exposing hazards in chemical factories, explaining how "super-rats" were breaking out of a poison ring in mid-Wales, and causing a most satisfactory fuss in Guernsey when I revealed how the government there was kicking out the English poor.

I also exposed a new scam in the property market when I investigated the plausible, highly-paid "winklers" hired by property companies and landlords to persuade families to leave their rent-controlled tenancies so that the houses could be sold on at a huge profit. At least a dozen "winklers" were operating in Islington and Camden alone.

I ran up against astonishing varieties of human greed: I got a tip that young Irish potato-pickers were being virtually imprisoned in filthy bothies in Scotland and beaten up if they attempted to escape. I hired several Scottish freelancers and we pieced together the story of the five Nevin brothers from County Mayo who had recruited about five hundred youngsters in the depressed west of Ireland to work in the potato fields of Ayrshire and Lothian. They had been told to expect lots of women and free drink, but what they got was backbreaking work, seventeen hours a day, seven days a week for a pittance paid irregularly. The few who tried to escape were tracked down and beaten before a couple of sympathetic Catholic priests set up escape routes for them. As soon as they heard of our inquiries, all five brothers disappeared leaving the Irish lads to get home by whatever means they could.

Harry Evans unfailingly encouraged us to name the guilty men so we could always tackle our stories without having to worry about letters of complaint or the possibility of writs. We were frequently threatened by someone or other but the office lawyer would sit down with us and compose a stiff, unambiguous letter asserting that the complaint was baseless and the complainant should therefore push off – or words to that effect. This often shut them up – issuing writs was very expensive and we *were* careful who we picked on.

The paper was booming at that time, making a lot of money for Lord Thomson and developing a new line in "adventure journalism" particularly after the circulation-boosting success of Sir Francis Chichester's solo yacht voyage around the world, for which we had bought the rights.

I was asked to follow a climbing team tackling the as-yet-unconquered south face of Annapurna and would get telephone calls on a crackling line from Chris Bonington who was either bogged down in a blizzard or worried about an imminent monsoon.

"Shout a bit louder, Chris," I would shout back at him. "I can't hear a bloody word."

For a year or so I had been doing well, getting big and regular hits in the paper and enjoying all this colourful company whether it was Murray Sayle in the Blue Lion describing the bombs exploding all around him as he flew in a chopper into Khe Sanh or Ron Hall talking about the book he was writing with Nicholas Tomalin about the strange voyage of Donald Crowhurst which ended up with Crowhurst's mind disintegrating and him jumping off the end of his boat and drowning.

Almost everyone was either writing or thinking about writing a book. David Blundy and I had approached the agent, Elaine Greene, to see if she could get us a publishing deal to write about communes, a fashionable lifestyle at the time. Harry liked us to write books but exploded one day when he discovered almost all his reporters were absent working on books, and there was almost no one filling up the paper. A ban on book writing was put in place, but quickly forgotten.

Those early months in Muswell Hill were the sunniest ever. As a family we never had much spare money, but we did acquire an old Hillman Minx for £20 which took us around London on Sundays, introducing the boys to the zoo, the Natural History Museum and, their favourite, the Imperial War Museum. They loved everything to do with bombs and bullets. We were all Londoners now, running amok in old London town.

Liz and I threw lots of parties which became well-known for huge quantities of drink, dope and loud music. One night we all danced in a line around the living room for a couple of hours waving joints the size of cucumbers to repeated renditions of McGuinness Flint's *When I'm Dead and Gone* or the other favourite of the time, James Taylor's *Fire and Rain*.

My old university friend Neil Kinnock, future leader of the Labour party but then an MP, turned up to one which ended with him doing a soft shoe shuffle on the pavement for half the newsroom. He was always good with the Press although (lawyers please note!) he never did dance around in our living room in a long line with a joint in his hand singing James Taylor's *Fire and Rain*.

Yet as we reporters scoured the world looking for melodramas our own lives were becoming enmeshed by the smaller but no less potent dramas of painful marital breakdowns. There seemed to be some sort of virulent anti-marital virus roaming around Gray's Inn Road and there were times when the whole office seemed to be infected.

The deputy news editor, Adam Hopkins, spent most of his day racked with visible grief and guilt over his passion for one of the reporters, Wendy Holden. Nick Lloyd had been furtively seeing his future wife, Eve Pollard, for years. Anne Robinson was having an open affair with John Fielding, a reporter with Insight and you never knew where David Blundy was going to lay his tall, angular body down at night. I often had to follow a long trail of telephone numbers if I wanted to talk to him about our projected book on communes which didn't, in fact, work out. David had women everywhere and, just when he looked to have settled with one, another bobbed up. In spite of all this activity I don't think he ever enjoyed a truly happy day although, oddly, he retained a terrific relationship with his wife, Ruth, whom he rang every day, usually to complain about how his women were treating him. "This new one has got the body of a young boy but the brain of a frog," he might tell her and she would listen and burble with sympathy like a loving and indulgent mother.

"You should have never left Ruth," I kept telling David when yet another relationship ended in blood and tears and he always mournfully agreed.

Even our leader, Harry, was soon bogged down in a long affair with Tina Brown that would cause him years of depression and guilt until he finally left his wife for her. Mike Randall had got through six marriages and his ex-wives would still ring him up and give him grief.

Apart from the widespread liberal ideas of the early Seventies I suspected then – and now I know – that alcohol, aided and abetted by the weed, was responsible for much of this scalding promiscuity. Alcohol was the engine on which journalism was run: you could only ever find out anything interesting in a pub after you had developed a relationship with your interviewee by loosening him up with a few drinks. Most key editorial decisions took place in the pub or over a long, alcoholic lunch and, with our better judgements suspended, if not pickled, in alcohol, it was always from a pub that we took off with whomever to some distant flat, invariably on the top floor of some huge house in Earl's Court, rather than going home where we belonged.

The two most successful journalists I knew, Hunter Davies and Philip Norman, who were churning out a book every six months or so *and* writing regularly for the paper, didn't drink at all. I couldn't imagine how I could become like them and sober up, didn't know how I might manage even a day off it, let alone give it up for good. Even after serious, drink-related illnesses I still kept drinking doggedly like all the others, still kept seeing drink as a friend when it was a clear enemy, still kept believing drink was making me feel better, which it did for a few hours, before making me feel worse.

Apart from industrial quantities of drink my general health wasn't helped by a thirty-a-day cigarette habit: almost the first thing I did in the morning was to spark up a fag in bed, enjoying that first divine whack of nicotine surging around my brain and I had less of a clue as to how to give up cigarettes than drink.

"All I ever wanted to do was write like Brendan Behan," Anne Robinson wrote of that period in her memoir. "But all that happened was that I learned to drink like Brendan Behan and ended up writing like Mrs Behan."

TWENTY FIVE

One Tuesday morning early in the summer of 1972 Michael Hamlyn asked me to go to Belfast for the features department. There had been a particularly fierce gun battle in Hooker Street the previous weekend which they wanted to reconstruct.

I knew nothing about Northern Ireland except that the Protestants and Catholics had been bogged down in decades of hatred there which had escalated into gun fights and bombings during the past few years, and which, with uncharacteristic understatement, the Irish referred to as "the Troubles". But Michael said all I had to do was establish the details of this particular gun battle, through eyewitnesses, and come up with a "hairs on the knuckle" piece about what had happened. The idea was that, through the microcosm, we would get something of the smell of the macrocosm. Tony Clifton was going to "do" the Catholic side and I was to "do" the Protestant. Such a piece would give the reader an insight into what was happening on the ground.

The academics in the features department were always coming up with fancy ideas like this, which only occasionally worked, but I was flattered they were beginning to see me as a writer in their midst – and on a standing with Tony Clifton, another of the Aussie mafia, who became a distinguished correspondent for *Newsweek*.

Thus that Tuesday morning I began a most unwilling relationship with Ulster that has lasted to this day. I never liked the place but seemed to be dragged back there again and again, for later reportage, to see friends, promote books and make appearances in the local media, including a film that was banned there. I almost had a stand-up fight with the panel of BBC4's *Moral Maze* after I had told them my views on what had gone wrong in Ulster and even ended up lecturing the members of the Orange Lodge on their "enemy within", an enemy who was no less powerful because no one had quite worked out who he was.

Not that I could have foreseen any of that on my first arrival in Belfast, sitting on the bus from the airport, frazzled with nerves and looking around me. The first thing you noticed about the city was the magnificence of its setting, ringed by low hills and the natural harbour of the sea lough, its waters shivering with pale sunlight which highlighted the huge crucifix shapes of the cranes of the Harland and Wolff shipyards. People were bustling about their business on the pavements and you could have been in a busy city anywhere in the United Kingdom, with much the same shops, the same Victorian schools and even the same drunks with their shirt-tails hanging out leaving the same pubs to make their unsteady ways to the same homes.

You might be slightly awed by the sudden vistas of sea or hill at the end of some streets. Fresh, briny breezes bumped around corners, carrying the ubiquitous smell of frying chips but, the more you progressed towards the centre, the more your initial impression of normality began unravelling. The British Army, rifles at the ready, patrolled ceaselessly in armoured trucks and on foot. An Army helicopter whump-whumped overhead. Rolls of barbed wire were stacked up high on walls with security cameras atop poles. Coloured swathes of graffiti unrolled across these walls. STUFF THE FENIANS, PROVOS OK, UP THE BRITS, UDA FOREVER. The gable ends of houses were covered with huge murals of soldiers holding Armalite rifles or a tableau of some ancient war involving King Billy, perhaps, which the artist wanted to celebrate and memorialise.

At one road junction loomed a tower, covered in wire mesh and bristling with electronic dishes – a heavily fortified police station. Many of the shops were fortified too, particularly the off-licences which had turnstiles fixed at their front doors like those at a football stadium. Republican flags fluttered in some streets while others were festooned with Union Jacks, the edges of the kerbs painted red, white and blue.

The newsroom had booked me into the Europa Hotel, home of the international media circus, and I sat in my room for a while, still feeling tense. I was no war correspondent and had never wanted to be. Many reporters found they could cover the Troubles perfectly well from a stool in the bar of the Europa where they would share tips and information while making regular check calls to the Army who were supposed to tell them what, if anything, had been going on throughout the province. Visiting reporters would also study local newspapers for useful material, though there was rarely anything worth lifting in them.

But, in the very nature of the piece I had been charged to write, I couldn't do this story from a bar stool with a pile of local newspapers. I had to get out there and find it for myself.

Belfast people are exceptionally hospitable and friendly, almost as in defiance of their warring public image, and quite soon they had directed – and even personally escorted me – to Hooker Street, which has long been demolished, but was then a mean crouching street a-flutter with flags rather like all the other mean and crouching streets a-flutter with flags in Belfast where the Protestants had been fighting with their Catholic neighbours.

I spotted a scuffle in a nearby street and took a closer look. There was a lot of shouting, mostly by overweight housewives, and a family was loading its possessions on to the back of a large truck. They were being driven out of their house of fifteen years for no other reason than that they were the only Catholic family left in the terrace. Last week everything had been quiet, if uneasy, but now this family was being religiously cleansed. The father of the evicted family was beyond bitterness, smoking furiously and staring hatefully at those housewives who had long been his neighbours and were now yelling at him to get out.

I went to a barbershop on the corner of Hooker Street and had one of the most savage haircuts of my life while trying to extract information from the barber about what had happened in that gun battle. I didn't learn a lot from him, but others who came in to be shorn by his brutal clippers were chatty as they told me what had gone on, ransacking their memories for times, dates and the number of shots. They showed no shame, expressed no regret about what had taken place in their name; seemed keen to give a good account of themselves and the role, if any, they had played in getting the wounded to hospital.

They were clearly accustomed to reporters knocking on their doors, even calling their kids out to elaborate on or confirm what they had said. Everyone had something to say and I was picking up some lively bits of colour but, in truth, it didn't add up to much, certainly not enough to write the envisaged feature. What I needed was to talk to a gunman or two.

Dusk was thickening as I walked back to the Europa feeling down and in need of drink. Ragged children ran wild almost everywhere and I came across one little boy busy arranging a pile of stones on the kerb. I asked him what he was up to and, as best I could understand him, this would-be Che Guevara explained that he was getting ready to fling the stones at the next passing Army patrol.

Next day I began digging into the gun battle in Hooker Street again but didn't come up with anything useful. Most of the shots had been fired at night by anonymous men who had quickly disappeared into the city, so there wasn't much to work with. Certainly no one would admit to firing a shot let alone explain why he had done it.

A reporter in the Europa suggested I might contact the press officers of one side or the other who could well come up with the name of someone who had fired a shot or "knew" of someone who had fired a shot.

"Everyone knows someone who knows someone else in Belfast. You'll always get there in the end if you keep poking away at it. Try a few of these numbers."

It seemed barely credible that both sides in this ugly conflict had a press officer with their own dedicated telephone line, but that was the case. A visiting pressman could ring a certain Belfast number and arrange an interview with a spokesman for the Provisionals. I rang the Sinn Fein number and later presented myself at their heavily guarded offices in the Falls Road. A television camera was mounted outside with a twitchy young man vetting visitors before opening the metal gates. The walls outside were splattered with the blackened whorls of petrol bombs and the waiting room was airless because the windows had been bricked up.

Yet my welcome was warm enough. They couldn't help me on the Hooker Street gun battle, but I was consoled with a cup of tea, a chocolate biscuit and a few political ideas they had been developing.

Everyone was fighting for the ear of the media – particularly the ear of the *Sunday Times* which enjoyed high prestige in the province. The Protestants had their own press man too and the British Army had no fewer than six press officers. They all wanted me to be their mouthpiece to the world at large although the actual terrorists, with their guns and bombs, had the best understanding of the media, knowing that, as far as we were concerned, their words and ideas were pointless. All we wanted was violence and, once offered that, we were putty in their hands.

No matter how we dressed up our lofty motives the *Sunday Times* was also only interested in violence which was why, of course, I was here. Newspapers like the *Guardian* and the *Times* were always writing high-minded leaders about the future of Ulster but their reporters here were only preoccupied with violence: it was all they ever searched for and all their news desks wanted.

I still couldn't understand what this conflict was about although I was beginning to develop a few insights. People often said the Troubles were about bigotry or cultural and religious divisions or loss of civil rights but if only on the grounds of common sense, I never believed that. The two sides weren't all that divided culturally. Both sides were white, they both spoke English and even their religions were nominally Christian, both attached to that same lonely figure on the Cross. Both listened to the same radio, read much the same newspapers and watched the same television.

What *was* clear was that the riots were going on in working class areas, between the poor, the unemployed and the uneducated. I doubted if the people I had spoken to in Hooker Street knew too much about cultural divisions and was certain they didn't care enough about them to go shooting one another in their name. There had to be other, deeper reasons for this conflict and my common sense was already telling me they were at one another's throats precisely *because* they were listening to the same radio, reading the same newspapers and watching the same television.

This province was one of my visions writ large; this was a society that was dying and in deep turmoil in a long season of black rain. The media was the problem here, not so much the international media, which certainly didn't help, but, more specifically, the local media which had become corrupt. I had already learned, on the *Western Mail*, that the media can become the nervous system of a community. Apart from the odd aberration, I never thought of the *Western Mail* as corrupt but here, surely, a corrupt media had destroyed this community's nervous system. They were seizing on violence everywhere and making it routine. It was now difficult to pick up a newspaper or turn on a television without seeing a violent image.

Such notions had been washing around in my head for a while but the first real clue that my analysis was right came when I was watching television in my room in the Europa before going down for dinner with the rest of the hacks. The local news differed from the national London news insofar as the television services in Belfast made it their business to report, in full, the details of every bombing, riot, murder and funeral. Their pursuit of violence was relentless and it seemed more than possible that this pursuit was inflaming and even encouraging each and every terrorist in their various outrages.

There was also the larger consideration of the effect of this coverage on the population as a whole: not on the educated middle class, who could see it for what it was and whose areas and suburbs were free of turmoil, but on those poor, unemployed and uneducated in areas like Hooker Street where most of the fighting was taking place. Surely they were responding to what they were seeing and hearing almost twenty-four hours a day in their media? If a riot broke out in one area, another would start in a completely unrelated area miles away and it was as if the same wave of violence was breaking over the province, not disconnectedly but in one sweep like a high-rolling winter wave.

All right there *were* cultural differences and there *had* been a loss of civil rights, but this didn't explain why they kept beating one another's brains out throughout the province and at much the same time. This point was developed in a slightly different way by the Dean of Londonderry, the Very Reverend George Good. "Sometimes they only had to set up television cameras and a riot would follow within minutes," he told me. "Then everyone longed for six pm. That was when the mobs went home to watch themselves on the box. Re-invigorated, they'd come pouring back on to the streets."

It was clear to me the people here were becoming what they were seeing. They were mirror men as, in a sense, we all are, created in the images and reflections of others. In another way, this was a society that was being eroded and broken down by a constant drizzle of violent imagery: an ongoing storm of black rain.

Even the most cursory study of the local newspapers showed that, like television news, their business was to show this violence on page after page, again not analysing it in any meaningful way or putting it into some sort of context but reporting every blow and blast in full with many a graphic photograph of the dead and dying or that visual cliché of blood spattered over shattered glass on a bomb-blasted pavement.

No less questionable was these newspapers' preparedness to picture men dressed up in their military uniforms, showing off their latest weapons for the cameras or gathering around the coffin of one of their fallen for some huge funeral for which the IRA (Irish Republican Army) would often build a special grandstand for the photographers of the international media.

(The most chilling photograph I have seen from Northern Ireland had nothing to do with blood or violence but was a shot of maybe five hundred photographers on a grandstand built by the IRA in Milltown Cemetery for the funeral of hunger-striker Bobby Sands. In his death Sands finally gained the publicity he had set out to achieve in his life.)

Almost no atrocity would be planned by either side without first asking how it would run in the media and all this attention, it should always be remembered, would be devoted – by Army estimates – to the activities of no more than a hundred active gunmen in the IRA, with a further three hundred who might support them with food or shelter and probably around the same number for the UVF (Ulster Volunteer Force) another small gang of thugs who went on to kill more than the IRA.

There were more practising Buddhists in Northern Ireland than active terrorists but you would have to read a lot of newspapers in Belfast before you ever found what the Buddhists were doing – simply because Buddhists do not practise violence.

The IRA even conducted seminars on how to deal with the media, explaining how to time bombings and hijackings for maximum impact on the evening news. In those early days of the Troubles terrorist acts often came at four o'clock in the afternoon in good time for the six o'clock news. Shooting incidents were also timed for the news and one analysis of sixty explosions in July 1974 found that more than eighty per cent of them were timed to obtain maximum coverage from the news.

When a terrorist plants a bomb he is not looking for a territorial advantage. Some are not even trying to kill – in Ulster they would usually telephone a warning. They never risked an open confrontation with the Army either, because they knew they would lose. The IRA was only ever after three things: publicity, publicity and publicity.

And because the media is what it is, that's what they got. "Terrorism feeds off publicity," Lord Annan wrote in his 1977 report on television. "Publicity is its main hope of intimidating government and the public: publicity also gives it further chances for recruitment. The acts terrorists commit are each minor incidents in their general campaign to attract attention to their cause ... By killing and destroying the terrorists are bound to extort publicity – and hence one of their ends – because such news will be reported."

Most reporters in the Europa never entertained such concerns. They did their job and got drunk, sometimes picking up one of the local girls and hauling her off to bed. There is nothing remotely subtle about your average seasoned reporter. He is untroubled by complexity and, if you can't drink it or shag it, he doesn't want to know. Visions happen to other people after they've drunk too much the night before. They do have feelings but all they want to do is report the facts of the situation strung out with a few appropriate quotes. You could read the life's work of your average seasoned reporter and never learn a single thing about what was going on inside him.

Reporters never seemed to worry about the impact of their work on the community either, content to relate what they could find out and seeing their roles as merely descriptive. The real pain of the bombings or woundings was always left to be inferred: reporters gave the facts of the matter, leaving the long-term traumas of these people to be guessed at.

No, your average seasoned reporter is determinedly and genuinely neutral. "Here's what they've been up to today," a reporter would tell himself as he picked up a phone to file his copy. "They are all, on both sides, brain-dead but it's not up to me to make any judgement about that. So don't shoot the messenger because you don't like the message. I am just doing my job and, when I've finished this, I will get drunk and sleep the sleep of the innocent. In time I will go home and wait to be sent to another hell-hole."

With piles of television equipment lying around the floor of the bar and notebooks in pockets, just in case, the reporters did indeed drink a lot and talked obsessively about the Troubles. You learned a lot from this chatter such as, for example, who you could approach for a quote and who you should stay clear of. Politicians were always good for a quote and anxious to feature in the media – it was a part of their job. The terrorists, too, were keen to talk and more than happy to explain why they had blown up that police station the previous Tuesday.

Much as we all liked to drink and chat, we always had our ears cocked for breaking news even late in the evening. One made regular calls to the Army while another monitored the local television news with a small portable set on the bar and someone else had a tiny radio with an ear-plug to keep a check on news from Belfast's Downtown Radio.

Downtown Radio usually got the tip first because it had the best contacts in the community, and would be broadcasting news of the bomb or riot almost the minute they exploded. This would be picked up and passed to the television cameramen in the bar, who would be up and off with their equipment, while the local newsmen might also shift fast if they were up against a deadline. Fleet Street's finest wouldn't budge unless they thought the story was big. Then, sober or not, they would take off in hastily summoned cabs to watch the bodies carried out or a riot in full spate. They would ring details into their offices and, depending on the size of the atrocity or the number killed, this news would spread exponentially to the news desks of the world.

"Kill one and frighten ten thousand," Sun Tsu, an old Chinese philosopher wrote more than two thousand years ago. A lot has happened since he coined that aphorism and now, thanks to the media, the IRA and UVF could kill one and frighten the whole world.

This was surely a primary evil promoted by journalism and terrorism which had entered into a symbiotic relationship. The weakness of the journalist was his romantic attachment to violence and the real cleverness of the terrorist was his recognition of that weakness and his ruthless exploitation of it.

But what could I do about it? I could hardly have rung the *Sunday Times* to say there was nothing in the Hooker Street gun battle but I had an interesting insight into the Troubles inspired by a vision I had seen in Malaya years ago. They would have had a good laugh in the Blue Lion about that.

All that was left for me to do was what the others in the Europa were doing: complete my job as best I could and get good and drunk. Drink would quieten the voices and ideas that kept babbling in my brain like some mad Greek chorus, making it throb with percussive anxiety. In drink I could laugh with the others about the follies of the people of Ulster, even invest in a few large gins and entice a local girl into my room. But the truth was I was always too drunk and tired to try anything that energetic after a day running around Belfast getting nowhere.

The next morning I began the day with my usual long puke of gastritis in the hotel bathroom; even so young, a duodenal ulcer was already firming up nicely which would mean that I would start most days like this for years to come.

I wandered back to Hooker Street to have another look around. I hadn't gathered nearly enough information for the feature and hadn't even seen Tony Clifton, with whom I was supposed to collaborate. I was pretty much locked in a hungover depression that was going to last until Easter.

By now I was even more convinced that I was right about what was happening here. Clearly I wasn't going to get any further with my assignment while harbouring such ideas so I flew back to London early that Friday afternoon to write up what I had. Tony Clifton later filed some more from Belfast but, in truth, his wasn't much better than mine and Ron Hall spiked the lot.

In fact, Tony Clifton stumbled across a real story later that Friday night when he had come across a shooting in West Belfast and ended up in a sandbagged foxhole with the Army as shots zinged all around the street.

So, while we hadn't managed to reconstruct some old violence, we did have some fresh violence instead, which was run on page one. For all our fine words, the *Sunday Times* was doing much the same as everyone else.

The *Sunday Times* sent me back to Belfast a few months later when the government reintroduced internment, but I can't say I acquitted myself all that well on that assignment either. I just couldn't do the work and kept going missing from my reporting duties, wandering up the Falls Road in pursuit of some mysterious "contact" perhaps or looking around Milltown cemetery, scene of quite a few later spectacular atrocities involving guns and grenades and staged for a wildly appreciative media.

Perhaps the news desk could see that my heart wasn't in it – even if they were never told the real reason why I never seemed to achieve what I had been sent there to do – and, anyway, I was soon being seen as a different kind of reporter who could do a different kind of story.

TWENTY SIX

Perhaps fortunately for my career and increasingly fragile sanity I began moving away from hard news features with some social bite and on to light, colour pieces that might make the reader smile or even laugh out loud.

Harry Evans was keen on such stories, saying the paper shouldn't be too full of long investigations or boring quasi-exposures. We must always remember that people are reading this on a Sunday morning when they don't particularly want to learn about the end of the world or the activities of some grubby racketeer, he'd say. They need a break from the workaday world. We can't always be seen to be taking ourselves too seriously. Every page should have a smile on it. Like every other editor, Harry was always fretting about the right mix, trying to balance the heavy with the light, insisting entertainment was often as important as information.

Such pieces were a quiet joy to write because you didn't have to telephone people asking them questions they didn't want to answer. They also meant you got out of the office to look at all kinds of events, be it a pop festival or a huge Greater London Council planning inquiry to which no one had bothered to turn up. There was also the opportunity to back yourself into the limelight as when I was photographed half-naked being violently massaged by a large girl in hot pants in what was being touted as the world's first clinic for hangovers, recently opened deep in the porn shops and seedy night clubs of Soho.

I wrote about a plague of rats and mice which had invaded London's Stock Exchange – rats usually like open-ended sewers but mice can and do get everywhere – and enjoyed working on a story which "exposed" seaside resorts for fiddling their rain and sunshine figures to make them more attractive to tourists. The guilty resorts would place their thermometers near buildings where the cold winds couldn't get at them, I discovered, and they put their rain gauges in places sheltered from the rain. Sun recorders were put on the top of multi-storey hotels to catch every available second of sun.

I also did a sketch of the 1971 Oz obscenity trial when the three defendants – Richard Neville, James Anderson and Felix Dennis – were charged with producing a magazine containing "diverse, obscene, lewd, indecent and sexually perverting articles, cartoons and drawings and illustrations with intent thereby to debauch and corrupt the morals of children and young persons within the realm and to arouse and implant in their minds lustful and perverted desires".

It was a bizarre trial in the Old Bailey's Number Three Court, not only because of the people in the public gallery, with their garish clothes and little faces peering out from beneath vast mops of hair, but also because of the trio in the dock who had only one suit between them which they shared on a day-to-day basis. Judge Michael Argyle had to keep asking people not to laugh but it was difficult when the various subjects under discussion included how and why Rupert the Bear had sexual intercourse with Gypsy Granny, how the Marble Arch was pushed forward five inches by meditation, not forgetting the life and times of the Fabulous Freak Brothers.

The story of mine which provoked the biggest reader reaction was about chastity belts. The Chancellor of the Exchequer had lifted the eleven per cent purchase tax on these belts and, after some inquiries, I discovered a general practitioner, Dr Alan Gardiner, in Leytonstone, east London, who, strictly as a sideline, was in the medieval hardware trade.

He could provide a scold for a nagging wife, a chastity belt to protect her from welcome and unwelcome assaults, a torture rack to give her a quick stretch and, should she decide to counter-attack, a made-to-measure suit of armour in which to hide. He also did a nice line in thumbscrews, iron boots and a siege machine that could be used for lobbing a hundredweight of scorpions or a severed head into a hostile neighbour's garden.

Chastity belts had recently been classified as safety devices and your Middle Eastern sultan would now save himself 2p in the pound, a concession which was expected to cause a small trade boom. So, together with his armour maker Terry English, Dr Gardiner was now augmenting his stock of medieval belts complete with fiendish spikes. He was even bringing out a new modern outfit made from brass plates which came with little chains, a natty padlock and two keys. The other key was for the purchaser's bank manager, the doctor said, deadpan.

His Leytonstone home, Doom Villa, had, in addition to a stack of armour, a couple of cannon in the doorway, a small brewery in the cellar, five dogs, four cats and two iguanas. Dr Gardiner said most of his business was done with Americans, who liked the curiosity value, but he'd also had a couple of men in Doom Villa who looked as if they hated the whole idea of Women's Lib.

In the week following the appearance of this story I had about two hundred letters asking the same question: how could they get in touch with Dr Gardiner so they could buy their own chastity belt. He sold so many he sent me one free. It was a great talking point at our parties and one drunken night I tried but failed to get it on Liz. Within a month it was stolen, perhaps by someone who had a real need for it.

My transformation into a light feature writer was made complete when Michael Bateman, our Atticus diarist, took a month's holiday and Harry asked me to do it with David Blundy, Michael's leg man on the column. David could write with a wonderfully light and funny style but agonised over every word – and then agonised some more – although his career soon pretty much went in the opposite direction to mine. As I became more frivolous, hiding my black and still very active demons behind the mask of a clown, David became more serious, later taking on the job of foreign correspondent with the *Independent on Sunday*. He was killed by a sniper in El Salvador in 1989.

David and I wanted to do well on this diary which had been written by many famous writers including John Buchan (*The Thirty Nine Steps*), Ian Fleming (James Bond) and Sacheverell Sitwell. In more recent years it had been done by Godfrey Smith, Robert – *Call My Bluff* – Robinson, Phillip Oakes, Hunter Davies and the illustrious Nicholas Tomalin, thought by some to have been the best Atticus ever. Like Blundy, he was killed on a foreign assignment: a Syrian rocket hit the car he was driving on the Golan Heights in 1973. Blundy and Tomalin, as it happened, had finished their pieces but, in the spirit of the perfectionists they were, both went out of their hotels to have one last look before filing.

Diary skills are very different to those required by a reporter. You can comment on people and issues in a diary; you are expected to create interest not only in the people and places you encounter but also in yourself and your world view. You can even live out some metropolitan fantasy on behalf of your readers wherein you trundle around the city attending receptions and parties, meeting famous people at almost every turn and even, if the mood takes you, putting the boot into their often fragile egos. This would never be a complete hatchet job but you could present them in an unfavourable light which often drove people mad since everyone knew this was the one part of the paper everyone read. Many said it was the *first* item in the paper they turned to. Crooks didn't seem to mind being called as such but went ape when you made any adverse comments about their personalities.

All this I was to learn in time but, just then, David and I weren't really up to it; we tackled the job like the provincial reporters we still were (he had got to the *Sunday Times* about two months ahead of me), filling the column with any "funny" news stories which caught our fancy and, far from creating a well-written metropolitan fantasy involving famous personalities, casting our nets over Britain and writing about the problems with starlings in Glasgow or what makes a good holiday home for cats in the Home Counties.

We didn't have the confidence to resort to that well-known diary tactic of describing the indescribable tortures which you went through to get a story only to reveal you had ended up with nothing. David later became particularly good at this kind of non-interview as when he described his various attempts to talk to Robert Mitchum. After many a long wait and partial promise David finally stepped in front of the great actor and asked if they could talk but, after a brief pause and a long sigh, Mitchum told him that he'd much prefer to have a piss.

We didn't attempt to "write" anything up in a particularly clever-clever style, employing parody or irony, which was completely alien to our training and what we wrote, in diary terms, during our month with the Atticus Biro, was no more than all right, I guess: maybe four out of ten. We even behaved like competitive provincial reporters when the diary was planned and being put to bed, practically having stand-up fights about where we thought our stories should go, which should be cut and whose name should go first on the by-line.

The executives on the paper didn't seem to think much of our diary efforts either: David and I were too much alike, with similar talents, preoccupations and experience. Ron Hall always said Nicholas Tomalin and Hunter Davies had made a brilliant team when they were co-writing Atticus: Nick, the urbane and witty sophisticate who played the oboe and Hunter, the chatty Northerner who liked pop music and footy.

Yet what I came to adore about writing a diary was that you could go where you liked and speak to anyone who took your fancy. A positive piece in a diary in a quality Sunday paper had a powerful effect on the sales of a book, so it would be a rare author, no matter how famous, who would not want to talk to you. Thus I began an informal project to interview every leading writer in the world. I didn't conceive it quite so grandiosely but that's how it turned out and hardly any major writer came to London over the next twenty years who I didn't interview.

There were several related aspects to this project, including my continuing ambition to become a writer in my own right. Not that I was making any progress on that front, largely because my spare energy was leaking out almost everywhere except on a typewriter. Yet I did quiz the writers I met about their craft: asking how they worked, why had they picked on this particular theme, what was the pattern of their day and, if they seemed reasonably candid, how much they earned.

Every aspect of writing absorbed me, particularly the way writers' ideas worked in their real lives. Why had this nice man managed to make a mess of all his relationships? How did the shy, extremely courteous JP Donleavy come up with the wild and often violent Sebastien Dangerfield?

Some responded to my insolent questions while others offered crumbs with which I could do with what I liked. A few, like WH Auden, didn't give a toss. "Oh just make it all up. I don't care in the slightest." Despite their fame and fortune almost none of them seemed in any way happy and I often detected deep levels of desperation in them whose real nature I could only guess at.

Perhaps I was also, yet again, looking to them for some kind of further insight into my Malayan visions. If artists and communicators were attacking the world how and in what way, if at all, were our *writers* attacking the world? Was there a corruption in them that I had once found in myself? Did they ever think there might be anything suspect about what they were doing? These were troubling, deep questions to which I never got any real answers.

There was an even weirder question here, which I couldn't start to understand, which was how could a man see a vision of the world being attacked by its artists and writers and, within a few short years, get perhaps the only job in the world which would put him in almost daily touch with these same artists and writers?

I had already met many writers, but my first plunge into their world came in that first week as a temporary Atticus when I travelled to Dublin to try and meet the large number of them who had moved there because the Republic had declared itself a tax haven for artists. Up to that date in 1973 about two hundred and forty artists of many nationalities had been granted tax exemptions by the Department of Finance.

Wolf Mankowitz was there, as was Ernest Gebler, former husband of Edna O'Brien. Gerald Hanley, who wrote *Year of the Lion,* lived there and the novelist Catherine Gaskell had just fetched up in Cork. Names of such diverse authors as Gore Vidal, PL Travers, the author of *Mary Poppins,* and even good old Mickey

Spillane were rumoured to be coming in on the next plane. JP Donleavy had long been there, in his manor, Balsoon House in County Meath, enjoying the tax concession given to writers even though his work had been banned there: *The Ginger Man* had recently been re-banned after the original twelve-year ban had run out.

The first writer I went to see was the author of *The Manchurian Candidate*, Richard Condon, a huge friendly bear of a man who had bought a large, down-at-heel mansion in Kilkenny where, he said, he sobbed himself to sleep every night over the bills. The saga of the ruinous expense of taking over such a folly kept me laughing for hours. Only the previous week new carpets had arrived after a three-month wait – but they didn't fit. On another occasion a man had crept up to him and said in a deep Irish brogue, "About these curtains. There's this agent from the CIA and he has taken them to Vienna."

"My hair has begun falling out," said Condon, "and if I don't get at least three novels out of this I'm going to want to know why."

He had come to Ireland because he loved the place. In nine years he had lived in six different countries and, it was said that as soon as he got to know five people he moved. Now he was running an open and hospitable house – Mick Jagger and a heavily pregnant Bianca had been there only the week before – and it seemed as if you had run into a solid wall of booze almost as soon as you walked through the front door. Everyone was getting Mexican food that month because – along with his lovely daughter, Wendy – he was writing a Mexican cookbook and visitors became guinea pigs for the next chapter.

Condon was possibly the most professional writer I've come across. He always wrote up to six drafts of every novel. Once he got the story he wrote it out and, if the first draft came to nine pages, that was it. He would keep doing this again and again, just continually expanding it until he got to page 240 when he'd call it a day. You kept your story tight in this way, he said. He would set the story in whatever country he deemed to be fashionable when the book was published. As befits a former Hollywood film publicist who had seen thousands of films, his books were always visual and many had been turned into films. He seemed to know all the stars, confirming that Sinatra's mates really had once put a horse's head in a film producer's bed to get Sinatra the part in *From Here to Eternity*.

Condon put me in touch with Len Deighton, who had found true love and happiness in an old bungalow in a leafy dell near the mountains of Mourne. There he mooched around like a big rumpled hamster and was growing vegetables, he said, the likes of which the land had never seen. Sometimes he took his vegetables to friends like Condon but the accent was on privacy and he put up a stout resistance against any tourists, journalists or would-be writers who tried to get near him. He'd always had a bit of a kink about privacy and, in London, had even gone so far as installing a telephone that only made outgoing calls. He was finishing a manuscript on the Hollywood film business and, since he got more neurotic as the deadline approached, the fewer intrusions the better. Once famous for his writerly gadgetry, he had got rid of all his electronic gear and he was saving a bundle in taxes too. Money meant a lot to Deighton.

It was on that trip that I began a love affair with Dublin and, if Belfast had become the face of my nightmares, Dublin became that of my sweetest dreams. I had been there often before, as a student, but the Atticus name opened all kinds of doors, bringing me close to the city and many of her literary figures. I seemed to crash in through one door and out the other, hardly ever eating as much as a cheese sandwich but certainly drinking a lot, particularly savouring writer Ben Kieley's story about a friend who had gone out for a box of matches in Dublin one morning and woken up three days later *under* a bed in Ballybunion. What he couldn't work out was how he had managed to get shaved.

My first contact in the city was with the Welsh playwright, Alun Owen, who would talk in a scintillating mixture of Scouse, Irish and Welsh accents and, with his fluent Welsh and current address in Dublin, had become something of a Celtic scrambled egg. For him the tax concession was an added attraction because, for a variety of reasons, he was living there anyway. Yet he had only sold his London flat and Welsh home the previous week and was not even sure he could go back to England, even for a visit, for fear the taxman would nobble him.

He said he had found British taxation crippling and kept having to do half-hour plays for quick cash. But here he wrote what he wanted and he displayed no sign of homesickness being at his funniest and most crushing when talking about Wales. In Wales they would, if they could, tax you double for daring to want to be a writer, he said with one of his big sorrowful shrugs. To make it in Wales you would have to be an Alexander Dumas on a motorbike, driving over the mountains and flogging your stuff to all the local newspapers for a pittance.

It's a pity Owen hadn't stayed in Wales, since all that drink in Dublin, with all those world-champion Irish piss-artists, took a severe toll. He did get back to Wales years later when he tried to clean himself up but it was all over for him by then and he had serious mental problems brought on by drink. He could be quietly and warmly funny one moment, then, after he'd had a couple, become intensely paranoid. While it was a pleasure to meet him it was an even greater relief to get away.

One of my favourite Dublin writers, who always seemed a positive island of sanity in all this swirling madness, was Hugh Leonard, a bulky playwright with a silver thatch of hair and the saddest blue eyes that ever got stuck under a pair of eyebrows. He had thought Dublin was bloody dull until he read about Ireland's budget announcement in his London home. Jesus Christ! He had shouted so loudly his wife thought he was having a heart attack. At the time he was doing a lot of television scriptwriting but the income tax treadmill meant that, more and more, he was doing bread and butter work for which he had no enthusiasm. With a joyous whoopee he filled in his forms, told the English revenue men they'd had all they were going to get and hightailed it to Dublin. That year alone he expected the move would save him about £20,000 and when I met him he was sagging with happiness in his luxury flat in Dalkey which directly overlooked the Irish Sea and was only half a mile from Joyce's Martello Tower which features in the opening of *Ulysses*.

But Leonard had become very gloomy about Dublin. "This is where the permissive society started," he moaned. "You go out to buy some groceries and never get home again. I'll learn to live with it though. These days I have a skinful and go out to play chess. Drunken chess is marvellous."

One of my liveliest visits to me jewel an' darlin' Dublin was with writer Edna O'Brien. We flew there together from Heathrow when she launched one of her books, *Some Irish Loving*. It was a strange, flirtatious few hours on the journey with buttercup sunshine suffusing the tops of the clouds and champagne fizzing in our glasses as we talked, mostly about love.

She was very cagey about her age and every time she had a new book out, her publishers issued a photograph which made her look younger. But her skin had a tremendous clarity. Oh to be sure there was that tell-tale cobwebbing around her pale blue eyes, but with the softness of her skin and the craven youthfulness of her talk, the way she kept touching your arm to make a point and the mellifluousness of her soft Irish accent, together with her astonishing candour, the impression was of a teenager who has fallen in love, for the first time. My conversation with her on that plane was the closest I've ever come to making love to a woman without actually doing so. Edna was romanticism made flesh, a thin bundle of yearnings and passions. Everything inside her ran on high-octane cries and whispers which made their own scattered and unruly rules.

"I'm very emotional and could do with some French blood to calm me down," she said. "When I fall in love I really fall and I dread the endings – men are always cowardly about the endings – and I used to end up as a wreck although I'm getting better at that now."

"Ever with married men?"

"Of course." She threw up her hands as if mine was the dumbest question of the year. "What other kind is there unless you're lucky enough to catch a widower on his way home from the cemetery? I chase by energy rather than request. It's the way you look at him. He knows."

"Do you usually get them?"

"Oh more often than not."

We both disappeared into the thickets of the city only to meet up again the following Friday for her launch party in the Shelbourne Hotel where I was staying. Even by Dublin standards this was an extremely drunken party with a beautiful young girl telling me I was welcome to go to bed with her as long as her boyfriend could come too. Edna was appalled when I told her about this and tried to get the couple thrown out. "What would the Pope say about that then?" she kept asking with comic outrage. "What would they make of that in the Vatican?" She'd had quite a few drinks.

There was almost always some sex on offer in Dublin although another reason why I have always been so fond of the place is that, whenever I'm there, I find it inspirational and seem to be reaching for my pen and notebook. This must be something to do with the shadows of great writers that hang over you. Here is the corner where Joyce met his Norah Barnacle; that's the house where Oscar Wilde was born; Bram Stoker got married in that church; Brendan Behan fell over in that pub and that cathedral was once run by Jonathan Swift. A whole mob of them emerged out of Dublin – Shaw, Wilde, Yeats, Joyce, Synge, O'Casey, Beckett – and their work set up a dynamic interaction between the slumbering Irish and the overweening power of the English imperialists. Their art prompted an intense period of self-examination and taught the people to say "No".

Most of Dublin's legendary characters had long gone, as had most of the pawn shops. There had been Love, Joy and Peace, who inscribed his name everywhere; President Keeley, who made loopy speeches around St Stephen's Green – "The sun will never go down over Dublin; it will do exactly as I say" – and Johnny Forty Coats, so-called because he wore nine of them.

I heard that the great Bang Bang – alias Lord Dudley, who created panic in the streets of Dublin by shooting people with two big silver keys, shouting, "Bang, bang, you're dead" – was being looked after in a home by the Rosminian Order in Drumcondra. Bang Bang terrorised buses, cinemas, anyone who walked. Grown men dived for cover when he came toting his keys down the pavements.

I went to visit him in Drumcondra and met a delightful man, stooped, with a sort of Adolf Hitler hair-do, his eyes the milky grey colour of the blind. He asked to take my hand.

"They've caught me in here now sir. Caught me unawares they did, unawares. I shot them all. I showed no mercy. Never missed. The city was mine."

He produced two large silver keys from his pocket.

"These were my 45s sir. People tried to get away from me but they couldn't. Dublin misses me sir. The people miss me. I want to get back there and sort them all out. But it's the eyes you know. I only see shadows now sir. Your hand, sir. It's so warm."

The next day, with a faint trace of blood in my alcohol and my head spinning with all these characters and stories, I caught a taxi for the airport and finally managed to follow a line of people and sit down on a plane. There was a long delay when they found out I shouldn't be there because the aircraft was going to Las Palmas. That's how you get after a week in what Brendan Behan called the biggest open-air lunatic asylum in the world.

TWENTY SEVEN

Everything was continuing to burble along nicely in Muswell Hill apart from a few quiet feuds with the neighbours, mostly about their yapping dogs, while my circle of friends kept growing interestingly.

On hot summer days I would go to the Hampstead Ponds where men sunbathed nude in their own enclosure. One day, much to my irritation, a little fellow took a shine to me and followed me around as I swam.

I hauled myself on to the pontoon in the middle of the pond and complained to a man lying there sunning himself about being stalked by this little sod who duly came splashing up out of the water next to me. The man, who made sympathetic noises, turned out to be the actor Nigel Hawthorne. We met at the ponds from time to time to have a chat on that pontoon and it never crossed my mind that he was gay. He gave the impression of being silkily butch and only "came out" many years later.

I also developed a somewhat odd relationship with the Persian owner of an abortion clinic near Park Lane: we didn't go out drinking or partying together, but I sent quite a lot of customers his way. It was difficult to get an abortion then but not impossible, given compliant Harley Street doctors who would say it was a medical necessity, and I interviewed him about his booming business.

He was a dark, kittenish character with a wonderfully toothy smile and, at the end of the interview, he mentioned that should I ever need his services he would be happy to help. I thought no more of his offer until one of the secretaries in the *Sunday Times* got pregnant – nothing to do with me, your worship – so I sent her along to see my Persian pal who fixed her up, complete with her own room *and* pink sheets for a token £20 when the going rate was about £350.

Naturally word got around about Tom's new pal and I sent him a few more pregnant girls including one who had become pregnant in Italy by a Welsh friend. You couldn't get an abortion for love or money in Italy but my Persian pal fixed her up too, again for a token £20. He didn't seem to mind how many girls I sent him – and his charges never went up – until he sent a message via one of them saying that, if I intended to knock up every girl in London, perhaps it was time I started *thinking* about contraceptives.

Oh blimey! I thought. He believes *I'm* responsible for all these pregnancies and I never sent him any more.

I was still a news reporter but achieved a little notoriety when I stood in for Peter Dunn, who had been writing a new column for the paper called Private Ear. The column was just high-class gossip and, with a bit of stirring in mind, I managed to inveigle an invitation to the weekly Wednesday *Private Eye* lunch at the Coach and Horses pub in Greek Street.

Private Eye was – and is – a scurrilous, infantile magazine written by upper middle class or even aristocratic men, who come up to London for a few days to write sensational, often inaccurate, scandal before disappearing back to their country houses. Their speciality was savage lampoons of members of the royal family or politicians, but their most popular feature was the Street of Shame column in which they were incestuously and endlessly fascinated by the disreputable private antics of the press. Most people hated the *Eye*, particularly those who were ignored by it, and the magazine crawled along precariously on a circulation of fifty thousand.

Much of its gossip came from their weekly lunch when assorted people from the media and Westminster ate well and drank plentifully and then paid for it by spilling the beans on their bosses and colleagues. Presiding over this prattle was editor Richard Ingrams, usually aided and abetted by Paul Foot who, while the wine flowed and the tongues loosened, took out a notebook and jotted down every indiscreet word. Given the drunken circumstances it was a wonder they got anything right. Not that they ever worried about that. When one of them was asked if he had checked the story he came out with the immortal line that he hadn't because it was such a good story he didn't want to risk spoiling it.

The other feature of this lunch was that the assembled diners were guaranteed anonymity. Purely in the interests of childish malice, I described the proceedings in my new column the following Sunday and listed the names of all those present including Michael Astor, Naomi Lethbridge, Alan Watkins, Ann Chisholm, Andrew Osman and Patrick Garland.

Almost as soon as the piece was published frissons of rage and delight swept around the Street of Shame and various people were called in to see various bosses who now had a good idea who was leaking the gossip from their offices. Ingrams wasn't happy with my exposure, denouncing me as a "rat" in the next issue of the *Eye* and a "greenhorn" because I had got a few of the names of his lunch guests wrong. But what really riled him was that I was threatening to reveal the names of his lunch guests *again* and he tore into me calling me "the weasel-faced Welsh worm" on his news pages, a name which Peter Lennon swore was pure poetry and which stayed with me for a long time, even becoming a clue in one of their Christmas crosswords.

The *Eye* took a revenge of sorts years later when they filled up the whole of Pseuds' Corner with a dozen different excerpts from my work in the *Observer*, a unique accolade to this day, I believe.

My life and career took on a new direction when I came in one morning and was asked to leave the newsroom and work on a newly revamped Atticus column with Allan Hall as editor. Allan had been editing Look, the lifestyle section in the paper which he had also launched.

Harry Evans had decided that Atticus would become a super-gossip column taking over the whole of the back page of the news section. Stanley Devon, a veteran and much-admired photographer, would be assigned to the column permanently and the secretary would be Deirdre, a rather posh girl who spoke as if she had just ridden her pony in from a point-to-point.

Allan, a flamboyant and dapper personality in his early forties, was always Savile Row suited, often with a carnation in his buttonhole. His hair was thinning, swept straight back and rakishly long around the collar. He spoke with soft, amused public school tones, often gently sending up those around him. He oozed charm when the mood took him and, as a conversationalist over a few drinks, he was peerless.

Many of our harder-nosed young Turks on the paper hated this *bon viveur*, denouncing him as a poseur and a lackey of the public relations industry, a portly symbol of an outdated Fleet Street which wouldn't last much longer. But I was fond of him, finding him effortlessly funny even when drunk which was most of the time. He was on the sauce night and day, but I never once saw him fall over or heard him slur his words. Your only clue he was well canned came from his eyes, which went coldly small and dark. He would sit at his desk with the curious, indefinable aura of a boiling egg about him. Champagne was his drink of choice, but he put away a fair bit of fine wine too. One of his boasts was that he had never drunk a bottle of cheap plonk and, alcoholic as he clearly was, he also steered clear of spirits.

He was a genuine original and I knew I was going to learn a lot from him. It was also thought we would make a good team: him rolling around town with his raffish chums and me doing the lower life like writers, actors or his real *bêtes noirs*, pop singers. He loathed them, claiming that, when he became a Member of Parliament, he was going to promote a Bill to melt down all the amplifiers in the land and have the last pop singer strangled with the last lead of the last electric guitar.

It was soon clear there were no office hours as far as Allan Hall was concerned: he didn't believe he had to be in the office except to write the column, have a rest from his drunken wanderings or look at his invitations and do his expenses.

He made guest appearances when the mood took him; it was left to me to get into the office at some time in the middle of Tuesday morning when, together with Deirdre, I tried to get some early shape to the column. This mainly involved winnowing down the landslide of invitations that came with every post.

There can seldom have been a postbag like it: an invite to a champagne breakfast in Park Lane, a letter from a publisher who would be pleased to arrange a lunch with the author of a new book, a new record by a "hot" new band, a couple of tickets to the opening night of some American singer at Talk of the Town (with drinks afterwards), a reminder that there was still a seat going for a lunch for a retiring politician in the River Room at the Savoy, an offer of a free trip to Paris to meet some actor to discuss their new film.

Such invitations kept snowing in, along with the inevitable telephone calls following them up, and I picked out those I fancied, leaving the rest to Allan. He would show up eventually to tell Deirdre which invitations *he* would like to accept, usually something to do with champagne or food or both. Champagne breakfast – YES, he would write on the stiffie for Deirdre to deal with. Art exhibition – NO. A wine-tasting – YES. An anti-apartheid gathering – NEVER. Prison reform - NEVER IN

A HUNDRED YEARS. Deirdre would sort out his diary and, if he was stuck for something to do during his endless perambulations from watering hole to watering hole, he would ring in and ask if there was anything in the diary where he might while away a few hours.

His wife, Connie, liked to keep up with his whereabouts but, by and large, she knew no more about them than I did. Allan's insomnia, coupled with his enthusiasm for drink, meant he was always on a journey whose stops and starts were determined by licensing hours. The best you could do was *guess* where he was on the basis of past behaviour, but it would be a brave man who would set out to track him down. The West End is a big place with many bars to hide in.

At noon he might head for the Connaught where he would hold court in the champagne bar before moving on to the Colony Room Club, of which he was a founder member, in Soho's Dean Street. This club stayed open all afternoon when the pubs were closed. Then he, the last of the gentleman diarists, would launch himself off into the wilds of the West End, taking in Churchill's or the Stork Room perhaps. More often than not he would end up in Covent Garden with the porters who worked all night in the fruit market where the pubs had special licensing hours. He glad-handed everyone *en route* and always greeted each newcomer as if their arrival was the greatest thing that had happened to him that week.

He also picked up a strange bunch of characters on his travels, Olympic gold medal drunks in their own right: Frank *Fings Ain't Wot They Used To Be* Norman, Sandy Fawkes, Jeffrey Bernard, who had worked briefly with him on the Henry Fielding column, Francis Bacon, the current king of camp in the Colony Room who had recently begun an affair with a burglar who had fallen in through the roof of his studio, and Molly Parkin who had worked with Allan as fashion editor on the Look section of the *Sunday Times*.

Allan could be uncharacteristically considerate to the two main women in his life – Connie and Deirdre. Even as he wandered the city in unsteady circles, he might give one of them a call to say that he was missing them or had just been thinking about them.

"The trouble with women is that they'll often believe anything you bung them," the old sexist sod would often say. "They'll believe anything you tell them because they *want* to believe it."

Connie and Deirdre, meanwhile, had developed their own odd relationship, born out of frequent isolation from their beloved Allan, and would often ring each other and chat for hours, usually about where they *thought* the old fox might be hiding out. At times Deirdre was even more protective of Allan than Connie, which led me to suspect that they might have been occasional lovers. But, on the subject of sex, Allan was ambiguous, to say the least. Some say he didn't just drink with the Covent Garden porters: my guess was he danced on both sides of the ballroom as the mood took him and that he carefully nurtured Connie and Deirdre for other reasons.

Deirdre often got into the most furious white-faced paddy and he had his own way of dealing with that. He could defend himself stoutly if necessary, but never said a word until he had consulted his diary, checking on the days ringed in red, which denoted the start of her period. If the day was clear he would respond to whatever Deirdre might be shouting about: if it was circled, he would put his diary back into his pocket and, without a word, disappear fast.

If he thought he had gone too far with Connie, he would go to extraordinary lengths to placate her, sending bouquets of yellow roses if the situation had become desperate. When he did go too far, Connie would seize the phone and dictate a memo to Deirdre to remind him that their house in South Audley Street wasn't a bed and breakfast; that he should *not* keep taking her for granted, because she could always leave him and, unless he shaped up, she was going to have all the locks changed and he could move in with all those drunken rogues in Covent Garden. These memos always worked and he'd take her out somewhere grand like Annabel's. But these conciliatory gestures rarely lasted for more than the night in question.

Whatever Allan might be proposing to write about in the column the following Saturday morning – if he knew at all – he kept to himself all week but I had usually lined up a subject or two for myself by Wednesday morning. My fascination with writers remained intact, not only because of my own continuing ambition to become one but also because writers were easy to write about since they were megalomaniacs with plenty to say for themselves. They also gave the column some much-needed gravitas, I thought, after Allan had been plugging some fine wine he had just discovered or another restaurant where he had been dining of late.

Another feature of his work was that it reflected the charm of his personality. His prose was suffused with a warm benevolence, often at odds with the cormorants and caterpillars he was writing about. He could never slag anyone off: everyone in the world was a chum, a possible future source of a meal or drink.

"I'm not making any new enemies in my old age," he would say. "And if a column isn't to promote your chums, what else is it for?" He never tried to stop me being critical though. When I had a pop at Mensa once, accusing them of yet again acting with all the signs of an arrested intelligence, the outraged boss rang up and complained furiously. The following week he and Allan lunched together, and soon they were enjoying regular strolls around the lake in St James's Park discussing the great issues of the day.

Anything can be defused with a little joke, Allan reckoned. One morning I was in my old Hillman Minx on my way to interview Elton John when the singer's office rang to say there had been a hitch and the great warbler couldn't manage it that day. Allan explained that I was already on my way and they asked if I had a phone in my car.

"Oh sure," said Allan, "but the trouble is his chauffeur is on it all the time."

Writers always had such wonderfully complex personalities you never knew what you were going to come up with.

There was the delightfully potty poet, Robert Graves, who I went to see at a house in Edith Grove where he told me he was having trouble with his eyes and had become so fed up with writing he was spending most of his time cutting hedges and digging potatoes. His face resembled a huge hulk with an enormous prow of a nose which sloped up into a balding dome with grey twists of uncombed hair. His memory wasn't too clever but his brain fizzed with stories like a shaken bottle of pop.

Occasionally he would stop talking about the gods or the Mafia or Irish poetic techniques, gaze abstractedly out of the window and remark on the quality of the sunlight or a Welsh professional safebreaker he had met the day before.

He thought there were a lot of deficiencies in John Mortimer's television adaptation of *I Claudius* but didn't elaborate before denouncing the attempted rape of Snowdonia by Rio Tinto Zinc in their search for gold. Then he began complaining that, although he had lived in Majorca for forty years, the Spaniards had only just twigged what Senor Graves did for his pesetas. They'd begun hailing him in the streets when he went out for a loaf of bread and he didn't like that at all.

I found Al Capp, creator of *Li'l Abner* and former darling of American liberals, who had now moved so far right he'd become a close friend of President Nixon, funny but darkly offensive. He claimed to speak to Nixon regularly on the phone and had been giving him advice on his speeches and how to conduct himself at press conferences.

"You know, Nixon is a great intellectual," he said, and I all but fell off my chair laughing, although that might also have been something to do with his broad-striped Al Capone suit, fashionable perhaps with Peruvian pimps.

"Sounds crazy doesn't it? A bit like saying Charles Manson is Father of the Year. Where I come from anyone who says anything like that is regarded as certifiable but this guy Nixon can think clearer than anyone. Look at LBJ. His heart was broken because they hated him on the campuses. Nixon couldn't care less. Every time he looks at student demonstrations he thinks of the millions who stayed at home. He doesn't worry about the media either. You can't get a job on television unless you hate Nixon.

"I keep telling Nixon he needs great phrases. You know, meaningless phrases but exhilarating ones, so you're on your feet shouting and cheering but you don't know what you're shouting and cheering about. That's his problem. His language is hopeless. He's a doer, not a sayer."

High on Capp's hit list were the student crazies. His speech really fired up when he went on about the "puberty worshippers" who went down on their knees before the "ill educated, the insolvent and the graceless" who should be "helped, sheltered, ignored and clubbed, if necessary".

All that didn't stop him touring the campuses and giving them lectures telling them they were demented little bed-wetters.

"They're always a sell-out. I get forty-five thousand dollars a go and I wouldn't take a nickel less. I used to give my fee to the widows of cops killed in student riots. That really got the crazies foaming in the mouth. They're coarse but I've got a treasure trove of coarseness when I get going."

Along came the sleepy genius of WH Auden whom I went to see one damp morning in Oxford where, with a fag in his mouth and octopal hands deep in baggy pockets, he spoke about how he hoped to do only the occasional lecture in his year-long tenure at Christ Church.

"I have been back quite a lot since I came up in 1925," he sighed. "I've still got quite a lot of good friends here and Oxford is so calm. You know, when I told the police that I was an author, they wrote down 'No Occupation'. I liked that."

Indeed it had been at Christ Church, when barely twenty, that, with Stephen Spender, he turned out his first book of poems on a hand press. Eyebrows were raised by this new nervy voice which later fashioned such arresting lines as: "Doom is dark and deeper than any sea dingle".

"I'm hoping to meet the students in the local coffee bar at, say, four in the afternoon but, for the rest of the time, I shall be working. I value my privacy. I first left England because it seemed like one big family where everyone knew everyone else."

When he was not in New York Auden lived in a small house in an Austrian village which he liked partly for the wine and partly for the German language.

"In New York I used to keep a five-dollar bill in my trousers in case I was mugged. You were just supposed to hand it over but I was never bothered. They've even got mugging in Oxford now."

His voice, like his poetry, was bright and brittle and his sentences often tailed off at the ends. There would be a long pause and he would look bored, throwing in a few "ums" and "ahs" as if about to start talking again, except he didn't. The silence grew ever longer as he waited, wheezing over yet another fag, for the next question.

"I think everyone should live in two countries apart from their own. This helps you understand it, but I shall not be living here too long this time." Chester Kallman (his lifelong friend and lover) had a premiere of their new opera in Brussels and then it was back to Austria.

He had become such a ritualist, he said, that even a pleasant surprise made him cross. He had a telephone call when I was with him telling him that his "grace and favour" cottage had not yet been renovated and he became very cross indeed. Annoyance quivered those tortoise features, that savage and famous geography which invited startling, outrageous similes and which he himself described as like a wedding cake left out in the rain.

You had the feeling that this man knew what it was to have suffered, to have been isolated, set adrift. He said he planned to live until he was eighty-four, when he would have said it all, which left him about nineteen years to go. He thought art was very small beer and the only serious things in life were not to be a parasite and to love your neighbour.

"I hope I'm not a parasite and we never do enough about loving our neighbour."

Oddly enough, despite the fact that he hardly exerted himself when he was with me and he put up with my fumbling questions with a weary patience, Auden was the most memorable writer I've met and I sometimes find myself missing him. Despite all that he had achieved he seemed full of defeat, overwhelmed by pain.

By Thursday afternoon I'd be trying to write up a few of my interviews, in between fielding the constant telephone calls, most of them for Allan. You had to ring a lot of times to catch him and, on one morning alone, Larry Adler must have rung at least ten times, his voice ever more exasperated when he was told that Allan was *still* not around and would return his call when he got in, if he got in, because he never worked to a known timetable.

219

"I'll ring back," Adler would say and slam down the phone. The mouth-organist lived for publicity and wanted to get his name in wherever he could. If you wrote a column you always got calls from Larry Adler.

Allan sometimes made an unexpected appearance and, if Larry Adler did happen to catch him, you could only wonder when you saw Allan grab the receiver with both hands excitedly and go on about how he had been thinking about Larry only that morning and they really must get together soon for a glass of champagne.

"It's all we've got left Larry. Champagne is the only love life we over-forties have got left."

Allan would sit at his desk and fret over his bills which, despite the lavish plugs in his column, most of his restaurants kept sending him. He messed around obsessively with these bills even reading the odd one out loud if it seemed particularly extravagant,

"Listen to this one. One Brouilly, one Muscadet, one Côtes du Rhône, one Châteauneuf, three glasses of champagne. Not a mention of food anywhere. Me oh my, I usually have a bowl of soup or something."

(Some of these meals were for astounding sums and when, later in his career, he became what was laughingly known as the Good Life Correspondent on James Goldsmith's *Now* magazine, Allan and his cronies managed to run up a lunch bill for £11,000. The magazine paid up and closed down a month later.)

It was permitted to put a lot of these bills on his expenses, of course, but he knew there'd be trouble if he submitted too many in one go largely because he often entertained whole *gangs* of liggers. Above everything else he was always a survivor – so he would shuffle and re-shuffle his bills trying to work out what he *could* get away with.

Then he'd fish around in the back of the drawer for the blank receipts he habitually picked up in restaurants and get Deirdre to fill them in, dictating the food orders and prices, while she struggled to keep disguising her handwriting, often working with different coloured pens and using her left hand. She demanded – and often got – ten per cent for her part in this forgery and, if the finished product didn't look convincing, he might pour a drop of red wine over it and elbow it around his desk.

His other expenses included taxi rides, endlessly criss-crossing the length and breadth of London, the most extravagant backhanders to society watchers for their tips, liberal donations to doormen, the Society for Distressed Gentlefolk, the Journalists' Widows and Orphans Fund and any other credible fund he could think of.

It looked as though most of London got something out of Allan although he liked to tell the story of how he came out of a restaurant one afternoon and was swaying on the pavement with a cigar in his mouth waiting for a taxi when a few members of the Hari Krishna Temple went dancing past holding out their wooden begging bowls. Out of the pure goodness of his heart, he magnanimously tapped some expensive cigar ash into one bowl.

By Friday morning, with less than twenty-four hours to go before our deadline, Allan could never be contacted anywhere and I'd be panicking, typing up almost any rubbish that came my way in case he forgot to come into the office altogether. It also fell to me to do the birthdays, a particular favourite of Harry's. Stanley Devon would have taken various photographs of that week's interviewees and laid them out on Allan's desk, hoping for his approval. Stanley took great snaps but his nerves were shot and his hands were so unsteady he could barely drink a cup of tea let alone hold a camera steady. This meant he had to use a load of tripods, screens and arc lights for our jobs which I had to carry around for him. On some days I'd be so exhausted whenever we went to see anyone I hardly had the energy to think of a decent question.

Late on Friday afternoon the number of calls and callers stepped up because everyone thought that Allan *must* be coming into the office with less our final deadline so close.

Some of London's super-crazies managed to evade the doorman and get up to our office in search of him. Allan's favourite loony was a man who had arrived holding a cardboard box under his arm. "The contents of this box will revolutionise the whole of the aviation industry," he said. "Alternatively they would make a very decent coat-hanger."

I always got in early on Saturday morning in the (usually vain) hope of getting the column away early but, by ten o'clock, Allan had often failed to show. By one o'clock I had to take a page-proof to Harry Evans for his approval, and all we had so far was what I had written. The lawyers liked to have a good look at a page-proof early on Saturday because we had long learned that almost everyone we wrote about in the column was super-sensitive. When I wrote that George Steiner was arguably one of our greatest intellectuals (in a piece about a chess championship in Reykjavik) Steiner, through our theatre man, John Peter, sent word that he'd asked his lawyers to take a close look at my use of the word "arguably". A joke, of course – or at least I hoped so – but we really did have to think carefully about every word.

Not only was there little to legal but the page was half empty and Stanley Devon was still shuffling his photographs around, trying to decide which ones were the best. He had taken a terrific one of Auden's craggy face and the one of Al Capp had well captured his saturnine Nixonesque qualities. Then just as Deirdre began ringing around known watering holes, lo and behold, Allan would enter, complete with cigar and a carnation, lit up like a Christmas tree and closely followed by Jeffrey Bernard. They had just come from some doomed pub in the all-night hell that was Covent Garden and were clearly in much the same state.

We are often told we should not think or write ill of the dead – Bernard finally managed to drink himself to death in 1997 – but I loathed the very sight of this misanthropic old bastard who always appeared in the office at precisely the moment we needed Allan to justify his week of fun by doing the business.

Bernard looked as if he'd been freshly dug up, and glared at everyone with brilliant, cold, psycho blue eyes. His was a well-known face around Soho – or, more specifically, the Coach and Horses – although he was soon to become very famous indeed after he was fired from *Sporting Life* for puking up in front of the Queen Mother at a race course. Then he wrote his low-life column in the *Spectator* (John

Osborne described it as the longest suicide note in history) only to be later immortalised in Keith Waterhouse's hit play *Jeffrey Bernard is Unwell.*

"I'm not unwell," he'd often groan with real feeling. "I'm f..king dying."

This play invited us to laugh along with his loser's philosophy of women, vodka and racehorses but, in those days, I have to say I never once heard him say anything interesting or funny. I just wished he would go away and let us get on with our work.

Then, with Stanley pointing out his best snaps, and me lobbying to have Auden at the top of the page, and Deirdre passing over a new memo from Connie asking when Allan was next coming home for bed and breakfast, Bernard would start harrumphing, saying it had been a long walk from Covent Garden and they should at least have a couple in a pub over the road to settle everything down. As he said this, he'd move towards the door like a dog impatient to be taken for a walk.

Bernard once put a famous ad in a magazine saying: "I have been commissioned to write my autobiography and would be grateful to any of your readers who could remember what I was doing between 1960 and 1974."

I could certainly have filled him in with what he was up to on Saturday mornings during most of 1972. He was being a pain in the arse, forever trying to get the Atticus editor to go for a drink when the Atticus editor should have been busy writing Atticus.

With a grand flourish Allan would take a fountain pen out of his inside pocket and sit reading my copy for a few minutes, changing a word here and there and always saying he liked it, even when he didn't, since the consequence of not liking it might be that he would have to do a lot more work than he intended. He would then sketch out a rough page plan, complete with a few of Stanley's photographs – photographs which were weekly getting bigger because that meant fewer words.

Thus Allan could see exactly what was required from him – one piece of nine inches, another of eight and maybe a few fillers. He always had to know their exact length before he started work so he didn't have to write one word more than necessary. He never counted his words but always seemed to know when he'd done enough.

Bernard would continue to smoke fretfully and harrumph about drink and at last Allan would hoist his typewriter on to the window ledge (he always wrote standing up to stop himself falling asleep at the sheer boredom of his copy, he would say) and, miracle of miracles, he would begin *tapping out a story.*

He would occasionally stop typing to search his pockets for the notes he kept meaning to take down all week and, failing to find any as usual, plunge on again, drawing on his vast experience and intuitive skill as a raconteur. As the story was written, so it appeared in the paper: he never changed a sentence or altered a word.

Can it be possible that divorce, which drove the Duke of Windsor from the throne thirty-six years ago, kept his nephew, the Earl of Harewood, away from the funeral last Monday?

The phone would ring and Allan would pick it up and start a conversation with someone he had been thinking about only that morning, fervently hoping they might meet up soon. "We must put away a glass or two of fizz soon, Henry.

Champagne is the only love life us over-forties have got left."

The fact is that Lord Harewood was not at the funeral. The fact is that he was not asked. The fact is that, fearing an invitation had gone astray in the post ...

Then, unbelievably, Bernard would begin harassing Allan again, jumping up and down from his chair and I'd lose my rag and start shouting: "For Chrissake, Jeffrey, let him finish the f..king column first."

...the charitable theory of oversight is not convincing since the earl's younger brother, Gerald Lascelles, was invited and attended.

And Allan, in between tapping out a few more paragraphs, would take Bernard's side. "You worry too much, Tom. I've always told you that gossip is the art of writing bugger all about bugger all. Nothing to it really. We'll all get there on time. Just stop worrying."

"But why can't you just finish the column and *then* go to the pub. I've still got to sort it out on the stone *and* take it to show Harry."

"He writes better when he's had a few drinks," Bernard chipped in. "Don't you Allan? You always say your fingers work better when you've got a lot of alcohol flushing around you."

"That much is true Jeffrey. That much is true."

One doesn't complain if men want to get together from a club they are committed to and exclude whomsoever they wish. I just observe that if such extraordinary sensitivity were exercised to greet whomsoever should come across one's door, social intercourse in this country would cease to exist.

So, having finished just one story, Allan indicated that he and Bernard should go and have a quick one and our deadline was only half an hour away.

Twenty minutes later they would both be back in renewed alcoholic fluorescence. Bernard would have put away a couple of large vodka and tonics which he drank so greedily he caused small storms of vodka and tonic to swirl around his lips. But at least he would then sit quietly for ten minutes while Allan filled in the missing pieces of the columnar jigsaw, often with little pearls of gossip which had been distilled from the alcoholic vapours of the week.

There has been considerable refurbishing at the Albany, that elegant pull-up for prime ministers in Piccadilly and at last the new tenants have moved into Mr Heath's old apartment: Baron and Baronne Philippe de Rothschild.

I have to admit that, in spite of my anxieties, he always finished it on time, never a few minutes before or after, but right on time. The lawyers were happy with the page proof, Harry was happy because I'd put in a lot of birthdays and the printers were happy because they'd hammered it all down in plenty of time for the first edition.

And, of course, Allan was happy too, having done a good half hour's work at the most to justify his enormous salary and now on his way to the Coach and Horses where they would doubtless get rat-arsed all over again together with other low-lifes, including a man who really did sleep on the floor there at night and another who had once lived in a hollow tree on Hampstead Heath.

Most of them, including Allan, are long gone. The wonder is not that they died so young but that they lasted as long as they did.

TWENTY EIGHT

Journalists who get bogged down in affairs often withdrew into a shell of barely concealed misery and just got on with their lives as best they could. That didn't happen to me because when I got stuck in one, my life and work fell apart almost completely within a matter of weeks. I simply couldn't believe how fast it happened.

She was Sally Walker, a secretary in the newsroom, and it began late one drunken night when I gave her a lift home. I had never been in the running for the Monk of the Month award up to that point and this, after all, was a London which had long been liberated by the permissive ideas of the Sixties: if you fancied doing it you just got on with it, whether you were married or not, almost always on the first night. You didn't even have to be charming or particularly polite about it.

Sally was a darkly beautiful girl with a powerful sexuality and, after we ended up in her flat in Portobello Road I knew I was embracing a new and extremely dangerous darkness. Had I known or even guessed at the pain that would issue for so many for so long from that night I should have jumped up out of that bed and run out of that house without even getting dressed. But I didn't and soon found myself enveloped in an affair in which the scaffolding of my life was completely pulled apart and would be a long time coming together again. After saying goodbye in the dawn, I went down to my car in the awakening Portobello market and smoked a cigarette thoughtfully.

I thought it might pass but it didn't work like that. The strange thing was that I often found myself hating Sally – something I had never felt about Liz – but I still couldn't break it up and walk away. Barely eating, I was soon losing weight and interest in everything. Liz stood back and hoped it would all go away – I blamed the work – while I found myself staring into space and wanting to be somewhere, almost anywhere except where I was.

My absences from home were getting longer and longer and, if I took myself off on an interview in the country, Sally would often join me for the weekend. Perhaps all this added to the unreality of the affair but I was now spinning down a deep hole without so much as a toehold to help me get out again. And my work really was going down the pan.

What I didn't like about what had happened to me, particularly in the cold light of the morning, was that it was so banal. I had violated everything I had come to believe in and was also hurting a wife who had never done a single mean thing to me. There were also the boys, who plainly needed a father. It would have been unbearable if they had grown up rotten. Not that there was any sign of that but it was a worry among a hundred others.

"One day I'll wake up from this nightmare and get my act together," I kept telling myself. But soon I was so stricken with guilt I barely wanted to go home at all. What was happening to me seemed to be happening to someone else. Perhaps the real problem was that Sally had a much stronger personality than Liz: she knew what she wanted and stuck to it with the tenacity of a veteran limpet.

Yet Liz was more understanding and intelligent than Sally: she understood the nature of the beast, never approached anything in a confrontational way and would never give me an ultimatum so I never really left. Even when things were bad between us she always remained my best friend, the one I took my troubles to.

When I finally decided to confess all, the results were predictable. Liz announced that she wanted to return to Wales and cried herself to sleep every night while I tucked myself away in various corners with various bottles, quietly falling apart. I would have preferred Liz to have stayed in London with the boys because I wanted to continue working at the *Sunday Times* but, given what I'd done to them, I wasn't in any position to dictate terms so I took my pen, wrote another house ad and phoned it into the *Evening Standard*.

A sun-filled house in marvellous Muswell Hill goes up for sale this weekend. The spacious living room has a suspended pine ceiling and comes with a stage with state-of-the-art stereo speakers built into it. It has four bedrooms, many varied and talented neighbours and a view of Epping Forest. An absolute bargain at £12,250.

Again my ad enjoyed a tenuous relationship with reality: you could only see Epping Forest by standing on a chair in the top room and focusing on a slight green line ten miles away. Most of the neighbours got on my nerves, particularly as they had been told what I had been getting up to and were getting hoity-toity about it.

I had heard that houses were making good prices in those days and, at £12,250, this represented a huge and unbelievable gain on the £7,600 I had paid for mine. Maybe we'd make a bit but nothing prepared me for what happened. I had been on a job in Birmingham and rang Liz on the way back to ask if there had been any interest in the house.

"At one stage," she said, "there were a dozen people in the house, three in the garden, three upstairs and six sitting around the table writing offers. The last offer – wait for it – was £23,500 in cash."

Welcome to the first Seventies property boom!

No one seemed to know about this property boom – not even on the *Sunday Times*, where they were supposed to know everything. When word swept around the office, everyone in rented accommodation rushed out to buy something, *anything,* thus fuelling the boom even more.

After budgeting carefully for month after month we could hardly believe we had £23,500 in cash, about ten times my annual salary. On the morning we sealed the sale I was driving to the office in my old car when a woman drove straight into my side in Highgate. She was dreadfully sorry, she said, but I told her not to worry, hailed a cab and left the car at the side of the road.

Back in Cardiff there was even better news awaiting us: there hadn't been anything resembling a property boom there and we could have our pick of almost any house in the city and have a big pile of money left over.

We ended up paying £12,000 for a twenty-room house with a large garden in Peterston-super-Ely, a pretentious, middle-class village with two pubs in the Vale of Glamorgan just outside Cardiff, but it did need a lot of work. We also acquired a randy labrador, a couple of sports cars and the immense added attraction of my favourite writer and Welshman, Gwyn Thomas, as a neighbour. Then sixty-six, Gwyn had written fourteen books, five plays and was a veteran of *The Brains Trust* and *Punch* when it was funny. Richard Burton described him as the greatest talker in the world.

Within four weeks our lives had been turned upside down and I was commuting to London to work on the Atticus column, staying in Portobello Road during the week and coming back to my country seat for weekends in a house which was already filling up with old and new friends who came for the night and never left. I also threw a big house-warming party that, in the setting of a pretentious, middle-class village, was a mistake.

All I wanted to do was throw a great party which everyone would remember and, doubtless buoyed up by our new-found wealth, which was excavating a deep vein of madness in the whole family, I put a barrel of beer in every room and a plastic baby bath half filled with fruit by the front door. Every bottle brought to the party was poured into the bath, regardless of content and, at one stage in the evening I could have sworn it started smoking. We also ordered in three-dozen chickens, five-dozen French loaves, a traditional jazz band, a discotheque and two strippers.

Both pubs in the village that night were heaving with strangers getting boozed up and ready to land. And land they did around ten o'clock, about five hundred of them flocking through the front door like a storm of locusts, clutching bottles of this or that which went into the baby bath. The party took off like a ten-pound rocket and the man in charge of the discotheque worked the guests remorselessly. Neighbours who came to complain were invited in and didn't go home again. Someone fell through a window, people fell into ditches on the way home and a fireman was picked up by the police, taken to a lock-up and interrogated about a murder in the Bay.

When Gwyn Thomas left he said: "Tom, we've got enough trouble with falling leaves every autumn without you moving in here."

I was drinking so much and making such a noise, I now realise, to cover up my hurt and deep disappointment with myself. The affair with Sally continued, mostly in the pubs of Portobello Road, but I was mostly annoyed that I'd discovered yet another level of romanticism in myself which I never thought to be there. There were so many depths to this disease – hit one and you immediately found another. It was everywhere within and without and nothing – families, marriages or children – grew in its shade. Only idiots – romantic idiots – left their partners and children I believed, but here I was wandering down the same rocky path of lies, pain and drunkenness as so many other poor saps on the *Sunday Times* forever loading their possessions into bin liners and moving in with someone else. It was to do with sex, of course. Everything goes wrong when sex pokes its nose into the proceedings.

I continued travelling up to London each week and, arriving in the office one Tuesday morning, I found that Allan had taken a fortnight off and "they" had given the column to Jilly Cooper.

Quite why "they" didn't ask me to do it – particularly as I was writing most of it anyway – wasn't explained, but I'd always liked Jilly, a round-faced, gap-toothed, blue-eyed siren.

Her problem, it soon emerged, was that she was simply terrified of writing the column. When I first met her sitting at Allan's desk, she was emptying a box of Kleenex as she wailed her eyes out. There was no possibility, she cried, she could ever fill up something *that* size. Her fortnightly column for the Look section had filled her with terror and now she was faced with Atticus.

"Oh, Tom, the page is absolutely enormous. I don't *know* that many words. How am I going to fill all *that*?"

"Well, apart from the fact that I'm being paid to help you, it's just like falling off a log," I explained. "Allan says gossip is merely the art of writing bugger all about bugger all. Write about your dogs, kids and stuff. Anything that comes into your head. A bit of lusty sex might help too. That's what you're famous for anyway."

Unconvinced, she ran away for three days, then came back in with enough copy to fill a dozen columns, dumped it all on my desk, told me I could do what I liked with it and ran away again.

There was some vintage Jilly Cooper stuff here, including a splendid rumination on the muscular back of the English rugby captain. I edited it and it took me a dozen calls to track her down and convince her it was all terrific.

One day at Peterston, Malcolm, the man bossing my house conversion, put a proposition to me. There was a coal yard for sale in nearby Penarth dock, he said. It would only cost me £2,750 and, if I bought it, he would run it and we would split the profits.

Thus it came about that I returned to my family roots and began a long, grubby adventure in the coal trade.

I should have read the portents as soon as I clapped eyes on the place. The coal yard, once an old pump house for the now derelict dock, was on a muddy bank of the River Ely. Buddleia and nettles flourished in the crumbling cement of the brickwork of the main building. The yard gate had to be lifted off its hinges and opened backwards because someone had lost the key to the padlock, one of the wheels of the delivery lorry pointed east, another west and there was a visible droop in the chassis.

In the yard itself was a little mountain of coal and a geriatric tractor. This loaded the coal into a hopper which shook it down into 28lb polythene bags stamped with the trading legend Cosy Coal. The bags were then transported around the shops and garages of Cardiff and the Valleys and sold for a *substantial* profit.

Everything went wrong on the first day. The tractor refused to budge, so we decided to tow it down the dock road with the lorry. The lorry refused to budge, so we had to tow that with a car. The car refused to budge so we had to push that. I was convinced on that first rainy morning watching a cavalcade of clapped-out vehicles towing the tractor up and down the dock that Cosy Coal was never going to make a profit of any kind.

The tractor did finally start, belching black smoke out of its exhaust and with further worrying explosions inside its engine but, as soon as the other towing vehicles were untied, it gave a death rattle and stopped. The pattern soon became clear. If the tractor was working, the lorry wouldn't budge; when the lorry was working, the tractor would lapse into a deep, jealous sulk.

The hopper was eccentric too. When a button was pushed it was supposed to shake down 28lbs of coal on to a small conveyor belt. Occasionally it managed this small task but more often than not it sprayed a heap of nutty slack over you and you got more over your shirt than you did into the polythene bag. Or else it shook out a couple of small lumps, you stabbed the button again and all but disappeared under the stuff.

Despite all these setbacks we managed to get the coal to the shops and took an amazing £560 in our first week of trading. We went out that Friday night and got gloriously drunk, euphoric with extravagant visions of founding a chain of coal yards all over Wales; seeing a fleet of lorries speeding up and down the land and even turning over the possibilities of buying our own coal mine.

I wanted to rename the company The Real Welsh Coal Trucking Company but Companies House rejected that because your title cannot suggest that you are bigger than you are and, anyway, I had to admit that our coal came from England. We decided to leave it as Cosy Coal in the end, a title too appalling to be bettered.

In fairness to the professional moneymen, they didn't share my euphoria. I had been with National Westminster Bank ever since I was a student, but when the disbelieving manager heard what I was doing, he closed my account. So I went to the Bank of Wales who, it has to be said, stuck with me through thin and thin.

My accountant never understood how the business kept going at all. He reckoned that it was rewriting the basic laws of accountancy and when I protested that we had taken £560 in our first week his nose gave a startled twitch and he pointed out that I had paid £420 for the coal and polythene bags and £130 for wages which left me with £10 to pay for such boring overheads as petrol and electricity. We were probably losing money. He was proved right – though not for his reasons.

Even after a long winter, when we had moved an awful lot of coal, the books were not showing any sign of a profit. I couldn't understand it.

Then I received an angelic visit. The yard was plummeting into real debt and for the first time in six months I had gone to bed completely sober. (I had a night off the booze about every six months as a form of penance.) I was lying in bed looking at the ceiling, wondering if I would ever sleep again, when I saw the coal yard books in a form of a flickering vision. In a flash of insight I knew all.

"That bastard is at it," I yelled out in the insomniac dark.

The sales figures had been fiddled. Just by looking at our customers who had paid by cheque, I could see that dozens of cash payments had gone missing. A few phone calls to regular customers confirmed all. I immediately went into the yard and sacked Malcolm who, I later learned, emigrated and bought a farm in Australia where he had died. And a mighty big one at that, I'm sure.

This meant I had to run the coal yard myself since, with the summer almost on us, it would be almost impossible to sell, even if I could show a decent set of accounts. I had grown fond of the filthy place anyway, so the next week I resigned from Atticus and announced I was about to return to Cardiff to concentrate on beefing up Cosy Coal.

TWENTY NINE

The final decision to leave the *Sunday Times* after nearly three years was surprisingly easy. Apart from putting over a hundred miles of the M4 between me and Sally, Gareth Wyn Jones, a producer with Harlech Television, had asked me if I might be interested in presenting an arts programme in Wales and we'd had a few lively discussions about that, envisaging a satirical review that would involve the local poets and troubadours.

Another compelling reason for leaving was that I still wanted to write a novel and had even got a story and a title, *The Electric Harvest*. I had managed to get the literary agent, Pat Kavanagh, interested in the project after she had written to me saying that she had enjoyed a lot of my journalism in the *Sunday Times* and, if I had any literary ambitions, I should get in touch.

My story would be set in the future, in a London increasingly overwhelmed by media-inspired violence. Football supporters would be banned from the grounds of soccer matches, which would be played just for television. Official attempts to control crime would include secret labour camps and televised corporal punishment. Civil war would be raging in Ulster after the troops had been pulled out. The black and white populations of the city would be forcibly confined to their own ghettoes with armour-plated cabs cruising the streets.

The weekend after leaving the *Sunday Times* in 1973, I returned to my big house in Wales and began tapping out the first draft of *The Electric Harvest* on my Olivetti. Progress was erratic and slow because there were so many other demands on my time which included keeping a floundering coal yard afloat and putting together the forthcoming television show for HTV.

The big mistake most aspiring writers make at first is that they think can somehow tap out a book in their free time after finishing their day job and before going to the pub. It never works like that. Every ounce of creative energy should be jealously guarded, which was why I was so very far from being the writer I wanted to be. Anyone could get me to the pub and, anyway, there was too much noise in my life and mind.

The men who were supplying my coal were complaining about their unpaid bills and threatening to stop my supply while the Customs and Excise people were popping in unannounced to check that my bags contained the 28lbs they said they contained or handing out confusing forms to fill in about VAT.

We also had to deal with the ongoing problem of our close rivals in the pre-packaged coal business in Cardiff, Jolly Coal. They undercut our prices and lured away our better customers to the extent that we often rang up Jolly Coal posing as potential customers to check on *their* prices.

Then, just when the yard looked as if it really was done for, we might have a few freezing weeks and take a couple of grand which would ease our problems. Freezing weather and pack ice take on a different aura when you are a coalman: the mere sight of a sheen of frost first thing in the morning can make the most miserable coal man get up and dance.

Yet, at the end of the yard's working day, sitting on a pile of green plastic bags, smoking a cigarette and with my every muscle aching from delivering and bagging coal, I was sure this was the ugliest place I had ever known. There was nothing remotely romantic about that yard: it even looked disgusting under a foot of snow. Rats as big as cats foraged on the mud banks of the Ely river as it slid past the front door, brown and slow and smelling of rotten eggs.

I still don't know why I wasn't writing about the yard rather than a future London overrun by violence. This yard was a perfect metaphor for industrial Britain; under-capitalised, inefficient and continually besieged by officials all doing what they were paid for but offering no help whatsoever. But, there again, young writers often miss what's actually under their noses.

Harlech Television's new arts review, *Nails*, got off to a bad start when it was discovered, half-way through the local jazz band's opening number, that the pianist was playing a different tune to everyone else and the performance degenerated into a shouting shambles.

As the presenter, I was dreadfully nervous on the first show. Never the steadiest of people, I found I could present the programme properly, that is to say steadily, only after a few pints in the bar although the discovery of the autocue did wonders for my presentation and we often managed to generate some heat with cracking discussions and a few lively short films.

The undoubted star of *Nails* was the venerable John Tripp, boisterous performance poet, wicked mimic and all round funny man who crafted some seriously subversive scripts. He once rang me to ask me out for a drink and caught the moment and its ramifications perfectly in a poem that he later sent to me.

TOM'S HOPELESS MOMENT

I rang him to ask if he wanted
to come out to play. His sexy wife
answered, she gave him my name
and I heard a deep sigh
in the background. It was the last
animal moan of a good man
caught in a trap.

231

At the time, he was covered
with a thin layer of coal dust
from a dead coal yard he'd inherited;
there was a bill he couldn't meet
in his hand; and his attractive mate
was pissed. Life had brought out its
cudgel again, and now
a garrulous poet was on the line.

(At that moment, the entire rubbish of history,
like some dead coal yard,
must have loomed inside his tired brain.)

It was all Tom needed
to complete his day.
My radar clicked, and I sensed
this was a moment of heavy weather
in a week of storms:
the tide was coming in again,
the dog shitting on the lawn, the children
impossible, the clowns ruining his tulips,
and the barbarians at the gates
of his palatial drum,
his marvellous, expensive folly.

(It was something that whisky
and his friends, not even on the *Sunday Times*
could solve.)

The shreds of my bruised compassion
Went out to him and I said, piping cheerful crap down the
line: "Some other time, Tom, some other time."

Many thought, with justification, that *Nails* was the worst series in the history of television yet we had a marvellous time putting it together. Every programme was as different and as vivid as a slap on the cheek and John Morgan, one of the founder members of the group which successfully bid for the HTV franchise – along with such as Richard and Liz Burton – told Gareth Wyn Jones we would take *Nails* to London one day.

Somehow – and I'm not at all sure how – I managed to complete a first draft of *The Electric Harvest*, but it wasn't much good and Pat Kavanagh called for so many changes I put it in my bottom drawer, disheartened.

Nails was re-commissioned for another series and we were asked to put together a political review for Friday nights in the six weeks when the regular political show

232

took its annual break. We lined up a lot of guests and commentators for that, hoping to introduce some new ideas into the form.

Things were looking promising and I was picking up the siren smells of fame After all, presenting two shows every Friday night, there weren't going to be many this side of Offa's Dyke who wouldn't recognise my face. I would surely end up better known than Tom Jones.

Then, ominously, the National Union of Mineworkers, the most militant union in the land, went on strike and all my ambitions disappeared the moment the Prime Minister, Ted Heath, appeared on television in February 1974 to announce that, because of the increasingly bitter strike, the country would move to a three-day working week and that, in future, television would close down at 10.30pm to conserve electricity.

This meant that in the week I was due to present two television programmes, I lost them both and my coal supplier announced that he couldn't get us any more coal. I was overwhelmed by so much bad luck. I had failed as a father and a husband, failed as a novelist, failed as a television presenter, failed as a Christian and even failed as a bloody coalman. I went home that night determined to stay indoors and not drink, smoke drugs or talk to anyone at all for a week. But the next day, I had a telephone call and the caller saved, if not my life, then what was left of my collapsing career as a man of ink.

THIRTY

The caller was Peter Crookston, a former colleague on the *Sunday Times*, who had been hired by the *Observer* as a news executive to beef up their news pages. Did I fancy doing a story for them, he asked, and I said yes I did.

He had read a paragraph in the diary of the *New Statesman* saying that the welds in a £24m oil platform being manufactured in Nigg Bay by a company called Highland Fabricators were all wrong and had to be done again. This would delay the company's venture into its new Forties oil field by some months. There might be a strong story there so would I fly up to Scotland and take a look at it.

I flew to Inverness the following day and hired a car to take me to Nigg in the wilds of Ross and Cromarty where the stunted trees were bent almost double by the North Sea winds. This would be a difficult story to put together and my best hope was to dig around the bars and meeting places until I came up with something. But there were no bars or meeting places in Nigg, a hole with one pub where you half expected to come across tumbleweed and Clint Eastwood.

Finally, I knocked on the door of the Highland Fabricators' offices and announced that I was from the *Observer* and writing a general travel piece about the area, an old ploy I often used to relax people: had I said "I've heard you've messed up all your welds", I would have been flung straight out on my ear. The office manager was quite affable, told me a lot about the area, which I didn't want to know, and added, apropos of nothing, there had been a lot of rubbish written about what they had been doing in Nigg and only the other week there had been some crap in the *New Statesman* saying that they'd got all their welds wrong. The story was complete bollocks and they'd got their lawyers on the case.

A flat denial at the outset seemed to have flushed my first story for the *Observer* straight down the pan and I was despondent as I walked slowly back to Nigg. Then I saw, wandering towards me, an oddly familiar man with a broken nose and tattooed fingers, quite smart in a dog-track sort of way and with more oil on his hair than they were hoping to drill out of the North Sea.

"Hello Tom," he said smiling broadly. "What are you doing up here?"

It was Ivor Hutchinson, one of the large Hutchinson family from Cardiff Bay, most of whom were either about to go to prison or already there.

"Trying to do a story here for the *Observer* but it's not going very well. What are *you* doing here, Ivor?"

"Keeping law 'n' order on a ship just down the way. There's been so much fighting they've hired me and Bobby Turner to act as bouncers to keep the peace. You wouldn't believe what some of them get up to."

"Well, well," I said, fondling the notebook in my pocket. This sounded a better story than the one I had been sent to dig out.

Ivor showed me around the ship, a former Clyde pleasure steamer, the *Highland Queen*, which was providing temporary accommodation for the workmen on the rig that was alleged to have faulty welds. The situation aboard had become so unruly that the ship's lounge was known as Madison Square Gardens and Highland Fabricators had brought in Ivor and Bobby ten weeks ago, paying them £80 a week, plus free board and flights to South Wales on their leaves.

Most of the men were gentlemen, Ivor said, but there was nothing for them to do except drink and get on each others' nerves and there were a few who carried razors or even guns. Two youths told me they lived in a two-berth cabin about six-feet high and four-feet across for which they paid 85p a night. It had no port-hole, just a small air vent and they had trouble sleeping even after a hard ten-hour shift.

The only entertainment was a local caravan where two women did a lively trade and the pub, the Nigg Ferry. Highland Fabricators said they were well aware of the accommodation difficulties but their work did attract some rather rough types. This shortage of accommodation was thrown into vivid relief when Ivor took me to meet three men who were living in an old pillbox on the beach. They had arrived there last Monday and begun work as labourers on Tuesday. As the company made it a policy not to let men "sub" on their wages they were penniless and living until pay day on crabs and mussels and any spare bread rolls the men on the *Highland Queen* could give them.

By putting this mayhem into the context of how lack of accommodation was severely inhibiting the country's search for North Sea oil – which, ahem, gave it an important national significance – I managed to write a cracking story and it made the page three lead the following Sunday.

I had been lucky with my first story which was well-received, and I began getting regular assignments for the *Observer*. Soon I was almost regarded as a member of the staff even though I chose to stay freelance (in those days it had enormous tax advantages). It was a mistake, as it happened: when the paper ran into dire financial troubles, the freelancers were the first to be fired.

Under the editorship of David Astor the *Observer* was very much a writers' paper where you were allowed to loosen up your shoulders and spend an adjective or three. The *Sunday Times* always kept a tight grip on its reporters' style whereas, on the *Western Mail*, you weren't supposed to have a style at all. Here you could describe a face, evoke an atmosphere and even try a gentle piss-take if the mood took you.

I worked hard to be readable. A description of Robert Farrant on trial for witchcraft at the Old Bailey: "He stood in the dock wearing a black coat with sleeves too small for him, highlighting his large hands and long fingers which he occasionally raked through his tangled, sandy hair. He had sprinkled salt around his windows, salt around the doorway and kept a large wooden cross on his pillow, the court was told. He tried, in Highgate Cemetery, to raise the ghost of a pirate but all he raised were the police who arrested him on the stroke of midnight. An architect got into his car near the cemetery one night and found a headless corpse propped up against the steering wheel. Farrant had been trying to pinch the corpse but dumped it in the car in a panic when he thought the police were after him."

On a somewhat darker note there was also the terrible story of Markham Colliery, one of the largest pits in Europe, where a cage plunged to the bottom of the shaft killing eighteen men and seriously injuring a further twelve. This was one of the saddest stories I had worked on: the miners had tears in their eyes when they spoke about it and I described how the whole pit was in mourning for its dead and how some were now too afraid to go back into the cage. They knew only too well what had happened to their mates. Ankles had been shattered and the telescoping effect resulted in hip and spinal injuries and, in at least one case, castration. None of the survivors would go down the pit again. The story made me think hard about the propriety of owning the coal yard which I had not yet managed to sell. Was this bastard coal something I should be involved in? Should anyone ever try and make money out of it?

Yet working on the *Observer* could be a strain on the nerves: you never knew where you were because neither did anyone else. Many of the executives were quite useless and barely impinged on the haphazard workings of the paper although they were not above firing people ruthlessly, something that never happened on the *Sunday Times*. "We are such a small paper we can never afford to carry our wounded."

My saviour Peter Crookston was never clear what he was supposed to do since they already had a perfectly good news editor in the shape of Tony Bambridge, a smiling Cockney with an absurd dicky-bow. They had merely told Peter where to sit and, without a real job description, he promptly began building an empire by telephoning me, the only redundant reporter he could think of, albeit one trying to run a coal yard in Wales. For a long time I was pretty much the whole of his staff and he shuffled me around the country until he was made editor of the colour magazine and he passed me to Bambridge.

These shambolic tendencies were clearly inherited from David Astor, who was occasionally spotted hurrying to his office hoping no one would talk to him before he locked himself in. Astor, cripplingly shy and otherworldly, once asked at a news conference if someone could explain to him what a mortgage was. He was guyed mercilessly as the shy editor in Michael Frayn's *Towards the End of the Morning*, still thought by many to be the best book about Fleet Street.

You certainly never felt you were approaching a great newspaper when you went to its offices in Blackfriars, more a back street brothel as you skirted carefully around an overflowing skip before going into a small, unguarded entrance in a back lane, taking a lift to the third floor. You went through the magazine, where no one ever seemed to do much work, passed the specialist desks where, if it was Friday, Clive James might be frowning over his television review. You might spot a shrivelled old woman, sighing and tearing her hair over a typewriter (Norah Beloff, political correspondent) and continue into the newsroom.

There was never much of a pub culture in that newsroom and certainly never anything remotely approaching even a mild frenzy when a deadline approached.

Most did what they had to do quietly and without histrionics before drifting out again. There didn't seem to be any office affairs going on (practically *de rigueur* at the *Sunday Times*). Most of them didn't even drink, apart from the sports department. How could you possibly trust and work with anyone who didn't drink?

We occasionally met our foreign correspondents, Mark Frankland or Gavin Young, but they were never very forthcoming about anything and I always reckoned, on the basis of no evidence whatsoever, they might be spies using the *Observer* as a cover. A good precedent had been set by Kim Philby, who had once worked for the *Observer*.

You were never very sure what any of them were up to. The deputy editor, Donald Trelford, was typical: he never seemed to do much work and avoided confrontation at all costs. He existed in our office somewhere on the edge of our consciousness, never making enemies or rocking the boat. Men like Trelford rise to the top of any organisation, even newspapers, just by being unthreatening and pleasant.

The one editorial department that did work well was the sports department, under the editorship of Peter Corrigan. He had gathered some real stars, including Chris Brasher, Geoff Nicholson and the awesome and difficult Hugh McIlvanney, thought by many to be the best sports writer in the world. But Hugh's problem, to put it mildly, was that he liked a drop to drink and, almost alone, made up for the general abstinence of the rest of the staff. At the beginning of every week Corrigan's first job was to think of an idea for Hugh and get him working on it immediately. If he stumbled or failed with an early idea all would be lost: Hugh would be off on the piss and that might be the last you would see of him all week.

I continued to enjoy reporting for the *Observer* for most of 1974 but there was continuous trouble in the paper's finances. As a regular freelance I had no job security and went in one Tuesday morning as normal to be told by Tony Bambridge that they all liked my work but, they were sorry, I had to go. I had never been fired before and returned to my desk where Ken Obank's secretary asked me to go and see him. Curt as ever, he said the paper really was in financial trouble so could I go immediately?

Two minutes later David Astor's secretary came and asked me to go and see him. This was getting excessive even by the *Observer*'s often mean-minded standards. I had never exchanged one word with Astor, who didn't like exchanging words with anyone, and when I entered his office he was standing near the window, twanging his braces awkwardly and with the friendliest of smiles on his moony face.

"Ah Tom it's really good to meet you at last," he said with such warm relief he might have been tracking me halfway around the world for the last six months. "I just wanted you to know that I had lunch with Lord Justice Scarman last week and he said that you had given a quite brilliant performance in your evidence to the Red Lion Square Tribunal."

Oh did he now?

Jeremy Bugler and I had reported on the street battle that had taken place between the police and demonstrators in Red Lion Square earlier that summer. The protestors had set out to break up a march by the National Front protesting against any further immigration and Jeremy and I had been watching them march past a line of mounted policemen when a helmeted group, the International Marxists, broke away from the main body and attacked the police horses. In the ensuing *melée* a student, Kevin Gateley, was struck on the head and killed. Lord Scarman had chaired a public inquiry and I had given evidence on what I had seen.

"Furthermore," Astor went on, continuing to tug on his braces and with his daft smile broadening, "that story you wrote last week was very brave and beautiful, I thought, standing up against the unions and in the finest traditions of the *Observer*. What I really called you in to say was that you have a great future on this paper. Well done."

He nodded to indicate that the meeting was over and I was too concussed to ask him the obvious question: if what you are saying is true, why the hell am I being fired?

I couldn't even quite remember what I had written the previous Sunday and when I checked it out, it was extraordinarily boring and not anti-union at all. A few of us had long suspected that Astor didn't know what was going on in his paper or that he even read much of it except the leaders. This was probably as a good a proof of that as any.

I went straight back to Bambridge on the news desk and told him what had happened. He said he'd look into it and, about ten minutes later, got back to me. "Apparently David *does* think very highly of your work," he said, "and as you've also had Lord Scarman's seal of approval, you'd better stay."

"Can I have a staff job then?" I asked, sensing an opportunity to stabilise my position there.

"We're in an awful lot of trouble, Tom. Stay as you are for a while and we'll see if we can do something for you in the future."

They valued eccentricity on the *Observer* and it was clearly a matter of pride that one of their reporters had a secret life as a coalman even if, after some long and sticky negotiations, I had finally managed to sell the yard for more or less the £2,750 I had paid for it. Not that I had anything left over after paying all the outstanding bills for wage, coal and bags. About £25 was blown on a celebration party for the staff in the local pub.

I went back to Cardiff most weekends to see Liz and the boys, although she had long accepted that I was with Sally in London and was getting on with her own life, working as a press officer in the Welsh Office. But that job, which was temporary, came to an end and, unable to find a decent job in Cardiff, Liz decided she wanted to return to London. So the grand house in the leafy countryside was swapped for a small terrace house in Stoke Newington.

My literary ambitions continued to itch: I was still keen to tackle the great blight of romanticism in our lives and there were moments when I became quite chilled by its overwhelming and threatening presence in our lives. One night Sally and I had gone to see the newly-released film *Taxi Driver* at the Odeon, Hammersmith. This film, directed by Martin Scorsese and written by Paul Schrader, is about the life of Travis Bickle and starts hypnotically with shots of eyes everywhere and lone figures moving along unfriendly New York pavements. We meet Bickle, played by Robert de Niro, driving his taxi around the alien streets. He is an ex-marine and a misfit, given to headaches and morbid introspection. He hates blacks and mutters racist slurs. He drags through his meaningless days on a diet of cereal topped with sugar and peach brandy. He is addicted to pornographic films and worries about his mind: "I've got some really bad ideas inside my head".

He sends his parents glowing accounts of the successful life he has been living in his fantasies: "I've been dating a girl for seven months," he writes from his solitary room. "I know you would be proud to see her." Later he does indeed meet a girl, Betsy, who is a well-connected campaign worker and who appears to him like an angel. He becomes obsessed with her. "You are the most beautiful woman I have ever seen." He pursues her, sending her flowers and trying several times to call her.

But she rejects him after he takes her to a pornographic movie and he becomes ever more hurt and dejected until his life assumes a new focus when he acquires an arsenal of guns – a hand-gun, a revolver, a Colt automatic and a .380 Walther. He begins to get in shape with fifty press-ups each morning. Every muscle must be tight. The idea has been growing for some time: use force and all the king's men cannot put it back together again.

He starts stalking the presidential candidate for whom Betsy works. He wears the accessories of his new militancy: sunglasses, an olive-drab field jacket, black ankle-high pull-on boots. A twelve-year-old prostitute, played by Jodie Foster, enters the story. She is being abused by her pimp and Bickle just wants to talk to her. He wants to help and protect her. He wants to give her money to get her away from her pimp.

"Now I see things clearly. I see that now. There has never been any choice for me."

The film blazes into awesome violence when he storms the pimp's stronghold, guns blazing, blood spurting everywhere as he shoots the pimp but gets shot himself. Bickle holds a bloodstained finger to his temple in a smiling gesture of triumph. He has sacrificed his life to save hers.

The film then becomes magic fantasy. Bickle recovers to become a local hero, transformed by this bloody act of violence into a very important person. Betsy is eager to be with him and goes back to school. The pathetic failure has become a great celebrity, loved and applauded by all.

Sally was in a terrible state when we came out of the cinema. She said that it was one of the most evil films she had ever seen. Films didn't normally affect her but *Taxi Driver* had got right to her.

I wasn't quite so upset by the film but what had shaken me was that it was almost a perfect definition of that romantic vision which God had once told me had become such a destructive force in the world. Here was an *alienated primitive*, the outsider, living in a hole in the wall, given to *morbidity* and *melancholy*, who uses extreme *violence* in the defence of the *innocence* of a young prostitute before setting out to win the *love* of a *beautiful* young woman.

There it all was in the fullest detail; another squall of black rain driving the world down what DH Lawrence called an increasingly dangerous valley of days. I was to learn much later how completely this film had affected a young man in Denver, Colorado; how completely the images and story of *Taxi Driver* had entered his imagination; how this impeccably romantic film became, for this young man, a myth that enabled an attempted murder that shook the world.

THIRTY ONE

I was now trying harder than ever to become a good reporter whose stories said something. This was occasionally possible as when I was sent to an estate in Barlanark just outside Glasgow – known the locals as Bar-L estate – to look into the world of Mary Cairns, aged nine, who had become the youngest child sentenced for a crime in modern times. She had stabbed her friend, aged eleven, with a bread knife during a quarrel.

We weren't interested in the crime so much as the circumstances surrounding it and, merely by standing on various corners of the estate and chatting with the passers-by I felt I'd obtained an insight into how and why little Mary Cairns had done what she had done. My first clue came from standing on the balcony of the fourth floor flat in Pendeen Place where Mary had lived, watching the tiny rituals of violence of the children playing in a scruffy patch of ground directly below.

Some thirty children were ricocheting around together in play. Suddenly, one boy punched another to the ground. He got up and kicked his assailant with startling viciousness – but there was no retaliation, all was shrugged off as casually as it had begun. Nearby, three children were breaking off the branches of a recently planted tree. A button of a girl leaned over a neighbouring verandah, shook her fist and bellowed: "Geroff that f..king tree. Geroff or I'll f..king come down there an' gie yer a wee punch in the gob."

The crude language and casual violence were basic to all levels of life on this estate, a down-at-heel development of more than two thousand mustard-coloured council flats piled up on top of one another. Graffiti shouted from every wall and the estate was being called the toughest in a tough city. There were ninety empty houses in the area, many extensively vandalised, which the council could not even give away.

By night gangs glorying in such names as Bar-Toi, Bar-L and the West Rebels roamed their own territories and fought any who dared trespass. The previous Thursday the Bar-Toi had engaged with the Bar-L in a bloody clash a few blocks away from Mary Cairns' home: one boy was stabbed and two received broken noses.

The main problem seemed to be vandalism which had reached terrifying proportions. Mary attended a local school, St Jude's, and the caretaker was out in the grounds every night chasing away one group or another. In one weekend eighty windows were broken. Two of the caretaker's guard dogs had been poisoned. A small school for the disabled, opposite Mary's home, had not been spared either. The previous year two classrooms had been wrecked and, of the seventy-two trees planted in the grounds for Conservation Year, only seven remained.

At a meeting of the area's community council the members were considering the provision of fencing for some of the back gardens near Mary's home. They discussed whether the projected fencing would be strong enough to withstand the inevitable onslaught. It would be five feet high, cost £6 a yard and made of steel. What's more, the blacksmith would be asked to spot weld it and not use bolts. "But they'll still have it down," sorrowed one policeman. "They'll soon have it away and sell it for scrap."

Another item under discussion was the projected community centre that, twenty-five years after the estate was first opened, was due to start being built the following month. One member said they had a serious problem here because one end of the centre bordered on one gang's territory and the other bordered on another's. "They're very strict on demarcation. Unless we watch out we'll have one gang using one half of the centre and the other gang the other. Or one gang will take over the centre and the others will never use it."

Canon Martin Docherty told me that boredom and neglect were at the root of a lot of the social problems here. "There are no facilities for youth and the council seems to take a cynical view. They don't cut the grass and wait for a shower of rain to clean the place." Another resident said he couldn't remember the last time he had seen a corporation cleansing van. Certainly the pavements showed no evidence of ever having seen one. Law 'n' order on the estate was maintained from a wooden police caravan manned twenty-four hours a day but much to people's concern, this was soon to be moved to the nearby Easterhouse estate and replaced by a phone kiosk.

So this was the atmosphere in which Mary Cairns stabbed her friend with a bread knife. As I wandered around this vision of hell I reflected that, yet again, I was walking across the fields of a blighted harvest after a long season of black rain. Through the front windows of all those apartments you could see the little heads of children watching television programmes, featuring the most graphic images of brutality and violence. In the darkness you could see the flickering glow of televisions wherever you looked. The end of the world would look something like this, you thought. Our man of lawlessness will get everything like this in the end.

This might indeed be the most violent and derelict estate in Britain and you recognised, with every fibre of your being, that what caused this mess was busy making the same mess in every other council estate in the land. Soon they would all be going in the direction of the Bar-L estate: into a living hell where little girls stabbed other little girls, all lit by television. These were the original killing fields where the crime and violence of our time were busy growing in every dark corner, carefully fertilised by all arms of a media which was quietly growing into an aggressive cancer in our midst.

This seemed so clear to me I couldn't even start to guess why it wasn't so clear to others. Not that any such thoughts had ever appeared in the liberal *Observer*. Most everyone who knew me had no idea what was going on inside me.

One autumnal morning, Ken Obank sent me a terse memo severing my connection with the paper, adding that it wasn't necessary for me to come to the office again. With no David Astor or Lord Scarman to save me this time, I was finally booted out of my journalistic spiritual home.

All the freelancers received similar memos. Some disputed them hotly but I couldn't be bothered, picked up the phone and rang the features editor of the *Sunday Telegraph*, Ralph Thackeray. In true Fleet Street style, he saw me that afternoon for maybe ten minutes, offered me a staff job as a feature writer and asked me to start the next morning. You could never accuse newspapers of being rule-bound or bureaucratic. Even this, the most conservative paper in the land, seemed to fly by the seat of its pants.

Being hired by the *Sunday Telegraph* wasn't my proudest moment: it was a lumpen, boring broadsheet of the Right with no sense of design or visual flair. Photographs were often the size of postage stamps and its writers could go droning on about nothing much for column after column. As long as the space was filled, that was enough. There was no sense of innovation anywhere and all editorial executives peddled the same advice: "Now look, the way we've always done it is …"

The wonder was it sold as many copies as it did. Probably it picked up most of its sales of around four hundred thousand as a direct spin-off from the *Daily Telegraph*, which was produced on the floor below and printed on the presses at the back of the building. The *Daily Telegraph* prided itself on its blanket news coverage ranging from every move in the City and business to a near pornographic report on page three, usually drawn from a court case, which would involve so much graphic detail it would be considered too risqué even for the most reckless tabloid. If you want to know everything read the *Daily Telegraph*, they boasted; we'll give you all the salacious detail but don't expect photographs of nudes with big tits because the *Daily Telegraph* would never demean itself with that kind of thing. Hypocrisy was as rampant at the *Sunday Telegraph* as it was at almost every other newspaper in the land.

The Telegraph organisation had impressive offices in Fleet Street, complete with neo-Egyptian façade and sculptures of winged Mercurys over the front door. The wide, high foyer, full of white marble and dark mahogany, announced that these newspapers meant business even if the white-capped commissionaires never challenged anyone as they went in. You could be carrying a box labelled BOMB and they'd still wave you in with a smile. A rumbling lift took you up to the third floor where many of the staff secreted themselves in small offices behind thick wooden doors. The overwhelming impression of the place was of cavernous, brown gloom, somewhere you might come to dispute a tax claim or register a death.

Overweight secretaries in white, starched blouses, whose job it was to prevent the members of the public talking to their bosses, clattered past on high heels. Groups of sightseers were shown around in the afternoons and helmeted motorbike messengers in leathers wandered about like lost spacemen.

The newsroom was the smallest office with eight reporters who never seemed to do much. In the sub-editors' room they seemed to do even less. Down the other side of the corridor were the offices of senior executives such as Peregrine Worsthorne and the huge editor's office where, in a corner behind a large desk, sat the editor, Brian Roberts. Roberts, a tiny former production editor of the *Daily Telegraph*, had in his day been known as one tough bastard who could even stand up against the fearsome, bullying print workers, but the word was that he had long given that up as a bad job. I spoke to him only once in my two years there to ask for a raise and all he said to me was "No". How he had become editor of a big Sunday paper no one could ever explain.

The owner of both Telegraphs, the uninspiring and ineffectual Lord Hartwell, formerly known as Michael Berry, had a penthouse on the fifth floor complete with garden and gardener. He came in on Saturdays to read the galley proofs and scrawl comments on them in such spidery handwriting only the managing editor, George Evans, could decipher them. George was Hartwell's representative on earth. He would go wild with delight if his Lordship wrote a few words of praise on a proof, hurrying to contact the writer who had been honoured with this golden mention in dispatches. Hartwell did this on a couple of mine, much to my dismay, since what he thought to be good I always thought useless. His Lordship loved anything that was dull.

On my first morning I was directed to the features room and given a desk next to the features editor, Malcolm Williams, a jolly chap who didn't take himself seriously, and who immediately took me to lunch at Simpson's-in-the-Strand where we ate vast hunks of their famous roast beef washed down by plenty of fine claret. Malcolm, who could be a bit of a Champagne Charlie when he got going, loved such lunches and I got fond of them too. There was supposed to be a licensed canteen at the back of the *Telegraph* building but I never found it.

We often sauntered out of the office at noon and staggered back at around four, full of hiccups and happiness, bloated with food and wine. No one appeared to care if we came back late or even if we didn't come back at all. The paper seemed to drift out spontaneously on Sunday mornings, without any help from any of us and I was always mildly surprised to see it on sale in newsagents.

I soon got to know the other writers in the features room who were relaxed with life on the *Sunday Telegraph*, not unduly worrying about anything except their expenses or what time the pubs opened. Most of the building decamped just after noon to the King & Keys next door, a narrow dark pub that smelled of stale beer and vomit. I quickly realised the *Telegraph* organisation was fuelled by a tidal wave of alcohol.

The journalists on the *Observer* were decorous and sober; those on the *Sunday Times* worked hard and included a fair few drunks in their ranks, but they *all* seemed to be hardened boozers on the *Sunday Telegraph* and I stayed more or less permanently drunk on that newspaper for two years. There was nothing else to do.

Many of the leading members of the Tory hierarchy were to be found in the King & Keys at lunchtime, including the amiable Bill Deedes, said to be the model for William Boot in Evelyn Waugh's *Scoop*, Colin Welch, the deputy editor of the Daily, Peregrine Worsthorne, our deputy editor, and a general sprinkling of interesting women on the look out for Tory big bugs.

The biggest Tory bug in the business, the doleful, stone-faced genius, Michael Wharton, always arrived late at lunchtime, having finished his column, for his regular two large brandies and ginger ale together with a corned beef sandwich without mustard. He wrote the matchless Peter Simple column, mandatory reading even for Lefties, introducing us to such immortal grotesques as Dr Spacely-Trellis, the go-ahead Bishop of Bevindon; Mrs Dutt-Pauker, the grizzled Hampstead thinker; Dr Llewelyn Goth-Jones, the head of Malebolge Pharmaceuticals and the extremely sad and defeated man of letters, Julian Birdbath, who lived at the bottom of a disused lead mine in Derbyshire where he dreamed of being invited to glittering literary parties.

Michael often compared the King & Keys, with its half-mad regulars, to the Theatre of the Absurd, claiming in his autobiography, *A Dubious Codicil*, that this same smelly dump was a resource and a catalyst always on hand when he needed it.

"Immersion in this anarchic riot undoubtedly helped to construct, in my column, dreams of ideal beauty and hierarchical order," he wrote.

Yet the truly hilarious feature of many of these leading Tory gurus, who were always banging on about family values or railing against the permissive society in their editorial columns, was that they had all kinds of skeletons firmly locked in their closets.

Apart from a multitude of other indiscretions, Perry Worsthorne had been having a twenty-year affair with an actress. Colin Welch had been having a long-standing affair too. Even the saintly Michael Wharton had the odd affair while his wife, Kate, also had a long affair, and a child, with another journalist. You were never sure what exactly any of them were talking about when they referred to their "homes".

In a further twist in Toryland, Claudie Worsthorne, Perry's long-suffering wife, was Michael Wharton's secretary on the Peter Simple column. Tiny Claudie wore a beret and rode a bicycle down Fleet Street like the French resistance fighter she had once been. She could speak perfectly good English but had decided to keep her French accent, and she was a gifted mimic, always taking the piss out of her wayward Perry.

"Poor boy, 'e 'as not a pea to 'is name."

Claudie had a strange relationship with Michael Wharton. Many a time he tried to sack her, but she never took any notice. According to Perry, Michael was so mean he always picked a fight with her at Christmas to get out of the obligation of buying her a Christmas present.

Even more bizarre was Claudie's relationship with Perry. She never discussed the state of her marriage with me in the King & Keys, although we discussed almost everything else, but I assumed she wanted to maintain the marriage for the sake of their beloved daughter. Perry's actress love was also married but that hadn't stopped him moving out of the family home a few times, once to stay for six months with novelist Kingsley Amis, another Tory monster who had his own problems coming to terms with the institution of marriage.

With all this – and much more – swirling around us, the gossip in the King &

Keys was wonderful, particularly in the evenings when we might start off with a few half pints of beer before engaging in a short discussion about whether it might be time "to go nuclear" i.e. large scotches all round.

The cost of these rounds could reach ten or fifteen pounds but no one flinched because expenses were always good on the *Telegraph*. The real trouble with this practice, however, was that, having heavily invested in one round, you had to hang around until everyone else bought their rounds and you could end up in hell of a mess.

There was always a moment in the proceedings when the assembled hacks might explode into shouting insults and even violence which the landlord, Andy Macnamara, sorted out with implacable firmness. Andy had been there for ever and one night when Brendan Behan had tried to get in, Andy, a soft-spoken man, had ordered him straight out again. In English and then, for good measure, in Irish.

We all played our parts in this Theatre of the Absurd and, one night, trying to hail a cab in Ludgate Circus after yet another nuclear session, I was staggering around the pavement to such an extent that no cab would stop for me. I was wearing a white silk scarf and I tied myself by the neck to a traffic light to try and keep myself erect. I was so drunk that, when a cab did stop, I strode forward, and all but hanged myself. The cab accelerated away at high speed.

It was just as well that the atmosphere on the paper was always festive and drunken because I wasn't going to get much job satisfaction there. For my first feature (it ended up on the spike) I wrote a thin and predictable piece about the death of the novel.

Ralph Thackeray, our features editor, with the bald head and soft furtive air of a Scottish back-street abortionist, went through every word and line, savaging the piece in a way that hadn't happened to me since my old philosophy professor had drilled through one of my essays like a deranged woodpecker.

"What do you mean by this? When you say that, how many would it be? How many pages exactly would be too long for a normal publisher? When you write about a usual advance then how much, exactly, would a usual advance be? What I like are nutty pieces. I like a fact and figure in every line. That's good journalism."

I was mortified. Not only was the kind of stuff I'd been writing for the *Observer* clearly unsuitable but I was back with the *Western Mail*. These same views had been preached to me years earlier by my first editor, John Giddings. I had hoped I had left all that behind. The real problem with such "nutty" journalism, of course, is that it is extremely hard work. You can't waffle in "nutty" pieces. Where one paper had made me the journalist I had become I was now very much unmade by another.

After much trial and error I finally learned how to play this particular game. When preparing a piece, I assembled all the stray facts and figures and crammed them in together in the second or third paragraph. This device seemed to make Thackeray happy but I could never see how any reader would get through my second or third impenetrable paragraph to read the rest. But you had to do what you had to do and I was already beginning to run out of newspapers.

"The *Sunday Express* is it next, Tom?" Robert Chesshyre asked me one day in Fleet Street. "How many to go before you hit *Tit-Bits*?"

One of my features for the *Sunday Telegraph* was about the boom in house squatting and it would have been a pretty determined reader who could plough through my opening paragraph which took me a morning to compose and went: "Some 30,000 people, many of them from middle-class backgrounds and with full-time jobs: this is today's estimate of the number of squatters in Britain – twenty times as many as five years ago. The figures – 20,000 in central London and 10,000 elsewhere in Britain – are the estimates of the squatters' own advisory service and compare with 1,500 in 1970."

I had never written a piece like it before. Smuggling the key words "middle-class" into the intro always went down well on the *Sunday Telegraph* and the figures made it almost unreadable. But Thackeray thought it was wonderful and told me I was sure to do well here, a line that I had now heard more than once.

Apart from "nutty" journalism, the other feature I had to come to grips with was the newspaper's Tory politics. I was never directly told I must toe the party line but you generally knew what the news executives wanted to read; you soon learned to see the world though blue-tinted spectacles. If you forgot to put them on, your work simply wasn't used. The executives would never give you a good wigging or ask you to rewrite it. Your stories just disappeared down the corridor, never to be seen again.

I learned that my work would get big displays if I pontificated about how profligate councils were forever wasting ratepayers' hard-earned money. Lord Hartwell let it be known he couldn't get enough of this and my first two or three features concentrated on the "massive" salaries of local government officials; how money was being thrown away on sports grounds or theatres where those arty bastards might stage lefty plays, and I was positively encouraged to foam at the mouth if I caught some hapless council wasting ratepayers' money on strawberries and cream at some pointless fête.

Another of the paper's many *bêtes noirs* was the National Council for Civil Liberties and the executives would almost do a little dance of joy if I had a go at them. I once described them as the champions of squatters, cannabis-smokers and various other disaffected groups who had the unmitigated gall to demand the abolition of the crime of incest and wanted the lowering of the homosexual age of consent to fourteen.

By God, that's brilliant!

Students also got it firmly in the neck if they spent excessive amounts on pop groups for their union dances or dared speak out about anything when, with their huge grants, they should have had their noses stuck firmly in their books every night. Agitprop or the slightest whiff of revolution was a disgusting blight on civilisation as we knew it, while the trade unions in general and the miners in particular were enemies of the state, particularly when they manned unruly picket lines and tried to stop a man carrying out his lawful work.

Anything that issued from Tony Benn's mouth was, by definition, rubbish.

I had never been particularly political – no more than a token left-winger – but was surprised at the reactionary gusto with which I was soon getting stuck into the various manifestations of the loony left. The more biting I got, particularly on the "right" subjects, the bigger and better my display on Sunday.

Thus we can perhaps understand how an uncommitted writer might become a notorious right-wing journalist: he merely starts out writing what the newspaper requires of him, if only to hold onto his job and get paid a lot of money for doing very little, but, in time, he comes to believe his own propaganda. His ideas become one with the newspaper. He becomes a willing mouthpiece for the paper's lies. Any dissent is merely stupid: if you want to become a naysayer join that commie rag, the *Daily Worker* (where, in fact, you would enjoy even less freedom).

This was the same office that had driven the saintly Malcolm Muggeridge mad, encouraging him to write thundering right wing leaders which he did by drawing on the passions which had fired him as a young communist. No newspaper is independent and neither is any reporter, no matter what he might claim. I have never believed in a reporter's objectivity: there is no such thing. Unless he is a star columnist, the reporter must reflect the newspaper's line. Most of what masquerades as objective reporting is propaganda and lies, tailored to meet the prejudices of the proprietor. Journalism is an extremely poor servant of the truth, even so-called quality journalism, particularly the variety that was practised on the *Sunday Telegraph* in 1976.

Like poor old Julian Birdbath in his disused lead mine, I still dreamed of writing the great novel but it *was* only a dream since I had to continue making money. So I settled down to the easy, drunken life of the *Sunday Telegraph*, writing breathless pieces about the rates and cramming as many facts and figures into my little narratives as possible.

The news executives never interfered with my work but why would they? I was giving them what they wanted, although how anyone could read any of those pieces, still less enjoy them, was beyond me. But the pay was good and, rather oddly, they never seemed to worry about any mistakes in my copy, taking the somewhat eccentric view that mistakes provoked letters. The diary editor of the *Daily Telegraph* had once decreed that every item should have one fact, one generalisation and one inaccuracy since that was the recipe for lively letters.

Most of the staff were singular, to say the least. The *Telegraph* never fired anyone, except one reporter caught with a periscope in the women's lavatory, and this policy undoubtedly enhanced the ever-present feeling that that you had wandered into a morgue by mistake. Here you kept plodding on until you died and no one would necessarily notice even that.

But I made some good friends there such as Ivan Rowan, a real writer who had been on the staff since the paper was launched in1960 under the editorship of Donald McLachlan, a former English teacher at Winchester, who was described by all who met him as a madman.

He had staked out a place for himself for ever in the lore of the King & Keys when he decided to hire the delightful but blind Peter Utley as a television critic. McLachlan argued that the pictures would unsettle a television critic's judgement. He was finally persuaded to abandon the idea and hired the tall, genial Phillip Purser instead. Ivan was once called to McLachlan's home in Hampshire to discuss a project and told to sit on a deckchair to read a paper before they discussed it. When

McLachlan didn't return, Ivan went into the house to look for him – only to be told he had gone back to Fleet Street.

I met a strange lady in a really disgusting caff, Mick's, a few doors away from the *Telegraph*, groaning and sighing over the crossword. She had the best job on the paper, she told me: she came in each morning for half an hour to see if the next day's crossword could be done. If she couldn't manage all the clues it was reckoned no one else could and it was referred back to the compiler. She was paid a salary to do this.

The news editor never seemed to do much except look as if he was on the run from the cops and quite what Derek Tapsell, the picture editor, did – except tell crude stories and laugh a lot as he scratched his balls – was an even bigger mystery. He must have been the only picture editor in Fleet Street without access to photographers: there was never any question of sending one with me if I was out of town on a job as had often happened on the *Sunday Times* or even the impoverished *Observer*.

They didn't really understand the power of photographs to enhance and present a story. Small was beautiful in their eyes, the smaller the better. I had been sent to Immingham on Humberside to cover what came to be known as the Fish Finger Armada of local fishermen blocking the port entrance to prevent foreign trawlers bringing their catches in. This blockade was lively and noisy so, more in hope than expectation, I rang Tapsell and told him there was a good snap here for him. He agreed but, as usual, didn't have any photographers because he didn't have any money to pay them – or so he said. Could I get something like an Instamatic from a local chemist or somewhere and take a snap myself?

No I couldn't. My nerves were always far too ragged from too much alcohol to point a camera in the right direction let alone hold it steady long enough to take a photograph.

"Get a local photographer to do it," he went on. "Give him a couple of quid, get him to bang off a roll and bring the roll back in your pocket. We'll try and find a way of developing it."

Try? *Try?*

I wrote only one piece in my years on the *Sunday Telegraph* that I was proud of and that was an investigation into the state of the London Hospital in Whitechapel in the East End. The skeleton of the Elephant Man is preserved there and local folklore has it that it was in its operating theatres that Jack the Ripper learned the surgical techniques he practised on the prostitutes in local back alleys.

The routine when you get near a major government building, particularly in the National Health Service, is that you are met by a battery of press officers paid to put a thick gloss over everything. Truth is always the first casualty when journalist meets press officer, leaving the journalist, if so inclined, to dig out what he can from other sources.

Yet when I rang the London Hospital to ask if I could sit in their midst for three days – as part of a more general inquiry the paper was making into the state of the NHS – they not only didn't tell the press office what was going on, but took me around to the heads of every department who agreed to tell me the truth, the whole truth and nothing but the truth.

In summary, I discovered that almost all the junior doctors were applying to work in the United States and the operating theatres were so archaic and unsafe that wasps were flying around during open-heart surgery and birds getting in through the ragged wire mesh on the theatre windows. These theatres had no air-conditioning: they had open sinks and the steriliser put the temperatures in there up into the nineties in summer. The consultant surgeon would point out to visitors the mould growing under the sinks and show them where the rain poured in.

The main danger was from cross-infection and there was no shortage of places where germs could gather. There were yawning cracks in the old terrazzo floors built on wooden frames; lifts opened directly to the operating floor, and the doors to the theatres were cracked and often slightly ajar. Earlier that year, all surgery had been carried out in a tent set up by the Army for the two weeks it took to install a new system. A whole new development programme had been deferred for lack of cash. The effect on staff morale was disastrous. One, planning to leave for America, told me that he had twenty-five years to go and could look forward to no improvements here. Why should he continue to work in this squalor? This hospital was in one of the poorest districts in London.

Money was not their main complaint. Most of them were exasperated by the appallingly inefficient administrative machine landed on them by a recent hospital re-organisation. This had spawned innumerable committees and sub-committees. There were the Private Wards sub-committee, the Safety Committee, the Control of Infection Committee, the Notes sub-committee and more. One surgeon sat on twenty-three committees and spent more than half his working time on administration.

Everyone had to apply to someone else who applied to someone else for an item when before they had simply to ask for it and either got it or didn't. A surgeon had waited nine months for a curved needle. Another ordered a wooden mallet which came two years later and was the wrong size.

There were huge waiting lists and delays of up to two or three years – the waiting list for general surgery was 384 days, for orthopaedic 658 and for gynaecological 600. To try and speed up the treatment the neurological department had something like a one hundred and fifty per cent occupancy rate, a remarkable statistic achieved by lodging patients in other wards or corridors and an almost constant game of musical beds when new patients arrived.

I went on writing like this, moving from one clapped-out department to the next, for a three-thousand-word piece which gave a chilling portrayal of a hospital that was falling apart. Everyone I spoke to answered my questions with a candour which I had never experienced before – or have since – and some doctors had shown me their salary slips in case I didn't believe how little they were being paid for such long hours.

What made the piece even stronger, I have to admit, was that it was packed with facts and figures. I wrote it without any personal comment, just let the facts and figures speak for themselves and, oh my, with what eloquence and force they did so.

The difficulty with this form of journalism is that you rarely come across a group of intelligent people prepared to supply such facts and figures. They usually want all shortcomings and blemishes hushed up or swept under the carpet, but here they were queuing up to tell me the whole story in all its messy and ugly detail. For once I felt I had said something important about the macrocosm of the health service by concentrating on the microcosm of an ailing hospital.

I never found out if my piece did the London Hospital any good, but some of the staff sent me private notes in which they said they felt a good deal cleaner and more optimistic now that the state of the place had been so fully and carefully exposed.

For once I could feel quite proud of myself that Sunday morning as I marched my hangover down to the newsagent's and bought a copy of the *Sunday Telegraph*. They had even run up posters for the newsagents' billboards suggesting they were as proud of it as I was. On that sunny morning, I read my piece carefully from beginning to end on the pavement and, in that one moment, I might have dared to believe that journalism was more than the grim diet of sensation, prejudice and downright lies that it so often appeared to be.

It was early evening in Portobello Road and we had just eaten when the phone rang. Sally answered and said it was my wife. Liz had never rung me here before so I knew it was serious before she said something that knocked the bottom out of my world: "Tom, I don't know how to say this, but your mother has died."

I left for Paddington Station and Sally offered to go with me to Cardiff. But I could hardly go to my mother's funeral with a girlfriend I wasn't supposed to have. I sat on the train to Wales, alone and shocked, thinking about my mother who had always looked after me when I had come home on a train like this, often in a complete mess after yet another misguided adventure in some part of the world. She had always managed to patch me up, always put the pieces back together until I got strong enough to get out and make another complete mess of things. But not any more. Not any more.

She had long known about Sally and been unhappy about it but kept her disapproval to herself. She knew that no one ever stopped me doing what I wanted to do, insisting that these things would pass and I would sort myself out one day. She'd had her own troubles with my father in their early days together, she might hint, particularly if she'd been on the gin-and-orange. He'd been a bit of a wanderer too.

I still didn't quite believe she was gone, not even when I got to their house in the sprawling estate of Llanedeyrn on the outskirts of Cardiff. The whole family was gathered there in a state of tearful shock. Mam had not complained she was ill, simply succumbed to a heart attack while asleep.

I just couldn't shake off the thought that I should have done more for her and became convinced that, if I'd been a little more attentive to her and not so obsessed with myself, she would still be fine and not lying upstairs dead in her bed.

We drank tea and talked a lot about her but I have no recollection what was said. My shock was complete and even whisky – Graham Greene's medicine for despair – did not work for me that night when my own despair seemed terminal.

As the eldest the funeral arrangements fell to me – my father was barely capable of even lifting a pint of beer - I did whatever was necessary and struggled to come to terms with my loss. I was mostly surprised I could do all this and cry at the same time.

There wasn't a great deal that needed doing. The funeral home took charge of everything from the crematorium to the announcement in the *Echo* that they wrote themselves. The undertaker didn't seem much worried about when he was going to get paid but I don't imagine there would be many who would try and avoid payment for their own mother's funeral. When I went to her bank I learned she had managed to save £220, a surprise to my father, since they had never had any money. He had a small pension from the steelworks and she had been a cleaner at the local college.

The day of the funeral was a blur. I remember nothing about it except for standing in the backyard of the family home with my tears still falling and my Uncle Bob telling me one of his dirty jokes. Incredible! I hated his dirty jokes – and kept telling him so whenever we met – and here he was at it again, expecting me to burst out laughing when all I was capable of were tears.

I have often thought of the death of my mother and the grievous loss of that love which is so selfless. Yet, in retrospect, I believe there was a meaning in it even if I couldn't see it at the time. Things get passed on in death that take us a long time to understand. We really can take something valuable from unbelievable adversity and that certainly happened in the case of my mother: through her death she achieved for me what she could never quite manage in life. After the funeral I returned to London, ended my affair with Sally and was shakily restored to my wife and children.

THIRTY TWO

The *Sunday Telegraph* was never much interested in the affairs of Northern Ireland, believing that the Irish deserved everything that was coming to them. They gave bare news coverage to the big events of the week, if any, and our features department generally managed to steer well clear of the Province, much – in light of my private beliefs of what the media was doing to its people – to my relief. I really hated going there.

But late in 1976 I was despatched, at a moment's notice, to track down the burly, smiling Frank Maguire MP, the Government's majority of one, who had disappeared somewhere between fogbound Heathrow and fogbound Belfast when urgently needed for a crucial vote in the House of Commons.

The province had been unusually lively that week: a 500lb landmine had blown up a Ferret patrol car and shots had been fired at a house in Lisnaskea where Maguire lived. Those Pavlovian dogs, the media, were salivating in packs in the Europa Hotel, as they invariably did when IRA or UVF violence broke out.

But I hadn't been asked to cover anything like that, merely charged with tracking down Big Frank – or the Fermanagh One as the Press was familiarly calling him – who owned a pokey pub in the middle of the control zone of Lisnaskea, a straggling, much-bombed town near the border in County Fermanagh.

Everyone else was looking for this Republican publican too and I didn't give much for *my* chances of finding him: he had a deep mistrust of the Press and a way of disappearing into the wilds of his constituency, the so-called Lake District of Ulster.

Big Frank had long been a friend of the Provisionals, visiting them in English prisons and agitating for better conditions for them but this didn't seem to stop bombs going off around his pub. His sign, Frank's Bar, had been blown into a hundred bits and the front window of the taproom shattered three times. Big Frank wasn't terribly bright, it seemed. Even the IRA had managed to work that out.

When I got there I found the taproom had thick, bullet-proof glass riveted to the windows and was apparently run by his wife, Philomena, who had gone missing too. Sometimes Big Frank helped out behind the bar with his brother, an archaeologist. Frank and his brother liked to travel to India "to see things like the pyramids", a regular told me.

I never managed to clap eyes on Big Frank but, as I was there, the news desk told me to hang around in the Europa for a few days. The national and international media was out in force. The usual faces from the *Times*, Reuters and Press Association were in the bar, exchanging stories or rumours in their cheerful boozy manner.

The terrorist groups all now had code words, given them by the media to authenticate their messages. Thus someone would ring a newsman to tell him that so-and-so had been killed with such-and-such a weapon. A code word would be given and the line would go dead. The journalist was free to use the information without bothering to check it back with anyone. If the code word tallied he could just phone the information to his news desk. But who, anyway, could he have checked it with? You couldn't ring up someone on the run, with the Army hot on his tail, and ask him if he really had just flung a bomb into a bar in Inniskillen.

Newsmen were routinely rung and told to be at a certain place at a certain time. They would be shown something or someone – usually a display of weapons or a wanted man. They never tipped off the police about this – much to the police's annoyance – and, while that is not the function of the Press, I was again able to detect a growing and strengthening relationship between terrorism and journalism.

I once had a long chat, in this very bar, with an unofficial fixer for the BBC, and was struck by his cold and knowing insight.

"Of course we're here for the bombs," he said. "No one is interested in talk but, if we left, they would let off larger bombs to fetch us back. If we still didn't come back they would let off even bigger bombs. It's like a bad marriage: we are stuck with the terrorists, and they understand us. They understand everything about publicity. They know everything about news.

"The IRA have had a good run just now, so what I'm worried about is that the UVF will decide they're losing the publicity race and get back into action themselves.

"The way it works for the BBC is that Ulster television carries all the funerals and London takes what it fancies. There's been so much trouble just now we've all come from London as a back up. We've been doing a lot of internal worrying about these funerals – the tearful widows, the lowering of the coffins, the displays of arms. There are new unofficial ground rules and the thinking is that people should be left with a nice feeling. No too much agony, you know. But we *are* manipulated all the time. We know it and they know it. This could go on for another twenty years. There's no end in sight."

On another visit I spent some time with the Army who also go to considerable lengths to get the media on their side, usually beginning with a detailed briefing about the Troubles. The IRA and INLA (Irish National Liberation Army) had generated ninety five per cent of the violence against the security forces, I was told, and the Loyalist terror groups were the UVF, the UFF (Ulster Freedom Fighters), the Protestant Action Force and the Red Hand Commandos.

The terrorists liked to operate on their own patch, using local knowledge and often running south of the border. The IRA still had a small hard core of men who would shoot a soldier, plant a bomb or take part in an attack. In addition there was a larger group who would always help a gunman. The IRA was fond of knee-cap-ping people accused of passing on information or of anti-social behaviour.

The IRA was no longer a cowboy outfit, the Army spokesman went on, having learned a lot from their mistakes. They had abandoned car bombs because they were indiscriminate weapons that could go off accidentally which the Army mordantly described as an "own goal". It appeared Gerry Adams had decided they were "bad for the image" of Sinn Fein. A few years ago they were attacking commercial targets, but were now concentrating more and more on the security forces.

"They do ring the changes. Once they used homemade Drogue bombs. Next they had rocket-launchers for attacking security vehicles but three years ago they attacked an Army Land Rover, missed and the warhead went through a school where a nun was teaching twenty-seven children. It didn't go off but was a disastrous public relations blunder.

"Terrorists have all the advantages," the Army spokesman added. "And they have all the options, especially in terms of public relations. Unlike the government they are not accountable to anyone. A terrorist can state something as a fact when it isn't. He is rarely challenged. They keep it simple. 'Brits out!'"

These days their statements were routinely used in the Press and some were extensive. The *Times* had recently carried six paragraphs warning building contractors not to accept contracts with security services or they would be shot. These were new developments the spokesman emphasised: formerly terrorist statements were not reported. "Let's keep remembering the IRA barely has a hundred active servicemen. Even most Catholics do not support what they do. No one voted for them and they only ever represent themselves."

Despite my personal reservations about our role in the Troubles, I didn't much mind talking to terrorists, who were at least fighting for their beliefs, but there was one group in Belfast that unfailingly drove me around the bend, with their weasel words and whining drivel, and that was the BBC. These people, all well educated and who should have known better, had assembled an extensive collection of clichés and bogus arguments to justify the way they worked. To this day the BBC persists in the fantasy that it is in no way responsible for this (or indeed any other) conflict. It is merely *reporting* it.

Meet John Conway, former editor of news and current affairs for the BBC in Northern Ireland who told me about his work with so little prompting it suggested he had done so more than a few times before. A BBC press officer carefully monitored our conversation from the corner of his office.

"Our guidelines are taken from the BBC Yellow Pages' case law dealing with violence and conflict," Conway said. "But they are only guidelines and a starting point for journalists on the ground. We are constantly updating them for our policy group. Major events like prison sieges in Scotland are analysed and regional news editors travel to London for weekly meetings.

"At a recent IRA funeral the ITN crew was present for the gun salute in a back street. We were not present, but we did use a still. It looked to the viewer as if it had been staged. Personally I do not like gun salutes but they might be tolerable if shown in the context of a funeral when both sides are making political points. If people were firing shots we would be negligent in not transmitting those shots.

"Paramilitaries supply us with videos. Sometimes we show them and sometimes not. We show them on their news value. An IRA roadblock stopped traffic for twenty minutes. We thought long and hard about it and showed some of it in the context of security. A local MP was making the point that a bunch of heavily armed men were taking over a road. We thought that was in the public interest.

"Our work is very difficult. A lot of the players have been at it for twenty years and have become quite sophisticated. They issue contradictory statements and ninety per cent of their propaganda goes in the waste paper bin. It is always difficult to work out who comes first, the chicken or the egg. If I were a worker anywhere I would like to know if I was under any sort of threat so I could take precautions. And we must remember that seventy eight per cent of all violence takes place away from the gaze of the media."

"Would a withdrawal of the media have any effect?"

"No. It would be unworkable and unenforceable. The Republicans have their own newspaper. You would never get the Irish newspapers to comply nor the American or the French. Rumour would flourish and encourage terrorists to commit even more spectacular crimes. People would be easy prey to the paramilitaries. We do chase ambulances, but this is all about dispelling rumour. We are reasonably comfortable with what we are doing. The problems are not as bad as they were a few years back.

"We cover all funerals unless a family asks otherwise. Orations put a man in the context of his community. We are always aware that we operate in the full glare of a very critical populace. The point is that, if you are going to kill people in a spectacular fashion, you are going to get a lot of publicity."

"Should they get it?

"You get back to news values. If you get killed quietly you get treated quietly. Spectacular deaths generate spectacular amounts of publicity."

Sir John Hermon, when head of the Royal Ulster Constabulary, expressed his views on the media at a private meeting: "Is the freedom of terrorist organisations to disseminate their propaganda through the news media a price we must pay for the maintenance of democracy? Is it acceptable that the terrorist should have the freedom of radio, television and newspapers to justify murder, to threaten more murder, to intimidate, to poison people's minds and to spread fear, hatred and division? Or should the safeguarding of life and the protection of the quality of life place a limitation on the freedom of the media? Should the terrorist's abuse of this democratic freedom be denied him in the interests of the common good?"

I never did much work in Belfast. Often I merely wandered around those forlorn streets at night wondering how we so frequently manage to mess everything up so completely.

Belfast promoted severe paranoia. You always got the feeling that the government was spying on your every move. All those cameras are watching *you* – and every delivery and every visitor to every home. Those dishes around that police station will be listening to every conversation. The amount of every electricity and gas bill is monitored on some internal computer and checked for any inexplicable variations. Telephone calls are routinely tapped. The violence of the IRA and the UVF had stoked up fear until everyone was afraid of everyone else.

The real problem with violence on our screens is that it doesn't actually represent anything other than the sickness of the few: the sickness of a small gang of terrorists who commit the violence, of course, but the deeper and far less forgivable sickness of those who write our newspapers and put together our television news bulletins.

In these streets, as in streets all over the world, the flickering glow of televisions through windows intensifies the darkness and every wall testifies to a widespread fear. There were new walls, ruined walls and walls covered with military murals and, more significant than these, the so-called peace walls: architect-designed metal structures just that little bit too high for anyone to heave a petrol bomb over late on Saturday night. These walls are tribal boundaries of the mind, constricting it and imprisoning our thought.

What I kept seeing on such watched and walled walks were the hands of all the major players in this conflict – the television companies, the Press and the terrorists – all reaching out and interlinked beneath the water. In public, they were eternally at war; in private, they had settled down into a long-standing, secret affair from which, rather like a lot of other long-standing, secret affairs, they were having great difficulty extricating themselves.

If modern worldwide terrorism began anywhere, it began when the media and the terrorists came together so secretly and intimately in Ulster in the Seventies. Neither side has ever publicly acknowledged the existence of this affair, which was first struck up in the dark and shadowy corners of Belfast and Londonderry, but perhaps that's what people do when they get bogged down in a relationship with shades of incest, of which they are heartily and secretly ashamed.

THIRTY THREE

John Dyson, one of the main characters of Michael Frayn's *Towards the End of the Morning*, is a Fleet Street journalist in charge of invitations, country notes, meditations and crosswords, heading fast towards a nervous breakdown. He buys a house at 43 Spadina Road, SW23, where he finds himself trying to keep out the damp and rain with Polyfilla or encouraging his posh pals to move into his road in the hope of improving the value of his property. But his attempts are frustrated when his friends learn about the abandoned cars sitting on bricks in the road and his West Indian neighbours who throw their empty beer cans into his garden.

I've always fancied that Frayn had Newington Green in mind because it was the most seedy area I've ever lived in. It is little more than a traffic roundabout in search of a suburb, jammed in between imperial Islington and the decaying grandeur of Hackney. Even after you had lived there for a few years you could never quite believe the reality, this collection of down-at-heel terraces with hedges sprouting half-way across a pavement always liberally dotted with dog turds, this no-man's land which was neither rich nor poor but offered temporary shelter to a rabble of council workers and journalists, gardeners and doctors, publishers and the unemployed.

Liz never took to our little jerry-built house in Newington Green after our fine mansion in Peterston, but we stayed there for eight years. The boys attended the local primary school where they learned how to bash drums in the school's steel band but not a lot else.

After being told – at twenty-eight – she was too old to start training as a journalist in Wales, Liz's career took off in London. She took a speedwriting course in Oxford Street, joined *Management Today* and then became a sub-editor and columnist on the *Investors' Chronicle*, tipping movements in the City – a sphere about which she knew zilch – before moving to the *Sunday Telegraph*, all in the space of a few years.

This was why people were prepared to live in the slummy suburbs of London. You could do anything here: opportunities never failed. She didn't even apply for the job on the *Sunday Telegraph*: it was offered to her one night when she came to pick me up at the King & Keys.

She became great friends with Kate Hoey over the road, a teacher who was later to become an MP and Minister for Sport. Kate liked to throw parties and for these she would bring peat over from her parents' farm in Northern Ireland. It gave off such an acrid and disgusting smell when it was burning that most of the party would end up outside on the pavement in the freezing cold.

I liked these people well enough: we were all misfits trying to make our way in the big city and, whatever its faults, the big city was kind to us. We could all make money and build a career of sorts here, although the plan was always to retire to the country or seaside when our working lives were over. That dream kept most of us going; no one wanted to stay here a day more than necessary.

What I really didn't like about Newington Green was the education my two boys were receiving but, more by luck than judgement, I managed to turn that around. I had been involved professionally with an ongoing ruckus at the William Tyndale Junior School in Islington. As it was almost on my doorstep I had written about it a few times: the teachers there had gone on strike, picketed the school gates and become a national *cause célèbre*.

The dispute was between the radical teachers and the more conservative school managers. The teachers, all under thirty, were said to be very left wing and had introduced participation and democracy into the classroom. This, the parents noted, often involved flowerpots being hurled out of the school windows upon the heads of passers-by. The managers claimed a breakdown in discipline and that the teachers were too much concerned with politics and too little with education.

After the teachers staged a one-day strike, worried parents began pulling their children out. Calls were made for the dismissal of the headmaster, Terry Ellis, petitions were drawn up and a public inquiry announced. Staff were leaving in droves and the Inner London Education Authority, under the full glare of national publicity, drafted in their best teachers to turn the school around. Classes had now shrunk to eight or nine pupils (my boys were in classes of forty or more in Newington Green) and one ILEA inspector told me that they were now determined to make this school the best in London. "Inspectors will be crawling all over it," he said. "Anyone even thinking about a spot of political agitation will be straight out the door."

That was enough for me. Within two or three days, I had taken my boys out of Newington Green Primary and put them into the William Tyndale Junior School where they did indeed receive one of the best educations available in London at that time.

I was becoming restless at the *Sunday Telegraph*, a feeling barely assuaged by the arrival of John Thompson from the *Spectator* as our new editor. If I'd had little to do with Brian Roberts I had even less contact with this man who seemed dull and ineffective although his soft, genial manner was liked by many. "My door will always be open to anyone," he said on his arrival, although, as the weeks went by, we noticed it becoming more and more closed.

The work remained dull and predictable but never onerous. I had even become something of a rock correspondent although, this being the *Sunday Telegraph*, it never meant that I had to file any words on the subject, only that I could always represent myself as such to record companies and pick up the best tickets for almost any concert I fancied. Pink Floyd, whom many on the *Telegraph* would probably have thought a new cocktail at the Ritz, presented their new *Animals* album at Earl's Court that year, one of the best concerts I've seen, full of giant inflatables and shimmering laser effects. I also caught the legendary Bruce Springsteen in his first concert at the Hammersmith Odeon, and a Frank Sinatra concert when the old trooper was so near I could have reached out and ruffled his rug.

I might have taken the Hartwell shilling indefinitely and lived the rest of my life with a desperate and often drunken unease like most of the other hacks there. You could do a lot worse – indeed, given the ruthless competition on most newspapers, it was difficult to imagine how you could do better. My family life was going well too or as well as could be expected after being torpedoed by a long affair.

So I seemed to have settled down at last and might even have found myself breathing the familiar smell of vomit in the Kings & Keys in about twenty years' time with a large scotch in my hand and asking my drinking pals, "What the hell happened to our lives? Where did it all go?"

When you have serious thoughts about leaving your place of work it is in some ways similar to deciding to sell your house: in time you can't bear to stay there a minute longer, can't understand why you have been there so long and every part of you becomes sick with anxiety to get out.

I became tired of the King & Keys and all the Tory hypocrites with their messy affairs and public talk of family values. I was fed up with the sheer wanton drunkenness of Fleet Street where lives were so empty they were spent boozing morning, noon and night. But far more than any of that I was sick to death of this crapulous newspaper with all its crapulous preoccupations with such as agitprop students, the need to restore the death penalty or who was wasting the ratepayers' money.

Most journalists who write their memoirs seem to like Fleet Street but mostly it left me with a fury of loathing. Hacks can get very sanctimonious about their craft but it all seemed to me a drink-sodden heap of crap. I had to get out and was about to give in my notice when I was offered an unusual assignment: would I like to spend the next six weeks or so travelling around the country with our deputy editor, Peregrine Worsthorne? We would take the pulse of the nation in the Silver Jubilee year of 1977 – twenty-five years since the Queen had begun her reign – and write up our findings in a series of perhaps six main features of about five thousand words each. We would visit large and small communities, dig out the famous and the unknown, find out what they were thinking and what celebrations they might be planning for the Jubilee. At the end we would share the billing and there might be a book in it.

This was a challenge. Perry and I could hardly have been further apart on every level. Although I had long been friendly with his wife Claudie, I had hardly spoken to him and hadn't even particularly wanted to. Claudie had invited us to their weekend home in Wivenhoe and we had packed to go when she rang Liz to cancel it. Perry had put his foot down about something and I'd thought no more of it – or him.

He had become well-known as a sort of English William Buckley, publicly supporting Joe McCarthy, capital punishment and the American presence in Vietnam – all positions anathema to me. But he had managed to once utter the word "f..k" on national television. His appearance could be laughable, if not alarming: I'd often spotted him marching down Fleet Street with his arms swinging back and forth and his long silver hair sticking out like a great-crested grebe which had seen a ghost. He had blue eyes, an exquisitely modulated, plummy voice, and a sense of dress best described as Eton College meets teddy boy. He favoured suede shoes, garish red socks, wide-stripe shirts, prehistoric fat silk ties with huge Windsor knots and a chained fob watch dangling on his portly waistcoat.

"Look at me, I'm the bee's knees," the ensemble proclaimed to the shuffling hangovers of early-morning Fleet Street.

I realised in retrospect that there was much the same thinking at work here as when I had been yoked with Allan Hall on the *Sunday Times*: the Garrick dandy and the scruffiest dummy in an Oxfam window; the right-wing ideologue and the left-wing rebel; the reactionary High Tory patrician and the weasel-faced Welsh worm.

Perry picked me up at my home and we set off through a grey, dank morning for the M1. He soon turned out to be the original shrinking violet. When he spotted a big brute of a lorry driver devouring a pasty in a motorway restaurant, he asked me if I thought the man might speak to us. I went over to ask him and, after a few minutes, Perry slunk up on the other side. When he realised the lorry driver wasn't about beat him up, he took control of the interview and managed quite well.

Thus a pattern was established: I would track down the quarry and corner it and, as soon as Perry saw there was no physical danger to himself, he would move in and mop up whatever it was that interested him. I don't know how he ever became a journalist: he was scared of *everyone* although most people were happy to talk to him, particularly when they learned who he was. They weren't *Sunday Telegraph* readers but they responded positively to his name because they had seen his well-fed features so often on television when he had been hauled in to give the right-wing viewpoint.

He performed these high-profile duties with such aplomb he might have been born in a television studio. But there he was, quivering with fear at the prospect of approaching a lorry driver. Working our way up the M1, we stopped to talk to the police monitoring the traffic, and to Perry's astonishment they informed him that his car belonged to the Telegraph organisation. Much of their work was to do with stolen cars.

I thought we made a good team, bringing various strengths to an improbable pairing. Apart from opening doors with his name, Perry brought far more energy to the operation than I did. When I'd had enough all I could think of was where we were going to stay and what we might eat and drink, but he always wanted to push on for a few more hours. He was like a kid in a toy store here, away from his beloved Garrick Club, meeting real people in a real world and enjoying every moment of it. I guess I had taken the terror out of reporting for him because, as soon as he got going with someone after I'd broken the ice, he was fine.

In Sheffield we walked out after dark into a brutal, modernist city centre and visited a disco where Perry interviewed the manager and I spent a pleasant half hour with the resident dancer asking her what she thought about while she was bopping on her little dais above the throng. Her boyfriend mostly, and her ailing mother. I also, through an old contact in Barnsley, managed to arrange an interview with Arthur Scargill in his National Union of Mineworkers' lair: a treasurable moment, the elegant Tory sitting down with the Commie bogeyman who was to give Margaret Thatcher more than a few sleepless hours.

"How are you going to manage when the Tories win the next general election by a landslide?" Perry asked him out straight.

Oh boy, there's going to be some fun and games here, I thought, but far from it. Scargill agreed with him that the Tories would win the next election by a landslide and he agreed with much else that Perry said in a civilised conversation which lasted about an hour and which Scargill showed no sign of wanting to bring to an end.

When he did end it, Scargill gave us a tour of his newly modernised office which seemed to consist of a cubby hole for making tea with an electric kettle. Pride in a new tea making system was not quite what Perry might have expected from Britain's boldest and baddest trade union leader. Outside, Mrs Scargill was waiting for him in a large station wagon with a sporting dog in the back. Scargill was not so much a budding commissar as a budding country gentleman.

Later we spent the evening in Knottingley Miners' Club as a guest of one of Scargill's lieutenants, Jimmy Miller. Music blasted out all night long. "Listen to the juke box," Jimmy complained. "Fifty years ago the miners wanted books and lectures to improve their minds. Now the only thing they like is pop music."

We travelled around the Lake District, reciting half-remembered lines of Wordsworth to one another on the banks of Windermere, calling at Dove Cottage, where we learned that a nun had recently been photographed in the garden trying to dig up one of Wordsworth's daffodils.

With a few drinks inside him Perry might feel sufficiently emboldened to tackle a whole bar in one of the smaller Lakeland villages. He would stand there like the country squire he so resembled, jollying them along and getting them to tell him what they were planning for the Jubilee ... commemorative mugs, street parties, that kind of thing. Some had already decided not to have a parade or decorate their cars because it would be too expensive. Others didn't particularly want any new streetlights. Maybe a bonfire or two.

So, slowly but surely, we were piecing together a tapestry of modern Britain which we began to think might indeed make a good book. Perry had the right contacts to set up something like that, maybe with his friend George Weidenfeld. We might get it out in time for the Jubilee itself.

Far more interesting for me than the picture of modern Britain that was beginning to fill our notebooks was Perry's character. You could pick around the scrambled egg of his personality all week and still keep finding new bits in it. A few drinks after dinner at the end of a long working day and he'd begin telling me stories that entirely subverted my earlier assumptions about him.

He had once got on a plane to attend a debate in Glasgow, he said, and found himself sitting next to Mrs George Melly. She made it clear that she objected to sitting next to this High Tory and, just to wind her up, Perry said: "Ah yes, but we do have a lot in common don't we?"

"What could that possibly be," she spluttered.

"We were both seduced by George."

George had seduced Perry on the sofa in the art room at Stowe School and he'd had a few gay amours like that before taking up with women. When I told him that I liked to smoke a little dope he confessed to having become addicted to purple hearts to keep him awake. Once, when asked what he thought the public might make of Lord Lambton being caught in bed with two women, he'd replied: "Of course I might be wrong but the public probably won't give a ... well, there is no other word for it ... they won't give a f..k." And this was at 6pm on the BBC's *Nationwide*.

He refused to make an immediate apology and was suspended while Lord Hartwell decided his future. The upshot was that he wouldn't be required to write a column for a few weeks or do any broadcasting for six months. And this little verbal indiscretion, Hartwell added, cost him any chance he might have had of becoming editor of the *Sunday Telegraph*.

In his relations with women he was even more disorganised. His marriage to Claudie was on the rocks and, according to his memoir, *Tricks of Memory*, he treated her abominably, even after she had been seriously ill. His affair with an actress lasted twenty years until Claudie died. Then he abandoned the actress for Lord Lambton's daughter, Lucy, whom he married.

"Every man should be faithful to his mistress," he told me one night in the Lakes when we were discussing such affairs although, knowing of my friendship with Claudie, he never actually told me much about his actress.

All his high Tory mates – particularly those in his Wivenhoe set – were subscribers to the tenets of the Anglican Communion and ready to explode with moral outrage at the drop of a hat. They were also unreconstructed polecats ready to bang almost anything that moved. Kingsley Amis, "in his manly noon" as his son Martin put it, was having affairs all over the place. George Gale, who ran a most hospitable home at Wivenhoe, carved the Christmas turkey there one year, ate it, then ran away the same afternoon to live with his mistress. Another of Perry's chums, Henry Fairlie, a distinguished political journalist and lifelong rake, led a life of such indulgent profligacy he often couldn't pay his son's school fees.

Perry was full of the same kind of humbug and it eventually led to his undoing when he did become editor of the *Sunday Telegraph* after the demise of Lord Hartwell. In a leader, under the headline Editors as Playboys, he attacked the editor of the *Observer*, Donald Trelford, and that of the *Sunday Times*, Andrew Neil, for cavorting in public with one Pamela Bordes.

Neil sued for libel and won, saddling the *Telegraph* with costs of £200,000 from a long case in which Perry was described by Neil's counsel as a pompous, sanctimonious and malicious hypocrite. More ominously, the tabloids began digging into his past and exposing his own private life. The full story wasn't pretty.

"The fault was mine of course," he said. "Before writing that leader I should have thought through the risks, not for myself but those close to me."

Perry postured a lot about public morality but he had a feckless nature and an unattractive character. He enjoyed nothing better than a discussion of high political ideas but there were breathtaking levels of superficiality in him. People did admire him but with nowhere near the passion he admired himself. He remains one of the vainest men I've ever met and, when I did later write about his overweening vanity in the *Observer*, he shrugged and said that, had he complained, it would only have confirmed that his vanity was supreme.

But I couldn't help liking him after our tour of England even though it proved to be a grave misjudgement. I spent the week after we had returned to Fleet Street typing up my notes and took them to his office. He seemed embarrassed to receive them and I noticed from his typewriter that he was well advanced on his own version of our tour.

I made no comment and when the first feature appeared the following Sunday, it was advertised as part one of an extensive tour of Britain by Peregrine Worsthorne. He had ignored the copy I had given him and, although I had been mentioned in the body of the text as a colleague, he attributed to me a few daft remarks I didn't remember making.

Such small betrayals are routine in Fleet Street and are hardly important but his version of our tour was poorly written. His reporting skills were second-rate and his descriptions of the people and events, where I had been present, didn't chime with mine. It read as if he was trying to write some kind of cheap novel in which reality was only occasionally glimpsed.

I should have foreseen that little would ever grow under the shadow of his megalomania but I was disappointed that, even at that stage in his career, he was so insecure that he could not share the billing on a project on which we had both worked so hard. There was no question that we could now do a book together, a real disappointment since it would have been my first.

I resigned with immediate effect, telling John Thompson I had been unhappy for some time. Thompson confirmed my low opinion of him by being totally unconcerned, calling me into his office and telling me that, if I ever found myself unhappy in any future work, I should let someone know. He also said that Perry had always been expected to claim sole credit for our journey – even though I had repeatedly been told otherwise.

I had saved a couple of thousand pounds and Liz was earning enough to keep our un-mortgaged home and family going in Newington Green so I finally said goodbye to Fleet Street and with a mixture of feelings, including not a little fear, returned to Wales early that summer to take yet another crack at becoming a novelist.

THIRTY FOUR

I had decided to return to a story that had haunted me since my student days and write about Evan Roberts, the leader of the last great Welsh religious revival in 1904. It had been a remarkable winter. The chapels had been full and the pubs empty and I further hoped to thread a love story through this huge event, the relationship between a young socialist cockle-picker and a deeply religious woman who looked to the chapel for answers. In the clash between these two ideologies twentieth century Wales had been born.

What fascinated me most about this story was the character of the revivalist Evan Roberts, a man plagued by visions he didn't understand, and a man through whom, many still believed, God had once chosen to speak to the Welsh. Evan Roberts was not the brilliant speaker you might have expected of a man who fashioned a mighty revival. He did have inspired outbursts but his manner in the pulpit was often tentative and he was given to long, bewildering silences. He began his sermons by studying the faces of his congregation, making them betray themselves, and then he told them what they already knew: that they were there because they were puzzled by their own interest in this meteoric stranger. This preacher had a doubtful sanity but I had long identified with him so closely that I believed we shared the same spiritual DNA.

How had he coped with God's demands? What sort of visions had he endured? In what way did he believe Wales was being menaced by a rising tide of evil? How had he come to terms with his sexuality? Did he ever seduce his lady singers? Was he no more than another Elmer Gantry? If I could answer such questions, I might be able to understand myself a little better.

I already knew a lot about the revival but my plan was to live in Cardiff throughout the summer, research my subject thoroughly in the Central Library, and then find a room somewhere near the sands of Penclawdd on the Gower peninsula where I would work through the space of one winter – the time-span of my projected novel – watching the changing weather, speaking to people from Evan's area, attending the chapels where he had first fired his revival and perhaps tracking down a few old-timers who might remember his sermons.

A friend of mine, Keith James, managed a betting shop on Penarth Road, a short walk from the Central Library, so I took up residence in a spare room on the top floor. The room had ragged curtains, the bed was a mattress on the floor and commentaries on races and their results percolated up through the floorboards. But we were surrounded by all the shops we needed and a few doors away from a good Brains pub from where we were allowed to carry pints of beer back to the betting shop. It was the writer's garret I had long dreamed about and I got down to work, spending full days – not the odd half hour – in the library's reference room, reading early reports of the revival in newspapers, dragging out dusty books on the subject and filing the information on cards in an index box under such headings as VISIONS. MEETINGS. GOWER. OTHER REVIVALISTS.

Cardiff seemed a particularly fine place to be alive that summer: shoppers crowded the bustling arcades, the skirts of the young girls seemed to be getting shorter by the hour and a good crop of street-entertainers – musicians, mime artists, conjurors and escapologists – set the pavements alight with their entertainments. On most days the summer sunshine scaled the castle walls sending huge cartwheels of golden light rolling along the city's three rivers – the Taff, Ely and Rhymney – before they came together in a galaxy of gorgeousness above Bute Town on the edge of the shimmering Bristol Channel.

After I had finished my labours in the library, I submerged myself in the lively pub culture of the centre, mixing with the reporters from the *Western Mail* and *Echo*, the jazz band who played twice a week in local pubs and occasionally going down to the Chapter Arts Centre, my old school, where they often put on a good film or interesting new play.

The Old Arcade and the City Arms remained my favourite city centre pubs. If Wales' greatest living Irishman, the journalist Dan O'Neill, wasn't in one he would certainly be in the other along with a number of other shady characters like Terry Downey, a parrot-owning photographer who wore failure as a badge of honour, the thriller-writer Robert Peart, forever busy trying to discover the secrets of life in the bottom of a pint glass, and Peter Harris aka the Major, a disc jockey and racing tipster normally flat broke and up to some scam because his chosen horses had failed to perform for him again. The rugby legend Barry John was often there, always ready to tell you another of his several million rugby stories.

My research was going well and I tried hard not to let my drinking get out of control, always a temptation in Cardiff. But, despite the deep spirituality of the story I was researching, I am afraid that almost every time the door of the betting shop opened at night a cavalry charge of women came storming up the stairs. Our visitors included a Norwegian lesbian, an apprentice lion tamer from Scunthorpe, twins who announced they liked threesomes and a bus conductress who would get her driver to stop his big orange bus so she could pop in to make a bet with Keith. But apart from one major hiccup otherwise known as a singer in the local jazz band, I was pretty much in control; I had suffered a lot on that front in recent years and didn't want to take that rocky path again.

When the summer came to an end I gathered up all my notes and took off to the Gower where I found a room in a house next to a pub in the small village of Crofty on the edge of the sands of Penclawdd.

The house was a strange damp place that I shared with a student and an odd couple who kept pet rats in dustbins in their bedroom. They let them out at nights for strolls around the house and the rodents often freaked me out when I met them on the stairs. The living room had been papered with small squares of sample wallpaper, which the skinflint landlord had decided on as a cheap way of doing the job, and I don't think I was ever warm there. When we lit a fire it glowed and spat but never seemed to give out any heat.

I already knew this beautiful part of the Gower from the time when I had been torn apart by *two* women at once: my wonderful and vibrant first love, Sandra, and the charming but withdrawn Kay. I had come here, plagued by their loss, as a student when I was first thinking about this novel and now almost every inch of the great sweep of the sands hissed with anguish and, walking on them, I heard the rumbling music of my breaking heart. Sally's absence still gnawed at me too – and the jazz singer hadn't helped - so, what with all that rain that winter, there was much to be miserable about.

The words of my story – a love story involving Beth, a local girl who gets swept up by the revival, and Michael, a cockle-picker who works the Penclawdd sands – came together easily. It was as if I had been preparing all my life to write this one story and I pounded on my typewriter until I could write no more. Then I might walk out on to the sands for an hour or so before making something to eat and taking a few pints in the pub, where I got to know all the local characters and their stories which I fed into my novel. It soon became clear to me I was distilling my past loves through my memory and restoring them to life in my work. This was my way of getting them back and, as I worked, I often felt them standing around my table, ready, when necessary, to advise me on how to drive the story forward.

In this way Evan's women also became my women and my women became his as I worked in his neighbourhood, breathing the same air as him, walking the same countryside, visiting the same chapels, crying out to him down a long Welsh century for help as I tried to work out what he had, what he knew and how he dealt with his personal difficulties.

On one eschatological battleground Evan and I met face to face, hand to hand, man to man – this great tide of evil which threatened to sweep us all away. Evan was constantly menaced by visions of evil and I too was often struggling to keep afloat in my long season of black rain.

Evan Roberts was in the pulpit struggling for words which kept drying up in his mouth. He swallowed hard. "The moon will bleed ..." The words dried up again and, staring over the sea of faces, his vision grew darker around the edges, more incandescent at the centre. Something big and black heaved in the white light like a whale breaking the surface and disappeared again. A huge hand of hard, solid shadow passed across the face of the earth. The face cried out in terror while the hand loomed over Evan's head like an eternal curse.

"He is coming, then, and will engulf the world," his lips said with the purest fire. "Satan and his dark angels have escaped from their dungeon in hell and are even now gathering for a final, desperate rebellion against God. Beware, my people, arm yourselves with holiness, for this destruction is coming down upon you with a terrible force. This hurricane will tear apart your lives in ways you do not understand. It will come offering money, which destroys charity; offering power which blights love; telling of the triumph of carnal knowledge which undermines fidelity; insisting right is wrong and wrong is right.

"This force will strew illusions at your feet. It will come bloated with gluttony and malodorous with the stink of its own corruption. Its walk will be slow, for it will be burdened with grudges and resentments, trailing ahead of the slime of its hatred. This invading force of evil will come as organised intelligence. Never underestimate it, for it will come dressed as men of respectability, anxious to serve you, able to convince you that Satan does not exist.

"But he does, my people, and he will cast a cloak of perversion right over the face of the world."

The winter rain kept pattering on the window in Crofty. The leaves fell and began growing again. The wild horses came wandering in from the marsh looking for food in the gardens. I smoked a thousand cigarettes. Bonnie Tyler sang *It's a Heartache* on the radio a million times. Occasionally there was a squeak of a rat wandering around the landing. And I just kept writing my love story, my eyes often filling up with tears as I drenched almost every page with melancholy and pain, making my very words surge with the minor-key passions of those great Welsh hymns so beloved of the Welsh soul.

The real struggle in that room was not between man and woman but with me and Evan himself as we both wrestled with the same rough beast slouching to Bethlehem. We had both seen him in our own ways and, although he had a more arcane, more Biblical language than me, we were both possessed by the same visions, both trying to pass on an understanding of a God preparing the world for the return of his Son.

The ending of my novel left Evan Roberts broken and alone in the chapel where he had started his revival. Beth was reunited with her baby briefly only for the girl to die of pneumonia and be cremated on the sands. Beth disappeared on the night of the cremation and Michael searched for her desperately until he rode his horse down to the sands to find her cloak floating on the fast flowing tide.

He picked up the cloak and let it fall back into the water. "Beth. Oh Beth girl what have you gone and done?"

The final thread had parted now, the night full with the promise of a coming storm. Already huge ugly clouds were piling up in a Himalayan range of evil which only forked lightning would disperse. That which was once loved deeply was lost forever. The die had been cast and the sand trickled out of the hand. The shadow of all that was hateful was striding across the sea. The dark days of cold love and shrieking pain had begun.

Oh Beth, girl, *what* have you gone and done?

After I finished the novel I returned to Newington Green in June, somehow purged after my own endless winter. More than anything, I guess I was pretty relieved to find that, by some miracle of human engineering, my marriage and family were still intact. In her own calm and independent way, Liz was leading a fulfilling life, juggling a successful career and children.

I didn't even get too despondent when several publishers sent my manuscript back. That it was set in Wales was a problem for them and the book certainly required a lot of revision. It had been written with too much passion and needed a little more lightness to balance it out. The research had also overwhelmed the story in places and the whole thing needed several years in my bottom drawer before being looked at again dispassionately and critically. That is almost exactly what it got before it was published.

There were now five manuscripts in my bottom drawer but I didn't feel I'd wasted my time that long Welsh winter. I had expected to serve a long apprenticeship as a writer – there is so much to learn and even more to forget. Writing was anyway always a great pleasure: nothing came close to the rapture of creating a good scene or describing a momentous event. I kept writing because I needed to; not wanted but *needed* to. Writing affirmed my humanity: my words underlined my fleeting passage through a teeming world. It hardly mattered to me if my words were any good or not, although I would certainly have liked to see them published one day in some form.

THIRTY FIVE

There was nothing else to do but find some work so I rang the *Observer* and began as a freelance reporter for them the next day. After the *Sunday Telegraph* it was a relief to get back to a newspaper which valued good writing. It had regained most of its old confidence now that it belonged to the oil company Atlantic Richfield which had paid all its outstanding debts and David Astor had been replaced as editor by Donald Trelford. My old pal Peter Deeley was news editor.

The newsroom wasn't over-endowed with talent and they liked my gift for the trivial and inconsequential. Not only did such stories almost always get a good show, often as the creeper or crawler on page one, but they also involved minimal work: you just went somewhere and described whatever you had seen or whoever you had met.

I started a long run as champion of animals and insects with a story about a man in Essex who could explain the swarms of greenfly which had been invading every vegetable patch in the country that summer.

Balding, with big hands and a voice like a record being played at double speed, Lawrence Hills directed a research station that experimented in poisonless pest control. Aphids, scale insects, mealy bugs, thrips, caterpillars and mites: you name them and he had ways of sorting them out. He sent armies of ladybirds in pursuit of the greenfly and established a Ladybird Hilton in his grounds where lady and gentlemen ladybirds could sleep together in the warmth of asbestos pipes for the winter. Ladybirds sleep all winter and copulate all spring, it seems, and then the gentleman ladybird dies, presumably from exhaustion.

In other attempts to marshal the natural world, Hills had tried to recruit glow-worms to eat slugs (no success), enlisted hedgehogs and encouraged soldier beetles to do the same (slight success) but his favourite, by a mile, was the hover fly (big success).

Another story I enjoyed was about fleas. The angle was that the last flea circus in Britain – in Manchester's Belle Vue – had finally shut up shop because the circus master could not locate a steady supply of fleas. They had been wiped out by the combined ravages of DDT, the vacuum cleaner and regular baths.

During my investigations I went to Cambridge to interview the world's leading flea expert. He explained that, far from being verminous bloodsuckers, fleas are the jolliest of creatures with an astonishing anatomy that includes two penises – a big one for penetration and a smaller one, curled around that, for foreplay – and an ath-

269

leticism that would have won them every gold medal at the Olympics. They also have been stars of stage, screen and circus, he went on, and are amorous beyond the dreams of the maddest, most nymphomaniac poets.

St Francis of Assisi called fleas pearls of poverty. They also have phenomenal stamina. Those in flea circuses could perform fifty ten-minute shows a day and carry on for a fortnight before conking out. A flea can jump a hundred and fifty times its own height, which, in human terms, is the equivalent of a man jumping over St Paul's Cathedral. During the jump it somersaults a few times but always lands on its feet.

With its two cocks, the flea possesses the most elaborate sexual equipment in the natural world and Miriam Rothschild, who was known as the "Queen of the Fleas" for her work as a parasitologist, said that any engineer assessing such a fantastically complicated mechanism would bet heavily against it ever working. Fleas make love for three hours and sometimes for as long as nine. There are fleas that live only in the tears of the hippopotamus; fleas that travel the continents of the world on the winds and fleas that serenade one another with dulcet love calls. The fleas that live on humans are the best for circuses. Now they've gone we have only a quarter of a million other varieties left.

I loved doing stories like this, but the pleasure came to an end when I was sent to Northern Ireland again to investigate a shooting in an Army barracks. The previous Sunday, Trooper Edward Maggs had been on sangar duty. Sangars are high lookout posts built of grey breeze blocks and surrounded by wire netting to ward off hurled bombs. Inside, it was a dark prison cell with photographs of known terrorists on the walls. In the summer it is boiling hot and in the winter freezing cold.

The man on sangar duty must look out through a narrow slit and observe any movements for up to four hours at a time. He may not read, listen to the radio, sit down or even urinate while on duty. If there is any action or "contact" he may use his general-purpose machine gun but only against men with two rifles or one machine gun. Otherwise he must use his own self-loading rifle. Soldiers regarded sangar duty as the most boring non-event in the universe.

At 2pm that Sunday, Trooper Maggs had slipped the safety-catch on his SLR and, in a brief and murderous twenty minutes, fired off round after round at his own men, killing one and seriously injuring another. A Yellow Card warning had been read out. When Maggs failed to stop firing, he was shot dead.

I was in deep despair as the shadow of the helicopter went spinning over the green, patched countryside below us. I wanted to write about killer ladybirds and randy fleas and here I was back again in the last place in the world I wanted to be. Violence again! Not the usual form of terrorist violence on which we had consistently gorged over the years, but violence nevertheless: that little delicious carrot which gets news desks everywhere dribbling with anticipation.

Some in the Army hadn't particularly wanted me there, I was told later, but the top brass had insisted that I be given "access all areas". These soldiers were as clever in handling the media as the terrorists.

One soldier told me, strictly off the record, that most of the listening dishes attached to their Londonderry watchtowers did not work. They were there to give the *impression* to the locals that somebody was listening to every conversation. Who was kidding who in this fiasco?

The Royal Welch Regiment, under the command of Lt Col Morgan Llewellyn, put on an impressive show of openness for me and I was allowed to investigate the private world of the private soldier.

We will never discover the full story behind Trooper Maggs' brainstorm but quite soon I appreciated the stress on the troops and the atmosphere in which he had turned that gun on his fellow soldiers.

That week the 605-strong unit was due to return to its base in Germany, having completed a four-month tour in Londonderry. That doomed city was still far from quiet. Most of the incidents had been the usual small-scale stuff, yet in their four months here, the regiment had discovered 23 bombs and 893 rounds of ammunition. Some 50,000 vehicles had been stopped and 23,000 searched. There had been 13 armed robberies in the city; 34 explosions; 50 bomb hoaxes and ten car hijackings. In the last three weeks there had been four kneecappings in the Creggan suburb alone.

About every six months the IRA would set up a sniper attack, if only to maintain media interest in them. "The worst part of patrolling here is late at night when the pubs kick out,' said Sergeant Arthur Ellingham. "You get some gob-shites full of Guinness wanting to have a go. Normally we just laugh at them but working out here is like fighting a war with both hands tied behind your back."

The most striking feature of the fusiliers' lives was the long and gruelling hours. They were not allowed outside their compounds – except on patrol – for the duration of their tour. A breakdown of the hours worked by the Royal Welch in Londonderry each week showed that, on average, field officers worked 93 hours; sergeants 85; corporals 96 and fusiliers 92. Many told of working a 118 to 130 hours a week, mostly on sangar duty. The lower ranks worked four hours on and four hours off for the full twenty-four hours a day, seven days a week, except for rest days, for four months.

Sexual activity was confined to talking about it or wolf-whistling the local women while out on patrol in the streets. The fusiliers' bedrooms were festooned with pornographic pictures; an incredible panorama of pneumatic poses which gave new meaning to the concept of interior photography. "We're all too tired to worry too much about all that," said a sergeant.

The fusiliers reckoned that almost two-thirds of their work involved sangar duty and at midnight that night I joined Tony Jones in a sangar just on the Republic's border. Fat snowdrops swirled around in the phosphorescent glare of the sodium lights outside and, inside, the cell was dark and claustrophobic. Apart from a machine gun and an SLR rifle, Fusilier Jones had a shot direction indicator and a telescope that magnified light in the dark and enabled him to scan the outlying fields for movement. Despite this firepower, he had only ever experienced one false alarm in his four-month tour of duty.

"This work bores me to tears," he said. "There's not a thing going on. I think about all kinds of things ... the girls I've known, the Welsh rugby team and how they're getting on. I don't mind the Irish – not like some of my mates – but it gets hard watching the lights of the cars all night. Between two and six in the morning there's not even the cars to look at."

The following morning I joined D company at their base on Piggery Ridge, which covers the Creggan, a Provisional hotbed. Piggery Ridge was the most bombed and shot-at base in Europe and the Creggan itself resembled some new hinterland of hell with the walls of its crouching, drab houses daubed with such graffiti as STUFF THE JUBILEE, BRITS OUT and, the most popular demand, SMASH THE H BLOCKS.

The area was patrolled four times a day and the men had to watch out for strangers and note such details as how many milk bottles were left on the doorstep. Domestic dogs were trained to run after Army Land-Rovers. The locals ignored the soldiers moving around in their gardens. The very young didn't even look up from their ice creams. The most lively part of the patrol came when school ended and the pupils, all dressed in the same blue anoraks with grey fur collars, gathered on one of the hills to hurl missiles at passing patrols.

"They throw everything: bottles, bricks, iron bars," said our driver. "The latest stunt has been throwing light bulbs hidden inside snowballs. I caught one on the cheek last week and got cut."

Indeed it was shocking to witness all these anoraked little squirts with their hard eyes and cheeks pinched white with hatred. They screamed obscenities and didn't seem to know the meaning of fear: they understood perfectly well the Army wouldn't dare take a shot at them.

What they were doing made sense in the context of their community. Kids elsewhere might grow up on American comics, rock'n'roll and a little light wanking. All this lot would have known was violence and hatred. If they were lucky they might join a riot and get their faces on the evening news: every kid everywhere wants to get his face on television. Could these kids grow up into normal people after being cocooned in such hatred? Not with television ruling their homes they couldn't. They didn't have a prayer.

Then, as is the way of journalism, everything changed overnight. Columnist Geoffrey Wansell, who was writing the Pendennis diary, went on holiday and Donald Trelford asked me to fill in for him. Unfortunately for Geoffrey, Trelford preferred what I did to what he had been doing and I was offered the column full-time, a staff job, my own secretary, Anne, and the use of a freelance of my choice three days a week.

"We all like you here," said Trelford, displaying a recently acquired belief in my abilities. "Follow your instincts. Put the knife in when you feel like it. Let yourself go."

Trelford must have liked my work a lot since I asked for – and got – my name on the column, the first time this had happened in the newspaper's history. I had almost half a page a week all to myself, on one of the best "Sundays" in the world, with my name in lights. Ah yes, journalism was the job for me.

I had tackled this kind of journalism before, on Atticus at the *Sunday Times*, but now, unfettered by the gluttonous obsessions of Allan Hall, I had a column which I could define in my own way. I didn't intend to write a diary as bored and cynical as Allan's, nor did I want to write it like Geoffrey Wansell's, which had been a grab-bag of bits and pieces: a few paragraphs about some starlet here, a few more about a painter, some minor political revelations not important enough for the news pages, a book puff or two or else some idle celebrity chatter. I also inherited a birthdays correspondent, Jeremy Beadle, whose particular speciality was giving birthdays to those who were long dead and whom I was going to get rid of as soon as decently possible.

I had in mind a metropolitan diary with only two or three pieces about my wanderings around the wilds of London acting out everyone's fantasy of meeting famous people in delicious venues. An absolute priority each week would be a beautiful, talented woman who would be flirted with and photographed lovingly. I would look for a serious, reasonably hard-edged subject to lead the column and balance that up with a quirky sketch of a challenging character like Malcolm Muggeridge or Dennis Skinner. It would be all about names: not B-list celebrity quiz show hosts or soap stars such as the tabloids drooled over but personalities who were achievers: people with intellectual clout.

But however I wanted to frame it I would, in short, be moving through our celebrity culture which had just become getting a total grip on the media, a wholly romantic culture, driven by a mania for fame and a search for sexual inconstancy. Such ideas were almost certainly Rousseauesque in their origin insofar as the old madman had promoted popular heroes, the worship of people merely because of their beauty and the mass identification with all such: the cult of the individual. Before Rousseau we venerated holy people or figures of myth; after him almost anyone could be worshipped whether it be a footballer with a mean right cross or a dizzy blonde prepared to get her tits out for the camera.

Not that I wanted to get near too much crassness in Pendennis. Writers would be obvious targets. I would certainly pursue them as I had on Atticus and I still saw talking to them as very much a part of my continuing education and ambition to become a writer. A grand scheme like this would take time to evolve so I began feeling my way at the start of my career as a diarist in the time-honoured manner with five or six random pieces about this or that. Then I had an astounding piece of luck in meeting an unusual freelance.

I had wanted to talk to Kate Bush, and got through to her people only to be told that Richard D North from the *Observer Magazine* was already there. I learned that he was profiling her for the magazine, so I asked him for three or four hundred words, which he duly supplied. They were oddly poetic, with some marvellous turns of phrase and I was even more impressed when Richard came into the office with bicycle clips on his jeans and rain dripping off his cycling cape. He laughed a lot and displayed a huge set of gnashers below a nose like a jackdaw's. He had been working on the eco magazine, *Vole*, where they were all certifiable, and fixed bicycles in Kentish Town at weekends.

He cycled everywhere, which was of interest to me at the time since the police had taken away my driving licence after an unfortunate incident with a Chinese takeaway and another car. Richard and I had a few drinks in the Cockpit pub next door and I offered him three days' work a week on the column, which he accepted. He could continue his other freelance work, I said, but any freelance would love to have a regular three days' pay a week, particularly with the small amount of work I had in mind for him.

He urged me to get on a bike and, somewhat nervously I did, surprised at how quickly the strength built up in my legs as I swanned around town. We were soon riding out of the city too, one night pedalling all the way to Wembley in the vain hope of interviewing Tammy Wynette at a Country Music Festival.

On the way home, after cycling up an endless hill towards Golders Green, we cooled off by removing our shoes and socks and riding around the pond at the top of Hampstead Heath. It was all a bit of a lark and I continued to be amazed at how childishly pleasant life had become since I started riding a bike. Afterwards we dried our feet with a Tammy Wynette T-shirt and I knew that serendipity had played a part in my life yet again. Through meeting Richard I had met the bicycle and, through the bicycle, I had done nothing less than save my life at a time when, doing this column, it could have easily fallen apart.

Yet as I continued pedalling around the West End, again and again I was coming across my Malayan visions made flesh, constantly surprised at how the romantic mind and philosophy was shared by so many of my interviewees and how they had become rich and famous because of it.

I could think clearly on my bike – something to do with the oxygenated brain perhaps – and it occurred to me that what God had been telling me in Malaya wasn't just about the violence which we hear and see so much about in our news media, nor was it particularly to do with the obsession with sexual inconstancy. It wasn't even the perpetual sexual frustration and heartbreaking passion in our pop songs, nor the routine perversions and violence of Hollywood – or even the gonzo romanticism of many of our major writers.

That which God had spoken of in my vision of the black rain was almost everywhere I looked because those who were rich and famous were romantics themselves. Between them they had created a romantic and useless popular culture in which we were all trying, but failing, to maintain some form of stability. Some of these artists were more capable and powerful than others while a few were decisively and trenchantly influential but, to a greater or lesser degree, they all fell under the same dark shadow. They were imprisoning the free world in a carcinogenic cocoon of romanticism which was not only leeching poison into the world's every pore but also attacking the very heart of us, engulfing us in violence, encouraging us to embrace infidelity, feeding us with horror and nightmare, leaving us sleepless and paralysed with fear. They were even attacking the very mind of God although not one of them would admit that or even understand the charge.

More scary by far than that frightening perception was the more personal realisation that what was leading the world astray was leading me astray too. This global disease lived deep in the heart of me as I kept discovering to my continuing cost. Open-eyed, I was suffering from it too and didn't see how I might recover. I was always ready to seek out new intensities, pursue empty dreams and indulge in alcohol and drugs to an almost destructive degree.

Not that I was going to write anything about this in my column: my visions were my business and there was certainly no place for them in a newspaper although, in the light of them, I did begin quietly exploring my life's theme by sniffing around a few romantic personalities who had been major influences on me when I was young and who, after what had happened to me in Malaya, I now saw rather differently.

My first target was the daffy JP Donleavy, author of *The Ginger Man*. His wholly romantic creation of Sebastian Dangerfield pursued stray women, drink and debt when he was not fighting and rampaging around Dublin. This book had had a profound influence on me when I was young and I suppose the most curious thing about Donleavy, when we met for breakfast at Claridge's, was the extraordinary contradiction between him as a person and the wild Sebastian Dangerfield.

Donleavy was a fastidious dresser with a smart tweed suit, a spotted handkerchief sticking out of his top pocket and a pin-striped shirt with an elegant tie: every bit the Irish country gentleman on his way to the horse fair. His features were gaunt and baggy-eyed and he studied me balefully with his head lowered like a dog unsure whether he was going to get a pat or a kick. He spoke in such a soft whisper you could barely make out what he was saying and drank his orange juice with his little finger sticking out. A truly annoying characteristic was that he kept standing up from his bacon and eggs every time anyone came near our table. This obsequiousness continued when we went to Broadcasting House where he was appearing on Radio 4's *Start the Week*, and he opened so many doors for me we practically began fighting when it came to opening the next.

Why was it then that as soon as he sat in front of a typewriter he experienced a violent personality change? His novels, beginning with *The Ginger Man* and right up to his latest, *Schultz*, the book he was plugging, were, not to put too fine a point on it, an avalanche of filth.

This filth wasn't even funny, there was hardly a trace of original creative energy in *Schultz* and the dialogue was often simply exchanges of "f..k this" and "f..k that" with no avenue explored that he hadn't explored a hundred times before. He carefully and repeatedly pointed out that his work might be obscene but never pornographic, a distinction I didn't understand.

How, then, when he looked out through the curtains of his Irish mansion with its swimming pool and football field, with the cows mooing in the distant meadow, how could he sit down and churn out such tired fantastical crap as *Schultz*? Did he feel any responsibility to his readers?

"No. If I allowed myself to worry about that I would never get anything written."

Did he feel he might have some duty to engage reality in his work?

"Not really but it is true that I tend to romanticise everything."

Did he think he might have any sort of pernicious influence on his readers?

"It's possible but none that I know of."

We got around to the writers he liked and admired and he spoke of Kafka, Fitzgerald and Joyce.

"Henry Miller?" I asked and he said, for I wrote it down, "Oh yes, Henry Miller was a tremendous influence on me." He also, it emerged, admired Truman Capote and Norman Mailer.

So what we had here, I thought, was another member of that band of romantic revolutionaries who feed one another's fantasies, ignoring the claims of real people and specialising in alienation, animalism and despair. He had firmly claimed his place in an artistic conspiracy that was destroying the world: the influences he had described were in that same conspiracy. Not that he saw it in such terms.

"Really I'm just a quiet businessman who writes books," he whispered.

A little later I came across the spent force that was Lawrence Durrell, curator of Greek legends, lifelong pal of Henry Miller and chronicler of diabolical doings in Alexandria.

Like so many others of a certain age I had been in thrall to the Alexandrian Quartet, with its effusions of gorgeous prose and shady characters with noseless faces, and I had pictured Durrell as a big, wild-eyed man with long, curling locks and a cavernous cloak under which he secreted bottles of wine, sheaves of poems and a nubile girl or two.

How wrong could you get?

I met him for a pint in a pub and found a tiny, tubby man with a big, blobby face; blue eyes; a balding, wrinkled pate and a soft, almost colonial accent. Far from secreting nubile girls under his cloak he was carrying a blue, empty shopping bag and I bought the drinks.

To make matters worse he was suffering badly with rheumatism and asthma. "It's absolute hell," he said. "I can't run, can't cut wood, can't do anything."

There was no rancour or self-pity in his tone as he sat on one leg in the pub, his hand playing with his sock. His short legs were very fat and, as he wobbled about, his whole frame seemed to be formed of spare tyres like some small Buddha on the blink.

We spoke about his health, his friendship with Henry Miller – "He left a great hole in the décor when he left us" – and TS Eliot. The one thing that stood out was the incredible level of rubbish in his conversation. I could hardly understand any of the quotes that I duly transcribed in my notebook and I found his new book, *A Smile in the Mind's Eye*, a study of Taoism, total bosh.

How had he got away with so much for so long? Even a semi-trained philosopher would have destroyed his every utterance in one minute flat. "Did he ever fear he had spent most of his life talking rubbish," I asked.

"Oh yes, all the time," he replied without batting an eyelid.

What next?

"Well death, I suppose, but we may all be dead already."

Gleeps.

"But then most of the gang have gone now. They've all gone. Anaïs. TS and Henry. I've just got old and grumpy, going around boring the hell out of everyone. I'm the last of an epoch."

Later in the winter of 1979 I managed to catch up with Norman Mailer in

Manhattan and, given that he had been such a decisive influence over me as a young wannabe writer, I got really stuck into him to the extent that when he flew into London on the Sunday my column about him appeared, he read it and wanted to fly straight home again. He said that talking to me had been a big mistake. "You get criticised in America but in Britain they set out to destroy you."

Mailer was so influential, I think, because he was often capable of recklessly brilliant bursts of good writing that the young identified with and wanted to copy. But he also influenced the general media with his macho celebrations of violence and murder. If you read the body of his work you understand how his ideas have fed so positively into Hollywood and television. You can see where most of the cinematic madness and mayhem is coming from: much of it has been inspired and sanctioned by his work.

Consider, he wrote, the actual case of two young men beating to death a sweet-shop owner. Did it not have its beneficial aspect? One murders not only a weak, fifty-year-old man, but an institution as well: one violates private property, one enters into a new relationship with the police and introduces a dangerous element into one's life.

In his novel, *American Dream*, Mailer describes a man's murder of his wife as a positive act in the development of his personality, a liberation, a catharsis. After the murder the illness passed from the murderer. This idea has a positive echo in the film *Lethal Weapon*, starring Mel Gibson, as one example among many. In the early part of the film our hero was suffering from a mental disorder but, after a long series of violent acts, he emerged smiling, purged, his sanity restored.

Mailer was promoting his new work, *The Executioner's Song*, when I met him and he turned out to be an engaging, immodest man, short and dumpy, with tiny cold blue eyes, no neck to speak of, a bulging chest which made his arms hang away from his sides as if to give him balance and a thatch of thinning grey hair. He was in good shape, working out in a gym every Saturday morning with a former light-heavy-weight boxing champion.

I found him likeable and with a beguiling ability to send himself up. The urge to write had long left him, he said, but there was all this alimony to be found for his sweet, battling wives and eight kids. Far from wearying of marriage, he suspected he might marry sixteen times before he was through.

One subject cruised into another and we got on to his latest work, *The Executioner's Song*, about Gary Gilmore, who had insisted on being executed for killing a motel manager in Utah. Mailer said he hoped the book would become a classic text in criminology but he then made a remark so startling that it brought me up short.

"There is something saintly about murder."

I wrote that down and looked at him without saying anything.

"I know you can spend the rest of your life explaining remarks like that. I am not in favour of murder but I am saying that murder can give you feelings of life."

He added that murder continued to obsess him and he had once thought of calling the Gilmore book *The Saint and the Psychopath*. His hands smoothed the table again. "Gary was an obvious psychopath with something saintly about him. I wanted to show that Gary was not insane. There is no record of him wavering."

There it was again: the romanticising of murder – the wicked refusal to perceive murder as the wanton, callous act of savagery that it is. Mailer's ideas were to get him into more hot water and lead to his involvement in a real-life murder. In 1977, Jack Abbott, a prisoner locked up for murder, began writing to Mailer. His letters described life in prison and there was much in Abbott's language that suggested prison was the best place for him.

"The judge sentenced me to the main penitentiary for the express purpose of having me raped by prisoners and reduced to a homosexual. To the authorities there is nothing seriously wrong with getting raped in prison. On the contrary, the idea excites them, they *enjoy* it. Here in prison the most respected and honoured men among us are those who have killed other men, particularly prisoners. It is not merely fear but respect."

Mailer was so impressed by these letters he helped get them published in a book under the title, *In the Belly of the Beast*, for which he wrote a gushing foreword.

"Crime is a positive experience for juvenile delinquents because it is more exciting, more meaningful, more mysterious, more transcendental, more religious than any other experience they have known," he wrote, adding that Abbott was an intellectual, a radical, a potential leader.

Along with like-minded celebrities such as Christopher Walken and Susan Sarandon, Mailer managed to obtain parole for Abbott in June 1981, celebrating his release with a dinner at Mailer's home. Within days, after a row with a waiter in a New York restaurant, this intellectual, radical and potential leader took out his exciting, meaningful, mysterious and transcendental knife and brutally stabbed the waiter to death. At the subsequent trial Mailer admitted to having blood on his hands but expressed no sympathy for Abbott's victim. At least Abbott was back inside where he belonged.

THIRTY SIX

Within weeks Richard and I had worked out what we wanted to do, the column was going well, my home life was unusually happy and, largely thanks to my bike, my relationship to the city had changed for the better.

Atop my saddle I cycled free of bus queues, truculent taxi drivers and, despite a truly sybaritic lifestyle, managed to stay reasonably fit. My greatest joy was discovering the intimate and attractive secrets of London contained in its overwhelming traffic-fumed largeness. I came across intricate Victorian railings in Smithfield and, in the next street to mine, happened on a Chinese noodle factory. If I heard interesting music coming out of a pub I could lasso my bike to a tree and pop in to listen to it. There was a three-legged dog that sat on a window sill in Islington and unusual pockets of beguiling fragrances hanging in the air around the wasteland that is Kings Cross.

Even at night you could stop at will to savour new surprises that, in a car, you would have missed. I loved ghosting through the city nights, free of the menaces of police and traffic wardens, my reflection chasing after me in the various shop windows and accompanied only by the peaceful ticking of ball bearings when I freewheeled down a slope. The parks were the best to travel across at these times, lonely nightscapes with a still freshness in the air, which you didn't always associate with London parks, and stooped figures mooching around in the bushes looking for love. Long journeys home were often a procession of new discoveries that you wanted to go on for ever.

As if this wasn't enough, I had begun mining a glorious seam of beautiful women, surprised so many of them were prepared to talk to me. I was to find that actresses were generally fragile, insecure women, believing they could be tied to the railway lines at any moment and who would do almost anything for a few kind words. One week it was Felicity Kendall, the next Joanna Lumley, Hannah Gordon or Francesca Annis.

They weren't all over-friendly as it turned out, particularly Francesca Annis even though she rode a bike and had agreed to meet me. Possibly I'd made the mistake of confusing her character with that of the genial Lillie Langtry who she had just made famous in a television series, but the long and short of it was she didn't think much of the Press.

"I want to keep my private life to myself," she snorted after turning up late and then getting difficult about the photograph. "On yer bike," she snapped later when I stooped to kiss her goodbye on the cheek.

279

Joanna Lumley was a strange one too. The living room of her flat in Holland Park was piled high with paintings, bric-a-brac such as old weighing scales and baroque mirrors, magazines everywhere and more flowers than at the Chelsea Flower Show. There were lots of old books too, first editions I guessed, and Joanna, dressed only in a shirt and knickers, wandered about unselfconsciously, showing off her endless legs to an extent that made me think that I might even get lucky here with a fair breeze.

Daughter of an Army major there was a lot of "jolly" and "gosh" about her but she neutralised it by swearing like a trooper. She talked almost non-stop and worried a great deal. "There's something I've forgotten," she kept saying as she ironed her dress for a do that night at the Savoy Hotel. "I know there's something I've forgotten, I just know it. My memory isn't what it used to be. I'm always going to Marks and Sparks to buy a bra and forgetting why I've gone there."

Later that evening, as she drove me through the West End, she was still fretting about her amnesia. "I know there's something I've forgotten," she began again, but was cut short by a dawdling driver ahead of her.

"Come on Noddy. Get a move on."

She wasn't letting on about any of her blokes, apart from vaguely admitting there were a couple around. No one had even been told who was the father of her son. "The Press are always giving me affairs I've never had and killed off a few I did have. After a while you learn."

We got to the Savoy, had another drink and she asked me, in a quietly lethal way, why it was that, the more I drank, the fouler my language became. I had no answer to that: her language had been far fouler than mine, I protested, but I took it as an invitation to push off so I did.

A big favourite of mine was Felicity Kendall. I liked to drop in and see her at whatever theatre she was playing and she would crack open a bottle of wine – although she never drank herself as she was usually about to go on stage. She was gorgeous, with those lovely cheekbones, and full of friendly curiosity about me, which always goes down well with men. We had some wonderfully intimate chats and I even thought there might be some internal combustion on offer. But it never was.

I was amused by the way I kept believing I had fallen in love with these women even when I was met with a polite but firm resistance (you would never get anywhere with a few gin and tonics with this lot) and I only ever got over my unrequited longings for Felicity when they were fully and finally transferred to Susan Hampshire, the best of all my romantic lost causes.

If I interviewed anyone theatrical the picture desk usually gave me as photographer Nobby Clark, a bluff Cockney who has had numerous exhibitions and photographed just about everyone who was anyone in the theatre over the last thirty years. One day I asked Nobby who was his favourite actress and, as he put his head to one side, there was a faraway look in his eyes. "Oh Susan 'Ampshire. She's magic. Makes me legs go all funny every time I looks at 'er."

Discreet inquiries revealed that Susan Hampshire also had a thing about Nobby.

"He's wonderful," she told me on the phone. "I'd say he's the best in the business."

I arranged a date and we converged next day at the Haymarket where Susan was appearing in some rubbish called *The Crucible of Blood*.

She was indeed a very beautiful lady and my own legs began to go weak as soon as I looked at her. There was an English classicism in those high, wide cheekbones and her face conjured up the click of croquet balls, the smell of cucumber sandwiches, lace parasols and fluffy white dresses at vicarage tea parties.

The problem was I wasn't quite sure what to talk about and with Nobby there, polishing his lenses and behaving like a proper gentleman – even looking at me sharply when I used a rude word – I felt lost and sat there like the original gooseberry.

Nobby began doing his stuff and I was looking at a blank page in my notebook when Susan uttered a sentence which floated across the room like a single, small cloud in a clear, blue sky.

"We've got five bikes in our family, you know."

She was a bike nut, always out on one on weekends. "I don't do it for exercise or to save money or pollution. I just love it. It makes me feel I'm on holiday. You can stop and look down streets. It's also nice knowing that someone's trees are going to have more leaves on them."

The blood slowly began draining out of my belly and we spent a very happy hour talking about bikes. Love and affection flowered everywhere. Women in sports cars are one thing: a woman on a bike is an entirely different proposition. The cohesive beauty of bikes. The sheer bloody agony of cycling up steep hills. The unalloyed bliss of cruising downhill. Messing about in country lanes. "Bikes are very sexy," she said. "The wind. A floppy lace shirt. White skirt. In the summer it's wonderful."

Overwhelmed, I stood up and offered her the rare honour of a ride on my bike, which was tied to the traffic lights outside the theatre. It was the very stuff of a young boy's dreams, watching her sail down the Haymarket with Nobby jumping around in the traffic after her, though there was a nasty moment when she smiled at Nobby and nearly got hit by a motorbike.

That week I wrote a piece in my column about me, my bike and Susan Hampshire under the headline *Love Among the Spokes* in which I acclaimed her play – even though I have not seen it to this day – the greatest triumph in the English theatre and certainly the most ravishing production ever to grace the West End stage. I even gave the prices of admission and the numbers of the buses that would get you to the Haymarket.

That one piece, Susan told me later, sold out the half-full theatre for two months and each night, after the show finished, she was given a standing ovation. All of which did not stop my heart being torn asunder when, no sooner had I gone abroad one dark spring, than she flung my love for her back in my face and married some millionaire Greek ship-owner.

Sigourney Weaver was in town, I heard, promoting the first of the *Alien* films and, as I'd long admired her intelligent work, I set off in hot pursuit of her.

Her publicity people fixed me up with an hour in her Piccadilly hotel and suggested that I might like to go and see the film first, followed by a press conference with its director. It was not a film I would normally have chosen to see but I went along anyway and, oh boy, was I sorry. This film was evil, one of the most Satanic eruptions of the romantic imagination ever. For much of the time I was under my seat, for the rest I watched, horrified, through a fretwork of fingers and hair. I felt sick almost as soon as it started and got sicker. Weeks later its effects were still fluttering, bat-like, around my mind.

Alien is the story of seven astronauts working a commercial starship. They encounter a savage beast and fight it, but what was truly remarkable was the way its director, Ridley Scott, had managed to pull together everything that was romantic and rotten in the contemporary cinema. There was its persistent preoccupation with the perverted, the morbid, the violent and the cruel. There were monsters, mayhem and murder – all even further removed from reality than normal because it was set in outer space. The only "human" member of the crew turned out to be a robot.

After the showing we gathered for lunch at the Café Royal where, at one stage, I found myself sitting next to Ridley Scott and other assorted film luminaries. He had weak features emphasised by a ginger beard and I just sat there, chatting with Emma Soames, wondering quite what crawled around the sewers in his mind.

He had worked for the BBC – an episode of *Z Cars* – before going on to make some three thousand television commercials including those for Hovis Bread, Strongbow Cider and Levi jeans. He had learned his sharp cinematography with those commercials and I was told he was a determined and tough operator who liked his horror hot.

In *Alien* John Hurt picks up a monster while exploring a distant planet. The alien lodges itself in his lungs until, when everything seems okay and the crew are enjoying a quiet meal, the monster bursts out of Hurt's chest in a shower of blood and runs amok on the starship. For this scene, which became known as the Chest Burster, Scott got fresh offal from the local abattoir and stuffed it into Hurt's fake chest. Scott didn't tell the other actors what he'd done and when the chest exploded, Veronica Cartwright caught several pints of blood and offal directly in her face that left her shaking for hours. Another scene, later cut, involved condoms packed with live maggots.

Now what kind of human being would do that?

I asked Scott if he was worried about the effect of such nastiness.

"No," he said, "and anyway my audiences are over eighteen and will have a rough idea of what they are about to see." He seemed genuinely astonished when I told him that I would never be able to sleep at night if I'd made a film like that. "It scares them," he said, "but there's no real harm in it."

Oh, really?

The next day I met Sigourney Weaver and asked her if she believed that films had any effect on people?

"Films do get into my head," she said.

Wasn't she worried that this film was going to get into other people's heads and possibly damage them?

"This film is no worse than *Midnight Express*. Did you see that? Some shocking scenes. And what about Sam Peckinpah's work?"

"I was rather hoping we could be talking about this film. You know. *Alien*. This thing you've just done."

"I can't be objective about this one. I can't get it into perspective."

Our discussion continued on these lines until, at one stage, she got really stuck for words when I added that I thought the film was evil. She didn't like that one little bit. She handled the usual publicity questions with ease but didn't seem to be able to answer my questions.

"They don't normally ask these kind of questions. They usually ask me things like why did I go back for the cat?"

She lit a cigarette and, when Nobby Clark began photographing her, she put it out, saying she was worried about the effect seeing a cigarette in her hand might have on children.

"Are you joking?" I asked.

"No," she replied seriously.

"So horror is acceptable but not cigarettes?"

We took some more photographs in Green Park and, on the way back to the hotel, bumped into the film director, John Schlesinger. I introduced him to her and she began complaining that I had been knocking her film. He'd seen it in America and thought it was fine, so what the hell was I going on about? I explained and he said, "Well you could also say that about Edgar Allan Poe."

"I do," said I. "I do."

"Oh dear," said he. "Oh dear."

Schlesinger's friend joined the argument and said if there was a really monstrous play around the West End at the moment it was *Bent*. He loathed that play and we had a really great row on the pavement with lots of passers-by looking around and various voices rising by decibels.

I'll never be able to understand these film people. They'll be the death of us all one day. I left on my bike soon after that and went to feed the ducks in St James's Park.

I crucified *Alien* in my column the following Sunday and the piece had an extraordinary effect on my readers, who were not generally the type to write letters to anyone. I received several hundred about that one column. Some were heartfelt.

"I know my children and can see how they are changed by such films," one mother wrote. "They are under attack and there is nothing at all we can do about it."

That column had a severe effect on Ridley Scott too, I learned with quiet satisfaction. He had been at a dinner party the night it appeared and had been too catatonic with shock to speak. All they could get out of him was: "If I ever catch up with that bastard Tom Davies I'm going to beat his f..king head in."

It was through my column on *Alien* that I entered into a deeper dialogue with my readers, many of whom seemed delighted that *someone* was challenging the violent and perverted heart of the film industry.

Certainly no one else was stepping forward to write anything out of the conventional line – this was the one industry where critic and film-maker were all firmly bolted to one another in the same bed – although my distaste for the film industry rapidly evolved into boiling hatred after a visit to the Cannes Film Festival where almost everyone I met was disgusting in one way or another.

To get some idea of this festival you need to cross the hyperbolic glitz of Disneyland with the torrent of lies told by the public relations industry, throw in a collage of Hollywood film posters, slap it into a giant hamburger and smother it with tomato sauce. Hang a sun lamp over the top of the lot and you are coming close to the essence of this horrific circus which sets up its tent each year on the edge of the Med.

All week I pedalled up and down the Croisette and all week I could not remember hearing such maddening music. This industry is run by people who exercise absolute power with terrifying irresponsibility. Their visions are of violence, murder, perversion and terrorism: none of them seems to understand or be prepared to acknowledge the intimate connection between ideas on the screen and the minds and conduct of the people watching. They looked at you blankly if you suggested they were reconstructing people's imaginations with their snapshots of horror.

There were the svelte women who looked as if they never ate anything more than a lettuce leaf; the ageing tanned men chomping on cigars and with bellies like Alpine landslips; hookers hauled along the pavements by grotesque poodles with diamante collars so expensive – the hookers not the collars – the likes of you and me would have had to raise a mortgage for the dubious thrill of touching their hands. There were taxi-drivers with mouths full of gold teeth and that wariness of eye habitual to working men who knock around with the rich; rock stars gone to seed and others still very much rocking.

Writhing about in all this detritus were the wheeler-dealers and the film stars themselves, talking a hurricane of nonsense about what and who they've been doing; what they want to do and, generally, how simply wonderful they are. All across the beach brown, topless women were getting browner; a sort of miniature Alpes Maritimes of tits.

My only good moment came when I was talking to Kirk Douglas, who was being really boring, only talking about his son's new film, presumably on the principle that, if that's all he talked about, that's all you'd be able to write about. I fell to studying the famous cleft in his chin and finally, in exasperation, asked if I might put my finger in it.

"Be my guest," he said. "It'll bring you luck."

It was exquisite. And I got my finger back too.

The best place to listen to the heartbeat of the festival – if this jamboree could be said to have a heart – was on the terrace of the vast Carlton Hotel. There, beneath film posters advertising their rituals of death and violence, just about everyone, my dear, wandered in and out and, if your nerve and pocket held (the prices of the drinks were astronomical), you could sit around, listen and look. There you could scrape away the plastic veneer and find the true plastic underneath. On this terrace French was spoken in broad American accents. A man went past. "Hello, hello. See you later." Heads turned. "Who the hell was he?"

A woman came in with a yapping poodle. "Rejoice I'm back."

Unimaginable sums of money were discussed in relation to unimaginative films. "I'm not sure what Lew would say about that."

Wandering through this carnival of self-publicity and image making came beggars, actually daring to show up at this court of the rich and famous and being shooed away like flies. They rarely received anything because the abiding quality of the rich was that they became rich by never giving anything away. But still the poor sods came … women with babies, old men on crutches, a young girl with a foam-flecked mouth – holding out their hands and accepting a magnanimous cuff on the ear. I longed to find the plug of a great, implacably smooth yacht, pull it and enjoy the most expensive gurgle in history. The other mad feeling surging around me was to get on my bike and run down a few of those poodles.

Photographic circuses began every half hour. Would-be and never-to-be-in-a-million-years starlets came mincing down the Carlton terrace, stripped off their tops and danced over the road and into the sea followed by packs of paparazzi. The word went out and others would come running; one, two, three … ten, twenty, thirty …until there were maybe two hundred of them whirling, elbowing and ricocheting around the knockers of some dame no one had ever heard of.

The same press swarmed all over Roman Polanski when he turned up later that week though we all knew what they wanted to talk to him about back in California.

The words "murder" and "death" feature in film titles more than any other words. Scene after scene after scene are stitched together into a never-ending embroidery of violence. Victims are run over by cars, shot, pushed off buildings, eaten by sharks, bitten by tarantulas, dropped into earthquake fissures. People are hung up, burned, strangled, stabbed and suffocated. Bones are smashed, tortured mouths cry out in pain. Body after body slumps as masked monsters wander the darkness with chainsaws.

But the film industry, as it gorges itself on the fluorescent evils of the darkest form of romance, is not satisfied with murder. It must glorify crime, encourage rape, gloat over incest, constantly slobber over the face of perversion. Its central vision is of a child prostitute in a charnel house fixing on heroin with a homosexual pimp masturbating in the background while some psycho is hammering on the door trying to get in with a Kalashnikov.

This industry's mortal sin is that in its relentless quest for the sensational it turns its back on the decent, truthful claims of decent, truthful people. When art loses its grip on the particular and real it is worthless. A moment of reality is a moment of truth and, where there is truth, there is God.

Our children were indeed under attack, as that beleaguered mother had written to me after my tilt at *Alien*, and there was nothing we could do about it although I did, on my rounds about town one night later that year, extract a small retribution on those bastards at a private screening in Soho.

I had gone with my friend, the poet Stephen Morris, to see *Rude Boy*, a film about punks and the National Front featuring music by the Clash, a band whose music I had always liked. The film was a celebration of animalism that left me almost speechless with rage.

"We've got to do something about this," said Steve, who has a long history of getting me into trouble. "What're we going to do?"

The only decent thing we could have done was burn the bloody cinema down but there was no future there. As we left, however, I was introduced to David Mingay, one of the film's directors and, perhaps proof positive that films about mindless violence do provoke mindless violence, I socked him so hard in the mouth my fist was still hurting a week later. Steve grabbed hold of Mingay too in case, as he explained later, I wanted to sock him again.

It did not end there. The punch was reported in Nigel Dempster's diary in the *Daily Mail*. I seemed to have proved my own point: the only time I have ever been written about in the national press followed my only act of violence against another man.

THIRTY SEVEN

The column was evolving, stirring people up, becoming oddly powerful. It was also inundated with invitations from those who had heard we could fill up a theatre, sell a shed-load of books or do wonders for the sales of a record.

I also, to my unconfined relief, managed to get rid of Jeremy Beadle. I had wanted to ditch him from the start but Donald Trelford had always insisted I keep him, arguing, as Harry Evans had, that people liked to learn about other people's birthdays. But, in the end, Beadlebum was the architect of his own destruction.

He had yet again managed to give a birthday to someone dead, this time to Andy Devine, a cowboy film star who had died years previously. Then he told us that next Sunday, Cliff Richard would be 39, Roger Taylor 38 and Roger Moore 51. We decided to check ourselves. We found out that they were indeed still alive – good going for Beadle – but that Roger Taylor's birthday was out by several months and Roger Moore was 52. How many mistakes can you make in one paragraph?

We reported these errors in the column and wondered how many other mistakes might be found in Beadle's new book, *Today's the Day*, a book of anniversaries he was clearly hoping would get a generous plug from us. He walked out in a huff after that and, glory be, we never heard from him again. Not that he was too concerned because, soon after, he briefly became a national television star with *You've Been Framed*.

I was to last some time yet but the seeds of the column's demise had been sown. I was making it too personal. Most decent columnists go on for year after year by acting as amused outsiders but, more and more, I was becoming the exasperated insider, introducing myself fully into the column and becoming a part of the story, making myself as important as the people I was writing about.

This was a mistake not only because I didn't want to give it up just yet but because I was also making myself vulnerable to attack. *Private Eye* was throwing me into Pseuds' Corner on an almost weekly basis and I was clearly driving the women's magazines mad too with *Company* magazine making me their Number One "Out" personality of the year.

I was breaking all the rules and certainly Trelford didn't quite seem to know what to do with me, largely backing off although he did complain in a memo now and again. Once it was about the off-hand way I had treated the actress Claire Bloom and a few times about the amount of alcohol that was swilling around the column.

"If you have a problem with alcohol do you think you might try and keep it to yourself?" he asked.

But whether people liked it or not – and there were plenty who didn't – the column was being read and often generated a frenzy of emotion. I was told of one literary editor on a national paper who would leap out of bed when his papers were delivered on a Sunday morning, rush down the stairs, tear my column out of the back page of the *Observer*, put it in the wastepaper basket, without reading a word, and jump up and down on it.

Yet the management would have been after me quickly enough if they weren't happy with what I was producing, I guessed, so someone, somewhere, had decided the best thing to do was let me get on with it. Like the hapless Jeremy Beadle I'd surely hang myself sooner or later.

Famous names were ringing me up, offering stories about themselves. These often led to hilarious consequences as when the disc jockey Kenny Everett, whom I had once interviewed and kept bumping into around town, rang me to say that he had just received a message to the world from John Lennon and Yoko Ono and was there anything I might do about it?

Any journalist would be interested in anything John Lennon had to say, particularly as he had long locked himself away in the Dakota in New York watching the world go by. He hadn't spoken to the Press for five years.

Yes, Kenny. Mmm. Very interested in that. I would love to run something like that. Maybe give it the whole column.

Phone calls were duly made and I ended up talking to Yoko Ono. At first she said that she wanted to take a quarter of a page advertisement for their big message in the *Observer*. I explained that might be a bit difficult at such short notice but I would be happy to run their message for nothing. There followed a brisk round of negotiations. Would I then use their message in full? Would I promise not to comment on it? Would I do this and would I do that?

More phone calls followed and the *Love Letter* from John and Yoko arrived, via Kenney Everett, the following morning. It was two foolscap pages and reading it was one of the great disappointments of my journalistic career. It was pretentious piffle from top to bottom and I wouldn't have used it in a bad week when I'd got nothing to write about and the deadline was half an hour away. As a species of writing it was best characterised as Jack Kerouac meets Barbara Cartland with quite a few hangovers.

It emerged they had both got involved in what they called the wishing process: The spring-cleaning of our minds! The people who come to them are angels in disguise, carrying gifts and messages for the Universe. There is love between them, the city, the country, the earth. Their silence is the silence of love and not of indifference. They are all part of the sky, more so than of the ground. They love everything – even the plants which one of us originally thought was robbing us of air.

The PS slaughtered me: "We noticed that three angels were looking over our shoulders when we wrote this."

I went to Lyme Regis to see novelist John Fowles in his marvellous house at the Cob, finding him a really strange cove, possibly the only man I've ever spent time with who I could never get through to, either physically or with words.

The formal side of the interview in his living room was a dead loss. There was so much sighing hesitancy about him and he mumbled; very shy, I decided, although there was a rather disturbing squint in his sharp eyes. He also kept taking his glasses on and off; he was obviously another who wasn't too keen on the Press.

"They get it wrong so much."

But he brightened up considerably when he took me on a tour of his garden, a wild, unkempt tangle that tumbled down two sloping acres to the sea. Everywhere there were strange trees and deep mysterious smells. Bees whizzed around in patches of sunlight and, what with the birds, animals and insects, the whole place seemed full of confrontation.

Bamboos went shooting up out of one clump of foliage, driving straight for the sky. He said they were probably the tallest in Britain and would need to be to survive the jungle beneath. No, he didn't pick the blackberries. They were left for the birds. He called his garden unmanaged and unmanageable and the place told us a little, I guessed, about the workings of his mind.

The sky was heavy with rain and, just walking down the slopes with him and hearing the distant wash of the waves, I felt a tiny shiver, almost able to picture the deeply romantic French lieutenant's woman gazing out to sea at the end of the Cob, pining for her lover, lost somewhere in France.

He also told me about trees which, for him, were symbolic and he had inherited a passion for them from his dad whose trees were the most closely pruned, cosseted and prayed over in the whole of England. His dad was also an authority on ants.

"There's a rare bird which nests in this tree. The tree's dying of old age but I can't bring myself to cut it down."

He said this with a deep, almost holy, concern and the implication was that trees were important and people less so. I can't say I warmed to this strange, miserable man in the slightest – another disappointed romantic, I thought.

I went to Chichester one bright August morning, accompanied by the photographer, Jane Bown, and a heavy hangover, to interview the actress, Jill Bennett, who was appearing at the theatre festival there.

Nigel Dempster had described her in his diary in the *Daily Mail* as one of the most interesting women in Europe – her name had been associated with many unusual men and she had been married to the playwrights Willis Hall and John Osborne – and I'd long been keen to interview her, but she had always refused. She'd never liked talking to the media but the Chichester Festival press officer had leaned on her hard to do this one. Apparently the ticket sales for her play had been flagging and it was thought a piece about her might brighten them up a bit.

"All right but tell him I'm not talking about my men," she grumped at the press officer, "and if I don't like him or he starts getting into areas he shouldn't, I'm just getting up and running away."

The warnings were duly delivered and I did indeed promise not to mention her men. As it turned out, unknown to me, the ballet star, Mikhail Baryshnikov, a jealous little sod fresh in from the Russian steppes, was hiding on the other side of the wall where the interview took place, listening to every word.

"Zis man is completely in love wiz you," he said the following Sunday when my column appeared, throwing the paper across the kitchen. "I zink you should not see him any more."

I zink I was slightly in love with her too: no man could help but feel something when he looked into that extraordinary face, with its angular cheekbones, tiny ski-slope of a nose and a mouth big enough to post parcels in. Then there was that high forehead, the strong fingers with the dirty fingernails and the cold, blue, Bette Davis eyes. And the laugh, the grungiest laugh in the business, full of money and the promise of a good time, not forgetting that smile with the curling upper lip, a little like a hamster which has made off with most of the nuts. I could have filled the whole column with a description of her face.

We chatted quite amiably as Jane fiddled with her camera. Jane is a marvellous photographer, then of a certain age, who carried her cameras in a shopping bag, always wore the same dark blue coat and looked like the cleaner who had sat down for five minutes to rest her legs. Even when she was being quiet, Jane was planning her shots or looking at the palm of her hand. She never carried anything like a tripod, arc lamps or a light meter – she worked out the light by gazing at her palm. One of the most fascinating discussions I have ever heard was when she and the film director, Elia Kazan, were trying to decide exactly how much light was coming in through the window of a Soho restaurant. Those two seemed to know all you could need to know about light just by looking at it.

The three of us soon began joking together, as if we'd been old friends in a pub, and what surprised me about Jill was her quirky, self-deprecating humour. She never stopped putting herself down, forever going on about how useless she was at everything.

"No good points then?"

"Mmm. I'm very disciplined in my work and a loyal friend. If you became my friend I'd never let you down."

She must have had a good hammering over the years, you guessed. Being married to John Osborne could hardly have been a laugh a month and the recent death of her mother, to whom she referred a lot, must have been a tremendous blow. But she had a sense of humour that would help her prevail. She would always get by.

"I'm still full of hope," she sighed. "But oh, would I like to get out of this humiliating business."

"What would you do?"

"That's the trouble. There's nothing else I can do."

Jane did her bit with her cameras and the session was breaking up when Jill asked me quietly if she could borrow my notebook.

"I forgot to bring it."

"Well give me a bit of paper or something I can write on."

What did she want that for? Was she going to give me her autograph? I gave her my chequebook and she wrote a couple of telephone numbers on it. "Give me a call sometime," she smiled, getting all flirty. "If you can't get me on the one number, give me three rings on the other and try again. We should get together for a drink sometime after I've finished work in this dump. And don't go putting that in your column."

Delighted as I was to be given her telephone numbers I never guessed that this was the start of a relationship which would last for many years. It was never an affair as such and my relationship with her changed on an almost weekly basis. Most of the time we were friends who met for a bit of fun. She was too mad to have a proper affair with and the reason we lasted so long was that, as soon as her mercurial mood swung towards danger, I ran home to Newington Green. Then I'd turn up a week or two later in her house in Chelsea as if nothing had happened.

I rang those numbers a few times over the next month but never got a reply. When I did finally catch her in, she was evasive at first, then finally agreed to join me for dinner in a Thai place in Kensington where they made us take our shoes off before being allowed to sit down on the vast cushions in the basement.

"If I'd known this was going to happen I'd have put on clean knickers," she roared at the surrounding diners. She was always attracting attention by that kind of behaviour then complaining no one would leave her alone. She looked extraordinary in the candlelight, though, her expression changing like the light on a river from dawn to dusk. I never tired of that face and it encouraged complete strangers to accost us in the street. Always because of that face. Once seen, never forgotten.

Our conversation in that Thai restaurant offered no sex – she said she hadn't had it with a man for almost two years but that might have been another of her many lies – and during the early months she behaved like a young girl determined to hang on to her virginity.

She had a gay Praetorian guard; any number of pretty men who orbited the sun of her enormous personality like attentive, adoring planets and always seemed to know where we were dining out – or else they would be at her home in Britten Street (a few had their own front door keys) waiting for us to get back. I later learned from the Tynan diaries that she had a taste for caning and spanking but I never worked her out sexually.

She was subject to dramatic mood swings when she would change straight up from first to fifth gear and denounce me as a worthless Welsh tosspot who should never have left the damn valleys. She could keep up these tirades for hours, the spittle spraying from her lips, most of the time about nothing. It took me ages to understand that these furious words were often the ghosts of her former roles coming out to play, almost as if, in her anger, they were seizing their chance to come alive again. I kept recognising odd phrases from plays I had seen years ago.

When the toys in the attic came out to play I would dive for the front door and my bike and pedal off pursued by bursts of foul language, ashtrays or anything else that came to her twitching hand. She had gobbled up and spat out most of the men she had lived with but, hard as she tried, she never managed to get a proper headlock on me.

In any case I was happily married. I would have been mad to have left my beautiful, calm wife for Jill and it never once entered my head to do so. Liz had even begun giving me marks out of ten for the feeble alibis I came up with for not coming home for a night or two. It was usually a grudging three or four although she did give me an astounding eight one morning when, as usual, I had been lying through my teeth.

"Do you know why I always like the autumn?" Liz once asked me.

"?"

"Because you settle down when the weather gets cold and stay settled until late spring."

Albert Finney used to put money on horses for Jill and post her winnings through the letterbox, often around midnight. She spent many weekends at Sir John Gielgud's house in the country and she knew all the *grande dame* actresses in town. One of her biggest pals, Rachel Roberts, would often come over to Britten Street and collapse on the floor in tears after another of her love affairs had broken down.

The Russian ballet star, Mikhail Baryshnikov, frequently came over from America and she fixed him up with appointments with various muscle and bone specialists. He kept asking her to marry him, she said, but it never came to anything and they also had the most tremendous fights. The Ambulance Job – as she called him – was also apparently useless in bed but he did enjoy putting on a pinny and cleaning the house.

"He keeps thinking he's in the middle of Swan Lake or something when we're in bed. Then he might have a complete breakdown in America and start threatening suicide, so I get Jessica Lange on the phone – they had a kid together – and she's asking *me* if I'll go over to New York and do something about him."

Having the kind of job I had she often invited herself along for the ride, once joining me in Paris for a weekend. The *Observer* still pretty much allowed me to do whatever I wanted and I would go missing from the office for weeks on end. Even their liberal souls would have been absolutely horrified had they known *half* of what was going on in their name *and* at their expense. But they always got their copy on time and that was all they really worried about.

There was something about Paris that opened Jill up and as we wandered around, once stopping for a long series of cognacs outside a restaurant, she began telling me the most amazing things about her life: how her mother had given birth to her clutching her favourite greyhound; of the failure of her first marriage after she had pointlessly bedded another man; of her one great love, the actor manager Godfrey Tearle; how it had all gone wrong with her second husband, Willis Hall, after she had yet again pointlessly bedded another. These were all the stories of a woman who had almost all her life stepped and stumbled on the cracked paving stones of romantic love.

She knew I wanted to become a writer and I told her about my great theme: my visions of the fungus and the black rain, why I believed the media were busy inciting the world to violence and, perhaps my main worry, that I might even be a prophet who, like many other prophets, didn't want to get involved and just wished that God would pick on someone else.

Naturally, this came as a surprise to her but she never once laughed at me – as I had feared she would. More than anything I had always feared being laughed at when I was talking about my visions. Indeed she took them seriously and it was about then that I began enjoying her respect too.

She had always loved writers and often referred to herself as a writers' moll. Writing was all that mattered: all actors did was transmit the words of writers. "Writers rule the world and, if you do have a message, you'd better deliver it. God needs all the postmen he can get these days."

Perhaps inevitably our conversation got on to her life with John Osborne who had been a great hero to many of us when young. She talked about him a lot and clearly missed him far more than any of her other men. They had been together when he was at his most famous and influential: there were houses in Cadogan Square and the south of France and, on some days, the tapping of his typewriter filled their house with magic and her with delight. There had been several miscarriages and a stillbirth. And he wasn't much good in bed, either, she said, often sadistically wounding her.

Her marriage to Osborne had broken down because of her affair with Albert Finney, but when she had gone to tell Albert that they could be together at last she had, for some mysterious reason, which she still couldn't understand, blown him out, leaving him crying in the rain in the middle of the King's Road. When Osborne found out the sorry truth, he began crying too and went to bed before suggesting that perhaps they should get another cat and try again.

Her funniest story about Osborne concerned their race to Zurich after the marriage had fallen apart to get the cash out of their joint account. She flew in with her secretary and was met by a concerned bank manager.

"The trouble is, Mrs Osborne," he explained after pouring her a consoling glass of champagne. "The trouble is Mr Osborne was here an hour ago and withdrew the entire deposit."

Despite all the evidence to the contrary Jill always maintained a belief in romantic love: she believed in it blindly and passionately and that is why she so often ended up in such a mess. "Long periods of celibacy and big affairs. That's what I like," she often said.

THIRTY EIGHT

Jill loved talking about my visions – particularly how the black rain had helped me understand the secret mechanics of the conflict in Northern Ireland – and even began a full-on campaign for me to give up journalism for serious writing.

"Do what you believe in. If you believe do it. That's how it works. Do it."

"I'm not sure I've got what it takes. I've already got four books in my bottom drawer and I don't think I could deal with the critics if one ever got published."

"Oh damn the critics. They don't know anything. They don't believe in anything. You've got what it takes. I know about these things. I supported Osborne when he was doing his best work and believe me, I know. You've got what it takes and you've got to do it. Just do it."

I found these passionate affirmations inspiring but the feeling would be shattered when she got unstable and menopausal again, making demands I wasn't prepare to meet. You never quite knew when she would start making the most ridiculous requests – so ridiculous they often made *her* cry – but that didn't stop her making them.

I usually managed to resist these demands and, when we next met, she would apologise before starting up the same tune soon after. She hated not having her own way and was constantly scheming to get what she wanted.

I could never quite understand why I had grown so attached to her: she was often a total bitch when she got going while John Osborne and Willis Hall had even formed a pact that if they heard that anyone might be thinking of marrying her they would rush to his side and warn the poor bastard off. A sort of Jill Anonymous.

But what has since dawned on me with some force is that while working on my column, I had developed a romantic obsession with celebrity. She really did seem to know everyone and I did find her circle of friends absorbing. So I was back down the same hole again and I did what I always did in those circumstances which was to reach for a large whisky and then another.

Her career was in the doldrums but she had just been offered a small role in the new James Bond film. This involved three weeks in Cortina and would I go there to look after her? Here she was, the greatest Hedda Gabler of her generation, playing an ice-skating instructor in a Bond film. The indignity of it! "I only agreed to do at after telling Cubby he had to keep my name off the credits."

She was getting seriously irritated about not getting me under her thumb and they had already started working on the film at Pinewood where, apparently, she amused the rest of the cast by sitting in a corner of the set knitting me jumpers. By the time she had finished, there were four and I had to leave them behind the bar at my local.

I hadn't seen her for a week or so when she rang me at the *Observer* one morning in a storm of tears and chokings of grief.

"Tom, I've just got to see you. Rachel has finally managed to drink herself to death and I just don't know what to do with myself. I must see you now."

As it happened I was about to leave for a weekend in Cornwall to interview some of the local artists, including one of my old heroes, Colin Wilson, so I invited her along.

My secretary, Anne, booked us into a hotel near Wilson's home in Mevagissey and we met on Paddington station to take the Cornish Express. On the train, helped by a few gin and tonics I just let her talk about her friend, Rachel. Her eyes kept puddling with tears as she spoke of the way their lives had shadowed one another over the years, including the golden period when they were filthy rich, Jill with Osborne and Rachel with Rex Harrison.

Rachel had never recovered from Harrison's defection, possibly in the same way that Jill hadn't from Osborne's, and they had all certainly camped it up mightily in the Connaught for a time. Rachel's death had given her a severe intimation of her own mortality. Jill was obsessed by her own advancing years and bitterly hated growing old. She always shaved quite a few years off her age when asked, if she answered at all.

On close inspection, you could see why she was so worried. Despite a personal hairdresser, her hair was thinning and her neck, which she covered with a scarf whenever possible, was becoming scraggy. Most revealing were the small bluish tucks of the plastic surgeon just below her ear lobes.

It was a poignant sight, this former beauty, who had enjoyed such wealth and fame, surreptitiously covering up reality with a tuck here and a scarf there. She still had any number of men at her beck and call, including a plastic surgeon – who I was never allowed to meet because that would mean acknowledging his existence – and a vet who would turn out in the middle of the night if her cat, Archie, was off-colour. She used all her men, including me, to pursue her various strategies and we were all happy enough to indulge her to the full.

Ava Gardner, another of the royal circle of ageing actresses living around Chelsea, always told her she should cherish every wrinkle. "You've worked your butt off for them, Jill, darling, so you gotta learn to love every goddamn line."

When we arrived at Mevagissey it was still daylight so I left Jill to walk along the shoreline and went to see Colin Wilson at his house a few hundred yards from our hotel. It was recognisable by a notice that proclaimed NO VISITORS PLEASE. The word PLEASE had been crudely crossed out.

This was a strange pilgrimage for me because Wilson's *The Outsider* had been a decisive influence on me when I was young, my first introduction to the dangerous world of books. *The Outsider* was a survey of the hole-in-the-wall man who stands outside society and sees too deeply and too much. What he mostly sees is chaos. He is caught between being and non-being, living alone and avoiding people. He finds the world full of misery and is surrounded by triviality and shallow thinkers. His recurring cry is that nothing is worth doing and his disillusionment will terminate in madness or suicide.

As an ignorant, unsophisticated young man I had been galvanised by these dopey ideas and the book helped me to win a scholarship to university. If you knew *The Outsider* you could easily pretend to have read almost everything that mattered and I did this to great effect in my scholarship paper.

I had much to thank Wilson for but also much to despise him for after my early romantic, derivative novel had blown up in my face in Malaya and I had been shown a world under attack by artists like him.

His work had achieved little for years but he had kept at it like the zealot he was and, although it would never be formally proven in any way, I believed he had also become a prime mover in our rotten media, that his sick romantic obsessions with violence, murder, horror and the occult were directly linked to the same sick romantic obsessions of our media, particularly in those programmes which made up so much of primetime television. Even though his books were largely slated or ignored these days – as he himself testified – he remained an important, influential figure, if only for the wrong reasons.

Nervously I knocked on his door and heard the tread of my freebooting, existentialist youth coming down the hallway to open it.

Wilson was affability itself, in a house stuffed with books and more records than I've ever seen in one place. He was generous with his drink and, with his vivid, high-energy philosophical chatter, much as I had always pictured him. His face was chubbily cherubic, he still wore his trademark polo sweater and I was surprised to learn that he, not his wife, Joy, did the supermarket shopping. He just went up the aisles and flung into his trolley anything that came to hand, he said.

What first struck me was his staggering candour. Writers seldom talk about their earnings, largely because there aren't any, but, unsolicited, he began telling me what various of his fifty books had made and how he was wrestling with an overdraft. It wasn't worth him being a tax exile because he didn't earn enough. His bestseller on the occult had made a lot but, spread over the three years it took him to write it, it wasn't that much. Unlike many other writers who had hit the jackpot, he had to supplement his income with journalism and he'd recently worked on the screenplay of a new Flash Gordon film that had made him £10,000.

For someone who appeared so bent on protecting his privacy he could get into a fair few scrapes. Only recently the police had called to ask what he had been doing on the night of October 29, 1975, the night the Yorkshire Ripper made his first attack. Apparently part of one of his books read like one of the Ripper's letters. He consulted his journal and told them exactly where he'd been: not attacking women in Yorkshire but locked in his lavatory in Cornwall.

Nothing much had happened to him for ten years after the ballyhoo around *The Outsider* in 1966. He had never thought of jacking it all in – "What else would I do?"

– and sustained himself through the bad years with his conviction that he had something important to say, that he was, well, a genius. He'd had his fair share of fame. "But what can you do with fame? You can't eat it."

He took me to his local where each week he met up with the same group of friends. He never went to any parties because, he said, if you go to one, you get invited to them all. I liked him a lot – he certainly wasn't nearly as twisted as John Fowles, say, nor nearly as talented – but I felt sorry for him too. Here was a man who had never managed to grow up; someone who had consistently sold himself short for so long: all his morbid romantic obsessions, far from being life-enhancing, were actually life-denying.

With an eye perhaps on posterity he had set out in his journals every last detail of his thoughts and doings which now added up to thirteen bound volumes. "I'm planning on not being forgotten," he said with a wry smile.

He had been working for twenty-three years on a vast novel, *Lulu*, about a girl who destroyed all the men she came into contact with. He just couldn't seem to finish it but parts might yet surface in a television series. Just then he'd got two books out: *The New Existentialism* (dealing with Husserl and Wittgenstein) and *Frankenstein's Castle* (outlining his two-brain theory which he said would overturn Freud). He explained his two-brain theory to me at length – twice – but I didn't understand a word.

He didn't believe in God, of course, snorting when I asked, as if it was the stupidest question that had ever been put to him. Romantic geniuses become their own gods, of course; they believe in the power of their individual minds to reshape society in their own terms. The world is full of them. They run most departments in the global media and are all full of passionate intensity and are silly putty.

As I left I mentioned that Jill Bennett was staying with me in the hotel in Mevagissey. Wilson got quite excited and begged me to bring her around the next morning.

I wasn't sure what Jill wanted to do. She was still feeling fragile after Rachel's death, and always got extremely fractious if she thought she was being paraded in any way. I had also promised to take her to the morning service in the local church where she wanted to sit and think about her old friend. "Maybe we'll find the time to call in after that."

I told Jill all about Wilson over dinner that night, interrupted, as usual, by some man on the next table complaining about her foul language. That was often the way it was: they complained about her language and then tried to get friendly with her. But Jill always ignored them and got on with whatever she was talking about, foul language and all.

Colin Wilson was dead right on one issue. Fame was a pain in the arse and it wouldn't have been so bad if you could eat or drink it. But she *was* keen to meet Wilson the next morning after we'd been to church.

She looked wonderful sitting in a pew in Mevagissey church the next morning, smiling and chatting to the parishioners rather like the Queen who had lost her way to Windsor. She often calmed down after I'd managed to get her inside a church; she wasn't afraid of much but was certainly scared of God. She had no real respect for anyone else.

Colin Wilson turned up his natural oily charm to flood level when they met, told her about his two-brain theory and presented her with one of his books in which he wrote an affectionate dedication, adding that we could always stay in a chalet in his garden if we ever found ourselves down this way again. Her fame always seemed to have the oddest effect on everyone she met.

I had, I'm not at all sure how, managed to drag my column into its second year – a record for me in any job.

But now I could feel everything unravelling fast and it was only my bike – my classical bike – which was keeping me together as I cruised the city getting drunk here or eating vast meals there, seeing the battiest actress in Chelsea and trying to hold together a normal family life in Newington Green.

The bike forced me to find answers within myself and not take them from others. I discovered for myself, for example, that, unless I ate the right kinds of food, my legs wouldn't work. You can't keep cycling on alcohol alone. After some time in the saddle my damaged lungs insisted I gave up smoking. Depressions never lasted long: after one sweaty ride home I might be knackered but was depressed no more.

"The secret of good health is feelings of wellbeing," the beautiful Clare, one of my doctor neighbours insisted. "Medicine is just a sideshow. That's why the depressed are often so ill all the time and the happiest often fighting fit."

She added that these feelings of well-being are rooted in regular exercise and the proper circulation of blood. The heart pumps blood at the rate of ten litres a minute, feeding oxygen and glucose to the muscles. The efficient functioning of the heart is vital to everything from our sex life to the quality of our thoughts and the one great unsung talent of the bike is that it acts as a second heart. The bike stops the blood pooling in the belly and feet; cycling legs tighten and squeeze the veins, sending the blood sluicing back up into the heart and on to the brain, where we find our ideas.

Physically, despite a life of abnormal excesses, I wasn't in too bad a shape although emotionally I was a mess. I wasn't sure who or what I was attached to any more and I was worried by the way Jill and I had started nose-diving into cocaine, catching myself thinking about it a lot and wondering when we could do it again. The thing about cocaine is that it really is all it's cracked up to be and I could see how it got people into serious trouble.

I needed to accept the logic of my ideas and pursue them fully, not just with my mind but also with my belly and heart. I had to reconcile my warring feelings and feckless pursuits and live more fully within myself, my bike kept telling me. I had to become more serious as I made my way along what DH Lawrence called the savage pilgrimage.

I longed to pursue my literary ambitions again, spend more time thinking about my visions and trying to work out their relevance, if any, to the real world. Liz always supported me whatever I did, but when Jill learned what was on my mind she became even more determined to get me to give up journalism and take up the cudgels with my life's theme, even offering to let me move into Britten Street or, if I didn't want to do that (even she could see plenty of reasons why I mightn't) there was the flat Albert Finney had once bought her.

The last thing I wanted to do was live with Jill in Britten Street – or in Albert Finney's love-pad come to that. I'd never have written a word with Jill around – she was far too forceful and noisy. But something had to give, since I was very close to burnout with my column. Then, as had happened so often in the past, I met a very great man, who bowled me over and changed my life.

David Watson, an evangelist, had been doing some extraordinary work in York that was seen by many as a symbol of Anglican renewal. Some had even called him the new John Wesley. With Easter coming up, he agreed to my spending a weekend with him in York and I went there with Liz and the boys who made it clear they had no intention of going to church but did fancy the Railway Museum.

I spent some hours with Watson and my feelings for him were simple. I liked this lovely and charming man from the moment I met him and still count that meeting as one of the great privileges of my life. He had a strange face with an enormous nose and narrow, slanting eyes which disappeared altogether when he smiled, which he did a lot. His voice was resonant and he didn't have a trace of religiosity or pomposity. His best feature was a gently subversive sense of humour which always came in handy with Christians, an often judgemental, humourless gang.

Watson was a disciple of the simple life: just as well since he earned only £3 a week and always wore second-hand clothes. He rode around York on a bike and lived in a rectory near the Minster with his wife Anne, two children, another couple and a teacher in an extended family.

I left Liz and the boys to explore York while I tagged along with him, learning he had been a humanist when he went to university but had been converted by an Anglican clergyman, John Collins, who had explained to him that God loved him, that he offered him total forgiveness for everything that had caused a broken relationship between them, that this forgiveness had been practised by Christ on the cross and, if he accepted it, Christ could be his friend. He simply had to open his life and heart to God.

What Watson learned from Collins and went on to preach was that Christianity is not a farrago of empty propositions but a living relationship with God. The key to it is simplicity. David Sheppard, the England cricketer and clergyman, had taken an interest in Watson and, more flattered than anything else, he was converted.

"It was nothing very dramatic, just a simple, unemotional commitment," Watson said. "At first I had a vague sense of peace and then grew in my experience of God."

He had been ordained in 1959 and, after curacies in Gillingham and Cambridge, came to York where he took over an empty church, St Cuthbert's, which had an average Sunday attendance of seven. Using dance and song he built up the numbers into the hundreds. "The whole point of the gospel is to reunite us with God and one another," he said. "We also wanted our homes to become house churches in the fellowship of St Cuthbert's."

Later he moved to the far larger St Michael's-le-Belfry in the shadow of the Minster, which quickly became world-famous for charismatic renewal, and was packed out every Sunday. Most of his success, he believed, came from prayer – he and his wife set aside one day a week for prayer and fasting.

Attending one of his services was a great joy with powerful waves of affection and love sweeping around the congregation. Many of them were young and be-jeaned and kept their arms around one another. People talked to me as soon as I walked inside the place and they sang as if they meant it. They also said their prayers with a rare passion. Elements of theatre had also been incorporated into the service. A man got up and told a joke and there was an intricate dance before Watson him-self spoke with simple force: "Jesus will not come as a thief in the night, but as a friend in the day. If he comes are you ready? That day when all heaven will be let loose. Yes, the best is yet to be."

I have always tried to develop a relationship with the people I write about but I had never developed such a strong relationship with anyone, least of all a man, so immediately and lastingly.

It was clear that people offered me their friendship because they wanted to pro-mote some product or themselves in my column but I'm sure that wasn't the case with David Watson. We remained close friends, who stayed in almost constant con-tact with one another until he was cut down tragically and senselessly in his prime by cancer in 1984.

Watson and I trusted one another from the start and he told me about his asth-ma and frequent bouts of depression knowing I could have put such confidences in my column and perhaps caused him trouble with the archbishop: clergymen are not supposed to have depressions or go around talking about their illnesses.

He also told me about his troubles with the more hard-line members of the church who would not sit down with Catholics or accept that dance had any func-tion in a place of worship or that you could ever speak in tongues (which was just a way of talking to God, when you weren't sure what you wanted to say). Had I revealed any of that I wouldn't have done him any favours either. The whole point of the Church was that, rather like the *Sunday Telegraph*, you always did it in the same way because that was the way you had always done it.

Somewhat amazingly, given the shortness of our relationship, I unloaded a few of my secrets on to him too. Far from expressing pious disapproval, he roared with laughter. There wasn't a judgemental bone in his body.

On our final night together I told him about my visions. I told him about the exploding book, the world being attacked by its romantic artists, the way God had shown me his grief and, most terrifying of all, the black rain.

For most of my adult life I had been haunted by these visions, I told him, and the worst feature was that they seemed to be true. They made sense of a world strug-gling with ever-greater terror, riot and crime because we didn't understand where it was all coming from. Did he think God wanted me to do something?

"If there is a purpose it will be revealed in time," he said. "But you should just live your life and take it as it comes. God is real and you should trust him. That's what it means to have an honest, loving relationship with him. Nothing else matters."

"Do you think I went mad in Malaya?"

"No."

"How can you tell?"

"Because you use your powers of discernment. These tell me that you did indeed have an encounter with God; that there is some sort of truth here which I'll have to think and pray about, and that perhaps he did light a fire in you there which you will one day honour."

Watson didn't convert me in York but he thoroughly discomfited me. His words kept rattling around inside me like the ball in a pinball machine: his personality set off chain reactions deep within me and, when I sat down to write my Easter column, I poured my heart and soul into it under the simple headline REVIVAL.

"This Easter less than eight per cent of the population will be going to church which even the dimmest now see means we are sleeping through a long, dark night," I began. "Exhausted as a social and spiritual force, the Church is failing to live together and dying apart. The pulpit has long lost its place as the centre of drama, poetry and philosophy. The pews are largely empty and the excitement gone.

"This is a monumental tragedy since there has never been a more desperate need for moral leadership: divorce is tearing our families apart, our loving relationships are being destroyed, our babies are under attack by brutalising images and there is growing violence in our streets.

"We look to the church to arraign sin and arouse the conscience but all it seems good at is pomp and cowardly evasion. The worry for us all this Easter, I believe, should be if there is any chance of seeing a real religious revival in our time or, if we are going to stand back spinelessly and let the barbarians take over.

I had been obsessed with the Welsh revivalist Evan Roberts for years, I continued, had even written a book about him and frequently wondered if there was anyone capable of starting such a movement today. I went on to describe the work of David Watson in York, telling of the way he had filled the pews there and introduced a spiritual and dramatic excitement into his services. I described the work he had done with his team in our prisons, including some notable work for reconciliation in Northern Ireland.

So yes, I continued, we could indeed one day see a revival in Britain and there were good and talented people like Watson who could lead it. But the sheer size and scale of the enemy was enormous.

About two thirds of my way into the column, which I always wrote in longhand in the back room of my house in Newington Green before taking it into the office for Anne to type up, I took a deep breath and fiddled with my pen for a bit. Evan Roberts was staring at me from a distant Welsh valley, the words of David Watson were alive inside me from York. These might be the last words I ever wrote for a newspaper, but it had to be done; I might even have been preparing all my life to write just this one column. If I was mad, I was mad; if I was fired I was fired.

I went on to say that I had become sufficiently confident in Watson to tell him about my own visions in Malaya and how my understanding of what these visions represented had become better and clearer over the years, particularly during my journey through the media and doing this column. I now knew, as an absolute article of faith, that the modern media has become the mother and father of all terrorism everywhere. It was also clear to me that a media in love with violence was responsible for most major crimes in our modern world from the assassinations of our leading figures, particularly in America, to the alarming spread of violence on our housing estates and soccer hooliganism in our stadiums.

This is the meaning and mystery of the black rain.

We mock people such as Mary Whitehouse at our peril, I concluded and, if we could fight back and give people like David Watson some real support, we could restore the Church to its rightful centrality in our culture and face a future with an increasing confidence. If ... oh my beleaguered, dying people ... if.

THIRTY NINE

The column about my visions and David Watson exhausted me and filled me with such anxiety I took off to Jerusalem for a couple of weeks to recover. It wasn't to be my last column but there wouldn't be many more.

I had made friends with Orde and Flo Dobbie, who ran the Garden Tomb, on a previous visit to Jerusalem and indeed kept a bicycle in the garden itself. Cycling in that singular city was an experience like no other, often an edgily miserable experience with everyone glowering at one another and the Arab drivers of trucks and vans pulling over in front of me, as if determined to knock me off.

Jerusalem itself, which Ezekiel called the centre of the earth, offered something of its strange and warring soul to you astride a saddle. This was a city of a hundred fantastic shunts; a unique place, steeped in centuries of blood and battle. More evil has infected these huddled streets than anywhere else in the world; even circa 1750 the citizenry here were committing an average of four hundred murders a year. Soldiers are constantly on patrol and there are bullet and shell marks almost everywhere you look with rolls of barbed wire on the fences around the holy places and bags (even schoolboys' satchels) being searched for bombs.

Freewheeling around these streets, so inspirational and so sickening, I kept picking up the tracks of Jesus Christ. You might toil up the Mount of Olives and look out over the sandy cubes and spires of the city where Christ wept when he foresaw its destruction. Then you might go down to sit in the Garden of Gethsemane where the olive trees now have huge blackened trunks with fresh green shoots coming out of them. These are said to be the same trees which winced all those years ago when Judas betrayed Christ with a kiss.

You can pick up Christ's tracks again by the Wailing Wall, the holiest of all holy places for Jews. Next to the wall was the gate Christ passed through on his way to the Temple to kick over the tables of the moneychangers, his only recorded act of violence. This is now the Moslem Dome of the Rock, built on the same rock, according to the Koran, from which Mohammed ascended into heaven. The Dome itself has huge shadowy rafters, alive with the wings of hurrying birds. Outside on the flagstones Arab women in yashmaks sit around gossiping.

The real heart-stopper was the Via Dolorosa; the winding, climbing street where Christ shouldered his cross on his last journey, to a place called Golgotha which, today, swarmed with patrolling soldiers, Arab beggars and visiting pilgrims. Shops and stalls were piled high with every known vegetable and the restaurants had elephant's feet of kebabs roasting on bright red bars of electricity.

I stood in this street of death and life holding the handlebars of my bike on the spot where Christ, exhausted by nights of examination and scourging, fell under the weight of his Cross and Simon of Cyrene was ordered by the Romans to help him. Somewhere on the next corner he met his mother and all the sorrow of the world was in the rapt and silent looks they exchanged. She knew he was about to give himself to the world on the cross as she had given him to the world on the floor of a stable.

Christ finally staggered to Calvary, where the Church of the Holy Sepulchre now stands, and was nailed through the wrists to the crossbeam of the Cross. His body was rested on the saddle of the upright and, in a moment of pure agony, the Cross was lifted and placed in its socket with him hanging there, the blood from the crown of thorns dried but breaking out afresh to mix with the bubbling sweat of his pained brow. On the top of the cross was written: "the King of the Jews".

"*Consummatum est*," he shouted in triumph, and died with a child's goodnight prayer on his lips. He died of a broken heart in the end and his spirit rose over the city which today fights on at his risen, bleeding feet.

The Garden Tomb is supposed to be built around the cave where Christ was taken after the crucifixion and I always found it a lovely oasis of peace and flowers next to a bustling Arab bus station.

"Well, if he didn't actually rise from here, he rose from somewhere very much like it," Orde would say, with an impatient flick of his hand. You would never catch Orde coming out with a PR line on anything.

I began drying out here – not all that successfully, as it turned out – and a new book was beginning to evolve which might finally enable me escape from the journalism that was now half-killing me. Nick Webb, who ran the New English Library, had enjoyed what I had written about my bike in my columns and suggested I might like to tackle a sort of Paul Theroux of bikes, a celebration of bicycling in different parts of the world. I liked this idea and had already begun collecting chapters. On this visit I hoped to cycle the two hundred miles from Jerusalem down through the Judean desert to Eilat. The first part would be easy enough, a glorious downhill swoop through Jericho, along the shoreline of the Dead Sea past Qumran, where a shepherd boy had found the Dead Sea Scrolls, before I hit the vast Judean desert.

Yet everyone connected with the Garden Tomb thought this idea stupid and lost no opportunity to pour cold water on it. Orde said there was a hippy colony in Eilat that would depress me. Stewart Henderson, the poet and Orde's son-in-law, calculated I would have to carry at least eight gallons of water on my bike and Lance Lambert, a local evangelist, warned of flash floods, snakes, scorpions and the deadly winds of the Sherav which were about to blow in earnest. For a professional cyclist it might be possible, but for a wreck like me, on my old bike, with an inbuilt wobble and a tendency to go sideways, impossible.

So, like the great and intrepid cyclist I was, I gave up the idea and took a bus instead, travelling down to the Dead Sea, the lowest point in the world, and passing Bedouin tribes with their camels and goats camped out on the bald, brown slopes of the Judean desert. There were hot sulphur springs and patches of boiling mud and I was glad I wasn't on a bike. I wondered how even scorpions could survive in such a hostile place. But the Israelis could clearly grow tulips on lumps of coal and had set up a kibbutz down there surrounded by fields of extraordinary fertility. Their secret was to drip-feed their plants with just the right mixture of water and fertiliser – all managed, naturally, by a central computer.

They had opened a fully subscribed hotel in the kibbutz, where visitors could take the mud and soak their aches and pains away in the hot sulphur springs. This place was the healthiest in the world, they said, by virtue of its being so low. The extra level of air filtered out the sun's more harmful rays and had twenty per cent more oxygen. They said.

Nearby was Masada, a hill fort built by Herod during another of his bouts of extreme paranoia. It stands on a high hill above the Dead Sea, looking out at Jordan. The original villagers killed themselves rather than give in to the Roman besiegers and the symbolism of the place retains a high priority in the Israeli psyche. To this day most soldiers are conscripted into the Israeli Army and presented with their own guns here. They will fight to the last man, if only because they understand that the first war they lose will be their last.

Later that afternoon the sun began sinking behind the Judean desert, its rays striking directly across the Dead Sea and lighting up the high cliff walls of the Hashemite Kingdom of Jordan: a luminous gold at odds with the featureless darkness of the sea. I saw it that day as God has seen it forever. As the land looked now, so Moses and all the prophets saw it as they travelled north looking for the land of milk and honey. Here was a landscape steeped in its own silence and colour, a place waiting with the stoicism of ancient rocks for the long-promised return of our Man of Sorrows.

When I flew back to London I learned that my Revival column had prompted several hundred supportive letters from readers with barely one against. "You will never write so much in so few words as long as you live," one ex-BBC man wrote. I also learned there had been a lot of discussion amongst the *Observer* management about whether the column should have been printed in the first place. But Donald Trelford had decided that the conviction in the piece was clear and it was "beautifully written". John Cole, the deputy editor, had said he didn't see it as his job to interfere with another man's visions so they decided to let it go.

I continued to do the column but had pretty much lost my way, drinking too much and still seeing Jill. She was great fun to be out with but I was at a loss to understand the nature of our relationship and kept thinking I should end it. I kept pulling back from the brink because I loved the way she might occasionally just stand in a room or out in the street smiling with a radiant happiness. "You've made one old bat extremely happy," she would say.

But she had a hold over me for sure. Maybe at the heart of it was my fascination with her multiple personalities, the way she moved effortlessly from mad teenager to ageing matriarch; from a mean, lying spinster to the most generous and beautiful disco-queen in the land. It wasn't an act; it was just the way she was all the bloody time.

With a contract signed to write my book about bicycling and a reasonable £3,500 advance from Nick Webb, I announced I was going to give up journalism. As the column had bizarrely evolved into a spiritual autobiography I wanted the last one to have a religious resonance. Patrick O'Donovan suggested I should go to Quarr Monastery on the Isle of Wight, which, he said, had the most severe and pared-down lifestyle in the land. As a practising Catholic he liked to go there himself, often with a good bottle of malt whisky which he drank in his room when the monks weren't looking. Journalists, eh?

Over a meal in a local restaurant one evening, Liz and I had discussed going to California to live. Her contract at the *Radio Times* was coming to an end; the boys at thirteen and twelve were not facing serious exams that year, and we had no mortgage to pay.

So, after Quarr I was going to fly to California to find a house in Orange County and start work on my bike book. California had long been thought of as the home of bicycles and sunshine so I would certainly get a good chapter out of that.

I hadn't told Jill that Liz and the boys were coming with me and she staged a horror show when I did. She barged through door after door as if trying to chase half a dozen burglars out of the house. You could never tell what she was going to do – or say – when she got like this and, yet again, I noticed the ghosts of her old roles fighting to be free of her, all brawling together in her mad antics. It was best to keep silent when this happened and, if possible, slip quietly out of some convenient back door.

I was full with every species of remorse when I turned up on the doorstep of Quarr. I had been drinking on the ferry and fell in through the monastery front door. Dinner had begun in the refectory, with a man in a small, brick pulpit reading from a book as the other monks ate silently and, when someone put a plate of beetroot and scrambled egg in front of me, I had to jump up and run out into the cloister garden, where I was sick all over their roses.

I had at least managed to resist Patrick's suggestion that I take a good bottle of malt in with me and, as the monastery day unfolded around me, I sat in my room, white-faced and shaking, very far from the Lord indeed.

Occasionally I left my room to look around at night, watching the rain washing down the leaded windows or listening to the wind bashing against the stout wooden doors. The sound of bells often hung in the weeping darkness as a silence trawled through the dark crypt, hung around the pointed arches of the cloisters and was all but deafening in the high, wide church itself, lit by just one guttering candle.

More bells heralded the start of Compline or evening prayer and, still groggy, I sat in the rear pew watching the thirty or so robed monks take their place in the choir stalls. They chanted and knelt before God, their black, rounded shapes revolving and dissolving into one another in the flickering light. At the end the abbot sprinkled holy water over them as an act of purification.

I wanted to purify myself. That was the door I had to get through to meet God or faith like these fine men around me. It was probably in that pew that I determined to pull my marriage together. I would never be able to live without Liz and so it was that I prayed that weeping night in Quarr that I hadn't left it too late; that my marriage hadn't been damaged beyond repair. I was going to reform, I was.

When the darkness came so did the Great Night Silence when all that could be heard was the wind hurtling around the monastery walls and the shaking branches of the pine trees in the gardens. May the Lord grant us a quiet night and a perfect end.

In the half hour between Matins and Lauds, Dom Taylor always had a period of silent prayer in his room, he told me. The monastic life was one long process of coming close to God. "Yet the closer you come the further away he seems to be. He is nothing like his created reality. The more you understand, the more you realise that you don't understand anything at all. God is only ever like himself."

These are mystical, lonely thoughts although, in the constant process of prayers, cycles and chants, you sensed something of the mystical, lonely search for God. Here the doors were constantly locked to protect the monks from outside interference; there were no newspapers, television or radio to poison their ideas or undermine their faith.

Quarr was only half full, I learned from Brother Denis Bradley: there was a shortage of the right kind of men with sufficient sympathy for Benedictine ideals. The basis of the monastery was academic, rather than physical, and Brother Denis tried to spend at least three hours a day studying theology with a view to becoming a priest. He enjoyed the full balance of the monastic day and laughed almost continually, something of a surprise since the others were solemn, devoted men. They owned nothing and even their clothes were loaned to them. "But we've actually got rather a lot," said Brother Dennis. That laugh again.

I left Quarr detoxed and replenished by these men weaving a great web of prayer for the world with Christ at its heart. They could see a time when God, in his disappointed wrath, might send in floods and tempests that would last for years; when people would cry out in fear and pain when they discovered the harvest was fully and finally dead.

I returned home and flew out to Los Angeles. I spent my first night there in a hotel in Santa Monica before taking a bus down to Orange County, to Laguna, a small arty town that had been recommended to me by a friend. I signed into a motel, rented a bungalow in Driftwood Drive for an initial period of six months overlooking the Pacific Coast Highway and called Liz to come with the boys.

My main surprise was how quickly and efficiently everything worked: all the utilities were connected on the day we moved in and I was further surprised at how joyful I was when Liz and the boys turned up and I took them for a giant knickerbocker glory on the beach. The boys' own joy was soon soured when they learned that, far from becoming beach bums, they were going to school the following Monday and, what is more, they would be expected to recite the Pledge of Allegiance with their right hands on their hearts every morning. After a few mornings of this Julian, not slow to speak his mind, declared that as a British citizen, he should be exempt.

I continued wandering around this heaven smiling like some lifelong sinner who had just been told there was no hell. We men of ink throw away our marriages and families so hurriedly and pointlessly, I've often thought. Squander them and for what? Now, here, I'd been a given another chance which I absolutely didn't deserve.

So it was that I came to sit out in our small garden with a giant notebook and began writing up my notes. It was like being in the middle of the best dream, sitting here in the bosom of my family doing what I had always wanted to do beneath a clear blue sky with the warm air so fresh to the taste that it might just have been fresh baked by angels only an hour earlier. The garden was full of birds, including those magical sorcerers of the air, the humming-birds who liked to hover in the spray of the garden hose. The glittering Pacific was at my feet and out at sea whales spouted by on their way to their breeding grounds off Mexico. The high surf kept pounding the beach and the sunsets were romping fantasies of colour liquefying and raging into one another. Occasionally the windows would rattle in their frames, telling you about another small earthquake. The Garden of Eden was modelled on California, they like to say, and it was easy to see why. And in the midst of it all I sat, a smile on my face and my family around me.

PART THREE

BOOK MAN

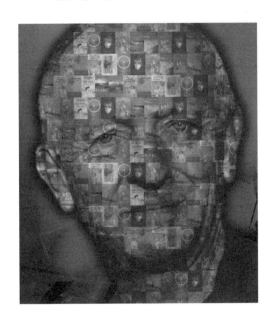

FORTY

Even had I planned it for a year I doubt I could have found a more idyllic setting to write my first book. Every Laguna dawn was a delight with dew settling thick on the lawns and the air as fresh to the taste as a lollipop straight from the freezer. Squirrels ran around the garden on squirrel business; exotic birds fluttered through the shrubs in sudden colourful flashes and, all the while, the high surf kept rising from the heart of a sea in waves which glittered like freshly flung diamonds.

The gardens rejoiced in a profusion of poinsettia and bougainvillea and many houses were covered with ivy which helped to stabilise the walls in this earthquake country. We were almost directly on top of the San Andreas Fault and from time to time there would be a rattle of cups in saucers or windows in their frames that gave me severe intimations of mortality and interrupted my work for a while.

The two boys, Julian and Steffan, quickly settled at their new school, which they enjoyed even though they were expected to learn everything parrot-fashion, and I worked until three in the afternoon when Liz and I went for a walk, sometimes around the hills at the rear of our house where we once came across a rattler, or down into Laguna itself, lots of one-storey clapboard houses set amidst bending palms in the Californian style. There was a library which we used a lot because television was often little more than vapid series about cops or doctors.

We had enough money for six months or longer if we took it carefully. Sitting in the ravishing sunshine of this Garden of Eden and pulling together a box of notes and notebooks to write up a global celebration of bicycling, I had my chance to become a serious writer at last. My plan was to view a city or country from a new perspective: the saddle of my bike. The idea had been knocking around my mind for a while and wherever I'd gone for the *Observer* I'd made it my business to get a bike and make extensive notes about cycling in different cities or parts of the world. Thus I had spent a week cycling around Amsterdam, the home of the bike; tried it around the bedlam that was Manhattan; cycled around Beijing in the rush hour; gone through a Bangkok dawn in a monsoon, and explored London times without number. I had bought an old bike here in California, which I hoped would provide me with a lot of new material, although I would still have a few more bits to fill in later that year in Greece and France.

My first chapter on Amsterdam was straightforward. I had roamed that fine city on my bike, picking up on the awful pong of the Heineken brewery, enjoying the higgledy-piggledy houses with hoist beams hovering on the edges of the canals and the freshness of the air that scoured my city lungs. Every lonely lock bridge framed a Dutch master just hanging right there. I met members of the old Provo counter-culture movement of the mid-Sixties and one recalled that, at the height of their notoriety, they had come up with crazy ideas like the White Bike Plan, which involved free bikes for everyone to be left wherever they finished a journey, or how they should get some lion dung out of the zoo because lion dung, one "intellectual" decided, would freak out the police horses.

I introduced a little man – or alter ego – into my narrative: Merlyn, who would bob up and comment on my odd moments of happiness or despair, in the book which was finally published under the title of *Merlyn the Magician and the Pacific Coast Highway*.

It was only after writing about Thailand in general and Bangkok in particular in my second chapter that I realised my book was not going to be a straightforward cel-ebration of bicycling. It would be something deeper and more meaningful since, astride my bike, I saw my chance to analyse the visions I had seen in my days with Voluntary Service Overseas in Malaya. I had cycled in Malaya during a visit there for the *Observer* the previous year so, during the course of the book, there was a chance to revisit the scenes of my visions and explore what they meant to me and their possible relevance to the world. Thus the book would also become a physical journey embodying a spiritual quest.

My main vision was of a luminous fungus growth – which I interpreted as the poisoned growth of my own romanticism – sprouting from the violence-riven man-uscript I was working on in Alor Star. This growth had then exploded into a swarm of attacking bees. Then there was the later one in Penang when a hole opened in a clear blue sky and a torrent of black rain came pouring out of it.

I decided I might as well use this book to try and understand, atop my bike, how the romantic heart and mind of the media had overwhelmed us. There was a sense too that, here in California, I was in the land which had practically given the roman-tic vision shape and heart, especially in Hollywood, the home of the film industry which, almost daily, released films which, in their persistent obsession with perver-sion, cruelty and violence, were blasting every corner of the world, fomenting crime and disorder, destroying the dreams of good people everywhere.

So I drove my pen on in my Laguna garden, touring the back alleyways of Thailand, Malaya, Singapore, Beijing and Manhattan each morning, with my remembering senses trying to tease out the city secrets, looking for their distinctive smells and tastes, watching out for strange moods, listening to street music and always shuddering when I saw a poster for a new Hollywood film celebrating mur-der, death, perverted sex or all three.

My chief reason for settling in Laguna was to take a long bike ride from here in Orange County right into the heart of Los Angeles and Hollywood. So one fine morning – all mornings were fine in California that winter – I took off and made my way up the Pacific Coast Highway.

Once past the town limits I coasted down a long slope, passing a ranch and two buzzards hovering watchfully on a breeze. More trees fanned out and all around me the unmistakable texture of Americana: The Church of St Michael and the Angels. Liquor. Hardware. Food to Go. Kentucky Fried Chicken. Auto Care. All Repairs Guaranteed. The roads were immaculately clean – as were the towns. Not a spot of litter anywhere. Yet every few minutes a helicopter clattered overhead on its way between San Diego and Los Angeles, leaving streams of black smoke in its wake. The cars were gas-guzzling monsters: Jaguar, Chrysler, Cadillac, Lincoln, Studebaker, Porsche, Colt – making empty announcements of their empty grandeur. One American dies in traffic every ten minutes: cars have killed two million here, more than the total death toll of the country's wars.

There was also a lot of Disneyesque imagery. A paddle steamer, the *Robert E Lee*, was parked next to the road, its great wheels motionless and silent. The sunshine remained brightly relentless and, over to my distant right, were blue, snow-capped mountains.

You saw things on your bike which gave you insights into the nature of this society: its fear, writ large in the profusion of locks, the barbed-wire, the red and white burglar alarms and notices warning of security systems and armed responses. The young beggars hanging around the beachfronts and boardwalks: druggies and dropouts, many barely fourteen, their minds full of blitzed ideas which, from the way they spoke, they had almost certainly garnered from the dustcover of a Kerouac paperback. That radioactive romantic detritus again; I spotted it seeping under every door like a creeping black tide.

After Huntington Beach came lines of oil wells nodding their heads towards me like mechanical Uriah Heeps. The air changed, got thicker, grubbier: way out in front of me was a dirty black cloud and, beneath it, Nuestra Senora la Reina de Los Angeles, otherwise known as Our Lady the Queen of Angels, otherwise known as LA. That cloud looked like something Satan had cooked up in a conference with General Motors – pure poison which dumped over a thousand tons of hydrocarbons on the city each day, the accumulated excrement of three million cars. Two-thirds of downtown LA was given over to cars and it was a rare moment when you could move through the city without those hydrocarbons stinging your eyes or catching thickly in the back of your throat.

Long Beach turned up next: clusters of shops on the palmed beachfront: Jack in the Box. Beach Motel. Eaglewood Furniture. Maggie's Club. Stars and Stripes hung from rooftops. Fly TWA. Way out in the bay was an oil well disguised as a tropical island with plastic palms. You could also see the three red funnels of that great old liner, the *Queen Mary*, once the pride of the seas and now a permanently moored hotel and home for Jacques Cousteau's Underwater World. A boarded-up castle followed and a few high-rise apartments. This was a society with itchy feet: almost every other home had a For Sale or For Rent sign.

I found the posters for the new films quite deranging. *Raging Bull* was a shrill hymn to animalism which that week had picked up fourteen Academy Award nominations. JUST WHAT IS GOING ON? This Garden of Eden, so full of such beauty and freshness, was swarming with snakes and, far from cleaning them out, these people fed, garlanded and honoured them. The new Jack Nicholson film, *The Postman Always Rings Twice*, had just opened: another essay in animalism in which the couple end up having sex on top of the corpse of her murdered husband. The new James Caan film, *Thief*, was another brutal celebration of crime and violence. Almost everywhere you turned the black rain was sheeting down.

It was late in the afternoon when I moved on out of Long Beach and towards downtown LA. All at once the beauty of the Gold Coast began transforming itself into a wasteland created by the car. Hub City. O&J's Tire Centre. Free Oil Filters. Credit for Everyone. Food to Go. Scott's Body Shop. Huge parking lots spread out everywhere, piled high with dead cars and sprouting with weeds. Credito. J&W Transmissions. The buildings were grey and electricity pylons trooped around me as if in a military drill. In the distance the swooping architecture of those enormous freeways. A line of coloured plastic flags hung forlornly around a garage forecourt. Body Shop. Tortillas. Burritos. *Se habla Espanol*.

A little cinema advertised *Blondes Have More Fun* and *Sex World*. A hotel had been gutted by fire. Air Conditioned Pool. Streaks of exhaust fumes and shattered coloured glass lay everywhere and I had to cycle carefully in case my tyres got ripped, moving past dusty trees, over a rail line and past a car with a broken windscreen, a huge frozen cobweb with a hole where the spider should have been. Charbroiled Burgers. Meat Market. Soto's Mexican Food.

John Lennon Forever – 1940 to 1980, said a painted legend on a wall. Oh John, my angel of love, how could they have done that to you of all people? Blown away by a scummy book.

We might take a rest from our ride here and think of a young American a lot like other young Americans, a lot like me in Mirror Man. He took drugs and played a guitar until, at the age of sixteen, he read a book about an arch-adolescent and phoney-slayer. Holden Caulfield changed Mark Chapman and his life forever. We have already met a lot of young people like Holden, the young Rousseau who doesn't like anything that happens to him. Our young man identifies with his new hero; he likes and admires him, seeing himself as the new Holden Caulfield, buying a Saturday Night Special in downtown Honolulu and travelling to New York to look for John Lennon.

See him now signing into room 2730 in the Sheraton Centre, laying out his clothes and possessions before sending for a prostitute. This was done by Holden down to the last detail; he even goes to Central Park and asks what happens to the ducks in winter – as Holden did. He pays the prostitute twice before sending her away. He's got his Saturday Night Special and is ready for the revenge slaying of Maurice.

At 10.50 pm Lennon was shot five times by two people outside the Dakota. Our young man drops the empty weapon again as Holden had done and began reading his favourite paperback in the lamplight. The other – the romantic hero of the hour-spins off into the cold Manhattan air. Both were catchers in the rye but who was who? *Who became who?*

Barely anything moved on the sidewalks as I pedalled past a gold-minareted mosque and into the LA dusk. The ghostly glow of television sets flickered behind almost every window. They were everywhere I looked. Hell was probably illuminated by the same palsied sheen. Things began moving around inside me again and I knew something else, too. Riding past the houses, factories and parking lots of downtown LA I knew I was travelling across that same silvery plain I had first seen in my Malayan visions with bands of artists standing on a cliff and shelling the people of the plain with their destructive romantic ideas. I caught on to something else in that fetid dusk too. Los Angeles was the home and lair of the fungus. I was on a bike ride into hell.

A tempest of evil came surging down these streets and I rolled up my eyes half expecting to see a cliff with rows of people on top of it, holding buckets and emptying the swill of their ideas into my head. This same tempest had been blowing through California for years and had met with so little resistance it had undermined the whole basis of the family, weakened all in its love of thrills; animalised all in its insistence on the worship of sex in the zinc shrine of the perfect orgasm; debased all in its wallowing in morbidity and incest, been so utterly remorseless in its attack that it had turned this – a Garden of Eden – into a valley of Valium and vibrators, an arena of divorce and leather queens, home to those who abandon their families in the name of better sex – this was the most venal and self-indulgent society on the face of the earth.

I pedalled on up Azusa Street as my mind began releasing thought processes which I neither understood nor trusted, possibly because, without actually planning or even realising it, I was pedalling under the eternal shadow of my old mentor and inspiration, the Welsh evangelist Evan Roberts.

I became the mighty Welsh dragon, riding my bike directly into enemy territory, my mouth bursting with long forks of fire. I was going to smash into Hollywood and release the most terrible ball of destruction in history. I was going to tear the roofs off the film stars' mansions with my fierce talons as I sent mile-long bursts of scalding truth all over those doomed hills. Everything was going to go up in smoke in my all-destroying flames and my huge legs picked up speed and began whapping down Azusa Street.

Evan was on my handlebars as I pedalled on, a man who had long had an intimate connection with this very street since it was his mighty Welsh revival of 1904 which had inspired, here in a warehouse at 312 Azusa Street in 1906, another revival that had gone on to directly inspire the Pentecostal movement in America and throughout the world.

This one had been led by Frank Bartleman who had written to Evan asking him how they might start a similar revival in America.

"Congregate the people who are willing to make a total surrender," Evan had written in reply and Bartleman, together with a one-eyed black American, William Seymour, gathered people here in a warehouse in Azusa Street in the same month that an earthquake had pretty much levelled the whole of San Francisco.

The scenes in Azusa Street were similar to those of the Welsh revival: fiery, twelve-hour meetings in which people spoke in tongues, were slain in the spirit and fell down in holy laughter. One reporter described a meeting as looking like a forest of fallen trees. The walls were covered with the crutches of those who had been miraculously healed. The Lord was bringing people close to him again: he was telling them that he was prepared to make everything new.

At first they called this the Latter Rain Revival, then the Early Rain of the Last Days. So what was the black rain? Was it the last rain of the last days? Was it actually the emblem of some new anti-Christ who had not only fooled us into presenting it with Oscars but was also ushering in the final days?

Evan remained with me, his spirit turning over and over inside me as I free-wheeled across this darkling plain. He was my comfort and strength as I pedalled on, ready to blowtorch out the eyes of God's enemies with the forking flames of my holy madness.

"He has come, then, and will engulf the world," Evan called out to these ruined streets, his lips framing the purest fire. "Satan and all his dark angels have escaped from their dungeon in hell and are even now gathering for their last desperate rebellion against God. Beware, my people, arm yourselves with holiness, for this hurricane of destruction is coming down on you with a terrible force. This hurricane will tear your lives apart in ways you do not understand. It will come offering money which destroys charity; offering power which blights love; telling of the triumph of carnal knowledge which attacks fidelity; insisting that right is wrong and wrong is right.

"This force will come scattering illusions at your feet. It will come bloated with gluttony and malodorous with the stink of its own corruption. Its walk will be slow since it will be burdened with grudges and resentments, trailing ahead of the slime of its hatred. This invading force will come as organised intelligence. Never underestimate it, since it is so clever it will come dressed up as men of respectability anxious to serve you and even able to convince you that Satan does not exist. But he does, my people, and he is going to throw a cloak of violent perversion all over the face of the world."

Driven on by Evan's mighty words, I reared up with a wheelie in Azusa Street, fire still exploding from my lips, trying to decide exactly where I was going to start my great purification ... Except ... it had got a bit late for all that and I was getting tired so I decided I would raze Hollywood and purify the world another night. I locked my bike up against a railing near the Greyhound bus station, signed into a motel and, far too tired to pray or even eat, collapsed on my bed and into a long sleep.

On a bike it is easy to tease out the spirit of a city – be it the jangling, ordered serenity of Beijing or the beautiful, moneyed elegance of central Paris. The personalities of these cities become known to you as you cruise their intimate places, away from their more visible attractions and along back lanes where you can find what most people like to be hidden: where they dispose of their waste, for example, or where the young gather to syringe their arms or raise a little drive-by hell.

But Los Angeles defeated my every investigative sense and, roaming her back streets, I couldn't pick up on anything distinctive, just block after deserted block, almost no one roaming anywhere on foot, all journeys done by car. With drive-in car washes, drive-in banks, drive-in movies and even drive-in churches it was possible never to get out of your car after you left home. Los Angeles was a ghost town, more a collection of empty suburbs disowned by the mother city.

The sky was its usual glorious blue with that distinctive dusty lollipop taste to the air but there were no kids playing, no dogs, nothing. If I did come across a walker I would see him shrivel with apprehension when I stopped and asked him a question, hoping he might tell me something I wanted to know, except he never did, hand fondling his mace spray in his pocket, perhaps, mumbling a few excuses and moving on.

I could offer no formal proof, of course, but it was clear to me that the blame for this dreadful social paralysis could be squarely laid at the doors of the television and film industries. My whole spirit reeled at the notion of a population locked behind alarmed and treble-bolted doors with their spirits frozen by the fear created by all the junk that persistently slopped out of their screens. And such as did make it out of their front doors were sitting in traffic jams on the freeways listening to advertising jingles and anxious to get home to learn all about the latest car smashes and murders on their televisions.

If you wanted to learn about the real lives of decent people in an ordinary world; if you wanted to find something of the sacred blaze of real love which holds together families; if you wanted insight into a true marriage which, even in its moments of exhaustion, takes the dog for a walk, forgives adulteries, keeps vigil on a sick child throughout the night ... you could watch Californian television for a million years and learn not a jot.

Adult television programmes featured five acts of violence an hour with eighteen acts an hour on children's. Victims of crime accounted for more than half the characters on the screen each week. Seventy per cent of allusions to sex on television referred to intercourse between unmarried partners or with prostitutes. Mass killer Charles Manson had recently been interviewed for forty-five minutes on Californian television. David Berkowitz, the Son of Sam killer, called a press conference to complain about his prison conditions – and the bastards all turned up with their notebooks and cameras.

Here was a vast edifice that celebrated crime and anointed the mass killer; an edifice built on rape, beatings and murder, a rabid rodent biting into every mind and home.

The next day I cycled over to Universal City, the largest film studio in the world, and explored the Back Lot: four hundred and twenty acres of offices, studios and giant sets which must represent one of the greatest attacks on truth ever mounted. With five million props and twenty-five thousand synthetic pot plants, they have called on every known technology to tan a star's face, make a wound look realistic and track a bullet through the air.

Everything is designed to make distortion convincing. On a tram tour you learn of false rain, of the ice cream which is cold mashed potatoes, of the plastic palm trees held up by sand bags, of the bricks made of foam rubber, of the revolving drum that is an earthquake, of the street where Doris Day once lived, married to a different man behind every one of the false facades and of how Moses parted the Red Sea. (This Feature Closed Today.)

This tour, which announced it was going to show us the truth of the movie industry, was no such thing. Most of the sets, like the *Jaws* set with the little man in his fishing boat on a pond with a big plastic shark bobbing up out of the water, had been built for the tourists. Even when the film industry said it was about to tell the truth all it could manage was another round of lies.

But I did understand the meaning of fear here. Fear was standing at the end of a lot watching forty people set up a simulation of a Chicago street scene. Fear was looking at the wires, the arc lamps, the rostrum cameras and the actors moving around on cue. Fear was seeing millions of dollars of technology employed by highly paid people drawn together in the cause of the ultimate obscenity. That day they were making *Gangster Chronicles*, an outrageous series that portrays, with some sympathy, the fortunes of three brothers who live by the gun. The programme had a monitored batting average of twenty violent acts an hour. Fear was learning that many of these films have blood editors who are responsible for the tone and colour of a whole range of bloods from thick to thin or granular to smooth. These set the atmosphere and impact of the movie, ensuring that a spatter of light blood will set a light atmosphere, say, and that a dark blood – and lots of it – will make everything darker and bloodier and the darker and bloodier the better. Get the heart fluttering with a light downpour of blood on the pavement and absolutely pounding as it pours off the roof and down the walls.

Before we leave America we must meet another young man who, at the very time Chapman shot Lennon, was sitting in a room in his home in Denver playing Beatles records and drinking peach brandy. He was very insistent that his mother only bought peach brandy which he poured on his cornflakes. In his cupboard was a gun together with a ski mask with holes in the eyes. He had books on the Nazis, Ronald Reagan and Lee Harvey Oswald. But there was another book here which he had read and re-read; a soundtrack he had played constantly and a film which he had seen literally dozens of times.

Our young man ended up firing six bullets at President Ronald Reagan and his entourage on the steps of the Washington Hilton on March 30, 1981. John Hinckley's defence team at his subsequent trial continually blamed the same figure, the alienated one who had captured his imagination, the outsider in his hole-in-the-wall who was given to violence and pornography. We remember him well; Travis Bickle upset my old girl friend Sally all those years back. And this taxi driver is with us still, driving around our streets still, taking shots at all and sundry until he is stopped. But who could stop him, particularly when he keeps pleading that he's not there, that all this mayhem has nothing at all to do with him?

FORTY ONE

Once back home I worked every morning for three hours, had lunch and cycled around London in the afternoons, which gave me new ideas. After Liz came home from work, we ate and put away a fair bit of Scotch before bedtime. Everything works in a routine and nothing more so than writing. You never need to do too much but you do need to do it regularly, and the body of your work will keep putting on weight steadily within that routine.

Greece as seen from a saddle was still a missing chapter so I bought a Bickerton, a lightweight aluminium portable, which folds up into a bike bag, and flew to Athens – quickly offended by the way the car had mugged this once-great city. Almost everywhere I rode in those choking streets there was a dead or dying tree, its leaves turning brown in the exhaust fumes. Taxis, cars, buses, motorbikes and scooters were jammed together, furiously honking at one another as they made their slow way along the scalding, melting tarmac. The Parthenon was barely visible in this shimmering Nephos cloud.

The evenings were the best: most of the cars had long gone home and I ghosted those tinkling streets, full of shadows and bouzouki music where old ladies sat in bougainvillea-draped backyards with their stockings rolled down beneath their knobbly knees, making lace.

I left Athens for Patmos, the island home of St John who, in a cave, received his revelation in 95AD. The *Revelation* is a magnificently ecstatic poem to the sovereignty of God and his ultimate purpose to destroy all evil: a statement of the power of theology built around a series of mysteriously haunting visions which include a dazzling sight of the godhead, the talk of the seven thunders, the war in heaven between the angels and the dragon and the foul spirits emerging frog-like from the mouths of false prophets.

I was repeatedly ambushed by the purity of the place. From one high olive grove I could survey the whole of this volcanic island wrapped in great shawls of light. Over to the north, set in a sea of the deepest and most vulgar blue, was Samos, island home of Pythagoras and, southward, Icaria, Mykonos, Naxos, the mountains of Paros and Amorgos with Kos nearby, formerly the home of Hippocrates. As it was now, so it must have been when God first made the world, finally scattering all the spare bits down as the Greek islands.

This particular terrain, sculpted and whorled like a brain, had been cut into the mountain by hand. Trees grew over the whorls and every breeze brought with it the fragrance of mint. Sometimes those same breezes picked up the leaves of the olive trees and shook them. The whisperings of breezes in olive trees are said to be the way the oracles first spoke.

I thought the Monastery of St John the Theologian a real wonder, an ugly black castle on the outside and inside a mish-mash of pebbled courtyard, a church hall and various cells and stone chambers joined by a jumble of long arcades, cool corridors and stone stairs. Black-robed monks went about their business and in the treasury was a codex of St Mark's Gospel.

Come the night, the darkness gathered Patmos in its arms. Birds ranted in the gaudy sunset and a lone owl hooted as the lights of the calamares boats speckled the invisible sea. And look at those stars: brilliant clusters set against even greater clusters in which a shooting star occasionally fell. Here, in a distant orange grove, you knew that everything was indeed a mystery but life couldn't have been for nothing.

As I continued working at home, in that hot summer of 1981, with the chapters shaping up nicely, the country was engulfed in riots and all my old cranial throbbings came back with a fever as I watched television news. I usually tried to avoid the news, but I had to watch this and often needed at least two large Scotches to ease me through those frantic bulletins. There was a riot in Liverpool's Toxteth: petrol bombs were being thrown, mostly but not exclusively by young blacks, and lots of them were locked up.

So far so ordinary, but the next day there was an extraordinary tension in the streets of Newington Green which I picked up when I went for my afternoon ride. Large gangs of young blacks were gathering on corners and, in the main street, a window was smashed. Shoppers began running or cowering in shop doorways, they knew not why. Even larger gangs formed in Clissold Park and they turned their backs on me and my questions.

That night there was a serious riot in Brixton, followed by riots in many other parts of Britain.

I knew what had happened: knew it as an absolute truth. Our television news, with its naked love of violence, had seized on the comparative isolation of the violence in Toxteth and provoked copycat violence all over the land. Street rioters are almost by definition unstable, unintelligent and unthinking; ideal fodder for the rough beast that our television news had become.

Indeed, television news was doing nothing less than what it had been doing with the unstable, unintelligent and unthinking in Northern Ireland although on a somewhat larger scale: now riots were spreading throughout the country, even into normally quiet areas with low immigrant populations like Cirencester and Aldershot.

We had entered another stormy period of black rain and those who should have known better were again destroying us, dredging up their self-justifying clichés like the "public's right to know what's going on in their streets" while almost no one except perhaps Margaret Thatcher and Mary Whitehouse seemed to have the slightest idea of the real reason why it was all erupting like this. "Please consider the effect of your news coverage on the behaviour of the rioters," Mary Whitehouse wrote to the BBC and ITV. Both transmitted her message without comment.

A parallel riot was raging in the media. A succession of po-faced experts hastened into television and radio stations and sat gravely in their chairs offering reasons for this rioting: over-zealous policing of the black population, drug trafficking, lenient sentencing. Most of the blame for almost everything was heaped on to the head of Mr Unemployment.

The extent of these riots came as no surprise to me. I had long known they would develop from the way television and violence first established their incestuous relationship in the late Sixties and early Seventies when huge waves of anger were sweeping across America – most of which, it seemed clear to me, if no one else – was orchestrated by American television.

I had been clipping pieces from newspapers about the effect of media on violence and it became clear that violence was the key to all news coverage. Gandhi had seen this years ago when he spoke of the value of British violence towards his people in enticing the media to India. Even Martin Luther King stopped a photographer helping a demonstrator being attacked by the police, saying he would be of far greater use to their cause by stepping back and photographing what was going on. Violence was a great help to them. Everyone in America from the Civil Rights movement to the panthers of Black Power and the anti-war movement, offered up violence in exchange for media coverage. In the age of television, if you didn't get coverage, you didn't exist.

Somewhere along the line television was not reporting events but instigating them, turning loose storms of viral imagery which would destabilise whole societies, first in America, then continental Europe and now in the largely immigrant sections of British towns and cities. When the man of lawlessness finally moved out of Belfast he went straight to Paris.

All sections of the media – television, radio, magazine or newspaper – had come together to form a global grid, generating violence on an international scale, embracing terrorism in Munich, fuelling riot in Chicago, fomenting student unrest in France and Mexico, seizing on any kind of trouble, encouraging the stupid to join in a vast chaotic party to which you could gain entry merely by offering yet more violence. The bigger and more entertaining the violence the bigger and more entertaining the party might get. There would be big rewards on offer too. Give me violence, particularly in the shape of a celebrity murder, which you may even have had something to do with, and I will bless and reward you with eternal fame.

Here in my little house in Stoke Newington there was almost nothing I could do or say. I was a redundant columnist. No one was interested in my ideas – still less in publishing them – so all I could do was push on with my bike book and, when the television news got too much for me, drink more. Then, slumped over yet another empty bottle of Bell's, I could tearfully curse God for landing me with these infernal insights in the first place. Or else, if I was feeling theologically alive, I might fling some empty beer bottles into the Spanish chauffeur's garden a few doors away where, despite my frequent overtures, his Alsatian dog was still howling with rejection at most hours of the day and night. That dog and I had much in common.

Later that violent summer, which only calmed down when the country was bathed in the fairytale imagery of Prince Charles' marriage to Diana, we went as a family on our bikes to "do" Paris for my book and took a train to Avignon before riding down through the Côtes du Rhône to the Mediterranean.

The weather was in one of its argumentative moods: one minute squally rain and the next glimmers of sunshine, but we all had fun on our rides around the City of Light, whether gazing at the amazingly geometric flower beds of the Tuilerie Gardens where you could often spot a couple kissing in the rain or in the thronged streets of Montmartre where grizzled painters, long gone in drink, attempted to sell their work for colossally inflated prices to tourists. We rode around like this, subsisting on junk food during the day and trying to have a proper dinner in or near our hotel in St Sulpice at night. Not that our two boys ever wanted a proper dinner: they would have happily eaten junk food forever. The French seemed to like the boys and always gave them careful and proper attention, often with a smile that suggested they actually enjoyed rather than endured them, particularly when they ordered *bifteck et frites*. We adult *anglais* were the ones who got on their nerves. It was no accident that this month of August was the time of their annual holidays and, with typical disdain, Parisians cleared off down south at the height of the tourist season.

After a week of messing around in Parisian gutters we took a train to Avignon where a boy was once sent by an angel to build a bridge. This lovely city, nestling beneath the giant stone walls of the Palais des Papes, was a mecca for bikes and almost as soon as we got there we felt as if we had been taken into a French fellowship of the road and it was all "*bonjour*" and "*ça va?*"

The next day we hauled ourselves up a steep hill out of the town and settled down into a grateful ease as we made a sun-flowered romp through Provence. There was something strange about cycling through fields of sunflowers with their black moon faces turning and watching us as we passed. When a shower of rain came they bowed their heads as if in prayer but when the sun came out again they stood to attention, heads and backs stiffly erect.

It was a wonderful day – perhaps the most wonderful of my life – and I didn't feel at all tired as we rattled into Montpellier, finding rooms in a hotel just above a restaurant in another Van Gogh square with a fountain and all the drinkers sitting around little wrought iron tables.

The boys went to bed and café cognacs followed café cognacs as we reviewed our day until we too went to bed and, as a fitting end to a great day, that was where our third child, another boy, Nathan, was conceived.

I wrapped up the manuscript of *Merlyn the Magician and the Pacific Coast Highway*, sent it to Nick Webb and settled back, anxiously awaiting a response – which never arrived.

This was standard practice in publishing, I was to learn, completely different to journalism, which works on instinct and immediate response. You don't think as a commissioning editor in a newspaper, you react. The idea either gives you a twinkle in your bollocks or it doesn't. Such reactions are rare in publishing where the concept of a reply by return of post is unknown. Everyone seems to need to consult someone else in publishing to find out what *they think*. Will it sell? How many? How will we package it? Is the author media-friendly? Some exceptionally bold souls have even been known to ask if the book is any good. The editorial secretary might well pitch in with her views and, despite all these competing ideas, whatever they come up with will still be ninety-nine per cent guesswork.

"We never really know what we're doing," Nick would say. "We rummage through one another's dustbins trying to find something which might make us a bit of money."

Nick, a smiling giant of a man with small beady eyes and a ginger beard, was much respected in the publishing industry and modest about his achievements. He had been the first to pick up on the radio programme, *The Hitch-Hiker's Guide to the Galaxy*, and got Douglas Adams to turn it into a book. NEL also made a pile out of James Herbert's horror novels, which Nick never really liked but, professional that he was, he kept his dislikes to himself. He also published Harold Robbins and Stephen King, strange stable-mates for me on my bike with my religious manias.

He lived around the corner from me in Newington Green and, often half-pissed, I would stand in the road late at night looking up at the lights in his house wondering whether he might be reading my book and when he might be about to deliver his verdict. My ulcer was rumbling at full throttle and my anxiety was compounded by the fact that I had not written what he had asked for. Even as I was writing the book a lot of unexpected stuff had come out; I felt I hadn't had control over a lot of it, often words splattered themselves over the page in great clumps of electricity. The final version had emerged as a sort of cyclist's visionary journey around the world as I travelled from city to city trying to work out the meaning of my Malayan visions while grappling with the nature of the media's growing threat.

My main difficulty was that I didn't know what to do with my life while awaiting Nick's verdict. Would *Merlyn* be successful enough for me to break out of journalism and become a full-time writer? The advance had long been spent and I wasn't due for any more until the book was published, which could be another year. Even if I got a deal for a new book that money would also be a long time coming. Liz seemed happy enough to keep everything going, but, with two lusty boys and another on the way, we had little to spare. Monthly pay-cheques were always welcome. Newspaper expenses were always worth having too, rarely reflecting what you had actually spent, and writing the odd thousand words a week could hardly be called work.

Yet there was a dark inner voice telling me that, if I did stay in journalism, my days were numbered. I would start drinking heavily again and fail to find my way home. Even though I was still cycling my health wasn't the best: apart from the ulcer I had also suffered from a bout of jaundice which made me throw up so many times it took the lining off my stomach. These ailments were all drink-related a doctor told me. If I carried on like this, I would soon be dead. Such warnings would scare me into a few days on the Coca-Cola but that was about it.

You couldn't do journalism without drink – I couldn't, anyway – so, with a great deal of trepidation, I went back to the *Observer* at least until someone else decided my future for me.

They seemed happy enough – although not exactly overjoyed – by my return but there was no question that I should write Pendennis again: after trying it out with a few others, it had been scrapped. Other worries oppressed me in the news-room, not least my loathing of the media which had hardened quite fiercely since my time in California.

Decisions at news conferences, again often to do with violence, amazed me. The editor, Donald Trelford, was angry one morning because we had missed some sort of fight after a political conference over the weekend. It was barely a fistfight, but other papers had carried it prominently so why hadn't we? What was he so worried about? Who cared? What did a few stray punches add up to in the scheme of things?

In another news conference the diplomatic editor, who always seemed lost in some sort of private dream, brightened my dim view of him when he asked why was it necessary for us to chase every act of random violence in Northern Ireland? It wasn't doing the province any good, he said.

"Believe it or not we are in the business of selling papers," said Anthony Howard, who was in the chair when a similar question was brought up. "We are here to sell papers and violence makes news."

Violence, violence, violence: it was a totally dispiriting business particularly when you considered that this was allegedly the most cultured, the most liberal and the most intelligent Sunday newspaper in the land. If *we* were doing this merely to sell newspapers, what were the tabloids getting up to? What kind of example were we setting the others? The Sunday broadsheets had a huge influence on every level of society and politicians were terrified of them.

I wasn't so much angry at what I was seeing as depressed when I sat in the news-room watching these clever, educated journalists beavering away often to such a negative effect. They weren't all writing about violence, of course, and I had to keep remembering that I was as imprisoned in my own ideas as they were in theirs. When I said there was too much violence on television news Ian Mather, the veteran foreign correspondent, said he believed there wasn't enough. We had a duty to report all these things otherwise we'd end up in a totalitarian state. All that again. Journalists so often hide under clichés in the same way most of us hide under umbrellas in the rain.

But the news desk never involved me in hard news. I was the descriptive writer and, though it was to be brief, I embarked on yet another career of relentless incon-sequentiality starting with a caption about a Shar-Pei dog. For this tiny effort: a hun-dred words, fifteen minutes' work, I was paid, as a member of the staff, £300 a week, about three pounds a word, plus expenses which could cover some serious lunching.

It was expected that you would write more than a hundred-word caption in the course of a normal week's work but that's all I did in my first week. I didn't do much more in my second and I still got paid £300. Could I give up all this to rely on the uncertain finances of writing books when, as I now know anyway, I could end up earning nothing from one year to the next? Added to that, this still being the daffy old *Observer*, rest home for spies and eccentrics, no one bothered if I came in late or not at all. I told the then news editor Robin Lustig that I didn't intend coming in on Saturdays in future – the one day when they might expect to pick up some real news.

"You can fire me if you like," I told Robin. "But I'm not doing Saturdays."

One of the first proper news stories I wrote was about Land's End, that massive valedictory pile of rock at the end of Cornwall – known to the Cornish as the End of the World – whose sale had just been announced.

The story, about twelve hundred words, took me a pleasant few days to research and I ended up doing a short tour of Cornwall in a new BMW which I had hired in Penzance. This sure as hell beat working for a living: this was the journalistic ground I wanted to make my own. Scatter a few adjectives and jokes around. Give everyone a smile with their cornflakes. Others could do the crime and violence.

The next week I wrote about a market gardener who had given up on conventional flowers and vegetables and, backed by the Nature Conservancy Council, changed to the production of wildflower seeds. Where there had been roses, vegetables and sweet peas there were now cranesbill, bishopswort and poppies.

Working on such stories was an unalloyed joy and for a short while I was happy. Even I couldn't get into trouble working on stories like this.

But no one is ever allowed to be happy in journalism for long; it is all but written in your contract. You get shunted around the country by a news editor's unfathomable whim, which is perhaps why we hacks always drank and moaned so much. No sooner had I settled back down on the *Observer* than the wheels began falling off everywhere.

I suppose it began in October 1981when I was asked to go to Wales to follow Princess Diana on her first tour of the Principality. Such stories are a nightmare because royal security is so tight I'd only catch sight of the back of Diana's head if I was lucky. The very idea of following her around my country was pretty sickening and I never could understand why the Welsh suffered a national nervous breakdown whenever she chose to show her face over the border. As her tour progressed, choirs sang, harps plinked and grown men cried.

Thus the royal tour rolled across mountain and down rain-swept valley in triumphant serenity. Hour after hour they moved through the smell of chips and expensive raincoats, swooped into gloomy mansions and mayoral parlours. Children were kissed and babies poked as the Welsh, a radical race, relived the heady days of Prince Charles' investiture.

The tour proved something we had long suspected: Wales was *two* nations. During the early stages of the tour through rural North Wales the response was warm but restrained. As soon as it hit the Valleys of South Wales, the traditional birthplace of British socialism, everyone – but everyone – went bananas.

When Diana attempted a bit of Welsh, sounding like an English girl speaking a bit of Welsh, they all collapsed at the honour of it. Well, Welsh, after all, *is* the language of heaven.

Just before the party arrived in Cardiff on Thursday a lone man on a milk crate was preaching in an empty, rainy street at one stage surrounded by five policemen. The police wanted him to keep his voice down and the man was trying to explain to them that he was preaching in the Holy Spirit and if the Holy Spirit wanted it loud then loud it would be.

Had he no control over it? one policeman asked.

No he didn't.

There was no keeping down the voices of the crowd when the tour turned up in Splott and all the smiles brightened when they were joined by the greatest smiler of them all, Jim Callaghan. He smiled and they smiled and he smiled back in a national Eisteddfod of smirks. It was as if Wales had been declared rugby champions of the world forever. But no, for a land of radical socialists, it was even more joyful than that.

Now that I am out of journalism I can admit that the whole of the piece I wrote was composed by watching the television news from a bed in the Angel Hotel in Cardiff, helped by a number of gin and tonics.

What I had written was fairly accurate and I can't have been the first newspaper reporter to take information from television news, but I'd only been back in the job for a few weeks and had already returned to my drunken, feckless ways. It seemed to go with the job and I was certain it was the drink that kept opening doors which should have stayed shut. For all my idealistic posturing I was just another drunken hack picking up information from the television and passing it off as my original research.

I am even sorrier to report that my piece on Diana went down well at the *Observer*. They used it with a huge Jane Bown photograph and, clearly unaware of the circumstances in which it had been researched and written, it was even selected by Donald Trelford to be included in the *Observer*'s 1982 *Pick of the Year* book. I felt even more uneasy when I saw that, but, of course, I never owned up. It was always half-expected you misbehaved in journalism - as long as you didn't get found out.

Then I got into another kind of trouble, again in Wales, although this time with myself and it turned out to be the death rattle of my regular journalistic career. There had been some new bother in Aberfan. The daily Press had been carrying reports of a possible explosion there and the way an underground fire was threatening the school built after the Aberfan disaster fifteen years earlier. Parents had attended stormy meetings, the name of the Coal Board was being vilified yet again so I was asked to go down there and take a look at it.

It was strange, even slightly disturbing, to go back to this blighted village where, in a sense, my journalistic career had begun in September 1966. It was the same village set in a brambled valley with the smell of cooking streaming along the terraces; the same mournful chapel and the same women with their hair in curlers standing with their arms folded, gossiping in their doorways.

What was different was that the killer tip had been cleared away and there was a memorial garden and community centre where the original school had once stood. A row of white archways stood in the cemetery, the children's graves, all blazing with colour. Parents visited the cemetery every week, some every day. I watched a man bring flowers to one and stand there for a full five minutes looking at the tombstone, his heartbreak as fresh now as that misty morning when the tip had broken loose and killed those children.

Yvonne, Jeffrey, Julie, Susanne, Jean, Janette, Robert, Megan, Islwyn, Graham ... even now the loss still flooded out of those tombstones and there were dark accusations against God too. "A heart of gold stopped beating, two little hands at rest. Why did you have to break our hearts to prove that you need the best?"

The evil which beset Aberfan on that terrible morning had not ended there. The second curse on the village was the appeal fund which came to £1.5 million or, with interest, £2 million. It was an amount which these decent, ordinary people could not cope with. There were quarrels, bickerings and wild words about who was to get what. Every week we heard of a new row and a new point of view which the media duly hardened up and delivered to the world.

Parents were standing outside inquiries holding up placards saying: "Is my child only worth £5,000?" Family was set against family and, in the end, £550,000 was spent on the community centre, £100,000 on a memorial garden and £150,000 towards making the pit safe. The unaffected school children were given £200 each which, invested in unit trusts until they were twenty one, lost money. The previous year the centre's swimming pool had run out of money and was closed. People who had grown up in the shadow of the chapel and in the fear of God reduced everything to money.

A man in the cemetery told me that "with all that money" they should have bought a better quality stone for the children's tombs. "With all that money" they should have done this. "With all that money" they should have done that.

But to my mind the greatest curse on Aberfan was – and remains – the media who hurried here to gorge themselves on the disaster and never left. They came back for anniversaries, protest meetings, any excuse to revive that nightmare day, to wallow in it all over again with their wretched clichés and exaggerations. All the previous week there had been headlines about how "fear was again stalking the valley of tears".

There had never been any explosion or underground fire, I soon discovered, as any of those hacks could have found out with a quick call to Mike Meredith of the Coal Board. There had been an underground *heating* which, at its highest, was 150F when a real fire needs 400F to get going. Three trees were slightly charred, as was a patch of ground which was nowhere near the school. It was, however, agreed to remove a gas main. The parents insisted that everything and everywhere should be checked – even under the faraway school. You could see they weren't believing a word they were being told. They had to check everything themselves. "Their main trouble is they've lost their faith too," sorrowed Mike Meredith as, under the eye of the television cameras, they kept asking questions to which they had already been given the answers a dozen times.

But I was there too, I had to remind myself. I was one of them, unable to leave this place in dignity and peace, coming back with my instant expertise, my unique understanding of the situation, handing out my ever-ready judgements on what was going wrong and who was to blame, feeling pressure to crank up the whole sorry drama again if only for ten minutes in a Sunday newspaper. I was one of them!

Just before Christmas I was sharing a desk with Neal Ascherson in the *Observer* newsroom when I said I was sick to death of journalism and he asked me what I was going to do. "I'm waiting for my publishers to pronounce on my book about bicycling," I said. "They don't seem to be in any hurry to say anything."

"Why don't you ring them and ask?" Neal said.

I followed this revolutionary suggestion and Nick Webb said: "Ah yes, I was about to call you. This is an amazing book, certainly the freshest and most original I've ever published. When you told me you wanted to write a book about bicycling you didn't tell me you were going to re-visit the Book of Revelation while you were at it. We're going to publish it next summer with maximum hype and you'd better come in and discuss what you're going to write for us next."

After all those false starts and a lifetime of dreaming about it, I was a professional writer at last.

FORTY TWO

Having had my first book accepted I did what any other writer might do in the same circumstances: dived into the unpublished, mouldering manuscripts in my bottom drawer to see what to dust up and send out next.

I selected the dog-eared manuscript of *The Electric Harvest*, a novel I had written eight years earlier when I had been running my coal yard in Penarth. It was meant to be a picaresque novel which would move my vision forward an inch or two, set in a London of the future where a gossip columnist, Binky Bines, is trying to wrestle one last ounce of fun out of a dying civilisation and we would follow him through the space of one week in which a young actress introduces him to the joys of high-tech sex while he is being pursued by a sundry mob of debt-collectors, deranged alchemists, vengeful secretaries and a frustrated, angry wife.

This London would be bursting with violence, most of which, I set out to show, had been promoted by the media, particularly television, but including the *Sunday Globe*, for which Binky Bines, the last of the gentlemen diarists, worked. In the final scene he got killed by an arrow in an outbreak of copycat rioting heavily orchestrated by the media.

It wasn't much of a novel and should perhaps have stayed in the bottom drawer, but Nick Webb thought it worth "a modest punt" and it was tightly edited by Tim Shackleton, who managed to hold it to its story and suggested some interesting futurology such as how Keith Richards, the only surviving member of the Rolling Stones, was about to buy Windsor Castle after the royal family had fled the country. We also had many a mad chat about how high-tech sex might work.

Publication day for *Merlyn* – September 2, 1982 – came and NEL hosted a launch party in Bedford Square. Book launch-parties are almost always useless for their main purpose of generating publicity, often achieving only a paragraph or two in the Londoner's Diary in the *Evening Standard,* if you were lucky.

But I was delighted the Rev David Watson was the first to arrive. He always came early to such parties, he said, because that was his only chance to talk to whoever they were throwing the party for. He was as funny and charming as when I had first met him in York, and had written a positively enthusiastic review of *Merlyn* for the Church of England newspaper whose staff had also turned out in force at the party. They were getting right behind the book, the editor said, one of the few Christian books she had read which you could give without embarrassment to a non-Christian. I hadn't seen *Merlyn* as particularly Christian – indeed I was already being referred to as a born-again drunk in Christian circles – but, as a steady and hungry market for Christian books existed, that might well be the road down which I ended up travelling.

David had also made a recent career change, coming down to live in a mews cottage in Chelsea with his wife, Anne, and children, Fiona and Guy. He would be leading a more flexible ministry and concentrate on evangelical work in connection with the houses of Lords and Commons. It was an interesting appointment, but he wasn't sure how it was going to work.

I was pleased he had come to London. He was one of the few Christians I knew who could help me in my own journey along the Path of the Cross. I sort of knew the direction – and might manage a few hundred yards or so on a good day – but I only had to lose concentration for a moment to be taking a toot of something illegal or finding some stray mad actress on my arm. I was still coming across them – there were times when London seemed full of nothing but – and my neighbours in Newington Green were still throwing parties awash with everything the police were keen to throw you into prison for so, yes, David might help me clean myself up. I got to know him quite well, often went to the services he led in Chelsea and hoped he would help me in the matter of faith, not seeing him as a John the Baptist figure holding up a light and leading me out of the dark desert, but as a complex, sensitive man often besieged by the black dogs of doubt and depression who also had trouble with a marriage which wasn't working as it should. Others probably looked for other things in a spiritual leader but he was someone I could identify with. He was frail and full of weaknesses; he was someone like me and perhaps we could even help one another now we were both living in sin city.

Indeed, as the launch party progressed I spotted him with a glass of wine in his hand and clearly enjoying himself chatting with Belinda, my attractive editor, so perhaps the poor man may even have been a little more like me than I thought. He gave a short, amiable speech to the assembled hacks and literary editors, who looked on him suspiciously, and I did get a paragraph in the *Evening Standard*, a little pisstake by Stan Gebler-Davies, who claimed, falsely, that I had told him that I'd seen the light and had given up drink as my hand "clutched a can of Coca-Cola".

This was far from true and afterwards we all gathered in the local Greek where everyone except David, who had long left us, got well-hammered at NEL's expense. Nick always tossed his American Express card around for the most frightening amounts but there seemed to be a real belief in my book throughout the publishing house: everyone thought it was going to do well.

It didn't as it turned out, but that wasn't through any lack of effort by me or them, since the next day I set off on an extensive publicity tour throughout the country with their Press man, Brian Harvey. Getting someone to buy your book is a tricky, elastic art barely understood by anyone. Unless you have a publicity budget of £100,000, with which you can buy ads in newspapers and magazines, about your only option is to get out there, make as much noise as possible and hope for the best.

I had interviewed enough big-name writers in my time and been on the opposite side of the fence often enough to know that it simply wasn't enough to write a book. Well-known writers like Norman Mailer, JP Donleavy, John Updike and Ed McBain had routinely put themselves out for me when I had been the diarist, Pendennis or Atticus, all busily hustling for their books as hard as they could.

I was never going to receive this sort of treatment now that I had jumped over to the other side of the fence. My name wasn't interesting or well-known enough to attract the attention of a broadsheet diarist and, for the same reason, no one was going to ask me to do a signing in a bookshop simply because no one would turn up. I did agree to do a signing for *Merlyn* – in a bike shop in Covent Garden – but, not only had the manager never heard of me when I turned up, he hadn't even got a copy of my book to sign. "What did you say it was called again?".

What the unknown author does, in effect, is go on the stump throughout the country, usually to provincial newspapers or local television and radio stations where, in between pop records and advertising jingles, they will give him five minutes to bang on about his book. The local radio disc jockeys are not interested in metaphysics or high ideas: with me they just wanted to talk about different aspects of bicycling, something to which their listeners could directly relate, if only because almost all of them would have ridden a bike as kids. It was a way of rediscovering the simple joys of your childhood, I used to go on; a way in which we could reconnect with important simplicities in the bewildering complexities of old age.

Sometimes I could work in a little rant about the evils of the media, but as we moved from Cambridge to Sheffield to Birmingham and Manchester, I mostly kept it low-key, trying to become a prophet of the bike, which I really did believe was the key to a number of important modern issues such as our health, faith and sex-drive. Brian, who accompanied me everywhere, liked this. Keep it simple, he would say, and always try and squeeze in a mention of the book's title.

The general idea was that the public heard you on the radio and there was a nice big pile of books in the local bookshop which they would search out. But if ever I went to a bookshop in between interviews I found no such pile. It was only in Edinburgh, in between interviews with STV and Radio Forth, that I did track down one in John Menzies in Princes Street. In Belfast, I walked into a shop to buy a newspaper, came across about a dozen of them and was so shocked and embarrassed I ran straight back out again.

A few of my local radio interviewers didn't seem to read books and none of them was ever quite sure what to ask. A couple could hardly have got through the words on the dustcover and there was one who I was pretty sure couldn't even read at all. Many of the questions were so annoyingly crass I was dumbstruck: What makes you think you can write about yourself? Have you ever had treatment for mental illness?

It's always good to get your face on local television and I managed both Scottish Television and Grampian, but the real problem with television is that it is terrified of ideas: what it wants is imagery, preferably of a violent nature. I realised, almost the first day I set out on the promotional road with my message on the way a violence-loving media was destroying us, that my publicity problems would only be solved if I toted a Kalashnikov down Oxford Street and fired off a few rounds or managed to hurl a bomb into a crowded House of Commons. My name, ideas and motives would certainly have whizzed around the world then.

The media are generally sceptical of journalists who cross over and they have always been understandably sceptical about my ideas, which denounce the very basis of their work. Journalists always take themselves seriously: it is impossible for them to do wrong and already Brian had taken a few abusive calls complaining about my "stupidity", particularly as I was questioning the media's role in Northern Ireland. They weren't having any of that – even though none had read my arguments - although there were a surprising number who privately agreed with me. But what could they do? They had bills to pay like everyone else.

The one thing that *can* sell a book is a clutch of positive reviews in the right places. *Merlyn* did pick up some positive reviews but they were often in the wrong places.

The Christian press was generally supportive and a few of the smaller papers, *Challenge* for example, were positively ecstatic, but the Christian book market was a strange business, I was learning. They would get behind a book and loved anything by Billy Graham or David Watson but I was an unknown, possibly dangerous writer who had a tendency to go too far. Even though I had read only theological books while writing *Merlyn*, to keep its spirit pure, I had used the word "s..t", as in "elephant s..t", in my first chapter and that had made me unfit for evangelical homes. Not all evangelicals reacted like this, but there were enough to ensure that *Merlyn* didn't get into any Christian bookshops. I was also a bit of a drunk, they had noticed.

I did well in Scotland, picking up an extraordinary review by Edward Campbell in the *Sunday Standard*. "This is a book written in righteous wrath by a man who has seen a vision and cannot lay it down," he concluded after observing that I was to the bicycle what Neville Cardus was to the bat. "In its picture of life – whether in the Church of the Nativity in Jerusalem, in the brothels of Amsterdam or the car-choked alleys of Athens or the fly-free streets of China – it is never less than brilliant. Whether one goes along with its major premise or not, this is a book that will be readable and re-readable."

My approval of this review was not because it had used the word "brilliant" – as might be imagined – but because Campbell seemed prepared to step inside *Merlyn* and go along with the book's lonely terror. Most reviewers accept a book only on their own terms insofar as it flatters their prejudices. It was never clear to me why my book did so well in Scotland: perhaps they are not a provincial people and enjoy seeing someone stand up for something.

The book failed critically and therefore commercially in the few places that really mattered: the national newspapers and magazines. The *Times* found *Merlyn* too cute and whimsical; the *Listener* liked the bicycling passages but hated references to the black rain and Richard Boston put in the boot in *Punch* maybe because I had once nearly had a stand-up fight with him at a party about what record should be played. Some literary types never forget – or forgive – anything.

Such problems were not shared by all the national reviewers: I did well in the *Daily Telegraph* although they were already laying down a template for future reviews. I could put together a sentence or two, it seemed; I even had a few interesting insights into bicycling or, as emerged later, into pilgrimage but, on the subject of the media, I was certifiable. My ideas on the media were so silly it was a wonder that any publisher would publish them let alone find any reader who might want to read them.

Generally speaking the reaction to *Merlyn* was mixed although, again unlike the newspaper world where everything became apparent quite quickly, it was a long time before you could see how a book was going to do. Just when you thought it had been forgotten something else would turn up. I received quite a lot of supportive mail about it, much of it from Tasmania where I became big. It was also short-listed for the Thomas Cook Travel Book of the Year award – much to NEL's delight since they had never won an award – only to lose out to Tim Severin's *Sinbad Voyage*. I was also asked for permission to translate it into Braille in South Africa.

There were other occasional delights spread over twelve months. For example Bono, the lead singer of U2, sent word through a mutual friend, Pete Williams, that he loved the book and asked if I would be his guest at a gig of theirs at the Hammersmith Palais. Being invited by a rock star to go and visit him, particularly when he was clearly expecting nothing out of it in terms of publicity, was a new experience for me and one that I wasn't looking forward to. I went to the pub next door to the Palais and had far too much to drink before Pete came to pick me up. I joined him and Bono's wife, Ali, on the mixing desk for the concert, where I drank a lot more and became quite squiffy.

Despite this unpromising start, I managed something of a conversation with Bono after the concert and he said that *Merlyn* was one of the best books he had ever read. "I'm going to make it famous one day," he added over a few more glasses of wine and I was surprised to read, in 2004, more than twenty years later, in an interview with a rock magazine, *Uncut*, he showed he hadn't forgotten it. He said that there had been two clear influences in his life: Kraftwerk, a Dutch band who had first turned pop electronic, and *Merlyn* which had introduced him to cycling as a help to health and a spiritual tool. "It's an amazing book about bicycling. Not being the type, but knowing the serenity of that book, I tried it out. I went cycling in Paris at midnight with Ali along the banks of the Seine. There is a kind of Zen thing with cycling and it's about as much sport as I'll need for the rest of my life. But I did it and they were at the back of my mind as influences: Tom Davies and Kraftwerk."

The Electric Harvest was published in 1984, but it would have taken a sharp-eyed person to notice. The few qualities it had were outweighed by patches of pedestrian writing and its main problem was that I had not yet moved away from journalism: I was still spooling it out as it came into my head and there was little real care in its composition. I settled for the first image that came into my mind: I wanted to fill up the space, meet the deadline and get on with something else. Journalists don't deal in thought or careful writing. Deadlines and pub opening times don't allow it.

The only review I picked up for *The Electric Harvest* was in the *UK Press Gazette* and that was little more than a blast against all journalists who dared try to write the great Fleet Street novel. The reviewer's main point was that hardly any of them were worth reading, particularly this one.

After recovering from the heady excitement of holding my first novel in my hand, I realised that I didn't think much of the book either. NEL did organise another publicity tour around local radio stations and provincial newspapers but, over dinner with a local hack in Edinburgh, I admitted that I didn't think the book was much good. I don't know why I said this – it might have been something to do with the amount of wine we'd got through – but say it I did and thus broke every rule of public relations.

Phone calls were made that night and, the following morning, Brian Harvey rang me to say that the rest of my tour had been cancelled and I should return to London. I didn't have to ask him why. That aborted trip might have been the end of my career as a novelist but I did have one further trick up my sleeve in the form of another novel from my bottom drawer, *One Winter of the Holy Spirit*, set against Evan Roberts' 1904 Welsh Revival. My agent, Elaine Greene, was trying to do something with this but without much success. Nick hadn't been interested and Elaine was on her sixth submission.

What I had learned from the experience of *The Electric Harvest* was the impossibility of engaging artistically with the media about its destructive love of violence without engaging with violence yourself. It has been estimated that eight hundred novels have been set in the turmoil of Northern Ireland over the last thirty-odd years. Everywhere you turned in these books soldiers were being shot and baggy women were bashing dustbin lids in back lanes. Then there were the plays, films and television dramas. Northern Ireland was where thriller writers went to find their plots. If they wanted a terrorist they went to the Europa Hotel and made a few phone calls; if they wanted gang warfare they took a taxi down the Shankhill Road and, if they wanted to learn about arms smuggling, they put the word out in the Ardoyne.

I can't suppose any of these novelists approved of violence or its spread or would plead guilty to the charge they were making it worse. But that's exactly what they were doing by reinforcing the nasty stereotypes, bathing in unremitting bleakness and extending the atmosphere of violence. This incurable romantic attachment to violence has soaked Northern Ireland in terror totally out of proportion to its reality.

FORTY THREE

I now had run out of literary road, which had barely lasted a few books, and, not for the first or last time, I didn't know what to do next. I couldn't think of a decent idea for a new book and, with my Revival novel still circling the publishing houses, I was not only stuck but couldn't remotely guess how I would find a subject which would extend my vision. Many writers claim they don't write with a message, but that's all that ever motivated me: had I not had that I don't think I would have written any further books and would have drifted back to Fleet Street. The *Sunday Express Magazine* under the editorship of my old pal from the *Sunday Times*, Ron Hall, often gave me a grand or two for a few days' journalism there. That was a lot of tempting money for old rope and my income as a writer had already become non-existent.

Yet my disillusion with the media's constant search for blood and pain had become complete and I was anxious to get away from it as far as possible. News had to be marketable; its function was not – as it often claimed – to understand ourselves and the world, but to serve up events as hot and bloodily as possible to make a profit. It was getting worse daily: the bloodier the images the fatter the profit: the more dead bodies on the front page the bigger the circulation. The more respectable the paper the more gross their offences. *All* their noses were in the same trough.

But my most worrying perception, almost impossible to handle with any sense of perspective, was the way it appeared that the media had become the central nervous system of the world. In my early days on the *Western Mail* I had observed how such a newspaper influences the community in which it operates. This perception broadened during my days on the *Sunday Times,* the *Sunday Telegraph* and the *Observer* but, after Pendennis, where I had a close relationship with the world of film and television, I saw that the media distilled a global poison. This toxicity was active and growing exponentially; its scope virtually limitless.

These were difficult, anxious and terrifying issues. More in desperation than anything else, I decided on a complete change of life and career and, after prolonged negotiations, in which they showed little enthusiasm for having me, I joined the London Bible College in Northwood for a two-year course which would lead me to something – I never quite worked out what – by way of a qualification in Biblical studies. All I wanted was to learn what was in the Bible and, perhaps, remake myself in the process.

Also, the arrival of Nathan meant we needed a larger house and that was more affordable in the suburbs than in central London. So we finally got away from the drug parties and cat burglars of Newington Green and found a pleasant house in Eastcote, near Northwood, a vast sprawl of modern bungalows with identical lace curtains, pansy gardens and neatly manicured lawns. There was not even one rebel who let his grass grow wild and roses sprawl over his paths.

Julian and Steffan settled into the nearby Bishop Ramsay School in Ruislip where it looked as if they might even pass an exam or two and for me it was writing or Bible College in the morning, walks with our new baby in the afternoon followed by dinner, television and a good slug of Scotch. For the hundredth time I gave thanks that our marriage had kept going despite all the blows I had inflicted on it: apart from enjoying it I needed its security to keep going as a writer; it was only when I wandered out through my front door looking for passion and intensity that trouble began. And surely I wouldn't get into trouble in Bible College.

Northwood Bible College was a group of modern, purpose-built buildings set on a hill and its four hundred burnished and bright students didn't look as if they had ever seen a Class A drug let alone taken one. The day began with a communal service then a round of lectures each started with a prayer delivered with various levels of fervour. The academic day was built on prayer: I guess it underlined why we were all there.

I was slated for several courses, including the Doctrine of Christianity, which was about God and his world; the book of the prophet Isaiah; the New and the Old Testaments and Christian Discipleship.

Isaiah, a prophet of exile, was the coolest and most far out cat in the whole of Israel. His work painted a picture of the great complexity of God and the way his power suffused the whole of creation. God, or Yahweh, the God of Israel, was supreme and Isaiah insisted that his worshippers should comply with his moral demands. The prophet was obsessed with the concept of holiness and saw prophecy as a call to holiness. He urged Judah to keep out of foreign alliances and trust in God: he was confident in the inviolability of Jerusalem – God's sanctuary on earth – and around those expectations gathered the hopes of successive generations of Jews. In a way Isaiah was the real father of the Jews, the one who always preached their durability and ultimate invincibility as long as they kept their faith.

One of his other main themes was a Way in the Wilderness, a good one for me who knew all about getting lost, so Isaiah became my new hero. He was going to lead me to a Promised Land, far from the fleshpots of Soho for a start.

Isaiah had also received a series of revelations that enabled him to understand the immediacy and particularity of certain events which made him the most important man in Israel. I was fascinated by the way he communicated as a speaking prophet and how his verses could be broken down into a wide pattern of voices. His voices had multiple sources, perhaps reflecting the complexity of the God from which they came.

I attended all the lectures on this strange, detached man. The lecturer himself just stood there, devoid of any sense of style or presentation, and often made me shiver with absorbed interest as he analysed the verses one by one, revealing their extraordinary depths. He demonstrated how one of the verses was built around five different lights.

I could have stuck to such studies rewardingly and even enduringly – and might have ended up as something of a Biblical scholar – but the trouble with many of the other lecturers, including the principal himself, was that they saw their work as something more akin to entertainment than scholarship and kept telling "funny" stories which never amused me or indeed anyone else.

I took extensive notes on Isaiah, but all I was doing in the other lectures was doodling, trying to keep at it but, perhaps because there was no one around to threaten me with dire consequences, soon not bothering even to show my face and spending most of my time in the library, where I began researching angelology (the orderly statement of Biblical truth about angels). These winged messengers of God might form the basis of my next book, I thought, even if I didn't yet know how.

Angelology had me hooked from the start and I went after it determinedly. Little had been written about angels except for one thin bestseller by Billy Graham. Most of the others, I had noted, had a tendency to whimsy, portraying angels constantly flying around the place wielding their mighty swords and doing heroic deeds. What I needed to do first was work out what I could about the world of angels from the three hundred references to them in the Bible.

"An angel is a spiritual creature without a body, created by God for the service of Christendom and the Church," Martin Luther wrote but I'm not even sure that accorded with the Bible. They were often invisible but could take on human form as we can see when we are told always to entertain strangers since they might be angels in disguise. Their corporality is also suggested by the fact that they cannot be in two places at the same time. Angels have their own individual personalities and a wide variety of functions.

Based in Israel, but with a worldwide brief, angels are unapproachable, unaffected by human needs and dwell in Yahweh's court. They often appeared in human form and stood before Abraham and Samson's mother. One appeared in a burning bush and only one was able to fly. "While I was still in prayer," Daniel wrote, "Gabriel, the man I had seen in an earlier vision, came to me in swift flight about the time of the evening sacrifice." The angels came with instruction and insight, messengers of God's thoughts, delivering messages as well as destroying and punishing his enemies.

As agents of the fear of God, angels could be fantastically brutal, destroying nearly two thousand soldiers of the Assyrian army and threatening to wipe out the first-born of every unbelieving Egyptian or Israeli household. "Where I see blood I shall pass over you." It was with the arrival of Jesus that their activities became more loving and they watched over him during the most important stages of his life. They announced his birth – "For unto us a child is born" – they ministered to him when he suffered in the desert; they were ready to defend him when he was captured, and strengthened him on the Cross. They were the first witnesses to his resurrection, having rolled away the stone, an act which also tells us they were strong.

We also know that angels are not to be worshipped in their own right, they never age or fall sick, they cannot fall in love or get married or feel randy. They are wise and know everything on earth. They will carry you up in their arms if you dash your foot on a stone and rejoice when a sinner repents with song and the music of heaven. The flapping of their wings usually presages some important event. Some commentators, including Thomas Aquinas, have tried to work out the complicated structure of the angel army with three archangels in charge – Michael, Gabriel and Raphael – followed by cherubim and seraphim and nine choirs of angels.

But perhaps the centrality of the story of the angels concerns their role in the outbreak of evil in the world, under which we have all been suffering more or less ever since. Michael and his angels engaged in battle with Lucifer, the most beautiful angel in all heaven, "who walked on the holy mountain of God, in the midst of the stones of fire". When Michael threw Lucifer out of heaven his tail, said John, swept away a third of the stars in heaven and threw them to earth.

Now, in his continuing war against God, Lucifer uses the human race, making them children of disobedience. He destroys truth, holding people apart from God, preparing for the last great battle against Christ who will finally stage his long-promised Second Coming on the plains of Armageddon. On this great day, this day of wrath, a date which is not even known to the angels, Christ will emerge with a shout, with the trump of God. There will be a great battle and all the forces of evil will be devastated. Lucifer will end up chained in a bottomless pit where he will be tormented for ever in fire and brimstone.

These are the bare bones of the story of angels and the problem with writing any sort of book about them was that any addition to or subtraction from Biblical testimony would be speculative. We can work out certain things about them from Biblical references, but not a lot.

When I did put in a possible treatment of a book on angels to the religious department of Hodder & Stoughton, the parent company of New English Library – with some sketches by the artist Mary Parkes on how angels might go about their work in the streets of London – someone who knew far more about the Bible than I, pretty much crossed out every line and wrote next to it: Biblical evidence? The synopsis was short when it was sent in, minuscule when it came back with a curt rejection. Angelology would have to wait for another day – which came about thirteen years later when I tackled the story of Conker, the angel whose grave misfortune it had been to be assigned Wales with her rain-sodden sheep and melancholic people.

That was the one positive thing about being a writer. Over a time – which might even be a lifetime – nothing is ever wasted. You work up an idea that goes nowhere and is turned down by everyone, and you throw it in your bottom drawer. Years later you work up another that goes nowhere and is turned down by everyone and you might think ah, I can graft it on to that old idea and, lo, something completely new emerges which might hit the publishing spot. In no career is the injunction "Don't give up" more appropriate. Everything will get into the daylight in the end: the real trick is not to despair, to keep writing for years on end, if necessary, until, for no apparent reason, it will fall into place and you will get on something of a roll again.

I was not on a roll in those Biblical college days: I couldn't put anything together and, with our finances stretched, I had to do some journalism to keep us ticking over. Out of the blue, I was offered an assignment which was also well-paid. The *Sunday Express Magazine* had decided to "do" a week in the life of the royal family and, with the full permission and co-operation of the Palace, various writers were asked to follow various members. There would be a book in it and I was asked to follow Prince Charles for a week for which I would be paid £3,000. I had long believed that, if I ceased to believe in my calling as a writer, I'd lose it. I'd met a professor of English in Dublin and we'd been discussing the many writers the city had produced and I'd asked him how they had managed for money and he'd said that not one of them had ever written one word for money. They had relied on friends or the patronage of rich women or their own wits and that's why so many of them had become great. You can't do it any other way, the professor said. For a real writer it's all or nothing: you can never be a part-time writer and make it work.

The professor's words resonated with me so deeply that I made almost nothing for years after that conversation but, at that stage, even with the words of the great and inspirational Isaiah ringing freshly in my mind, £3,000 was too much to turn down and, anyway, I thought I might enjoy being a reporter again, if only for one week, just hanging around in the background of Prince Charles' busy diary, constantly harassed by his nervous detectives, as I kept myself and my thoughts out of it, just carefully watching him and all around him.

There was no chance I was going to follow Prince Charles on television from a hotel bed either, even if I did carefully go through the *Radio Times* for that week to see if they were covering any of his events.

I continued attending Bible College and skipping most of the lectures except Isaiah, while continuing to work in the library where, having done angels in a manner of speaking, I began fattening up my file on the Man of Lawlessness, that Satanic parody of the true Messiah whose growing presence throughout the world had once vexed and tormented my spiritual godfather, Evan Roberts. He was written about in both Daniel and Revelation but the basic nature and detail of the prophecy are in the life and writings of St Paul.

Paul is widely acknowledged as the first man to understand the life and death of Christ, writing nearly half the books of the New Testament. If Christ was the light Paul was the beacon. Aquinas called Paul the professor of the Apostles and we know he was a man whose mind was on fire with new ideas at a time when the world was in ferment following the death of one Jesus of Nazareth, recently crucified on a hill in Jerusalem.

The first we learn of him was that he was a Jew, a proud citizen of the Roman Empire and that he hailed from Tarsus, a flourishing and determinedly immoral centre of learning and philosophy. He terrorised the followers of the Nazarene everywhere, entering homes, carrying off men and women and putting them in prison. These were gleefully pagan times with the stabilising law and order of the Roman Empire collapsing fast. Temples were still going up to old gods. Sacrifices were offered and sexual perversion rampant. Prostitutes conducted their business in the temples and the watchword "freedom" was used to justify going with them.

Sexual licence prevailed in Corinth with theft in Ephesus and drunkenness in both. Within this framework Jesus was seen as a trouble-making revolutionary, destroying the Jewish faith and upsetting the peace.

While on the road to Damascus, about his business as the bloody avenger of an outraged law, Paul received a vision of the risen Christ. He was blinded by Christ's appearance only to be healed later by Ananias. Like Moses, Elijah and John the Baptist before him he went off into the desert where, alone, he confronted himself and dedicated his life to God.

For fifteen years he worked as a missionary in Arabia, Jordan and Damascus. With his faithful sidekicks he often sailed the Mediterranean in sunshine and storm; trudged miles along old Roman roads, once rode horseback from Jerusalem to Caesarea. His first long missionary journey took him to Cyprus where he had a friendly meeting with the Roman governor in Paphos and he travelled up to the bandit-infested and dangerous mountains of Turkey to visit Perga. They passed Lake Egridir and visited the thriving city of Antioch, making for the synagogue where Paul began his address on Jewish lines but concluded by declaring a belief in Christ. The next Sunday practically the whole city turned up but Paul and his companions were moved on by the authorities. In Iconium they were threatened with stoning. At Lystra there were angry mobs. Wherever Paul opened his mouth trouble followed.

Some time after returning to Antioch his group heard Jerusalem had sent more hounds after them. Paul was denounced as a bogus apostle who was leading everyone up the garden path and it was then he wrote one of his letters, to the Galatians, probably dictating it to Timothy or Silas who wrote it down on papyrus.

Paul went to Thessalonica, a large city where a new vigorous church sprang up, largely with Gentile converts, with a Greek culture and under the domination of Rome. Yet again the Jews stirred up trouble against him. He went to Athens to found a church and was appalled at what he found. Publicity – the journalism of the ancient world – was based in Athens. People only wanted to tell and learn something new. Every interest, every shrine, every glory of the city was pagan. In its theatre real people were being crucified on the stage for dramatic effect. The games were orgies of eroticism and violence. Paul was anxious to get to Corinth where one of the liveliest of the Pauline churches was springing up.

It was in Corinth that Timothy came to him with a report. The church in Thessalonica, he said, was sound and in good faith. They were mostly Gentile Christians, but there were many spiritual problems. They had been drawn into a net of needless anxieties as they contemplated the shape of things to come. Many of them had stopped working, becoming idle and listless, waiting for Christ's return. When would Christ return? Why would they have to wait for so long? Or would it be long? What would happen if they died before his return? How could they tell if the end was indeed nigh? Such questions summarised the old Christian dilemma: caught between the sudden lightning of the First Coming and waiting anxiously for the apocalyptic thunder of the Second.

Paul dictated a letter to the church. He exhorted them to wait confidently for times and seasons which had not yet been revealed. He urged them to lead sober lives as "children of the light" and not get over-excited. The new age had yet to dawn. They were to be watchful and sober. Hold fast to that which is good. Steer clear of evil. He was opening the door to a trusting faith.

But he received more news that, despite his letter, his new converts were coming to believe that the Second Coming was imminent. They had misunderstood and were clinging to their new belief with a dogmatic certainty. So within a few weeks of his first letter Paul wrote his second letter to the Thessalonians in which he carefully defined the conditions which must precede the return of the Son of Man. At the heart of this letter lies a prophecy and a warning.

He described the Man of Lawlessness, a great and mysterious tide of evil which was going to sweep the world before the return of Christ. This evil tide will reach its climax under this man's leadership, he said; it will oppose Christ and be destructive of the very mind of God, making war on everything sacred and holy.

Now concerning the coming of our Lord Jesus Christ and our assembling to meet him, we beg you, brethren, not to be quickly shaken in mind or excited, either by spirit or by word, or by letter purporting to be from us, to the effect that the day of the Lord has come. Let no one deceive you in any way; for that day will not come, unless the rebellion comes first and the man of lawlessness is revealed, the son of perdition

So the Man of Lawlessness will be ruthlessly exposed in his own season. He will be known as the most famous Antichrist of them all, doomed to ultimate destruction. But Paul enters an important caveat. "And now you know what is holding him back so that he may be revealed in his proper time." This line has become known as the Restrainer in Biblical scholarship. Something will be *lifted* at the appropriate moment.

Paul added that when he comes he will come with all the "powers and miracles" of the lie. "And with all the wicked deception of those who are to perish. It will be a strong delusion to make them believe what is false."

What is the Restrainer? Surely it cannot be human because no human could hold back the word of Satan. One suggestion is that the Restrainer is the word and law of God. In the mysterious methods of his workings it is God who finally gives way to the Man of Lawlessness since this tide of evil somehow fulfils his ultimate purpose. He will lift his restraining hand gradually and somehow mobilise this evil in his quest to work out his original purpose in creating the world. When this evil has come to a certain point he will make a resolute attempt to restrain it. He will send back his Son and the career of the Man of Lawlessness will have run its course.

This might be so but surely it smacks of guesswork. We do not know God's mind. He does not think as we do. As the Thessalonians already "knew what it was" our best bet might be the simplest. By the Restrainer Paul might be referring to the restraining power of law and order. Paul had the greatest reverence for the law but he was worried he was watching law and order break down. He was emphatically not a revolutionary. The world, he said, was full of suffering and attuned to disorder. Roman law aimed at the triumph of right and the punishment of wrong. As it stood it was restraining a threatened outbreak of anarchy but, in time, this Restrainer was going to be moved out of the way and the world was going to slip into lawlessness which would find a leader who would both enshrine and encourage criminality.

As lawlessness grew a large mass of humanity was going to take a wrong turn. Light would become darkness. Everywhere people would give way to their unrequited passions; they would follow their own desires. The process was already at work but the leader had not yet revealed himself. Who was he? How lawless could he be? How much trouble could he stir up?

Sitting there in that Northwood library, I became increasingly convinced that Paul had foreseen, in almost every detail, the rise of the mind of the modern media as it fomented lawlessness and terrorism wherever its power and influence reached. Here was a philosophy – a Romantic philosophy which loved and valued violence more than any other – which supplied motive for murderous assaults on presidents and rock stars. It was almost a dictatorship with political control over well nigh everything to the extent that no politician would now get very far if he didn't look good on television or chose to ignore it. Newspapers consistently set the daily political agenda; politicians now hardly bother to talk to their constituents but they have plenty of time for the Press they fear and obey.

In line with the prophecy, the media had bemused the very elect of God since those with mitres and cassocks, almost more than the politicians, were clamouring to be featured on it and receive its approbation. The media ruled unchallenged on every hearth.

The prophecy also says that this man will come with "all the powers and miracles of a lie" and how well that phrase describes the very skin and bone of our modern media where it is often not so much difficult to locate the lie as pinpoint any stray outbreak of truth. Unless it is totally factual, most reportage is based on lies, on the sensational reading of sensational events which are then carefully edited to make them even more sensational. Almost every Hollywood film, by its basic fictional nature, is a high-gloss tissue of lies. Feature films, whatever the claims on their behalf to the contrary, are little more than a reflection of the workings of a director's imagination, often cut to give such workings a poetic or emotional effect. Most documentaries suffer from the same constraints and who could be worse offenders than those who make wildlife documentaries which are often wrapped around a sentimental story line involving some sort of race for survival? Even when they tried historical dramas the truth was always shredded ruthlessly in the names of dramatic tension, visual sensationalism or gratuitous sex.

When Paul said that "you already know what it is since it is already with you" could he have been referring to our fascination with – and indulgence in – the public manifestation of violence and cruelty which was as strong in Paul's time as it is now?

Crowds swarmed to the Roman games, many sleeping out in the streets at night in the hope of being close to the violence and death of the chariot races and gladiatorial combat. If Emperor Nero got bored he had sections of the audience thrown into the arena to face the lions. Wounds were entertaining, blood was thrilling and death was cheap. It can be no coincidence that violence seeped through every level of Roman society, threatening even its rulers.

Everyone was addicted to the games in much the same way as we are today addicted to "news". When we open our newspapers and turn on our televisions we do so in the same expectation of bearing witness to all the latest murders, violence and other associated outrages. Whether we accept it or not we have become as addicted to blood and pain as the Romans were although we, through various sections of the media, can satisfy this addiction almost hourly. Our media has erected a global Coliseum of cruelty where we can hear news and watch pictures of the fallen, the bloody and the dying because we enjoy it. The principles of this addiction are the same now as they were then: it's only modern electronics that make the circumstances of our enjoyment different.

These were troubling ideas and I couldn't see how I might be remotely suited or equipped to deal with them, if only because I was still drinking so much at night to calm me down. A real, faithful Christian would have put his prayerful trust in God wherein he would feel safe and secure. That never quite worked for me and, indeed, when I did attend church, as I did regularly in those days, I often came out feeling more stressed than when I went in.

One man who would have helped me out was David Watson but he had barely settled down in his new job in London when he had fallen seriously ill with cancer. He would spend whole days on the toilet, often listening to devotional tapes, he told me in a letter. It all sounded grim and I prayed for him earnestly.

Then, almost as if in sympathy with David, I had my own problems on the toilet one night in Eastcote when I sat down and felt a warm, blistering gush out of my backside. The pan was full of blood and I threw up several mouthfuls of blood. Amazingly calm in the circumstances, I went into the living room and told Liz that something had happened which might be serious. My long-standing ulcer had exploded, the emergency doctor said, and I was rushed to Northwood Hospital.

They put me on a gurney and the porter lost his way as he pushed me through the darkness of the hospital grounds in a light drizzle. I would have welcomed death with open arms at that moment. Life had become too difficult. Somehow I had ended up in totally the wrong place: I had become the Biblical loony with his placard walking up and down Oxford Street announcing The End is Nigh and, given the state of me on that gurney, the end might now be nigher than I had expected.

I was sickened by the way my career had evolved into that of a freelance prophet. It seemed to keep rumbling in that direction even when I slammed on the brakes or tried to take another more agreeable path. Freelance prophecy had nothing going for it, just one long torment of loneliness and rejection with people forever taking the piss out of your prophecies when not ignoring you altogether. There wasn't even any money in it. Even as I rehearsed these thoughts, with blood still sluicing from me, and the porter getting ever more lost in the hospital grounds – it was only his second day here, it seemed – my memory took me back to those terrifying days in Malaya when I had seen the black rain pouring out of a clear blue sky, telling me about a tide of evil flooding every corner of the world and bringing home a dead harvest. Oh yes, he had come all right. He'd taken control for sure.

That was the trouble with my visions. They were true and, wherever I looked, undeniable. The evidence was there. I couldn't contrive to lose them or turn my back on them. I was imprisoned with them and, wherever I went, they came along until I could get sufficient whisky down me to loosen their handcuffs for a few hours.

They put many pints of blood into me after the porter finally found the ward and I was given medication to stop the bleeding. The next day I discussed my exploding ulcer with a doctor and told him I'd had it almost for ever. Sometimes it was quiet but then it would flare up and I would control it with Tagamet until it calmed down. When I got worried it tended to play up again. The doctor asked me what I was so worried about and I settled for a lame "I dunno really".

I couldn't have even started telling him what I was really worried about. It would have been the first bus for the local asylum for sure if I'd told him the half of it.

Tests revealed I'd been lucky, the doctor said. Such ailments can kill but, in my case, the ulcer had healed itself which was why, for the first time in ages, I wasn't feeling a savage ache in the pit of my belly. But I had to give up the drink. That which had built the ulcer before would almost certainly do so again.

I did give up the drink when I got out and drank gallons of Coca-Cola, which made me belch all the time, before reaching for the calm of the whisky again: I was an alcoholic but wouldn't admit it.

I packed up Bible college because it was making my life too worrying, but I did take home another concept from Isaiah. I had been quite taken by his obsession with holiness which came from the Anglo-Saxon word *halig;* something which must be kept complete or inviolable; something which was one or whole; something which was of high moral excellence, spiritually perfect, of God.

Did holiness exist in our fallen world? Might it still be out there if I went looking for it?

From these questions, feeling better than I had for years now my ulcer had self-destructed, I began working up an idea for a book which would take me around all the holy places of Britain and Ireland. I consulted libraries and made calls to tourist boards. What was going on where and when? When did they have their festivals or pilgrimages? There was one night at Westport in Ireland when they all climbed Croagh Patrick mountain. They had a three-day pilgrimage in Lough Derg in County Mayo which was so tough people had died on it. I located a bus company that took people on an excursion around the holy spots of the north of England, including Durham Cathedral and the island of Lindisfarne. The last chapter had to be a walk along the Way from Winchester to Canterbury which had been followed by so many pilgrims.

The itinerary began firming up. It would take me a year and I would do each trip in its own season, noting the changes in the weather and describing the different people I met en route. I took it to Nick Webb and, although *Stained Glass Hours* — as I called it — was not what you might expect to find in a normal NEL list, he gave me £3,500 to write it and that next Easter found me cycling across the Fens towards Ely Cathedral with cold, wet winds blasting in my face.

This cathedral was founded in 673AD by St Etheldreda, a strange and beautiful woman of ice and flame who never washed in warm water and didn't believe in sex before or after marriage resulting in two immensely frustrated husbands. She remained a virgin until she died and you can pick up on this ice queen's personality as soon as you step inside her front door. The huge, dark spaces inside the cathedral do not tell of the human failings of ordinary people. There is no trace of sensuality in the flag-stoned floors. Every opening door whispers with disappointments of frigidity.

The high lantern tower had shafts of stellar light bursting through her windows and I signed into a local hotel before going back at night to try and find Etheldreda again, wandering through those ancient shadows outside, passing the dean's house where dark silhouettes moved around in the golden lights of the rooms. Insomniac birds fluttered past the spiky parapets and chipped gargoyles. Far away, the sound of choir practice. The cathedral was well on its way to being a ruin and there were no reserves, various notices said. The choir stalls were surrounded by scaffolding draped with huge polythene sheets. Those frigid draughts kept on getting in everywhere.

When I left Ely a few days later to take the road to Walsingham those Fen winds attacked me again with icy shotgun blasts of rain. Pylons marched across the flat landscape and, in the ditches, pampas grass with black beards whipped furiously in each and every gust of wind. I came across the numerous corpses of flattened frogs; it was still spring, the season of mass migrations and endless fornications for frogs.

As I cycled away from Ely, Etheldreda still haunted my mind, still reared up over and through me as if in one of those nightmares which cannot be resolved by wakening. The burst of transcendental light in the lantern tower, the draughts in the darkness, the scaffolding where there should have been holiness. She complained that I had completely misunderstood her and her home. My hands were red-raw and my face stung with the cold. It might have been her unforgiving hands that were clutching at my throat and, as two lorries roared past, spraying me with icy water, I had to stop cycling and bow my head, yelling out to her to leave me alone.

FORTY FOUR

I joined twenty-nine others for a coach tour of northern England and spent the week sweeping through countryside where red puffs of poppies dotted the silky green corn and trumpets of hogweed bugled along the banks of burns. We passed through villages with heart-rending names: Spennymoor, Seldom Seen and Pity Me.

We had viewed opencast mines, clambered over ruined castles, photographed Gothic ruins and stopped in towns where fluorescent bingo halls sat next to gilded curry houses. Now we were in Escomb to look at the Saxon church. There was a skull and crossbones on one of the graves. These were once thought to show that the death had been by plague or even the inmate had been a robber but this wasn't true, explained one of the more knowledgeable members of our group. The skull and crossbones were reckoned to be the minimum Gabriel needed to fix up a decent resurrection: only later did pirates claim them.

The church itself was a small untidy potpourri of mismatched stones. A sundial on the wall had only three lines, which suggested the original marks were concerned with times of prayer rather than hours of the day. Inside it had a simple whitewashed elegance with a spray of lilies next to the font. There were no windows in the north wall, the "devil's wall", and, during christenings, the door had always been left open to let the devil out. The pews were polished and stone floors spotless. "I love things that are looked after," said Pat, one of my fellow travellers. "To me that's lovely."

We had a "click" stop for photographs at Walworth Castle – "painted by Turner and written about by Shakespeare" – before cruising alongside a languid sea. The Farne Islands rose in the distance, mysterious in the small plashy waves. Oystercatchers wheeled overhead screeching their bad news at one another and a water tank sat on the horizon, a giant black mushroom. The day was going to be a scorcher.

After Bamburgh the countryside became flatter with lonely trees hunkering down against the bitter North Sea winds. We spotted Lindisfarne Castle for the first time and caught our breath. It was a bold fairy castle springing straight up out of a high rock as if, somehow, both had been created by the same hand at the same time.

Even as we crossed the causeway into Lindisfarne I lost my heart to the place and kept going back there, enchanted not just by the spectacular view but by the island's promise of holiness. Islands mediate the concept of holiness to us. They are one, whole, apart, places of pure solitude where man, alone, may seek out and attempt to understand the nature of the mystery. The surrounding sea is the very material of God – the way of baptism, regeneration and faith; the waters in which we must be born again. To such islands the soul might return after death.

Yes, there was a powerful dreaming holiness about Lindisfarne. It drifted on the great sea winds, through those wide stretches of sand dotted by pools and the curling mounds of lugworm. You could hear it in the fluting calls of the sandpipers, in the flapping wings of the storks pinning arcs of flight against the clear sky and the low distant rumble of the flooding tide.

Holiness is not evinced by a great edifice that has taken hundreds of year and thousands of lives to build. On Lindisfarne, it was etched into our minds by the line of old broken sticks stretching across the sands to mark Pilgrim's Way. Holiness is best expressed by the simple, the humble and the poor. Those sticks sang a song of holiness to the sea winds; they surrounded the journeying pilgrim with the music of the Cross as he made his way across the softly sinking sand to Holy Island itself. That day the island looked magical, the sun burnishing the huge pools around the causeway, goslings moving through the fiery yellow water as children on the other side tumbled down the high slopes of sand dunes.

This had been the island home of St Cuthbert, a saint with a silver tongue which could wreak havoc even among the birds. He had the gift of healing and Bede, the eighth-century chronicler of those times, referred to him as a child of God. He healed a woman's dying baby with a kiss; he would stand in the sea all night worshipping God until the seals came in the morning to dry his feet and breathe warmth back into him. Cuthbert was a key member of the Age of Saints when God sent in his chosen few to rescue the land from darkness.

Durham Cathedral was next, its great shadow falling over us as we gathered in the porch like a blessing from Gabriel himself. "The torch of faith stands here in Durham," said our guide, the sort of man St Augustine might have described as a hallelujah on two legs. "Stand still and look and study. Ask yourself how it has come to survive in a modern world. Remember that architecture is but history written in stone."

We shuffled behind this font of odd facts and learned that the bishop's throne here was the highest in Christendom; that the organist had a closed-circuit television to see what was going on in the services and there were twenty boys in the choir. Sixty people were employed here and since the building cost half a million pounds a year to maintain – with one hundred and eighty pounds a day to heat it – they had to run it as something of a business, making money where they could. In one year they get around a million visitors and only last week, the guide said, eight hundred came in during the Durham Miners' Gala.

As we wandered around listening to him talk I saw that there was much here that owed itself to Cuthbert. The saint's hospitality to strangers had been legendary, so it was only right the building should be a famous place of sanctuary where a criminal could seek asylum. Until 1540, when Henry VIII did away with it, six men a year knocked on the sanctuary door: the knocker was still there – a huge representation of a lion's head with flowing mane, huge eyes.

In the Galilee Chapel we were taken to the tomb of the Venerable Bede, monk of Jarrow and father of English history, to whom we owe so much of our knowledge of Cuthbert. His *Ecclesiastical History of the English People*, completed in 731AD, is a best-selling paperback today; he also translated parts of the Bible into Anglo-Saxon.

The tomb of Cuthbert at the other end of the cathedral was particularly moving: a long plain slab of stone surrounded by candles, with the name CUTHBERTUS on it. We stood in silence around the simple slab while our guide reminded us of the innumerable pilgrims who had come here before us, of how bishops had issued indulgences from this spot releasing people from the fear of their sins or penances imposed by a confessor.

Early summer saw me on a ferry pounding out of Oban to the island of Iona, the most holy place in Scotland. Tiny islands with ruined crofts dotted shivering lagoons. Way out behind me was the snow-capped peak of Ben Nevis. "It never gets above nought degrees on the top," said a man leaning on the rail next to me.

This was a radiant day after weeks of rain, sunshine striding across the sea like an American missionary in a white linen suit, beaming and full of himself, a black leather Bible under his arm, come to rescue and polish up our doomed souls. Travel bag on shoulder I was journeying to pray to another saint, St Columba: "Tender in every adversity."

The island of Mull: a hymn to desolation. Nothing moved except wind on stone. Nowhere to hide, run or even weep. The land had no primary colours, just light greys and faint greens with the odd dull smudge of crimson. Our bus passed a herd of shaggy Highland cattle and, later, a working peat bog, whole fields set out like line upon line of giant Swiss rolls.

We stopped at Fionnphort to take the ferry to Iona. From across the causeway, the place really did look like something recently escaped from the pages of myth: white shell beaches, grey crofts dotted around the tiny harbour, stone crosses, rugged cairns and, the object of my pilgrimage: the abbey itself, white doves fluttering around its slate roof. The sea heaved with continual eruptions of brilliance as we crossed it. I had been told the Scottish painters were obsessed by this Hebridean play of light on water; by the dark greens and purples of the seabed and the awesome vivacity of that white sand. We were surely confronted by the colours of holiness – in the tumbling waves on the isolated island, in the calls of birds in a wing-fluttered sky: the elemental speech of a God communing with the simple, faithful heart. The trails of two jets emblazoned a huge white cross on the blue sky and I took it as a sort of holy welcome.

The ferry's ramp clanked down on to the small concrete quay and I walked up past crofts to the abbey. An elderly woman was sunning herself on her doorstep, her hair in tight curls and her knees splayed out inelegantly. Midges eddied across the lane and in a tree by a small stone kirk was a furious babble of rooks.

"Och, they're nesting now, so they're that noisy," the woman said. "But they can be useful, you know. They keep the other birds away from the vegetable garden and dinna touch them themselves. My theory is they protect their own vegetables in case of emergency."

I came across the ruins of a nunnery – piles of rubble made tidy by the straight borders of closely cut grass. I could just about make out the nave and an aisle and the ruins of the Lady Chapel. There was something deeply serene about those old stones and I felt that sense of continuity, that feeling of human history you can often pick up on, alone, near something old and sacred. It was to these same ruins that the English moralist, Dr Johnson, came with his sidekick, Boswell, in 1773. "That man is little to be envied whose piety would not grow warmer in the ruins of Iona," Johnson wrote.

The air was warm with sunshine and the warbling of doves as I approached the abbey. It was not one of those great churches with a splendid ecclesiastical flourish, although there was a pleasing fitness about the stone cloisters and the granite church itself. The abbey liked you to book your visit in advance but I never did that throughout my travels, wanting to preserve the spontaneity and unpredictability of my journey. They let me stay after a bit of pleading and I found myself among a large party of German Lutherans from Munich. We set about cleaning, cooking and praying together in as jovial a gang as I have ever come across.

The next morning we gathered by the stone cross of St John for a pilgrimage around the island. A very strange gang of pilgrims it was too: sixty Germans in their Bavarian hats and lederhosen, some greying elders of the Church of Scotland and twenty kids from Glasgow on a week's holiday with the island's community centre: dirty wee sparrows with cuts and bruises all over their legs, ill-fitting T-shirts streaked with stains and thick brown coatings of nicotine on their fingers. No fancy bags or binoculars for them: they had what they stood up in.

We made our way up a rubbled stone track, tiptoeing around cow pats and across fields drowsy with daisies. Wisps of sheep's wool hung on the barbed wire fences. Even with many flies tormenting us everyone was cheerful and chattery and the Glasgow kids took turns to dump a fat girl on her backside. She always bounced back up again, waving her beefy arms and smiling in a way that suggested this was all great fun. We squelched along a ravine half bog and half rock until we came to an old marble quarry, its machinery eaten away by rust since its closure in 1914. Here our leader led us in a quavering rendering of the hymn, *Christ the Worker*.

Later we crossed a golf course to St Columba's Bay. The waves were collapsing, wheezing, into the shingle; a group of brown cows lay on the other end of the beach. It was here in 563AD that Columba and his disciples landed after a battle in Ireland where three thousand men had been killed. He came, he said, determined to convert as many to Christ as had died in that battle and the cairn next to the beach marked the spot where Columba's beloved Ireland had finally vanished from view. "It became the cairn that turned its back on Ireland," our guide said.

After a lunch of Spam sandwiches and an apple we trooped across more dung-littered fields and reached a ruined hermit's cell where the monks had once come to be silent with God. Our guide asked us to be quiet for three minutes, so we sat among the rubble listening to sounds the monks would have heard: that skylark busy whistling his brains out all day long, the dialogue of waves and beach, the thin, beleaguered cries of sheep and the wind quivering in the tense grass. Every such sound had meaning for the medieval mind.

It was to the accompaniment of such music that Columba came to this hut in the wilderness. In fervent prayer he sought to clad himself in the whole armour of St Paul to fight off the remorseless attacks of wicked spiritual forces. He had seen in a vision, he said, a host of black demons massing to attack his work on the island. He had engaged in duels with his arch-enemies, the Druids. But so worried had he become by the black demons that he had been bargaining with God for angelic assistance to drive them off.

By late afternoon many of the pilgrims had fallen away as we toiled up the final – and highest – hill on the island. There was a stupendous view over glittering blue water of the hundred and ten mile sweep of the Inner Hebrides; of the rugged outline of Jura where Orwell wrote *1984*; of the innumerable caves of Staffa, including Fingal's Cave, immortalised by Mendelssohn; of the wild, torn slopes of Skye with its whisky stills ...

Our faces had become as pink as prawns from being out all day in the sun and wind and there wasn't much chatter left in us. Only the Glaswegian kids were still leaping about as if they had just got up although the fat girl, fed up with her role as their private ball, had gone missing. A few of us had visited a nearby well where, according to pagan rite, if you washed your face in its waters, you could stay young forever. Finally we tumbled down the iris-spattered slope, back to the abbey for a shower and snooze before dinner.

Bells sounded in the glimmer din – as they charmingly called twilight here – and, dinner over, we crowded into the church for a healing service. Healing, in the spirit of Columba, is central to the Abbey's work and has been going on here since 1939. There is a monthly intercession whereby people can write in asking for prayers for someone in need of help. Lists of names are then sent to a hundred and thirty intercessors scattered over the country and the sick are prayed for daily. Tonight there was a laying-on of hands service. "We see this as very much the work of the church," said a speaker. "We do this because we have been commanded to do this. Mark said believers will put their hands on the sick and they will be healed. Touch shows sympathy and empathy. It shows Christ's love and compassion for every person."

A group filed up to the altar, placing their hands on their sick brothers and sisters. Lord, they whom thou lovest are sick. A tender moment in the flickering half-light, ministering to others in faith and, not for the first or last time on the island, I felt close to Columba, the great healer.

Next came Northern Ireland, a province which had long haunted my nightmares, where I tried to avoid my old journalistic haunts and began my journey in the countryside at Slemish, the boyhood home of St Patrick. I crossed to Downpatrick and was nourished by the cathedral, although the nearby glade where John Wesley had preached, was now the haunt of teenage glue-sniffers. Saul, the first church which Patrick had built there, had received no converts for years, and, travelling those forlorn streets yet again, with the burned-out houses, the high fences and cameras watching your every move, I again felt lonely and scared and saw the way the Troubles had violated the very mind and thought of God.

It was much the same story in Londonderry, founded by St Columba who called this city his "little oak grove". I was determined to seek out what St Paul had called "the good and deserving of praise: things that are true, noble, right, pure, lovely and honourable". Know these things and you will know God, we have been taught, but it was impossible. Here, anyway. The angels had long flown the oak grove but I did discover a real treasure when I was rootling around the cathedral: Bobby Jackson, the verger. He had a tiny, shrunken head mounted on a long neck with big, floppy ears, bushy eyebrows and the tightest of small mouths. He said he was "just eighty-three" and the oddness of his appearance was made considerably odder by the fact that he was as bald as a snooker ball, with tiny red veins running around his pate like a relief map of the world.

I met him in the vestry polishing a communion cup and singing. "Oh to be sure I'm the happiest man that ever walked on two legs." So why was he so happy? Well, he'd been having the very devil of a job with the graveyard gates but now workmen were fixing them and that made him happier than ever.

He showed me the various mementoes in the museum and a bomb mounted on a plinth in the porch. This bomb had been fired into Londonderry by an invading army in 1689. It did not explode and was said to contain a letter offering favourable terms to the besieged loyalists if they would surrender. They had been besieged for eighty-five days but still refused to give in, living on starch mixed with tallow.

All his life, Bobby said, he had got up at 5am and worked through to 6pm. No tea break. Nothing. But look what the workers do these days. "I was watching this man painting over some dog mess so he was. I told him he should clean that first. But no. No pride. That's the trouble, these days." He added casually he had twenty-four children.

Later that morning there was a tiny communion service and afterwards I had a chat with the dean, the Very Reverend George Good. I asked him if his verger really did have twenty-four children. "He does," was the reply. "Twenty-four children and a *very* tired wife."

Bobby specialised in the year 1689 and knew everything about it, the dean added. Even today he maintained the tradition of ringing the curfew at 9am and 9pm. It wasn't true that he was always happy: if he was wearing a cap that meant trouble. People suspected he was even older than he said he was. "The locals say he is eighty eight and he decided to leave out the war years."

It turned out that Bobby had come to them one day as relief verger and the first indication that he was permanent came when he painted his own name on the bottom of the church notice board. He had lost all his hair through shock after he had been upended into the brass funnel of a fire engine in a riot in the Bogside. All his hair fell out that night. The astonishing sheen of his head posed problems for television cameras when they were in the church. The technicians insisted on powdering it because it glowed like a Belisha beacon in their lights.

In the Irish Republic I queued up with about a hundred others to take a small boat into a lake where a grey building with a green dome sat on one of the many islands. The Basilica of St Patrick's Purgatory, Lough Derg. We were all quiet and thoughtful since we were about to spend three days and two nights on the toughest and most penitential pilgrimage in the world.

The sky was curdling from grey to black as we chugged across the water, sending out bobbing waves in our wake which swished against the tiny islands choked with shrubs and small ash trees. The water was the colour of rust – hence Lough Derg, the Red Lake.

The island ahead was already crammed with more than a thousand people, barefoot and walking around the crude stone penitential beds. A peal of bells mingled with the continual chanting of the rosary. Many were resting on the damp lawns, but most were trudging ahead or kneeling before stone crosses or circling the Basilica again and again or standing on the shoreline pushing out their arms three times to renounce the world, the flesh and the devil.

I was soon barefoot with the others and settling down into a couple of stations, each of which took about an hour, at the end of which we could have a short rest on the lawns. Under the watchful eyes of the priests we would have to keep doing this throughout the night and the next day, when we could sleep for the first time. There was no food to sustain us except for tea and rock-hard oatcakes or a cup of hot water sprinkled with red pepper – Lough Derg soup. No one bends the rules and when two women arrived with a bottle of milk for their tea, claiming they'd had a special dispensation from their priest back in Dublin, they were sent straight back home.

For Evening Mass sixteen hundred of us packed into the Basilica before a plain white marble altar with a giant chandelier hanging over it like a bright cluster of huge electric berries. The plain walls soared in clean straight lines and only the stained glass flared with anything like real colour.

The night thickened over the plain, yeasty waters of the lake as midges danced in the lights around the penitential beds. Our rooms were locked and we weren't even allowed a short snooze as we engaged in the Rite of Penance, all of us moving around inside and outside the Basilica as we chanted lines from the rosary through a long shuffling night.

It started to rain and then came the dawn, dark as a hangman's stare. Clouds of moths had been hatched by the glooming morning spreading out over the mirrored lake and the tiny fists of the islands in a dripping symphony of twisting greys and mordant blacks. The whole universe seemed to spread up outwards like a growing bubble and it was then, as we continued trudging around the Basilica, that I glimpsed something deep and rich in the Irish psyche.

This was not the bomb-throwing Irish beloved of the media but a nation in its purest and most noble posture. This was the seed-bed of the Celtic Church; the great spiritual energy of a fundamentally decent people prepared to stumble red-eyed throughout the night; prepared to punish themselves on their knees before a holy God whose first demand was that his people be holy too; still prepared to suffer the pangs of outrageous hunger; still prepared to walk over wet, hard stones as they chanted their litanies of love … all so that they could earn the right to drag themselves face to face with their beloved Patrick; that they might look up to the monumental majesty of their saint who also had suffered when he had bargained with God to ensure the faith and future of the Irish; the man who had fought demons for them in a purgatory on this very island for them. For them!

In this damp dawn we were in community with Patrick. His ineluctable personality was there with us, next to us, below us and above us. We had come to pay homage to this complete man who comforted us still.

We weren't as tired as might have been expected after such a hard night and we continued moving around our stations throughout the next day in slow amiable trances, occasionally meeting on the quay where we bathed our feet in the lake. There the cruellest thing happened. Someone over in the Priory was cooking bacon and eggs and the smell drifted over the water, churning up our empty bellies and almost lifting us up on tiptoe with the mesmerising deliciousness of its aroma. We sighed, but nothing was said. There was nothing to say.

When I did finally get to sleep, at the end of those two penitential days, no sooner had I closed my eyes than it was time to wake up after the most dreamless, the most complete and refreshing sleep I had ever had.

Then it was a further five hours of stations before we clambered back into the boat where I resolved I would come back and do this pilgrimage again one day – only do it better.

FORTY FIVE

I had felt the warm closeness of God throughout my various pilgrimages that year, and I was never worried or insecure even when stranded at night on the top of Croagh Patrick in a violent storm. His spirit seemed so abundant and real in the shrines and holy places I had visited – with the exception of Glastonbury – and I believe he opened interesting doors for me all along the way and watched out for me when things began to get sticky. I always met someone who helped me to get where I wanted to go or gave me a lively story. God talks to you in a number of ways, I have learned, often through the mouths of strangers. He'll always get to you somehow if there's something he wants you to know.

After each journey I returned to Eastcote for three weeks to write up my notes, hoping to walk the hundred and twenty-odd miles from Winchester to Canterbury, one of the most famous pilgrim routes in England, for my final chapter. But even as I worked in my garden shed, full of confidence and optimism, I was conscious that the media was still trampling unopposed through our lives.

The 1985 soccer season began accompanied, as usual, by bouts of hooliganism. There had been a serious clash between fans at Heysel Stadium in Brussels where rioting Liverpool fans resulted in the death of thirty-nine Juventus supporters.

I had long thought of these modern Vikings as the media's first-born, indoctrinated with the concepts of masculine individualism from such films as *A Clockwork Orange*, *Terminator* and the Rambo films, which glorified mindless violence and ruthless murder. We know those hooligans have especially admired such films and one of their leaders, Paul Scarrot, who received thirteen prison sentences over as many years, said he had seen *A Clockwork Orange* three times. "It was pure," he said. "If there was a modern-day Alex he would be chundering around Dusseldorf with a six-pack of lager."

In 1973 a sixteen-year-old boy who beat up a tramp had said he was copying one of the characters in *A Clockwork Orange*. Another youth who attacked another tramp said he was aping characters in the same film. The judge described the film as evil and even its director, Stanley Kubrick, who owned the licence, suppressed his film in Britain.

You prove yourself by how tough you are in a fight. You impress your peers by demonstrating how you can wound, maim or even kill. You are as capable as the next wronged man of exacting the bloodiest revenge to make the world a better place for your vicious standards. You are a man now; it is time to stand tall and fight all authority – particularly the police – for the honour of your manhood.

Such ideas were endemic in contemporary films but it was not quite so simple as that because the media made these thugs famous and aware of their own notoriety. The media built them up from within and without. It fed them with concepts of such as Rambo and, when they acted in the way they did, they were featured on the news.

We saw that these thugs revelled in this attention when, after some were arrested, they were found to have in their pockets newspaper clippings about their activities. Many of their fights at football matches were featured in the media – often at the expense of the game. Any skinhead with a Union Jack on his shoulders and a safety pin through his nose giving someone a good kicking in the street was more likely to make it on to the news than a goal-scorer on the field.

Routinely we were shown clips of fans fighting and routinely a commentator would wring his hands and tell us how hooliganism was ruining the game. This, he kept insisting, was nothing to do with television and, while he kept reassuring us on that point, all those small acts of delinquent rebellion, on and around the pitches, fed by ever more abundant publicity, became declarations of war on the streets. Soon, fed by more of the same, these declarers of war became marching armies, pillaging whenever they came together for a few cans of lager or a snort of amyl nitrate. They had become their public image. They were *e-e-e-e-e-vil* as the Millwall fans chanted, warriors protecting their turf.

Everywhere truth was twisted on an anvil of illusion and lies. Some hundred and fifty fans arrived in Greece for a soccer match to be welcomed by no fewer than fifteen hundred policemen and six television cameras. Throughout the subsequent match the cameras concentrated on this terrified little group, too scared to hiccup let alone kick anyone's head in.

The season began in Britain and the first Saturday brought the predictable disorder. Police arrested two hundred and thirty six Birmingham City "fans", including sixty juveniles, at Euston Station after they had run amok among passengers queuing for Bank Holiday trains. This attack before the match had even kicked off, coincided with soccer's lowest first-day attendance since the war.

Seventy nations showed British football on their screens and violence became endemic wherever the game was shown. In Stockholm football fans formed a Black Army, closely modelled on Manchester United's Reds, and already these foreign armies were exceeding even the excesses of British hooligans, emptying Dutch stadia with nail bombs, burning down stands in Italy, killing people in Greece and beating up referees in Asia.

Not all were blind. Jeff Foulser, the executive producer of London Weekend Television's *Big Match*, said: "Unless it is of major news value our policy is not to show fighting in the crowd among a bunch of yobbos. I am convinced the riots in our inner cities – at Brixton, Toxteth and Bristol – started in small pockets and grew out of publicity. People copy what they see on the box."

I was contacted by John Milton Whatmore, a television director working for Central Television, who wanted to make a documentary about me for their

Encounter series. As someone who had gone banging on for so long about the evils of television it seemed ridiculous for me to take up the offer, but John argued that if I really did have a message, this was the place to deliver it. *Merlyn* had sold maybe a few thousand copies but I would have to address a packed chapel every night for eleven years to reach the number of people who watched the *Encounter* series. This would easily exceed the total of all who had listened to Evan Roberts in the 1904 Revival. I could say what I wanted and he would edit it for sense or legal reasons only. He said he liked what I was saying even if he didn't agree with all of it. Someone, somewhere had to step forward and say these things.

John was a strong, determined director who knew what he wanted and was unafraid to stand up against those who employed him. He was particularly keen to have a stab at what I claimed the media was doing in Northern Ireland. When I pointed out I wasn't sure I was a fit and proper person to make a film like this, particularly given my past misadventures into sex, drugs and rock'n'roll, he said that made what I was saying better. I wasn't a Bible-thumping Christian who'd never had a bad thought or done anything improper in my life, and that sharpened up my credentials considerably.

"This doesn't have to be an all-out attack on the media," John said. "Let's just lay down a challenge and let the public decide what they want to believe."

If the film wasn't an all-out attack on the media it was something remarkably like it, opening with a shot of me bicycling around the Fens saying, in voiceover, that St Paul had told us to expect the Man of Lawlessness, a great and mysterious outbreak of evil, and he had come.

This man roamed the world seeking out terrorism and becoming its most potent power, I went on. He provided the main energy behind the rioting that had engulfed British streets several years ago; he presented us with the soccer hooligan and kept plunging a savage spear of distortion into societies such as Ulster and turning people against one another. His main diet was violence, crime and perversion and he had emerged stronger and far more evil than perhaps even St Paul had envisioned.

I described my visions in Malaya, the way a huge fungus had grown out of a highly Romantic, violence-loving manuscript on which I had been working, how the ideas in the book had attacked me like a swarm of bees and how I'd found myself, along with many other artists, standing on the top of a cliff overlooking a plain on which people moved around. All of us on the cliff edge were shelling people on the plain, making them riot.

Later, when things seemed to have calmed down, I had seen, in Penang, a most striking and unforgettable vision. It looked as if someone was trying to rip apart the clear blue sky. A large hole opened in it. Through this hole poured fat, black dots which I came to know as the black rain. What did this black rain mean? I had meditated about this almost every day for more than twenty years and almost every day had come up with a different conclusion. Some days I believed it might be a representation of what had been going on in Ulster for the last twenty years; the province laid low by a constant downpour of violent imagery, its stability destroyed by people like me.

Our Man of Lawlessness had been the engine of the Troubles there, I argued and, over footage of a riot in Londonderry, I explained that he had seized on every stray act of violence, exaggerating it, distorting it and presenting it as having meaning when it had none. Essentially, the Man of Lawlessness had latched on to every outrageous act of two tiny, unrepresentative gangs of loonies – the IRA and the UVF – and, in this process, everything had fallen. So many people had been blinded to the real truths of their situation that almost no one there knew what they were fighting about in the streets, least of all the street fighters.

Others gave their views in the film. Most were worried by or unsure about my visions and, after I had described them in my column in the *Observer*, the editor, Donald Trelford, said he had called a meeting of executives to try and decide if I had gone mad and needed a long holiday.

David Watson said he was confused by my visions and unsure of their spiritual meaning although he was sure they were real enough to me. Don Berry of the *Sunday Times* said that the violence in Ulster had actually been there from the start and had got worse when the media ignored it. Richard D North said that I'd only really managed to save my sanity by following his suggestion and getting on a bike. "A Welsh boy from the valleys, he knew it would automatically humble him and keep him fit."

The film ended with me wandering across the causeway to Lindisfarne surrounded by the shrieks of birds and following the markers of the old Pilgrims' Way. You could work out the meaning of holiness by looking all around you, I said, but if you listened very closely indeed out here you might hear something of the breaking heart of God. "I bring you his love. I bring you his tenderness. I bring you his wild word but, most of all, I bring you his most urgent warning that, unless this season of black rain comes to an end, the harvest will be dead."

On one issue I was quite wrong: that, in all these rolling polemics, I was on my own on my own platform with my own view of the world.

There *were* notes of dissent: the usual one being I had over-simplified a complex situation although I never did understand how over-simplification necessarily annulled what I was saying. I was cutting through the admittedly frightening complexities of the Northern Ireland situation, I argued, to offer a straightforward view which, if anything, made what I was saying more intelligible. That it was simple and intelligible didn't make it wrong.

Hundreds agreed with what I was saying and wrote to John Whatmore and Central Television to say so in what John described as the biggest reaction to any film he had ever made. I'd had a similar reaction to my *Observer* column about my visions but this reaction told us that there were even more than we had ever guessed out there who were deeply uncomfortable with the way the media was carrying on. The truth of the situation, surely, was that the media – as in the days of the medieval church or Hitler's Nazi Germany – tolerated no heretics in their midst, disabling dissenters by ignoring them, not publishing them or publicly vilifying them as idiots.

Censorship was a road down which I emphatically did not want to travel. I have never approved of censorship: it never works. If they wanted to see it badly enough they would find a way somehow. There was a further problem with this: I saw a religious battle unfolding which was way beyond the influence of any mere censor or human, come to that. In this flooding evil of violence I sensed God was trying to work out his personal relationship with the world. How it would all develop would soon become clear.

Yet I had to grant that, given what I was saying, Central Television had shown a liberal and refreshing approach in showing our film and after the film was shown I was offered the editorship of two small Christian papers as well as the money to start one of my own. But an example of the frightening and almost totalitarian control of the media emerged when John Whatmore and I were sifting through the piles of letters about the film.

There were no letters from Northern Ireland, where it had been scheduled to be shown and was the one place from which I had expected a real response. Informal inquiries revealed that Ulster Television had pulled the film before it went on air. They had a system whereby they could look at material relating to Northern Ireland before it was aired and, if they didn't like the look of it for any reason (which they weren't obliged to explain), they could pull it.

I had thought my ideas might make a difference in Northern Ireland, if only because I was pointing an accusatory finger at a completely different set of people than those who were always getting the blame.

But I never got close, never managed to land a punch on one of them.

The time had come to tackle the last chapter of *Stained Glass Hours*. I disembarked from a train in Winchester on a squally, cold day in February 1984 to start to walk the hundred and twenty miles to Canterbury along the Pilgrims' Way, a meandering track once taken by millions of international pilgrims after sailing into Southampton. This was the route pilgrims had taken to pay homage to Thomas à Becket after he was murdered in Canterbury Cathedral in 1170AD. I hoped to walk it extremely slowly, at what was once known as the "Canterbury Gallop" (which later passed into our vocabulary as the word "canter").

I checked into a hotel and went back to Winchester cathedral the next morning. The height and splendour of the nave – with twelve bays, the largest Gothic nave in the world – engulfed me like a great symphony. But it was walking down the side of the nave and coming across stone steps worn down by the footsteps of endless pilgrims, and moving through deep shadows, that I felt something of the real spirit of the place. My senses latched onto era after era of prayer that must have flowed up through this warren of archways and alleys and cloisters. I noted the cleanliness, smelled the polish, saw the sheen on the wood and understood the pure love that had been poured into every inch and corner of the building.

I suppose it was in that cathedral that I had a sense of how such buildings develop organically. Wherever I looked I could see how a bit of this had been added to a bit of that, all somehow cohering into a graceful whole. The cathedral's most unusual feature was the striking number and variety of chantries, chapels and tombs. I have never been sure why being near to tombs always makes me feel so peaceful or why I get such a deep and inexpressible feeling of human continuity staring at the face of unknowable death. Yet I was drenched in peace as I moved past those chantries. I was on knowing terms with the unknowable. Perhaps my consoling sense of peace sprang from this architecture of death since it represented, for those so interred, the ultimate freedom from all anxiety and pain.

I set out on the Pilgrims' Way, taking the North Gate out of Winchester on the Jewry Road, so-called because it was formerly the centre of the Jewish community, once in the thick of the city's commercial life, where all traffic would have proceeded past the moneylenders. Or so it said in the book that I was going to follow, *The Old Road* by Hilaire Belloc.

Winter held the land in a clamp and chilly winds erupted through the hedgerows, hissing angrily and shooting out fusillades of dead leaves. Everywhere the earth was thick with chalk, slippery and difficult to walk on even in my studded walking boots. The bare branches of the trees hung over me like cat o' nine tails and I wondered if the trees in winter had the same shape above the earth as below.

In New Alresford there was a lovely old church, St Mary the Virgin, where I discovered a memorial plaque for Mary Summer who had, in 1876, founded the Mothers' Union. It was the first of many intriguing discoveries in what was to turn into an extensive church-crawl. I came to love those moments when, after getting the keys in the rectory, I could sniff around those old churches alone. I always read the Bible open on the lectern to see what had hit the congregation the Sunday before.

There was a scratch dial near one door, which showed the times of various ancient services and I came across a church once run by a vicar who had invented the multiplication sign. In another there was a plaque on the porch commemorating the theft of a statue "by persons unknown". Always there was a spray of freshly cut flowers near or on the altar.

Sir Arthur Bryant, in another English country church, wrote: "All English history – its strength, its sleeping fires, its patient consistency – is here, contained in its sleeping silence."

I got to Alton Abbey with bleeding feet and several patches of blisters and had fun talking with the Benedictine monks, a jolly, worldly lot who watched television, read newspapers and made extra income from communion wafers and incense. They had recently made a fortune from the Pope's visit and supplied half a million wafers for his visit to Coventry alone.

Two days later I was off again on the Old Way, cut into the chalk by an endless procession of pilgrim feet. Belloc wrote a marvellous hymn to this chalk: "The chalk is our landscape and our proper habitation ... The chalk filtered our drink for us and built up our strong bones, it was the height from the slopes of which our villages, standing in the clean air, could watch the sea or the plain; we carved it, when it was hard enough; it holds our first ornaments; our clear streams run over it; the shapes and curves it takes and the kind of close rough grass it bears are the cloak of our counties."

In the village of Seale I rang home and discovered that my great friend and hero, Canon David Watson, had died. The *Observer* asked if I would write his obituary for them, but I was too upset to put together a single sentence.

David's death was probably the greatest blow to my growing faith. I knew all the usual arguments that death is a triumph in Christian terms and that, in time, we would understand its meaning, but I couldn't hear any such words: my heart was full of ruin and bitterness that this fine man had been taken from us. Almost alone he had led me to a real faith and, along with many others, I was sure that he would be healed of his cancer and restore our country to God. Now he was dead. Why?

I had come close to the practice and presence of God on my pilgrimages that year but, sitting broken-hearted in the old Saxon church of Compton, I felt I knew nothing about him. Nothing. I knew only the darkness of the dark night. God said he didn't think as we did and that much was true. When I thought he had come close he moved away again, leaving me chattering and shivering in the cold and damp. Outside, a grey, winter rain was falling on everything.

I carried on somehow, through postcard villages flung down around ponds on which ducks dropped their beaks into the water, heaving their bums up into the air as they foraged for food. Around the back of a churchyard a magpie flew across my path. These country lanes teemed with exuberance in the summer. Now there was just the damp sleep of winter with the earth waiting for the reviving kiss of spring. Like me.

My next stop was a Carmelite monastery, the Friars, in Aylesford where, after supper, I spent some time with the prior, Father Edward Maguire, a man with a puckish red face and silvery curling beard who gave off such an air of having lived life to the full he might have been a Montmartre painter or a Greenwich Village drunk. I told him about the death of David Watson and how I was feeling exhausted and angry with God.

"Well, anger with God is fine. That's a form of prayer too. If you are angry with him you should tell him so. It's even a form of passionate prayer. But he is not as we are. We each of us have sparks that we hand on to one another. That's all I know. In some strange way we are always looking after one another. Somehow there is a sense in which suffering fulfils God's sense of purpose. But how? I couldn't even start trying to tell you why six million Jews were allowed to die. And your mind will not help you with the loss of this man. You won't be able to think your way out of it. Neither is it so much a matter of time as a matter of acceptance when you will find a pattern, a reason. Then you can take it."

These were the good, concerned words of a good, concerned man and that night in my monastery bed, they rang as true and hard as steel, a poultice, at least, on the still suppurating boil of my grief. Pilgrimage was clearly not just the acquisition of knowledge or experience or even new ideas. You had to grant that suffering was part of the journey, if it helped us grow close to Christ, who suffered much. You had to grant that the turning over of treacherous words and slippery concepts would mean nothing and take you nowhere. You had to grant that there were times when you had to sit still and be; that there was nothing easy about coming to terms with the mystery of God and the meaning of holiness. We were back in the shifting quick sands of mind and thought again, this moving jungle of ideas that we had somehow to hack our way through.

Canterbury was an attractive jumble of brick and half-timbered houses with moneyed, rather self-conscious fashion shops, a sprinkling of pubs without much life in their bars and sudden, surprising aspects of waterways flowing cold behind the backs of sloping houses built in the Middle Ages.

First I tried to locate the Chequers of Hope with its dormitory of a hundred beds. This was where Chaucer and his fellow pilgrims had stayed: that colourful, motley crowd which included a prioress, a nun, three priests, a monk and a prior.

The Chequers of Hope no longer exists, but there were a few of its paving stones in a coffee shop beneath a new department store. I did find one genuine curiosity: a huge, red pump nailed to a wall above a leather shop. This pump commemorated the monks' practice of selling medieval pilgrims water red with rust. They claimed the water was tainted with the blood of Thomas à Becket.

A siren wind blew in freezing blasts around the flat lawns of the cathedral when I finally entered its precincts. I looked up at the great Norman arcading and the ornate stone traceries and inside was immediately overwhelmed by the size of the nave. There was little intimacy here but – as befits the Mother Church of Anglican Christendom – there was unmistakable authority.

At the far end of the cathedral Thomas's shrine stood empty and silent like the looted tomb it was. They needed twenty-six carts to carry all the treasures away at the Dissolution.

Christendom reacted with tremendous emotion to his savage murder and Thomas was made a saint within days of his death, long before his official canonisation. Miraculous cures were soon reported near this tomb, children were christened Thomas, stained glass windows proclaimed his glory as thousands upon thousands made their way here to be baptised in the font of their own tears. A madman was taken to the tomb, chained here for the night and his sanity restored. Cripples came and threw away their crutches. Swellings and ulcers disappeared. The blind saw again and it was reported that the holy water of St Thomas had, in some instances, made prisoners' shackles fall off. A man came here with a violent toothache and saw a vision of a man who asked him to open his mouth. Air was wafted into his open mouth and immediately the man lost his pain. In the high noon of medieval pilgrimage this shrine was covered with gold plate and jewels of every kind – rubies, emeralds, sapphires and diamonds – all surrounding the "brain pan of the holy martyr".

Henry VIII, Defender of the Faith, dissolved the shrine and the Canterbury pilgrims' wonderland came to end after almost four centuries. But Dissolution wasn't as bad as it was often painted. There was a historic inevitability in the arrival of men like Calvin, Knox and Luther. They were sent to purge the poisoned body of its multiplying corruptions such as the sale of indulgences.

But who was going to purge this present church which was not so much corrupt as fast asleep; not so much decadent as divided? Such a church has become just as much an enemy of God as a decadent one, all as pointless and empty as the cordoned-off empty space I saw before me. In many ways this looted tomb was the perfect symbol for what we now have – a forlorn space echoing to the chatter of tourists and the flash of cameras.

Just behind me was the Chapel to the Saints and Martyrs, its elegant altar surrounded by a vivacious mosaic of purple stained glass. "The blood of thy martyrs and saints shall enrich the earth, shall create the holy place," it said on a tapestry. On the other side of the chapel was a board which read: "A martyrdom is always the design of God for his love of men. To warn them and lead them and bring them back to his ways."

I took a candle and lit it for that great canon, saint and martyr, David Watson. It shone a bright yellow with a hazy, stammering black smoke drifting up out of its tip before settling again. Light flickered on the brown marble pillar behind. The candle said a prayer for the saints and martyrs that are the lights of the world.

He had all the qualities of the saints of old, did David. Just like Swithun, who travelled everywhere on foot, David got around on a bicycle and ate the simplest of meals. Like Patrick, David fought the demons of darkness with fervent prayer and fasting. Like Columba – "tender in every adversity" – David was prepared to teach even when wounded and vulnerable. Like Cuthbert, he taught goodness by the impeccable lesson of being good himself. His spirit straddled the modern world just as surely as those of the medieval saints straddled the old.

David's miracles were no less astonishing. He maintained the miracle of a deep and loving faith even when asthma kept him up throughout the night fighting for breath; even when he was beleaguered with depression that got the black dogs yapping; even when his insides were being eaten away by cancer. Even in all that pain he kept showing us glimpses of his greatness, he still held up a light in the darkness.

Holiness abides: that's what I learned on my pilgrimages that year. Institutions may fall and decay and the loved old will always give way to the hated new, but there will always be men ready to pick up the fallen torch, always another to pass it on and teach us again the way and meaning of holiness.

When I left Canterbury Cathedral groups of visitors were hanging back in the porch. It was snowing. Huge fat flakes came whirling over the city, falling softly on my face and dissolving in my eyes like tears. I walked around to the other side of the cathedral and found a small frozen waterfall in some leafless wisteria. The snow fell into the canals, disappearing soundlessly as it kissed the water.

Two schoolboys rattled past me on bicycles. A rabble of noisy winds rose up and spat, harsh and angry, over the grey, slate rooftops. Two birds were fluttering hard against these furious winds, fighting to get back to their warm nests, perhaps, or merely just wanting to go forward. They fought harder and harder until finally one of them fell away behind the cathedral cloisters. But the other battled on bravely, fighting every inch of the way against the chill winds of God.

FORTY SIX

My life settled into steady drunkenness and spiritual mutiny. Every day was twenty-four hours of rain-driven darkness. Unsure where I was going, if anywhere, I picked up the odd job from the *Sunday Express Magazine*. This magazine journalism was not exactly work and there was none of the stress of real journalism about it, no working against deadlines and you could wander off for weeks on end on your investigations if you wanted. I was being seen as something of a specialist in religious subjects and the commissioning editor, Pauline Peters, would often ask me to do jobs like following the evangelist, Billy Graham, around the country or going to Oberammergau to write about the Passion Play.

This might have been the one way in journalism that I could keep deepening my still-faltering faith. Such assignments lacked the spiritual intimacy of being on the pilgrim road, but they allowed me to report on people who acted in the name of God and others who claimed to speak for him. Many of those I met, I found, were compromised by media and Mammon.

I first saw Billy Graham in Ashton Gate Stadium in Bristol on May 12, 1984, at the start of his new national crusade. Walkie-talkies crackled and at least a hundred photographers milled around the large, be-flowered stage on the football pitch. A red carpet stretched across the halfway line. Dark clouds chased one another over the roof of the sky as the two-thousand-strong choir began singing *All Hail the Power of Jesu's Name*.

Even in such a large stadium, on such an unpromising day, the air was thick with excitement. Spasms of emotion rolled around the terraces. "We are here to welcome Billy back," Gavin Reid told us over the microphone. "Some of us think he belongs here."

Television cameras were dotted around the dais and, we learned, videocassettes of the service were going to be delivered to meetings in local churches. There was a message from the Archbishop of Canterbury: "My prayers are with you as you begin this mission."

I was sitting on the Press bench. We had been given the best seats and media packs and had even been excused from the collection. "We don't want you to pay," one of the stewards told us "It is our delight that you could come. We know you will be blessed."

Next to me was a reporter from the *News of the World*. I wondered aloud what interest *that* newspaper could have in a meeting like this. In the trade it was always said that no self-respecting haddock would want to be wrapped in the *News of the World*. There was a lot of interest, it seemed. "I was out chasing some nude murderer in the New Forest," he said. "I had a call from the office telling me to drop everything and get down here. I've never been to a meeting like this. What happens?"

It emerged that Billy Graham had been meeting Rupert Murdoch of late and the newspaper proprietor had shown the evangelist around his offices. The editor of the *News of the World*, Nick Lloyd, had offered Graham the use of his car and chauffeur. Graham declined but he had written an article for the newspaper and Murdoch had decreed that all his newspapers should give the evangelist the fullest possible publicity.

The steward gave us all a media pack which, I discovered on riffling through it, had everything anyone could possibly want to know about this campaign and Billy Graham. It gave a full biographical account of William Franklin Graham, with his educational qualifications, the names of his children (all now married); his books and many awards and honours. He had regularly been in the top ten of the most admired people in the world; been in America's top fifteen best-dressed men and, in 1975, was elected the Greatest Living American by the contestants of the Miss National Teenager pageant. He had preached to more people than any other religious leader.

This had been achieved largely through television. "Television is the most powerful tool of communication ever devised by man," he once wrote. "Each of my prime-time specials is now carried by three hundred stations across the US and Canada, so that, in one single telecast, I preach to millions more than Christ in his lifetime."

Back on the Press bench in Bristol we were being fed more information. There were thirty one thousand people in the stadium that day, two thousand in the choir, five hundred and seventy coaches, five thousand coming by car and four special trains. The strategy was that we hacks should never complain we had nothing to write about.

The opener was provided by George Hamilton, who sang a few rounds of his Rocky Mountain theology. "In just a minute Billy is going to bring us his message."

Graham came on stage and brought his message, occasionally distorted by the loudspeakers: "I want to speak to you as if this was the last sermon I will ever proclaim. May we be conscious of no one except him. Something like this may never come again. For God so loved the world that he gave his only begotten Son that whosoever (that includes you) should not perish but have everlasting life.

"Remember the tape at Watergate. They had everything recorded in the rooms in The White House. They had it on tape. God has it all on tape. When you stand at the judgment of God he will say to the angels: 'Let's listen to the tapes ...' God did not make you a robot. You can do what you like and there is nothing that God can do about it. Man broke God's law and that's sin. We have all sinned. We are all under judgement and under condemnation."

He had begun with warm, soft, enticing words but, as he went on, the tone became darker and more urgent. *The wages of sin is death. Hell begins here but hell is to come as well. You won't find the answers in drugs or sex. Change your heart, your way of living.*

Such injunctions always haunt the religious imagination and that old oratorical magic was still magical. I kept thinking of my other hero, the Welsh evangelist Evan Roberts, who had none of Graham's polish or bite, speaking in disconnected outbursts of passion, hanging in long silences in his pulpit, breaking himself physically with his convulsions. Graham was quiet, pleading, forever raising his hand and pointing his finger *at you*.

"So now I am going to ask you to get up out of your seat and say, by coming up here, that you are going to open your heart to Christ. You want to start again. Jesus called everyone publicly. He hung on the cross publicly for you. There must be discipleship. From now on Christ is first in your life. You must get up and walk. It may take two or three minutes and you will receive a prayer and some literature ..."

And, with the organ sorrowing softly, they began getting up out of their seats, drifting forward in ones, twos and small groups. That afternoon 2,352 came forward, according to another bit of paper sent to my home. The next day there would be 2,172. The next, 2,642. All figures were added up, analysed and fed into a computer. The commitments on this date were 8.8 per cent. The percentage commitments of total attendance were 8.3 per cent. "Anything over five per cent is exciting." The cumulative total commitment so far was 7,166 ...

That summer's campaign was being staged in six separate football stadia at a cost of nearly £2 million; sixty per cent of costs were collected in the first three weeks of the campaign – largely in donations from local churches. "You can say we are very, very excited," said Larry Ross, the executive in charge of media relations. "You boys from the Press have been very, very good to us."

Graham had developed something of a presidential style and it was difficult for anyone in the Press to get an interview with him that summer, largely, his aides said, because he'd had a serious sinus operation at the beginning of the campaign and needed to conserve his strength. I did, however, get a surprise phone call in my home in Eastcote early one morning saying that, if I hot-footed it to Bristol's Holiday Inn, he would give me half an hour.

The hotel suite, which had been converted into a temporary campaign office, was abuzz with computers, word processors and shaded-in maps. Everywhere were clean-cut smiling American youths.

Graham himself turned out to be most engaging, one of the nicest men I have met. It was his modesty which most took me aback: the way he genuinely seemed to want to know what you knew. The sheer certitude of his faith kept taking my breath away and, as we chatted, he was a continual picture of sunny and easy affability with piercing blue eyes and an immense nose, full of line and character. He was surprisingly tall but walked and sat with a marked stoop in his shoulders. There was a tinge of the hippy in his gingerish hair, which was rather long at the back and stretched down over his shirt collar. God would take a great pleasure in such a man, you thought.

He spoke of how much he missed his wife who had been recovering from an operation and how he loved her a million more times than when they had first married. "Now that the children have grown up she travels with me a lot. Without her I don't know what I would do."

I asked him about his curious relationship with Rupert Murdoch. They had first met in Australia, he said, and had been friends for a number of years. When Graham had arrived in London Murdoch had hosted a lunch for him to meet his editors. We all knew what the *News of the World* was about. Wasn't there a contradiction in him, a man of God, writing articles for such a newspaper? Didn't it legitimise the perversion, violence and degradation in which the paper routinely traded? "I just don't know," he said, leaning forward, his eyes a hard blue of questioning innocence.

Much of Graham's early fame grew out of his relationship with newspaper magnates whom he had always sedulously courted. When he was first starting in California, Hearst sent out a telegram to all his newspapers with just two words: "Puff Graham."

Yes, Billy Graham was a truly impressive man although we might recall that the Bible also tells us that, when the Man of Lawlessness comes, *he* will have such a powerful and dazzling personality he will deceive even the elect of God.

Even after brushes with the London Bible College and the great Billy Graham himself my faith remained on the wobble because there was still a David Watson-sized hole in it. I couldn't make any sense of David's death – took it almost as a personal affront – and seldom went to church finding that, when I did, I could not pray because I remained suffused with an unquenchable and mounting anger with God.

Pauline Peters sent me to the tiny Bavarian village of Oberammergau and my spiritual desolation deepened when I saw the way these so-called peasants were systematically fleecing the pilgrims. Audiences of around five thousand a performance were paying £180 each for a two-night package and, as there were seventy-five performances each season, that added up to an awful lot of sauerkraut.

The village was improbably picturesque with neatly cut piles of wood in the gardens of the cuckoo-clock houses. The clear, pebbled River Ammer curved through the outlying meadows and goats wandered up to visitors hoping to be fed. The surrounding snow-capped mountains gazed down on the village in the stony, majestic way that snow-capped mountains do and you half expected Julie Andrews and her singing brats to come dancing down the slopes any moment.

Church bells rang out over the rooftops and avalanches of flowers spilled over the balconies. Many of the walls had coloured frescoes although a large smelly cowshed in the centre provided a slightly jarring note. The cows had their tails tied up to a rafter and just outside the door was a pile of stinking cow dung, fresh and steamy, delighting the attendant flies.

You could work out a lot by looking around. There was nothing poor or peasant-like about this place. Rows of gleaming, high performance cars lined the squares. The church was well looked after and almost every grave in the cemetery had fresh flowers on it. The public swimming pool was one of the most modern I had seen anywhere, with a huge sauna, wave machine and a section which came out of the side of the mountain before turning back in again enabling you to swim out in the cold air in warm water, look around the valley and swim back in again.

The shops were piled high with devotional carvings and religious icons. Not the twinkling tat of Lourdes or Knock either: many of the carvings, Christmas cribs, dolls' houses and clock cases, were well crafted and expensive. A lot of the men had long hair and wild black beards. This hirsute look was for the passion play, which involved two thousand of the villagers, who were all paid a percentage of the profits to make up for any loss of wages. The director received £10,000. Many managed to work around their appearances like, say, Werner Richter, a local taxi driver, who drove the school bus, operated the ski lift and ran a guest house. As Esdra, a servant of Annas, the high priest, Werner only had to be there for the first half an hour of the afternoon session.

The old theatre, where they staged the play, looked like a collision between a huge covered railway station and a Greek Temple. The audience sat in the railway station and the actors froze as they moved around the pillars of the Greek Temple. Oberammergau is so high up it is pretty much freezing cold all the year around, even in the middle of summer. The actors rehearsed in ski caps and leg warmers and it did not help that when the play opened they had to wear togas. Back in 1980 it had actually begun snowing during the Last Supper, much to the pleasure of the audience and the despair of the cast. Rudi Zwink, a former Jesus, said he was up on the cross for half an hour and his feet were blue when they took him down. "I am not joking. They were *blue*."

The play was first staged in 1634 as a village thanksgiving to God for safe delivery from the plague. At the time thousands of people, even doctors, were dying fast. There were mass graves and inter-tribal wars. The villagers gathered and swore before the altar that, should they be spared, they would perform a Passion Play. From that moment no one else in the village died from the disease and, with a few breaks for wars, the play has been performed every ten years ever since.

It also managed the unusual feat for the time of bringing together Catholics and Protestants. Matthew Arnold in 1871 said it united people who "seemed as far as poles apart," something it still tries to do today. The bare story is of Christ's last days before the churches put their own gloss on it.

Performances have been known to produce real dramas as when, back in 1922, an irate spectator tried to shoot Judas. They have thrown him into the Ammer more than once and being attacked by angry women with umbrellas is accepted here as one of the hazards of the betrayal business. "Someone has to do it," a local plumber and former Judas, Martin Kratz, told me. Most villagers speak a passable English.

Hitler came to the village in 1934 and praised the play. "It convincingly portrayed the menace of Judaism," he said ominously. Some claimed the play made Christ into an Aryan hero, but it was less anti-Semitic than the Nazis wanted and they were always calling for changes. A number of changes *have* been made over the years – largely to deal with any suggestion of anti-Semitism – and it is now presented as a theatre for the people in which *everyone* is complicit in Christ's suffering.

Despite these high ideals, my conversations there always came down to money. Max Jablonka, a former Jesus, ran a souvenir shop in the town, and complained bitterly about the price of fame. "How can I sell my souvenirs when people are asking for my autograph all the time? I have a business to run. Shops like this do not go on their own."

The barber was even harder hit. All actors, except those playing Roman soldiers, must refrain from cutting their hair or beards in the run-up to any new production. "This play is a dagger in the heart of my trade," the barber moaned, flinging his fat hands into the air. "The visitors are only here for a short time so they are no good for business. Everyone forgets the barber. Would *you* like a haircut?"

Most of them seemed to be trying to juggle with what they saw as their two main tasks: meeting the needs of the play and making money. I tracked down two of the Pontius Pilates, George Glass and Toni Presinger, close friends and hoteliers. When they were not selling Christ down the river and washing their hands of what they'd done they were helping one another out in their businesses. They sent guests to one another if they were full and even the odd bottle of Scotch if one bar ran dry. Like pilgrims everywhere, those who went to Oberammergau drank like fishes. "The Benedictine monks are the worst."

So it was that enormous amounts of money poured into Oberammergau, making it the richest village in Bavaria. The villagers themselves seemed an honest, genial lot but they were all at the active heart of a huge capitalistic enterprise which had almost nothing to do with the teachings of the Man of Sorrows scourging the Temple and demanding that the power of money be broken. Jesus never came close of course. All attempts to break the power of money have always ended in failure.

As a writer, all my attempts to make money had ended in failure too and, apart from the odd, relieving cheque from Pauline Peters, my personal finances moved through three distinct levels: skint, broke and dead broke. I had published three books, two of which had received serious attention – one had won the national Winifred Mary Stanton award for the best book with a religious theme and the other had been short-listed for the Thomas Cook Travel prize – but I would have been far better off as a one-legged trishaw driver in downtown Bombay.

I wouldn't have minded so much if I could understand my publisher's annual royalty statement but they hardly ever gave any information about how many books had been sold. The statements talked about returns and mysterious retentions and foreign sales which might, in fact, be returns. All that was ever made clear was that you were not going to receive any money this time since you hadn't yet 'earned in' your advance. You might have a chance with the next statement but, between you and me, we'll have remaindered it long before that. Then, to rub salt into my wounds, the taxman in Finsbury Circus called me in to explain how I could possibly live on what I had declared I lived on and I had to tell him that I didn't know. The urge to survive is strong, even in writers.

I was worried I would have to give up writing books. I simply could no longer rely on Liz to keep us ticking over, particularly with three lusty young boys. I would have to find some soft, uncontroversial berth, perhaps in magazine journalism and make money there while continuing to write when I could. But that wouldn't work. What that Dublin professor had said was true. You can't be a part-time writer any more than you can be a part-time priest or philosopher. You've got to give it all you've got and even that probably won't be enough.

Then something of a miracle happened. I had pretty much forgotten about my first novel, *One Winter of the Holy Spirit*, just as I'd forgotten about my agent, Elaine Greene, who never seemed to want to talk to me. Right out of the blue, she rang me to say that, after thirteen submissions, it had been accepted by Robert Maxwell's publishing house, Macdonald, and would be paperbacked by Futura. They would pay me £3,000, not a lot, they admitted, but at least I didn't have to do any further work on it and they would also give me an advance of £4,000 for another one which should also have a Welsh theme. They wanted to develop me as the new Alexander Cordell.

Thus I could finally do what I had long dreamed: produce a series of novels about twentieth century Wales. Almost everyone I had ever met in publishing circles had advised me to develop a genre. You win readers with one book and build up their numbers with the next. All successful writers do that. There is really no other way, they said. One-off hits are like winning the pools.

Almost nothing about being a writer makes sense but I was able to see the value of having a well-stocked bottom drawer. I had called on almost all the manuscripts in mine and, if I had published one book at a time, writing each from the beginning, I would almost certainly have never survived the inevitable disappointment over the first to muster up the necessary enthusiasm to start the next.

My one real question now was what I was going to tackle now because I had almost exhausted that bottom drawer. As the new Alexander Cordell, I had to have a Welsh theme, so I decided to go back to Cardiff to see what I could turn up with the help of my old cronies there. I emphatically did not want to tackle anything to do with God or what bastards they were in the media. I wanted to get back to the business of writing about normal people in a normal world.

For me the wonders of the normal world were staked out by Cardiff's city limits and I went straight there thinking that I might tackle a big novel set in the city which would reach through her every level.

I took up lodgings again with my mate, Keith James, in the garret above the betting shop in Penarth Road and immediately began wandering around the city looking for new material and ideas. Sometimes I stopped at night to listen to the wives and girl friends of the old lags in the prison who would shout in the news from home over the high walls. The news was interestingly mundane: how she'd had trouble paying the electricity bill that month and they were coming to cut her off or what the baby was suffering from and how she'd got some new pills from the doctor. Did he know what prescriptions cost these days? No, he fu..king didn't. He was here in the f..king nick, locked up, in case she hadn't f..king noticed.

Then there was a man with twenty stray dogs who wandered around the Cardiff streets at night with them, sometimes with me following him from a distance wondering what he got up to on these epic rambles, which wasn't a lot except for calling at the back doors of restaurants to pick up leftover food. These dogs were never fed rubbish: they were the best-fed and best-exercised dogs in the city.

I wouldn't be able to start on any book until I had a story but I couldn't see one.

A Bay family saga perhaps? Shuffling through the decades in a flat, documentary style? That wasn't a story and it was pretentious. A variation on the Shirley Bassey story was a tempter, but it had become a cliché and anyway she wasn't really from the Bay – despite what her publicity had always claimed – and had fled the area as soon as fame came knocking.

But I was going to have to put up some sort of proposal to Richard Evans at Macdonald soon and, if I didn't put up an acceptable proposal, I wouldn't get the promised advance which, by now, I needed.

This problem required the lubrication of a lot of thoughtful pints, so I haunted the golden triangle between the Cottage, the Old Arcade and the City Arms, three of the oldest pubs in the city. I was sitting one night with my old mate, Dan O'Neill of the *South Wales Echo*, who did his haunting in the same triangle, and telling him about my Bay dilemma which, in a few quick sentences, he solved.

"There's a much better story sitting around than that," he said. "The British miners have all been on strike since March and there's only one pit left in the Rhondda, Maerdy. If the struggle for survival of the last pit in the Rhondda, which once exported more coal than any other area in the world, is not one great theme for your next novel I don't know what is."

FORTY SEVEN

The mining village of Maerdy sat at the end of the Rhondda Fach valley in the heart of the South Wales coalfield. Enclosed by high rock walls it looked as if it was at the bottom of a volcano. The cavernous Miners' Welfare Hall was at the far end of the village and a dozen or so terraces ran off its main street. Foaming lace curtains cascaded over the front windows of the houses some of which sloped dangerously because of subsidence. There was a church, a row of shops, a school, a chapel and a pub. About a mile from the Welfare Hall arose the stern, black geometry of the pit, now idle for six months because of the strike.

Most of the miners were brown and fit, having spent the spring and summer kicking a ball around when they hadn't been out to other coalfields on picketing duty or travelling to Norway and Italy to raise funds. Others had set up cells in Oxford and Birmingham – or put a permanent picket at such key places as Cowley car works.

On summer days the sun arrived late and left early, here at the bottom of the volcano. It climbed high into the sky in the morning and sent a great golden kiss thwacking down on the valley walls and wandering sheep. On other days you could see huge rain clouds building up in pillars above the reservoirs at the top end of the valley. These pillars came marching down the slopes, sheeting rain over the piled pit props. Sunshine might burst through the massed rain clouds, and raise steam from the pigeon lofts and allotment sheds. Sometimes this sunshine was so ferocious it created the illusion that the whole village was on fire. Even the coal tips looked new at such moments, the ferns on the slopes and the scabby sheep themselves shivering with a visionary luminosity. The housewives pegged out their washing when the winds came, bringing the back gardens alive with booming sheets.

I got off the X8 bus here in late summer 1984 and wandered the length of Ceridwen Street, the main street, as I wondered if I could live here for *any* length of time, let alone the long length of time it would need to build a novel. This street had a slightly desperate music about it: burglar alarms sprouted profusely on the walls of the houses and front doors were festooned with bolts and deadlocks. Everywhere the one-eyed dustbin lids of the satellite television dishes stared out.

Later, when the sun dipped out of the valley, skinheads gathered in the chip shop amid the electronic gunfire of the Space Invaders machines. The lights of the street-lamps shimmered on the tops of parked cars and another group of skinheads dashed from one corner to the next. You never knew what they would do next. One night

370

they poured petrol down the drain at the top of the valley and set it alight, making explosions of flame erupt from the drains all down the slope.

The main door of the Welfare Hall had been made of cast iron after repeated break-ins and the one-armed bandit in the hallway had been padlocked inside a cage so that you couldn't rob what robbed you. A few old-timers were kicking their heels in the bar when I first put my nose in there and told them I was a writer looking for lodgings in Maerdy. "Dilys Evans takes in lodgers," one said. "She lives right next door to the Hall. You wouldn't have to walk far for a pint if you lived there."

Dilys, an ample, elderly woman who lived with her handicapped son, Jeffrey, offered me a small bedroom at the back of the house where I could sit and look at the side of the Hall and over at the high walls of the valley. For £50 a week she would give me my food too and, after a short holiday in North Wales with Liz and Nathan, I moved in, nervous about what I had let myself in for. Glynmor, a local lad and friend of Dilys's, called and took me into the Hall that Sunday night to introduce me to the various key characters in the community and tell them what I was hoping to do here.

It was crowded in the bars and everyone was friendly. Some of them seemed stuck in a Sixties' time warp. A fair few still dressed as teddy boys and the girls wore mini-skirts that were no more than fanny pelmets – highly unflattering to their fat legs. I didn't yet know what the girls liked to read but it was nothing to do with diet since a lot of them had the shape of a badly-packed kebab. Most of them smoked and the music was rock'n'roll. Their talk was loud and they were forever taking the piss out of one another. "F..k" punctuated almost every sentence of the men's dialogue, but they cut it out when the women (who habitually used the word themselves) were present.

Glynmor pointed to a squat man with a severe face and black moustache. "That's Max, the f..king chairman," said Glynmor. "He lost his thumb in here a few months back. Fighting with those f..king skinheads he was an' one of them bit off his thumb. They 'ad to get Max off to the Miners' Hospital in Chepstow an' they found 'is thumb in the bar an' put it in a crisp packet to take with 'im. F..king ambulance ran out of petrol on the way there an' Max 'ad to sit in a lay-by wiv 'is f..king thumb while they got the RAC to bring some f..king petrol.

"The police rounded up the skinheads and charged one of them with grievous f..king bodily harm. But they 'ad to drop the charge in the end 'cos the skinhead said that he hadn't had his f..king false teeth in that night so 'e couldn't 'ave bitten off Max's f..king thumb."

This, I thought, was a glorious story – the first of a continual stream of glorious stories which dropped into my incredulous ears almost every day of the two years I spent in Maerdy – and right at that moment I knew I was going to get a real novel out of this strange, doomed village at the bottom of the volcano.

Within a few weeks I had almost become a striking miner myself: the men allowed me to sit in on their strike committee meetings on Sunday mornings in the Hall (when they planned their strategy and fund-raising for the following week); to go picketing with them when they took charabancs to other coalfields, and to hang around with them drinking in the Hall when they brought me any tasty morsels of gossip which they thought I might fancy. I might even have been a news editor with a team of the beefiest reporters in the world scurrying around the coalfield digging up stuff for me. Really good stories were rewarded with pints, but there was always argument about what constituted a good story.

With a few notable exceptions they were clever men with a clear ability to see only their own point of view. They were proud of the radical traditions of the lodge. "And remember now, boys, Maerdy pickets are like draughts: they can get in anywhere."

I particularly enjoyed chatting with the retired miners who could remember in vivid detail those times when the hooter would sound after a fatal accident and the whole pit would stop working to march back to the village with the body. The most terrifying noise in the world for a Maerdy woman was the clatter of the cleats of hobnail boots as the men brought their dead mate back home to his widow. These miners would talk of the rats swarming around the ponies' stables underground and the taste of black pats (pit cockroaches) in their sandwiches; of zinc baths hanging on nails in the marigold gardens and money stopped for candles, oil for the lamps and chalk for marking the coal drams.

Tell them a story of hardship and they knew another far worse. They knew everything about this, the hardest work under heaven. Horrifying stories of boils the size of rugby balls and lying on your side to hew coal in six inches of water. They remembered shaking Robin starch on baby bottoms because there was no talcum powder, and using baked bean tins for sand buckets on the miners' annual outing to Barry Island. They had seen men dying by inches in their beds, their lungs choked with dust. They understood the secret language of the pit props: of how their creaking might tell of a possible flood or how hard the rock was pressing down above their heads or whether to make a quick run for it.

In spite of this, these miners loved their pit – unlike car workers who always seemed to hate their plants – and kept one another laughing through the long shifts underground. A lot of them were comical, lyrical and exceptionally tender men who, as they often said around here, had a bell on every tooth. Making love was described as "having a bit of a rub", a man might be so boring he could "put a glass eye to sleep" and when a man was dying it was said his "tools were on the bar". A woman walked across the dance floor "as if her arse was chewing a toffee". Almost everything they said was colourful and I don't think I'd ever laughed so often and so much.

One of the most unusual features of this strike was the emergence of the women's support groups. Mining communities had always been bastions of male chauvinism but already the women were openly talking of how they were going to get the railway back when they won this strike. The women organised the soup-kitchens in the Hall (where any mining family could always be sure of picking up a square meal) and pressed local contractors for food and money, often raising up to £35,000 a week.

The women had clothes coming in from all over the world – including Alpine hats and Bavarian lederhosen – and broke all lodge conventions by standing on the picket lines themselves, a formidable sight: Sherman tanks in duffel coats with "Coal not Dole" stickers on them, fags in hand and daring anyone to become the first scab in Maerdy. "Anyone who tried to pass those women on the picket-line would get thrown straight down the f..king shaft," said Ivor England, one of the strike leaders. "Any scab here wouldn't last five f..king minutes."

I settled easily into all this, soon earning the nickname Tom the Book. In the morning Dilys woke me at nine with tea and toast in bed. After I had washed I worked on my novel until one o'clock when she gave me spaghetti on toast in the kitchen and I might chat with some of the strike committee who popped in for tea at that time. In the afternoon it was back up to my bedroom where I read and made a few notes before I left the house at four thirty and walked the length of the village for a half hour swim in the baths (which I always had to myself). If I was feeling pasty I would take a session on the sun-bed.

When I returned, Dilys gave me a cooked meal – usually roast beef with two veg and swimming with gravy – then left me alone on an armchair in front of the kitchen range where I read the *Times* until 8.30pm. Then I went into the Hall, where I sometimes set the quiz, and we all drank until we were thrown out at 11pm. I always returned home to an empty mug with a tea-bag in it, and a cheese and chutney sandwich. All I had to do was boil the kettle and, in two years, my diet or timings never varied one iota. I never got fed up with the same food at the same times, day in day out, never longed for any change. This iron routine enabled me to forget myself and let my novel grow in my mind from one day to the next.

I soon had about six main characters up and running, most of them given to me by the people I was drinking with every night. I developed my hero, the handicapped Huw Bungalow (so-called because he had nothing up top) into a Christian allegory in which the strikers struggled around him, armed only with their sense of humour as they pitched themselves against all the massing forces of Thatcher's government.

The Rev Mordechai, an eccentric chapel minister, also came alive in my pages; Gnasher the skinhead who beat everyone senseless if they looked at him the wrong way, and Emlyn Kremlin, based on a local trade union leader who was so left-wing he had sent Mao Tse-tung a telegram of congratulation each year on the anniversary of his seizure of power in China. The Chinese Embassy in London never failed to send him a Christmas card by way of acknowledgement.

As the characters inter-reacted in the story, which I had worked out from the start, I fed in the material I was picking up all around me: daft but true stories like the driver of a concrete mixer who went home unexpectedly for his sandwiches and found his wife in bed with the insurance man. The man backed his concrete mixer up against the new convertible car outside and filled it with ready-mix. The insurance man, meanwhile, leaped out of bed, pulled on his trousers, jumped on his bicycle and pedalled off up the valley.

Something silly was always happening: one night the Maerdy men went to picket the coal deliveries to Aberthaw Power Station only to discover, long after they had set up their banners and lines, that they were outside the cement works. The only violence of any kind happened when a picket threw a half-eaten pork pie at a dog, which ate it.

My novel was practically fed into me hourly. All I had to do was turn up at my table each morning with a cup of coffee and start working, always trying to tap out three pages a day on my little Olivetti. The book practically wrote itself and Dilys, who had become the mother I had long lost, wouldn't allow anyone to come up and talk to me when I was working.

I realised it was not enough just to tell the story of the strike: I had to dig out its causes and try and put it into its historical and social context. I tracked down all the material I needed from books and local historians. Every terrace had its own local historian.

The Welsh coal industry employed fewer than five thousand men, compared with its 1930 high noon of two hundred and thirty two thousand, and there were now only five deep mines in South Wales and one, Point of Air, in the north. These closures had brought, in their wake, large-scale and increasing social and health problems. According to the University of Southampton's *Atlas of Mortality,* the valleys had the highest premature death rate in Europe. The main illnesses are cancer, hypertension and respiratory diseases. In the five valleys, ten thousand people a year died of heart attacks. It took an average of five hours to get them to hospital. One in ten would not live to the age of sixty-five.

These valleys also had the highest youth unemployment in Britain, the highest proportion of permanently sick and the highest proportion of households with no bath or lavatory. Another report showed that four of the valleys – the Cynon, the Merthyr and the two Rhonddas – had the highest rate of depopulation in Britain. Most leaving were the young in search of work.

Not all these problems sprang from unemployment, which most commentators blame for almost everything, since these valley communities had come through far worse in 1926 when unemployment in Merthyr stood at eighty-five per cent. Many believed that it was not the effects of poverty that were causing the damage but a collapse of the spirit.

Such vibrant communities had given the world the first great prophets of socialism and the mighty chapel movement. These brilliant, insecure people took education seriously and every welfare hall had its own library and was the home of the Penny Readings and the meetings of the Hearts of Oak. Only ten years ago the communities had been largely crime-free and Yale locks unknown.

"All our family went down the hole," said one of the old miners, Wynn Thomas. "But if there was no work all we used to do was go out and kick a football around. We never thought of thieving like the young of today. And not only did none of us think of rape we didn't even know what it was."

The story of Maerdy again illustrated these terrible cycles from the time when, a hundred years ago, Mordecai Jones sank the Maerdy No 1 pit at the end of the valley. By 1909 there were seven thousand people housed in eight hundred and eighty dwellings and eleven chapels. The village school, erected in 1880, was enlarged nine times in twenty six years. The Welfare Hall had a dance hall that could hold twelve hundred people, a billiard room, a gymnasium and two reading rooms, one for women. The library was one of the finest in South Wales, with a huge collection of Marxist literature.

By the turn of the century, the Rhondda had established itself as the largest coal-producing area in the world. Townships sprang up around the newly dug pits all along the valleys. In sixty years the population rose from nine hundred and fifty to more than a hundred and sixty thousand in 1920. Coal was behind this growth: sixty-seven per cent of the people were directly involved with the mines.

Maerdy was a harsh, bustling place. In 1885, on Christmas Eve, eighty-one men died in an explosion in Maerdy pit. Between 1887 and 1905, another two hundred and ninety four men and boys were blown apart in the mines of the Rhondda and the remains carried home in sacks to their families.

On this dark and dangerous stage the miners struggled against the hated coal barons and, in the process, gave birth to ideas which changed the world and forged the early character of the valleys. Socialism made its first appearance in Merthyr in the shape of Keir Hardie, the new Member of Parliament for the unemployed.

Maerdy also produced fiery, articulate leaders who were among the first members of the British Communist Party. Noah Ablett and Arthur Horner had such influence the village was called Little Moscow. There were competitions for boxers to go to the Soviet Union; "Lenin Weeks" in the coalfield; funeral wreaths in the shape of the hammer and sickle and a communist football team. A reporter from the *South Wales Daily News* wrote of "lawless Maerdy" and "the red reign of terror", describing how strangers were called "spies" and children wore red sashes at funerals.

But perhaps the real character of Maerdy was forged by the chapels. The eleven in the village included Calvinistic Methodists, Congregationalists, Strict Baptists and Wesleyans. The chapels provided the organising loci for valley villages and were the key to understanding the culture of the valleys. The very soul of the valleys was pounded out in the pulpit where a glittering dynasty of great preachers transfixed their congregations with visions of the poor, broken Galilean nailed to a Cross of Shame. It was these nonconformist ideas which became the seed-bed of socialism. Some early chapel theoreticians argued that Karl Marx had worked on the same loom as Isaiah; that, in the love of God and the brotherhood of man, the preacher and the politician were talking of the same thing.

My spiritual muse, Evan Roberts, had conducted a five-hour revival meeting here in Maerdy, I was delighted to learn and I felt close to him as I passed the chapel in question on my way to my afternoon swim, often pausing to smile and imagine the cries of surrender coming from the now boarded-up, burned-down building; the angry, passionate tones of Evan's voice echoing in the charred rafters as he spoke about the devastating effect of sin on the human personality. Those in the packed pews rose to him again, their eyes shiny with ecstatic tears as he promised them freedom from loneliness and pain. A cat wandered out of a hole in one of the broken windows, its diamond eyes staring at me. Ruined chapels had become as common a feature of the valleys as closed-down mines.

Nearly a hundred years after his great work Evan was still presiding over many corners of my life: first making me a novelist with his inspiring story in *One Winter of the Holy Spirit,* which was going to be published soon, then dominating the whole night as I struggled up Asuza Street on my bike ride into a Los Angeles hell and now here with me again as I started on some ill-defined struggle with my people as they engaged in a long fight with the Government which might end up in their own death. This strike was do or die for them. If they lost this they would lose their pit, jobs and community.

Yes, Evan was still here in all this, still trying to make his voice heard as he testified to the Welsh character which put honour before all, which always insisted that, if you did nothing else, you should always fight for your honour.

Christmas came, the spirits of the men were high and the strike was going well. I often felt their new sense of political purpose was reviving the community and a spirit of defiance was renewing and feeding on itself.

Light showers of snow came in the days that followed as gangs of people, fat with layers of overcoats and jumpers, trudged up to the old tip with buckets. A few pushed prams so loaded with nutty slack they kept collapsing. The high valley walls seemed dusted with powdered jewels. There were frozen pools everywhere, many with bright cobwebs of ice on them where boots had walked. The triangular shapes of bird footprints and sheep hooves lightly marked the snow. Here and there were scattered the shiny, black olive pebbles of sheep dung.

Down at the pit itself only the odd iron dram poked up from beneath the white carpet of snow. Even the old mine looked spruce and tidy for once, drifts of snow banked high against the wheelhouse and the wheel itself, a giant spindle which had lost its way in a blizzard. In such conditions, with the cold winds flaying the skin off your cheeks, people were out there digging and riddling for lumps of coal on those glacier tips. Their working holes became a surrealist pattern of black gaping mouths on a great white canvas. They might have been a medieval army digging in for a long winter siege. The scrape of the shovels and the rattling of the riddles carried all the louder in the glittering stillness of the morning. There were stories of some of the strikers going down to the face to get their own coal for their own families. Whatever happened, the people would be kept warm.

Here we were, in the year of our Lord 1985, in Margaret Thatcher's Tory monetarist Britain, with low inflation, and we might as well all be locked away in some isolated Soviet gulag.

There were new stirrings of life in this gulag though; my people were actively embracing their spirit and history out here on these slopes. As they chopped up old railway sleepers or carted off sections of old fence even the young were learning that basics like heat could not be taken for granted. The women were finding that they had brains – despite what the men had long told them – and were busy using them to set up the soup kitchens and send out calls for financial help. The old were proud and walking tall again, welcoming visitors to the Welfare Hall and showing them the hooks where they had hung up stolen sheep in the 1926 strike to let them bleed.

Everyone was renewed with pride and dignity in these ancient hills of coal: they had got up off their knees and were taking on the Government in a fight that would fully honour the spirit of their forefathers.

FORTY EIGHT

I went home to London regularly but was always keen to get back to Maerdy, aware I had got close access to a key moment in Welsh history. It wasn't much of a hardship to be away from home at that time: my eldest, Julian, had discovered Pink Floyd and, despite frequent complaints from me and the neighbours, simply had to play it at top volume day and night.

Newspaper reporters hit a situation running, suck up anything that is going for a few hours and write up their findings hoping for the best. Here I was able to delve much deeper, living with these men, watching their changes of mood from day to day, particularly when things were going bad elsewhere. The battle of Orgeave, when mounted police charged the picket lines, had a troubling effect on them: they could make bellicose noises and sing "I'd sooner be a picket than a scab" like no other, but they knew they weren't up to fighting the police or the Army.

The mood of the strike committee on Sunday mornings was unpredictable. Sometimes they were bubbling with new fund-raising ideas and crackling with jokes; at others silent and depressed as when Nacods, the union of the overmen, announced their cowardly refusal to back them and continued maintaining the pits.

At three one winter morning we went off to picket Didcot Power Station and you could tell they were all fed up by the lack of snap in their banter. One told me he was going to slip off to see his aunty when we got there: another said he would have given anything to have stayed in bed and didn't see how we were going to last out much longer.

A banner was held up in front of the power station and, after a night of rain, a rainbow formed overhead in the swelling dawn, but not only did that fail to cheer anyone up, they didn't even notice it. No one was making much noise at all when, from some distant place, came the faint snicker of horses and the yap of agitated dogs. Phalanx after phalanx of policemen in riot helmets and with shields and truncheons began marching down the road towards us and, as had become the custom, we whistled the Laurel and Hardy theme tune (albeit half-heartedly, as you do, if you think you're about to get beaten up). A police helicopter chattered overhead ominously as we stood there feeling lonely, oppressed and not a little scared. There were only twenty of us. Twenty!

What had we done to warrant this lot running all over us? What kind of state was it that marshalled this massive army of police because twenty pickets from Maerdy wanted to tell a few lorry drivers in Didcot about the need to save their pit?

The National Coal Board wanted to close Maerdy pit and link it with the Tower in the next valley, they would explain to those who would listen. This would lead to the full closure of our pit which was claimed to be losing £140,000 a week. But there had never been any investment in our pit and much of our machinery was as old as the pit itself. Even the NCB agreed there were still eighty million tons of coal down there. We needed investment in our pit and, if we didn't get it, our community would die and the country would be that much poorer.

Later that winter you could almost see Maerdy dying before your very eyes. The local branch of NALGO, the local government union, called a vicious and cruel strike which, amongst other services, took out Meals on Wheels, the libraries and the refuse collections. (Not that you could notice any difference in Ceridwen Street where I lived. There was always plenty of litter in the gutters with fridges just flung out on the valley slopes next to exploded bags of rubbish or the odd, burned-out car.)

Maerdy became more and more famous, with its tag as the home of the last pit in the Rhondda, and the media arrived in droves, giving voice to voices which were already too loud, dramatising situations which were already dramatic enough. Anywhere the media turned up it always made the situation worse: one director even wired up all the pickets with microphones and they almost went berserk in front of the television cameras as they scrummed down with the police. The mere presence of the cameras always seemed to have an alarming effect on the men, who felt they had to do *something* when they were around. Cameras gave them a moment so they would be daft not to seize it. Everyone got their fifteen minutes of fame, according to that emaciated clown Andy Warhol, and this might be theirs.

Oddly, the sense of defeat could lift in a heartbeat and one night in the Welfare Hall a few of the women's support groups from Clydebank and Birmingham were welcomed with a concert and a dance. These women had been having the time of their lives, escaping from their traditional domestic duties (and not about to return to them either) as they travelled to other parts of the land to meet other women who were also enjoying new freedoms. The men were getting more and more perplexed. "Haven't you got any dinner to cook?" one miner asked a group of women enjoying an early pint.

The Birmingham contingent had brought its own band and the night was so cold everyone *needed* to do a lot of dancing to keep warm. The Hall had run out of coal for its heaters and double-glazing, in the form of polythene sheets, had been tacked over the windows.

Yet they soon seemed to be in the highest of spirits – almost as if they had already won the strike – and laughed uproariously when the compère took the stage wearing a duffel coat with the hood pulled so far over his head you couldn't see his face as he complained how it was "bastard freezing" in here.

"There was this man who came over to the club in Merthyr saying that Maggie Thatcher had a face like a sheep's arse. He was hit sick, he was, and kicked something terrible. 'I didn't know you lot were Tories,' he moaned as he lay on the floor. 'We're not, mun. We're shepherds'."

Yet I found myself increasingly wandering those village streets at night full of fear for the future of my adopted village. Depressions took hold of me. Many believed that, if they could somehow win this strike, which was already looking unlikely, it would restore the fortunes of Maerdy at a stroke. But there was an illness here that went much deeper than mere unemployment: the village's vision of itself and its sense of history had gone missing somewhere; everyone had gone for a long walk into some endless tombola darkness.

You could see this illness all around you as night fell on the slate rooftops and the bingo caller read out those all-important numbers from his plastic box of bouncing balls. You could hear his voice two hundred yards away: *On its own, number eight; all the threes, thirty three; old age, number sixty* ...

Even as you heard the numbers you thought about those men who had once sat in the library in that hall, reading the first socialist texts and the newspapers, looking at someone sharply if he made any sort of noise.

Five and nine, fifty-nine; was she worth it, two and six; all the sevens, seventy seven ...

I kept such thoughts to myself, at least at the time, and could only talk about them frankly with the local vicar, Andrew Morton, and his wife Ros, who had become friends. Andrew viewed nothing through rose-tinted spectacles although, for different strategic reasons, none of us ever said as much out loud. These villagers could be extremely touchy, particularly if you dared to mention any of *their* alleged failings. They always complained about dog dirt in the streets, for example, as if it was nothing to do with their dogs. The litter wasn't theirs either, or the old fridges scattered on the mountain slopes. They couldn't think who was torching those cars. No, it was all some kind of bastard Tory plot to do them down again.

A police car sometimes came down the high road from Mountain Ash and accelerated through the valley too fast to notice any crime that might be going on in those padlocked terraces. These villages were badly missing the bobbies on their bikes, men who knew everyone and could be in any burglar's house waiting for him with a cup of tea when he got home with his loot. By common consent there were about fifteen youths in Maerdy for whom nothing was too hot or heavy. They had recently even stolen a guard dog. A few had been spotted walking home in daylight with a rolled-up carpet on their shoulders. Yet no sanctions were ever taken against them. Everyone was too scared to confront them and merely added extra bolts to their doors or put up another alarm that often went off for no reason, adding a tangible sense of paranoia to the perilous village night. When one woman heard them breaking in through the roof at night, she cowered under the sheets, praying they wouldn't come into her bedroom, too terrified to raise the alarm.

One and eight, eighteen; all the fives, fifty-five; two and three, twenty-three ...

Down at the mine itself, the winding wheel was motionless next to a huge pool of naked light in the empty windows of the canteen which also lit up the rainbow whorls of oil in the puddles all around the pithead. No one was betting any money on that wheel moving again. There was even a television talking to itself in the canteen, almost as if it alone was waiting for the men to return.

This absolute enslavement to television worried me most: the way they had surrendered to its tinsel charms to the extent that they seemed to have no life or society beyond it, almost as if they had become enmeshed in the web of lawlessness which the busy loom of television continually spun in every home. They had rolled over on their hearths as the pit and community died around them. Most had thrown in the towel while the same empty vessels made the most noise in front of the television news cameras. "When our pit opens again we're gonna ... and then we're gonna ..." The sheer unreality of their position made you weep.

The miners' strike had become the longest industrial dispute in British history and, while it remained a hundred per cent solid in Maerdy, many once-staunch men in other coalfields were drifting back to work at an alarming rate, particularly in Yorkshire, where the strike had begun. Twenty-four pits were working normally, according to the *South Wales Echo*. Forty-two pits had men reporting for work even if they were not yet producing coal and fifty-one were totally strikebound. News of the returnees was fed to the media hourly. On Black Monday, three thousand one hundred and seventy scabs crossed the picket lines. (I had always loved Jack London's wonderfully trenchant definition of the scab: After God had finished the rattlesnake, toad and vampire he took the leftovers and made the scab.)

The striking miners bitterly contested these figures. "Every time the canteen cat walks in twice the Board counts it as two men back to work," sneered Arthur Scargill.

The South Wales coal field remained scab-free and the local union leaders declared, at least in public, that they were prepared to stay out for the rest of their lives. There was a nuclear war, see, said the joke, so Margaret Thatcher and her Government went into a bunker where they remained for five years. When they finally came out they came across a group of Welsh pickets in Whitehall. "The strike's still on," the men shouted.

This was bravado designed to keep everyone's pecker up. Most knew the strike was losing its will and way. Every lunchtime many of the strike committee came into Dilys' kitchen for the usual cup of tea and to listen to the one o'clock news when we would be told the latest scab figures. None of us was too sure what these figures meant but they sounded sadly impressive, as doubtless they were meant to. The grim-faced men would often make no comment, thank Dilys for her tea and return to their cold homes with little food and even less alcohol in the larder to put a bit of smile on their faces. Welsh Brewers reported a drop in beer sales in all the mining areas.

You could almost hear the cracks opening as the strike began breaking up and, after such a long struggle the sound was heartbreaking. This was the time to be a reporter, not a commentator, I thought as I continued writing, recycling the events around me into my work.

Scabs appeared in the South Wales coalfield and matters took a decided turn for the worse when two miners shouldered a pillar of concrete on to a bridge before dropping it on one such scab on his way to work in a taxi. It missed the scab but killed the driver and many heads were shaking in real sorrow in the Hall that night when it was learned that murder had come to the coalfields. Men were arrested and charges laid.

That same day the members of the Energy Minister's coal committee were served champagne. For the first time in a year more than one million tons of coal had been delivered to coal board customers within a week. The biggest return of the day was in Scotland, where seventy-eight men went back to work. Now there were three thousand working there and qualifying for a tax-free bonus.

And so the biggest and most continuous mobilisation ever mounted against the Government floundered towards its end. "The mineworkers' strike as a living entity, with some sap in it, is over," said the *Financial Times*. "The final moves are of vital, perhaps paramount, importance: but they *are* end game."

The strike finally broke up in a flurry of confusion and the leaders met in the Hall as they heard that the National Union of Mineworkers was telling them to go back to work without any agreement. *Without any agreement!* What about the eight men who had been locked up and the seven hundred sacked for picketing offences? And what about the scabs? How were they going to work alongside *them?* And were *they* going to be called scabs for going back? I'd prefer to cut my own throat than be called a scab.

Questions there were a'plenty and answers none. The secretary of the strike committee said he would never call anyone a scab who had been out for nearly a year. They had done all that was humanly possible even though the Welsh NUM announced they were giving up.

But, after all that heated argument in the Hall, in which many of them declared they were ready to stay out, they decided to go back anyway and, early the next morning, March 3, 1985, beneath a grey, weeping dawn, the men marched back in to the pit, together with a brass band and carrying the huge embroidered banner of their lodge, clenched fists held high in front of the television cameras as if they had just won everything. Gestures were all that was left to them: in the general confusion of those hours, no one wanted to think deeper than that. Anyway gestures always ran well on the television news. It was real issues, like the economics of the pit or the future of the miners, done with analysis and depth, that television news could never handle.

It had never been my intention to leave Maerdy when the strike was over: I decided I simply had to stay there for at least six further months to watch what happened to the community as and when the pit did close. My novel was going well and after *How Green Was My Valley*, which described the industrialisation of a Welsh valley, I hoped mine – *Black Sunlight* as it was now called – would describe the de-industrialisation of a similar valley. I had pretty much lived every hour of that strike and was prouder of this book than anything I had written.

One Winter of the Holy Spirit was due to be published in a few weeks' time and I was discussing running an excerpt from it in the *Western Mail* with the features editor, Gareth Jenkins, when I told him what I had been up to in Maerdy for the past year. The place had become a real mess and had been made a lot worse by the strike, I said. Everyone had run out of hope: even worse, they seemed to have lost their traditional pride.

No newspaper could afford to billet a journalist in a small mining village for a whole year, Gareth said, so I would be uniquely qualified to write about what really happened there away from the headlines. Without much further discussion I agreed to write an eight-thousand-word series for them about Maerdy.

I began by recalling the Aberfan disaster and the way, it seemed to me, the Valleys had begun sliding into deep trouble after that; how half the youth of the Rhondda had become unemployed and the area had become the new sick man of Europe, with the highest incidence of the diseases of poverty and the highest premature death rate. Ten thousand people a year were dying of heart attacks. It was almost impossible to get a doctor to an emergency in Maerdy, for example, and an appointment could take from ten days to a month. Even so, the average number of visits to a doctor was five a year while the national average was two.

Unemployment was clearly one of the most destructive elements in the weave: "Why should they care about their health when they don't see any future in their lives?" asked one medical professor.

I went on to describe how the community had suffered in the strike and how, on almost every level, the problems had got worse. Crime was up, the police missing from the street corners and skinheads terrorising everyone. The Welfare Hall, once the proud heart of the community, was falling apart with neglect and the main street filthier than a Bombay slum. Now that the strike had been lost it looked as if Maerdy would drift into terminal despair.

I had always assumed that the *Western Mail* wasn't much read in Maerdy: my first big mistake. Even if it was I didn't think they would take much notice: my second, even bigger one. They *all* read it and everyone erupted in fury. Even the village idiots had a view on my articles. On the morning they began appearing the women in the Post Office were reading out bits to one another and practically swooning with anger. The owner of the Post Office said that had I been unlucky enough to go in there at that moment I would have been lynched on the spot.

Dilys' phone kept ringing with complaints about me, one suggesting I'd be best off six feet under. Many shouted at me in the street and many more ignored me altogether. It was puzzling: I had *reported* the truth: not *made* it up but *reported* it. The police put a *sergeant* on a corner right next to Dilys's house and the council sent a man to sweep Ceridwen Street almost night and day so that everyone began complaining that Aunt Dilys and her loathsome lodger lived in the best-guarded house in the cleanest street in the Valleys.

The rage ebbed and flowed for a few days and I stayed indoors, thankful for the police sergeant who remained on that spotless corner. I had better leave soon. Although no one was actually pushing me out, I had caused too much offence. True or not I had probably not concentrated enough on the positive aspects of the community which, for all its failings, *was* full of hospitality and love. Indeed I had felt enfolded by this love almost from the first moment I had gone there: everyone always gave you the time of day. But not any more they didn't.

Yet I thought it would be sad if I did find myself forced to leave. Not that I thought myself important but because future artists and writers here might feel inhibited from tackling the death rattle of the valleys. Only artists have any real chance of tackling problems like this, I believed; of showing the people what was happening to them, albeit in a melodramatic and upsetting way. Naively I had hoped that my words might help them to get better, to pick up their coffin and walk.

People continued shouting angry words in shrill tones. Barbara Williams, the chairwoman of the Miners' Support Group, called a public meeting in the Welfare Hall which she asked me to attend.

A few hundred turned up in the Starlight Lounge with committee men standing around in disgusted groups and staring at me balefully. A lot of unfamiliar faces had turned up too and I couldn't quite read their positions. Rev Andrew chaired the meeting, hopeful of keeping law and order which really did look as if it was going to break down at any moment. The anger seemed to be ramping up by the second as speaker after speaker accused me of cynicism, exaggeration and destroying Maerdy's public image which had been so carefully and successfully built up over the strike years. "We've become world-famous and now look what Tom the Book has gone and done."

Apart from the local fallout from my series, which had continued to be reported in the *Western Mail*, it had been discussed in the Welsh Grand Committee at the House of Commons, deeply irritating Nicholas Edwards, the Secretary of State for Wales (a good enough reason for writing any series I would have thought).

"As a mother and someone who has always lived here, I say you have not given justice to this community," Barbara Williams stormed. "You have picked on one section of young people like those skinheads. You didn't look for both sides. You looked for the bad and didn't look for the good."

As the complaints mounted I saw that their famous sense of humour really had caught the last bus out of the valley and an extremely ugly situation was developing, which might have nasty consequences – all of them for me.

I had no choice but to stand up and dig in, first apologising for the imbalance of my articles but insisting that what I had written was true. They had clearly caught me out on the odd fact – the men didn't walk home from the pit with blackened faces, as I had written, because they all showered at the pithead first – but what I had said was true and, if they continued ignoring the social problems I had identified in my series, they could end up picking up the bodies of their own dead children out of their gutters.

Most ominously of all, in my view, the Maerdy youngsters were watching television and video films which, in their constant portrayal of animalism, had done more to destroy the spirit of the valleys than any other single influence. Indeed they were almost certainly destroying the valleys in much the same way they were even now destroying the world. When you look at young kids standing on street corners spitting and quivering with aggression, think of our modern film and television industries, think of the local video shop where they're getting it from. *Because they are not getting it from anywhere else.*

"Most of the terrible problems besetting this community – and the valleys as a whole – could be settled by a revival of community pride," I went on. "The truth hurts, but the real problem with what I have been saying and writing is that it *is* all true and only if you face that and do something about it will you start building a safe future *for all your children. It will be a start."*

I was starting to get a bit stroppy myself, wondering why so many of them seemed to be so wilfully ignoring the evidence of their eyes. How, for example, could anyone stand over the road from this Welfare Hall, I shouted, once the proud heart of a great community who believed in honour above all, and not shiver in disgust at its appalling condition? How much does a lick of paint cost? If there's so much litter around the streets and the council can't – or won't – pick it up, why can't we? We know all these kids who are stealing from our homes so why don't we confront them and their parents? Why aren't we patrolling these streets ourselves if the police haven't got the manpower to do it?"

People kept standing up, shouting and sitting down again. It was bedlam and Andrew was desperately trying to keep control, telling everyone to calm down and the mood changed yet again when the black and bulky figure of Alf Lawes, one of the leading members of the Royal Antediluvian Order of Buffaloes (the Buffs, as they were called), stood up and began speaking in soft, authoritative tones. "Tom the Book has shamed and hurt everyone and we have come here because we are really ashamed," he said in a soft voice. "But the real cause of our shame is that he has told the truth. All he has done is hold up a mirror to our secret thoughts; all he was saying was what we already knew. Yet the articles only scratched the surface. Is it not the case that it is all far worse than he wrote?"

Others spoke, raising other issues, and from somewhere deep in these quarrelling tides emerged a will to grab hold of something concrete before the impetus was lost. The best they could do that night was to arrange a public meeting to which the local MP, Allan Rogers, would be invited and they could discuss matters like attracting new industry and the possible reopening of the railway line.

After that everything moved faster. The next day Andrew called together a small ad hoc group which met in the headmaster's study of the comprehensive school to generate ideas to revive the spirit of the community. Within an hour it was decided to call the group Action Maerdy and print their own posters and letterheads. Other possibilities were a new adventure playground for the children; street mural paintings by the schoolchildren; getting the books of the old miners' library back from the University of Wales; visiting the youth clubs and schools to get them involved in a general clean-up and starting a community information sheet which, that week, was going into four thousand homes.

The jewel in the crown would be a new community centre which would take the youth off the street corners. There was plenty of local labour to build it, but they would need other sections of the community to start their own fundraising initiatives. The local lodge of the Royal Antediluvian Order of Buffaloes might take it upon themselves to approach famous Welsh artists and choirs to come here and give concerts for the new centre. The local rugby club could approach other clubs throughout the valleys and ask for the proceeds of one Saturday gate. The shopkeepers might set up a committee which would provide prizes for the best single initiative taken by an individual in raising money on his own. The Miners' Support Group could also use its international contacts, built up during the strike, to get support from abroad. The important thing about all these initiatives would be that *everyone* would be involved and the whole process would also be a lot of fun as well as hard work.

The next day another small group of community elders – Allan Ifor for the miners; John Eirion, a magistrate; Terry Williams, a headmaster, and Andrew, the vicar, had an informal meeting with area police chiefs over a pint in the Hall about arguably the greatest cancer in the community – drugs and crime.

An officer would soon be returning to live in Maerdy police station, which had been empty for ages, Chief Inspector Phillip Steele told them. Community policing would be increased to four officers on foot, mounting a twenty-four-hour patrol throughout Maerdy. Panda cars out of Ferndale would provide an umbrella cover. CID personnel would be increased to three working the area. The police were anxious to help in any way they could, they said. They had been worried by rumours that Maerdy was going to set up its own vigilante patrols so they were increasing their numbers and keen to improve their admittedly poor relationship with the community. The police also wanted to participate in any social activities and would even play the unemployed at soccer. They had access to money for local aid projects if only someone would set up an appropriate committee. Yes, they would deal with crime, but they had to have the full backing of the community.

The next night again there was yet another meeting called by Barbara Williams and it was decided to form a community council inviting representatives from the council, police, chamber of trade, churches, Buffs, clubs, youth clubs and the NUM. This council would address itself to the problems of the village including the plan for a new community centre.

Most seemed prepared to give it a go, but I could no longer be seen as a part of it and it was time to leave. My series had undoubtedly been a catalyst for action, but now it was down to them to do it in their own way – or not – and I couldn't suggest by my presence that it might be anything to do with me. I came as an outsider and left as one.

I had anyway betrayed my hand in the community – no longer the quiet observer who set really hard questions in the quiz but a vocal and potentially disastrous enemy who had views which he didn't mind expressing. Many remained angered at my articles and I might be sitting in the Hall having a late pint when a few who'd had a few too many would start shouting at me and inviting me outside. This happened in the pub too and it got so boring I stopped going out altogether.

People said it would pass, particularly when things were being seen to be done, and indeed it might all have settled except that, nearly a year later, *Black Sunlight* was published to a further chorus of outrage. For one thing, a lot of the characters swore a lot and, as we all know, miners never use bad language. Then there was the scene during a wedding reception in the Hall, when the committee chairman caught the bingo caller and the bride's sister having it off on the committee table. "Do you realise you have pissed on the holy altar?" my father asked me. "The committee will never forgive you for that."

They didn't either, although I suppose it hardly mattered that the incident I had described had actually taken place. That was the real problem with it and other incidents in the book – they were true.

FORTY NINE

W ith *Black Sunlight* safely delivered there seemed no alternative but to tackle the story of Cardiff's Tiger Bay with its multi-racial mix and clamorous past.

Macdonald were keen to do it *and* the proposed advances kept going up – along with my sales – so somehow a career path seemed to be opening up for me as a novelist of twentieth century Wales. This would also be a lot of fun, enabling me to live in different parts of Wales, wherever my novels were set, and there wasn't much competition at the time. Most of the great old Welsh novelists like Gwyn Thomas, Jack Jones or Alexander Cordell, with whom my work was being increasingly compared, had died or fallen silent. Indeed it was extremely difficult for a Welsh writer to find a berth with a large London publishing house then although it may have helped that my editor at Macdonald, Richard Evans, was from Carmarthen.

The problem was that I still didn't have a story for my book about the Bay: any number of themes, but nothing to tie them together. Maybe I could find one by living down there, mingling with the community, seeking out the keepers of the culture and spending most of my evenings in the lively pubs encouraging people to talk, a practice which, as it turned out, was very easy, the only problem being to get them to shut up. Everyone had a personal version of the story of Tiger Bay and his or her role in it. No outsider could understand the area as they did: it had been the most wonderful place on earth when they were young but now it was all going to the dogs fast. I'd heard that line a few times before.

I rented a room with a bathroom on Windsor Esplanade, an attractive terrace of large late nineteenth century houses built by the Dutch for sea captains. This terrace housed some extremely dodgy characters ranging from wild lesbians to poverty-stricken students and fat singers in the Welsh National Opera. It looked out over mud flats on which the sun rose on most mornings to frame the hundreds of waders out on the sea or wading in the mud. Many of these birds waded for hours, occasionally fluttering off to somewhere at great speed before returning for a few more hours of wading.

Directly opposite was Penarth and the quay where I'd had my coal yard and, way over on a further shore to the left, a line of gasometers each given a shimmering golden crown by the rising sun. On most mornings it rained or thick fog curled everywhere in the Dickensian manner. Sometimes the sun was no more than a thin golden line beneath a heavy grey sky. Every dawn was different on those mud flats. This was where the three rivers, the Taff, Ely and Rhymney, converged before debouching into the Bristol Channel in a great flood of water. Ferocious rip tides battled with the rivers in surges which caught the light and played with it all day.

My landlord was an eccentric artist who had somehow managed to gut the local Norwegian Church, derelict like almost everything else along the waterfront, moving most of the furniture and fittings into his house. His bedroom looked like the old church hall with a rackety pulpit. Musty and chipped Norwegian panels held the walls together throughout the house and this charming, medieval effect was only spoiled by his two incontinent dogs who shat and pissed everywhere.

He also brought back a worrying variety of sailors he picked up in the local bars or on the wharves and I was never sure who I might bump into late at night on the stairs after I'd come home from my own night out in the Bay.

I was still scouring the area looking for inspiration. This had happened often enough when I had been a trainee reporter on the *Western Mail*, buzzing from street to street in the Bay looking for something and only finding it when it rose up from nowhere to tap me on the shoulder. But I wasn't looking for an eight-hundred-word news story but a long story, with a good heft to it, which would sustain a novel.

There wasn't much left here from my days on the *Western Mail*: the demolition ball had wiped out whole communities and streets in readiness for the Bute Town redevelopment. At the start of Bute Street and over to the left had been old Irish Town which I remembered as a vibrant collection of terraces full of fat housewives in hairnets and pinafores and malnourished children with scuffed shoes and dirty knees, all ruled by tyrannical priests who bullied their flocks mercilessly. Those terraces had long been bulldozed and buddleia flourished on the rubbled wasteland. The corrugated sheds of light industry had taken over parts of the area with the odd gypsy encampment moving in, the scattered old fridges and spare tyres guarded by scabby dogs on the ends of long pieces of rope. Council workers with clipboards kept coming and threatening them with bulldozers unless they moved on.

In Bute Street the Charleston Club had gone as had the Adelphi pub and the Cairo Café. Even my old friend Sophie Salaman, once such a valuable guide to the Moslem community, had been re-housed to some new council estate on the outskirts of the city where so many uprooted docks people were almost terminally miserable, deprived of their old stamping grounds where they had been as happy as jackdaws.

One morning I traced the long low scar of the Glamorganshire Ship Canal, where barrel-chested horses had pulled barges piled high with coal and iron. I came across Greek Church Street with the Greek Orthodox Church still standing in lone vigil on the waste ground that was once the Greek community. They were clearly retaining this church in the Butetown development and I knocked on the front door of the house next to the church, which was opened by the minister, Father Anastias Salaptos, who lived here with his small family.

"The Greeks first established a community in Cardiff in 1873," he told me. "This church was built in 1906 and, with a Greek ship coming in every day, the whole community established itself around it. But by 1960 the work stopped and so did the ships. Now we get one ship a month. My people here have moved to all parts of South Wales."

Ghosts in a wasteland: faintly echoing memories, blurred by time.

Many Somalis had started coming here to escape the war back home but I found them difficult to get on with, particularly the young who struck me as insecure and aggressive, many carried knives.

I did manage a long chat with Betty Hassan one afternoon. Her father, a Somali, had served in the British navy in the First World War, later meeting her mother here.

"Tiger Bay was a beautiful area to live and there was no racial discrimination of any kind," she recalled. "There were Germans, Greeks, Jews, Norwegians and Dutch. You name them and they were here. The people were peaceful and you felt safe. Nobody ever bothered you. There are still a lot of Somali people here and the situation in Somalia is very bad with the war. The president is no more than a Papa Doc and the people have to become free from that regime. There's also a lot of forgotten children in that war. They have no clothes or toys or anywhere to sleep. They are living rough and running between the war zones. I want to set up a children's village, something which will be theirs, not just the bush or a begging bowl."

The Roath Basin dock displayed a sign that said: "It is absolutely forbidden to drown dogs in this dock."

I was growing ever more desperate as I listened to such stories, still not finding whatever it was I was looking for. I went to the city library to take a closer look at the circumstances of Britain's first race riot which had revolved around 250 Bute Street, once a lodging house for West Indian seamen, later the Charleston Club and now but another patch of wasteland offering no clues to its lively history.

A hot Wednesday night, June 11, 1919. The First World War had ended; unemployment was high. In time-honoured tradition the Press put the blame on the twelve hundred black seamen living in the Bay. A gang of whites jumped a group of blacks in the city centre and bystanders joined in. A shot rang out; a soldier was wounded. The blacks ran for the safety of the Bay and were chased by a group of soldiers. Shots were fired by the bridge and running fights flared up all over the area. Three blacks ran into 250 Bute Street chased by twenty whites who dragged them out and beat them up. Hysterical crowds roamed the Bay all night and a gun battle broke out. The police later confiscated a revolver, a razor, a pile of bludgeons and a length of brass wire with a plate on each end. Twelve men were charged and fifteen injured including a policeman. One man died.

My questioning went on for week after week and my little room in Windsor Esplanade had notebooks piled up on my table and pieces of paper pinned to the wall. The notes on these pieces of paper were interesting enough in their own right but, no matter how hard I thought about it, I still couldn't see the story which would bring them together. No novel could work without a story; it was pointless to start without one. Get the story right before you start and everything else will fall into place, Elaine Greene had always drummed into me. Get it wrong and you could end up wasting two or three years of your life on false trails leading nowhere. A chapter may be pretty or even beautifully written but if it doesn't advance the story, chop it.

One morning I was sitting in my room looking out of the window, as writers do, with nothing but a vaguely anxious emptiness inside me, which is why writers drink so much, when my eye caught the *Sunday Times* Atticus column written by Stephen Pile, a talented comic writer whom I had got to know when I had been writing the Pendennis column for the *Observer*. At the bottom of the column was an item about the Nanteos Cup, claimed by some to be the true Holy Grail, which had somehow made its way from the Holy Land via Glastonbury to end up in a safe deposit box in a bank in Cardiganshire.

You could tell by the tone of the piece that Stephen didn't believe a word of the claim, but I continued staring at his words, my blood running hot and cold. The Holy Grail. Mm. If that wasn't a unifying and compelling symbol for a story I didn't know what was. A good way to start my story would be at the turn of the century with the third Marquis of Bute, the richest man in the world, acquiring it for his wild and extravagant folly of Cardiff Castle. He was exactly the kind of man who had the means and motive to search for such a sacred object and it couldn't be too difficult to get this grail to pass through the hands of the different racial groups in the Bay, who either flourished or died in the continual battle for its ownership.

I decided to find out more about this Nanteos Cup which, it was alleged, was the cup used at the Last Supper or else made from the wood of the True Cross and had miraculous powers for healing the sick. Fifteen years earlier its owner, Elizabeth Mirylees, had taken the Nanteos Cup to her daughter who had suffered a serious riding accident and, after a prayer session with the cup, the daughter had recovered.

I learned that, according to the same story, Joseph of Arimathea had given it to the monks of Glastonbury. Years later, when these monks had to flee heathen invaders, they had taken the cup with them and, after wandering all over the place, ended up in Strata Florida Abbey in mid-Wales. When the last monk died he gave the cup to the abbot. After the dissolution of the abbey, some of the monks left behind were given a home for life on the Nanteos estate and they gave their hosts the cup which was how it became known as the Nanteos Cup. But it wasn't much of a cup today: half of it was missing and the remaining half held together by metal rivets. But by now the owner had died and I couldn't get to see it myself.

I tracked down a scientist at Aberystwyth University who had examined the cup and who told me that there had been many small slips of paper kept with it which provided a record of healing. Between 1857 and 1901 sufferers, mainly women, held on to the cup for about a month in their homes, leaving either a pound or a watch as collateral. On the cup's return, the slip was inscribed with the date and usually the remark "completely cured" or, in one case, "bleeding stopped".

My scientist had difficulty examining the cup because it had been damaged by the many people who nibbled pieces out of it to speed their recovery. After careful examination over two days with a number of other experts he concluded it was wych elm which rather undermined its holy credentials since wych elm grew in Europe – and was, in fact, the most common elm found in Wales – but never in the Holy Land. "There was no mention of the cup prior to the last century," he told me. "It is just a marvellous bogus story. I'm as romantic as anyone but this, I'm afraid, is a lot of mumbo-jumbo."

Whether it was romantic mumbo-jumbo or not hardly mattered to me. I was writing fiction so I began digging out the other grail books and quickly discovered that all the stories were romantic mumbo-jumbo.

The first reference to it in Wales came in the story of Peredur in the *Mabinogion*, a collection of Welsh folk tales. There the grail was presented as Peredur's cousin's head floating on a pool of blood in a platter. A much later writer argued that the grail was not a cup at all, but the landscape of Wales. Grails were dotted all over the place – including the one in that safe deposit box in that Cardiganshire bank which no one wanted to unlock for me. Valencia Cathedral had one, as had Genoa Cathedral, with another buried deep in a spring on Glastonbury Tor. Today, thanks to Dan Brown and his *da Vinci Code*, there's another buried in the glass pyramid outside the Louvre.

The more I read, the more opaque the stories became, all of them made up on the hoof by writers, undoubtedly like the one staring out of his window at the waders in Windsor Esplanade, wondering how the hell he was going to find his story and get going. But wasn't the grail, in a sense, the ideal metaphor for any writer, something which changed its shape and form whenever you looked at it, something which meant so much to so many different people, something which you could take to mean whatever you wanted it to mean? This was surely why the grail had attracted the attentions of so many writers over the years. You could prod it around a bit and get it to work for whatever narrative purpose you wanted.

So I had my subject at last and started the book with a careful description of the Bay on a sunny empty Sunday at the turn of the century, gradually working my way up to Cardiff Castle where we met the third Marquis of Bute standing on the battlements and looking gloomily out over the city as he suffered from a mysterious bleeding of the genitals like the Fisher King of grail myth. He was to cheer up considerably that night when a group of monks appeared on the drawbridge bringing him, after a long and expensive search, the Holy Grail itself.

The main story opened in 1918 when, the war over, a ship owner dies and his son, Edward, comes to Cardiff to claim his share of his father's company, Oriel: he is particularly interested in a windjammer, the *Solomon*, which is sailing from the Azores. I had already got my eye on this windjammer as a symbol of the Church, something whose fortunes would rise and fall in the narrative. The other partner in Oriel, the rich and enigmatic Hamilton – whom I saw as representing romantic evil, interested in violence, cruelty and medievalism – promises Edward that he could have the windjammer if he leads a team of thieves into Cardiff Castle to steal the grail.

A series of electric storms shivers over the sweating city as Edward takes his gang in through the sewers under the castle walls. Out in the Bay of Biscay the *Solomon* has been caught in severe gales and the waves look as if they have turned to fire. The thieves manage to raise the newel post where the grail was hidden and find a cup in which a heart seems to be still beating. They are spotted by security guards and panic. Edward grabs the grail and manages to escape by hurling himself into the swollen waters of the River Taff, raising the grail briefly in triumph as he was carried on down to the Bay itself.

Twaddle, for sure, but colourful twaddle that would serve my purpose.

Fire in the Bay, the title under which the novel was finally published, was not my best book and there were flaws in it which were to lead to my undoing as a developing Welsh novelist – but, in its opening chapters, I had managed to set up the story well and it subsequently ripped out of my pen, reminding me why I had become a writer in the first place as I mixed up scenes from the city of my birth with remembered moments from my childhood on the banks of the River Taff and in the shadow of Cardiff Castle, bringing them all together in a nice warm flow which also managed to include my usual themes of nationhood, the search for God and a coming tide of evil.

I worked steadily for day after day in Windsor Esplanade, often close to rapture, not needing to do further research: it had all been done and was pinned to pretty much every spare inch of wall around me.

I soon decided it was safe to leave Cardiff and return to the family home in London. Those tortured screams coming from my landlord's bedroom at night had been driving me crazy and you simply couldn't be drunk all the time. Even Pink Floyd at maximum volume had to be preferable to that.

In 1985 Liz left the *Sunday Express* to become a sub-editor on the *Sunday Telegraph* and so, to be nearer Fleet Street, and being more than a little fed up with the symmetrical bungalows with their symmetrical gardens in Eastcote, we moved to Greenwood Road just off Dalston Lane, Hackney.

I missed the ordered tranquillity of Eastcote almost from the first day. My boy Steffan, leaning out of a window one morning, saw a man being stabbed. We had bought our house from a minor Islamic sect who took security seriously: even the ladder in the garden was treble-locked to a fence. One night we forgot to secure a window properly and lost our television. But the thieves put down a vase of flowers in the fire-grate and folded up the connecting lead tidily before they left.

In the meantime, being near Fleet Street had advantages for my writing. I could often use an assignment from the *Telegraph* to cover some useful research which might not be available in the normal run of things. There would be a cheque in it too, which always helped.

Although I had introduced a windjammer into *Fire in the Bay* I knew nothing about them, but the *Lord Nelson*, a three-masted barque, was sailing around the country with a disabled crew. With my *Telegraph* hat on I negotiated a berth for her last trip of the season to give me an insight into what it might be like sailing on one. That trip cost me a lot of bruises: I can still feel the bumps and cuts when I think of her and relive that last furious night after we slipped our moorings in St Malo in France and set sail for Guernsey.

The sea air was full of storms and rumours of storms. Screaming winds whipped the sea and black thunderheads piled up on the horizon. Sheets of pink lightning stammered and, on deck, all was furious activity as lines of men and women in oil-skins hauled miles of rope to let down the sails. Another wave broke over the bow as the sails were set one by one ... the top-sail, the top gallant, the royals, the spanker ... eighteen of them in all, filling up with wind and booming softly like distant cannon.

By now the winds were ripping the tops off the waves and the air was full of stinging salt spray. The chief officer yelled for someone to get up into the yardarms to loosen fouled ropes. Wooden blocks cracked together like breaking nuts. The ship rode up the back of another wave and there was a brief silence, a holding of the breath, with just the harsh screaming of the winds in the rigging until the ship toppled forward again.

More oilskinned people were slithering over the sodden deck, hanging onto ropes or stanchions. As they hauled on more ropes, shouting: "Two, four ... heave! Two, four ... heave!" you noticed something almost unbelievable: most of them were disabled by multiple sclerosis and spina bifida and others crippled with arthritis or paralysed by spinal injuries. The oldest was seventy-one. A few had suffered from strokes that had nearly killed them. Others had clubbed feet or were paralysed below the waist and struggling to stay erect on aluminium crutches. Now they were hunkering down for the trip of their lives — straight into a Force Eight gale.

The ship groaned piteously up the next wave before another silence was followed by another groaning slide back into the screaming furies. Thunder bellowed and lightning stammered repeatedly. Most of us were silent, wondering what we had let ourselves in for. The ship had never before sailed when there was a gale warning but for this, the last trip of the season, our captain, John Fisher, had decided we were ready.

The *STS Lord Nelson* was a rare and thrillingly beautiful ship, named after England's most famous sailor. This was its first season afloat and it was a miracle that that it had been ever launched at all: two of its early builders had gone bust and at one stage the officers had to hijack it out of a yard.

Another belch of thunder and the rain came with fat slugs of hail that hit down on the deck savagely. The helmsman had a lame arm, but that was no excuse for not keeping the sails close trimmed to the winds. One youth in a wheelchair yelled at another as they hauled in the buntlines. For this watch I had been chained to the deck rail with a safety harness and was acting as lookout for the port side. A wave the size of a small house broke over me, sending torrents of icy water down my neck and freezing my hands into shrunken, cold claws. The ship bucked again and a man was thrown across the mess-room, to land, his shoulder dislocated, in an untidy and painful heap against a bulkhead.

On the *Nelson* blind people regularly took the wheel with some help from the able-bodied; the partially sighted had their own special bright-track radar screen. There were lifts between the decks to give access to those in wheelchairs. Everyone was expected to do their turn and everyone did. Those permanently in wheelchairs did not have to work in the yardarms, but one lad with spina bifida and no legs did haul himself up there with his own strong hands. All the blind people had gone up too and I found it the most terrifying experience, the winds ripping the breath out of your mouth as you tried to reef the sails while hanging on for dear life.

When first ordered up a yardarm five days earlier I had refused point-blank, claiming journalistic immunity but they ordered me up anyway. When they did prod me up the ratlines, I was too afraid to go out on the yards themselves and clung to Norman de Pead, who had left the lovely warm safety of the chorus of *Cats* to get stuck in all this.

After the boy with no legs got up there we had to force ourselves out, clinging on tight and whimpering plaintively. The rule was one hand for the ship and one for yourself, but no one had yet fallen. "When you know you're dead if you let go you don't let go," the bo'sun observed bleakly.

We were fifty miles out of St Malo with the ship sliding down the back of wave after mountainous wave and thumping down hard on to her bows. The sails boomed when the rain stopped and the rinsed, star-encrusted sky reeled over our heads. The ship's lights turned the masts and sails a ghostly green: we might have been a ghostly ship on a ghostly ocean come back to haunt the modern world.

Being lookout that night was the coldest ever, the winds slicing so easily through my oilskins I might just as well have had nothing on. I spent a lot of time jogging on the spot or shadow boxing the spray. What made it all the more miserable was that when I did manage to spot anything they had spotted it on the radar already. Nevertheless I got a right rollicking for negligence when I missed a lighthouse.

My partner on the starboard side, Adriana, was on crutches and managing far better than me – letting rip a few jovial Italian songs as we ploughed through those gale-scoured seas. On the bridge the captain checked our course, exhilarated by our speed. These were marvellous winds for sailing, he said, and we were travelling the hundred-and-ten miles at around eight knots. "Everyone on board will remember this night. I wouldn't have risked it if I thought the crew wasn't ready. But this is a good crew who have got over their seasickness quickly. Sometimes the less able-bodied can do better than us."

The bowsprit went spearing down into the waves again with the sea hissing up out of the deck sluices as Lindsay Taylor sat strapped into his wheelchair on the upper mess deck. He suffered from dwarfism. In rough weather like this he kept being thrown out of his bunk yet, pale and tired, he remained remarkably cheerful, talking freely of his disability and how he had often been written off as unemployable. On this ship he had discovered skills that he never knew he had. He wrote the ship's log and took the wheel. He had a sparkling sense of humour, saying that he tried not to drink too much gin and tonic (I have never seen anyone drink gin and tonic faster) because it was bad for his figure.

Seasickness hit everyone at first – able-bodied and disabled alike – and a lot of us kept throwing up. But it was interesting how the disabled often helped the able-bodied – rather than the other way around – encouraging us to get out of our bunks and get on with it, even though many of us would have been far happier curling up to die. It took a man with one arm to teach me the right way to peel potatoes: my father-in-law had one arm and could do more with it than I could have managed with four.

That morning run down to Guernsey justified every ache and terror, the gales finally slackening off and the air becoming warm as a grey dawn broke over the towering waves. A lone seagull had been gliding near my head almost all night and as I looked up around me at the shrouds and mainstays quivering with tension I saw how these extraordinary systems kept reproducing themselves all along the deck. It was then that I spotted something of the fantastic poetry of these great sailing ships and their deep intimacy with the wildest elements. We were at one with the winds, the sea and everything that moved on those heaving waves. It was ships like this that first brought the seven seas of the world together; first transmitted new ideas to distant continents and made world merchandising possible. They were once described as the most powerful instruments of civilisation that mankind had ever created and here we were just as those seafarers had been from the beginning.

But there was something else on those decks that morning. The windjammer, in myth, symbolised the risen church and it was not difficult to see why as I looked out along the nave of this great canvas cathedral, with ropes dangling everywhere like bell ropes, the vaulting majesty of the masts holding up the great roof of the sky, all driven forward by the beneficent prayers of the winds.

Two men in wheelchairs were fighting to control some flying halyards and another on crutches was offering advice. Others were hauling in the spanker ready to change tack and yet more were working in the rigging. Someone was shouting orders through cupped hands but his words were blown away. Here, surely, the metaphor of the risen church was exact in the creaking silence of this new dawn. For here the ship had survived a terrible storm and was now taking on the functions of the Mother Church, faithfully attending on and sustaining the poor, the unemployable and the disabled. The ship had taken them all into one family, working and resting them, providing food and sustenance as we sailed on, creakily tackling the first dawn of the rest of our lives.

Back home in Hackney, the crime in the area eroded my sense of wellbeing: you never knew what was going to happen next and, when it did, it was usually unpleasant. One sunny afternoon a man threatened his neighbour with a six-foot sword and even the police seemed scared of him. Within weeks I was campaigning for us to sell up and return to Cardiff. My career as a Welsh novelist was shaping up – *Black Sunlight* had sold five thousand copies in hardback, sixty thousand in paperback and was among the most-borrowed titles of the year in our libraries – and I wanted to return to Wales and become a part of what, if anything, was happening there.

But Liz enjoyed the buzz of newspaper life so we worked out that she would split her week between four days in London and three in Cardiff over the weekends. I would look after five-year-old Nathan during the week while the other two, now nineteen and twenty and both working, would share a flat in London.

Our subsequent move back to Wales was faster than any other. The Islamic sect who had renovated our house in Greenwood Road had done a thorough job, if you liked your living room green – their holy colour – and the bathroom done up in stained glass panels and intricate fretwork. Many of the bedroom walls were decorated in complex detail, but the house's main selling feature was that the whole structure had been renovated including a new roof and windows, making it unique in an area where most of the houses were falling apart.

My advertisement in the *Evening Standard* compromised between a modern house and ancient mosque, but it attracted a lot of interest and the house was sold almost immediately to a most un-Islamic publisher who gave us, after we'd been there just two years, £100,000 more than we had paid for it. Whenever we decided to move in those days seemed to coincide with a boom in the housing market.

As luck would have it there had been no sign of a boom in Cardiff, so we managed to buy a wonderfully spacious house (once lived in by a lord mayor) for cash in Ty Draw Road in the Roath area overlooking the playing fields and stream where I had played as a youth *and* buy a flat for Liz in Greenwich where she could spend her *Telegraph* days and walk to work now the newspaper had left Fleet Street and moved to Canary Wharf.

In another twist of fate, my father, on his own now that my sister Jackie had married, decided he could do a lot worse than live with us. I dreaded this, particularly given our bilious relationship when I was young, but he turned out to have a sweet side to his nature that I had never guessed existed.

FIFTY

On August 19, 1987 reports began coming though of a massacre in the small market town of Hungerford in Berkshire involving Michael Ryan. An old friend, Robert Peart and I were arranging our Friday night booze-up with the boys and the more details I heard from Hungerford the more they rang bells in my mind. "You know, Bob, I'm sure that guy is acting out a film fantasy," I said. "He thinks he's Rambo. He's got the same relationship with Rambo as John Hinckley had with Travis Bickle."

I'd seen the film *First Blood* while on holiday in Portugal a few years earlier. It was not a film I would normally have chosen to see but it had been raining heavily and I had taken my two eldest boys to see it if only to sit somewhere dry for a few hours. It was a violent, all-action film which, for some reason, lodged vividly in my memory.

"Come on, let's go and have a crack at the story," Bob urged. He had reported on the Angry Brigade bombings in the Sixties and was keen to see action again. So I rang Graham Patterson at the *Sunday Telegraph* and explained my theory that Michael Ryan was acting out a Rambo fantasy. If true, it would have serious repercussions for the film and video industries. "They're always saying they have no responsibility for modern violence, but this might be the one chance of nailing them," I told Graham who couldn't get us both there fast enough.

We drove to Hungerford and immediately picked up Ryan's trail in Savernake Forest just outside Hungerford where he had shot Susan Godfrey as she cleared up after a picnic with her children. Ryan shot her sixteen times but spared the children, aged two and four, leaving them to walk away hand in hand, looking for help.

Bob explored the surrounding forest, a tangle of pine, beech and oak criss-crossed by unmarked lanes. Red puffs of poppies sat in the ripening corn and wood pigeons called. Bob found a crudely made hut of branches, invisible from the road, where Ryan might have been planning to hang out.

We called at the Golden Arrow filling station at Froxfield on the main road to Hungerford. After shooting Mrs Godfrey, Ryan had driven here in his Vauxhall Astra wearing summer clothes – a white shirt and light blue trousers. In his boot was a forest survival kit which included a waterproof jacket, shoulder-holster, rucksack, Balaclava mask, drinking flask, respirator mask, waterproof trousers, kit-bag, NATO-issue poncho-cum-groundsheet, pouch with first-aid kit, underpants, ear mufflers and battledress trousers.

Ryan filled a gallon petrol can and put £15-worth in his car tank. The Asian cashier, Mrs Kakaub Dean, noticed that, as usual, he used pump number two. He was a regular customer, calling every two days. Ryan fumbled in the boot of his car for ages, Mrs Dean told me, then straightened up and faced her through her partition of reinforced glass, firing one shot which went straight through. He walked into the service station and she was on the floor pleading for her life when he fired a further burst at her until his gun jammed. While we talked Bob was busy in the station's video section, noting that the video *First Blood* was on the shelves among a variety of soft-porn and violent videos including *The Terminator* and *Daughter of Emmanuelle*.

As Ryan headed for the town of his birth, Mrs Godfrey's children had been found. Then came the 999 call from the garage. A rural police force, more used to dealing with Saturday night drunks, was about to find itself dealing with the biggest manhunt in its history.

Ryan returned to his home in South View and went upstairs to change. In his bedroom he put on a bandolier of ammunition and a combat jacket with some US army insignia on it. He had never worn these in public before, according to one of the local children we interviewed, although he had left them visible in his car. He did often wear a bandanna and was known locally as "Rambo" but these were clearly special clothes for a special day and he was about to launch a savage massacre.

He killed his mother with four shots of his Kalashnikov, two in her front and, as she fell down, two shots into her back from a distance of four inches. He also killed his black Labrador. He splashed petrol over the living room floor and fired it by blasting the television set, setting the whole house ablaze. Next he pumped ten shots into the petrol tank of his Vauxhall Astra trying, but failing, to set it alight.

Later he went down the line of terraced houses in South View, pumping bullet after bullet in the direction of his neighbours' television sets. The bullets punched holes the size of fists in the brickwork around the windows. He strode out on to the common, unleashing round after round at the grazing cows and playing children. A young girl, Lisa Mildenhall, told us he jogged back to South View like a policeman or a guard. She heard a cracking sound like a cap gun: "I could see he was carrying a great big rifle under his arm as if he was going to fire it. I paused by my front door and he stopped jogging. He was in the centre of our drive. I recognised him as Michael Ryan. I looked straight at his face and he smiled at me. He fixed his eyes on mine then crouched down and aimed the gun at me. I froze by the door and he fired the gun."

Lisa survived four shots but others were not so lucky. He made for the rustic High Street, giving them, in Rambo's words, a war they couldn't believe, and would never forget. A twenty-year-old woman lay dead as he fired indiscriminately at the townsfolk, none of whom he could claim as a friend. He killed fifteen people that day and injured a further fifteen. He had let loose a hundred and nineteen shots, according to a later report by a ballistics expert. Eighty-four were fired from the Kalashnikov and all but one of the remainder from a Beretta. One shot was fired by a 30-calibre MI semi-automatic.

Finally he made for his old school, crouching with gun in hand, US combat-style, being shadowed by a police helicopter. The police surrounded the school. He went to the top classroom and tied a white handkerchief to the end of the barrel of his Kalashnikov before throwing it out of the window. He repeatedly asked Sergeant Brightwell, who was trying to communicate with him, what had happened to his mother. "I didn't mean to kill her, it was a mistake," he shouted. "I just wish I'd stayed in bed." He asked the sergeant to give his dog a decent burial. Minutes later there was a muffled shot from the school and he died by his own hand from a single shot of a Beretta tied to his wrist.

The inquest jury returned a verdict of unlawful killing on each of the fifteen people. Ryan's motives were a mystery. The police later concluded that they had made no progress on the issue of motive and it might never be known.

After spending a day interviewing as many eyewitnesses as we could find in Hungerford, Bob and I went to a hotel and, together with the video of *First Blood* for which we found a VCR, we drew clear parallels between that and what we had learned about Ryan. There was a strong, detailed relationship between his actions and the film and we finally filed the story, The Man Who Thought He Was Rambo, which appeared in the *Sunday Telegraph* the next day. We argued you could clearly see Ryan's motives within the context of the film. Everything became clear when you saw the film (which was not, in fact, shown to the inquest jury). Our main points were:

Forest survival techniques: both Ryan and Rambo were experts in forest survival. Had Ryan made it back to Savernake Forest there is no telling how long he might have survived there. Certainly the elaborate survival equipment in his car boot suggested he had long been preparing for this. He had begun his murderous rampage in a forest and throughout the massacre there were clear echoes of the film.

The dress: Ryan walked around in military gear like Rambo. He had been photographed wearing an army camouflage hat and owned an army helmet. Both wore thin beards. Both wore combat jackets. There remained some dispute about the bandanna but the teenager we spoke to seemed a reliable witness. Doubt was also expressed on whether he owned a video but Bob and I found a VCR in the ashes of his home. The police thought it so insignificant they threw it away.

The weaponry: Both had similar carbines and both had bandoliers of ammunition slung over their shoulders.

The attacks: Ryan attacked a petrol station just as Rambo had in the film. Again and again Ryan was going for the petrol tanks of cars, clearly hoping to explode them into balls of fire. (Petrochemical explosions are the favourite images in Rambo films.) Ryan fired his own home in the same way as Rambo fired a shop.

The motive: Rambo's attack was revenge against the hick town that rejected him. Ryan had no friends in Hungerford. He, too, felt rejected. Both believed the world had given them a bad deal, both felt victims of "injustice".

Even the final scenes are bizarrely similar, both near the roof, both shadowed by helicopters. Rambo was on the point of blowing himself up when he was finally led meekly away to make many more millions of dollars with the sequels and franchises. Ryan died by his own hand.

There was simply too much confirmatory detail in both these stories for it to be the coincidence the creators of Rambo have since claimed. It is true that no one saw Ryan watch *First Blood* but the overwhelming body of evidence suggested that he had watched it again and again: that his imagination had entered into it as deeply as John Hinckley's had into *Taxi Driver*. Michael Ryan had become Rambo just as certainly as Hinckley had become Travis Bickle. Their imaginations had been taken over by two violent films that had fatally shaped their ideas and behaviour.

Bob had an interesting insight into the endemic violence of our youth culture when he spotted a huge poster for the film *How the West Was Won*, one of the most violent cowboy films ever, on a classroom wall in the school. Ryan had shot himself just a few feet away from it.

My personal interest in this case, of course, was that here again we glimpsed the romantic spirit of modern lawlessness. Here he was again, the alienated superman, a key romantic concept of which we get our first real understanding in the work of Friedrich Nietzsche – "the pagan philosopher with a hammer" – who became God in his own mind, the superman who looked down on suffering humanity like a hills man on the plains. He stood alone, "the only healthy man in a sick universe", while his clarion call that God is dead has echoed through the ages. Throughout his work he sculpted the role of the individual on a giant scale. God was dead precisely because *he*, Nietzsche, was God. In his mind narcissism reached insane proportions. It does not require much of a leap of the imagination to understand Hitler when you have grasped the ideas of Nietzsche.

Perhaps his most important book was *Also sprach Zarathustra*, a rhapsodic and aphoristic attempt to present his whole philosophy. His key ideas were based on the concept of Pure Will, untrammelled by the demands of reason. There was also the Will to Power: "The strongest and highest will to life does not lie in the puny struggle to exist, but in the Will to War, the Will to Power ..."

In *Also sprach Zarathustra*, he gave these concepts life and form, sketching the character of a new superman – super-prophet, super-hero, super-warrior – who would freely exercise the demands of his own will and only develop the greatness in himself. So Zarathustra, a preacher of extremes, extolled people to be either saints or sinners; to do anything except be mediocre.

"Where is the lightning to lick you with its tongues? Where is the frenzy with which you must be infected? Behold, I teach you the Superman, he is the lightning, he is the frenzy ..."

So the superman stood alone, the perfect embodiment of the individual whose frenzy was going to remake the world by whatever means available. He was the only healthy man in a sick universe and, if necessary, he would die alone.

The only snag was that Nietzsche was already suffering from tertiary syphilis and spent the last eleven years of his life writing books such as *Why I Am So Clever* and *Why I Write Such Excellent Books*. He signed his letters Caesar and the King of Naples until he finally died in Weimar on August 25, 1900 at the age of sixty five.

But his superman did not die with him and was to make a healthy and profitable home in our modern film industry.

If we were looking for a moment when the superman stepped into contemporary culture we could do worse than pick 1962 when Ursula Andress emerged from the sea into the arms of Sean Connery and, in *Dr No*, the superman fantasy of James Bond began.

In a phenomenally successful series which the producers were to describe as "sex and sadism for the whole family" we followed the fortunes of this snobby, invincible public school hero as he killed people and blew smoke off his gun, casually and callously seduced beautiful women, wandered through society with a "licence to kill", responsible only to M and his own desires. When not bedding women or drinking vodka martinis "shaken not stirred" this superstud assassin was destroying Blofeld's high-tech armies or blowing up SPECTRE's headquarters.

The Bond superman changed the whole concept of the English hero. He presided over the eclipse of the gentlemanly ethic including the ideals of service and courtesy to women. He was to herald a new movement in the cinema: the glorification of cold-blooded killing. Vicious and thoughtless, his only aim was self-gratification.

But there was a sense in which the Bond series redeemed itself by audacity and wit. Bond was parodic, uncomplicated and flamboyantly heroic. In other hands, however, this notion of the wise-cracking superman was to change and we began to see the spiralling growth of bloody violence on our screens and the promotion of the psychopathic outsider who spits on society's rules; the lawless superman who rides the range with a permanent erection and murder in his heart.

Bonnie and Clyde was the story of two young killers – "They're young, they're in love and they kill people" – that, in the year Martin Luther King was assassinated, won an Oscar. These perpetual adolescents, recognising no authority, killed people for money, fleeing by car until they were themselves killed. The Western had turned into the modern gangster film.

A new wave of films followed, including *Butch Cassidy and the Sundance Kid* and *Easy Rider*, in which America and her values were seen from the outlaw's point of view and rejected. Sam Peckinpah's *The Wild Bunch* was another degradation of women and contained slow motion ballets of orgiastic violence. In defence of his work this gonzo romantic argued that it was necessary to show violence in order to condemn it, an argument with which many directors persist to this day.

Sergio Leone made his Dollars trilogy of spaghetti Westerns in the mid-Sixties and, in them, Clint Eastwood began his rise to key icon in our culture. He was the bounty hunter with no name, cheroot in mouth and perpetually squinting into the sunlight. Everyone was gunned down in bursts of operatic violence and this creation of the invincible superman became its most studied in *High Plains Drifter* when Eastwood is the unkempt stranger deputed to protect everyone from an approaching gang. He appoints a dwarf as sheriff, casually dynamites the hotel and arranges for the town to be painted red and re-named Hell. When the gang turns up he allows them to fire and slaughter everyone before he puts paid to them. There is barely any dialogue and he shows no motive or emotion for his savage killings. With the whole town smouldering rubble he rides off into the sunset.

Eastwood followed the Dollars trilogy with the influential *Dirty Harry*, in which we meet the lone Inspector Callahan, scripting solo dreams of power and revenge.

In 1976, Michael Winner began his *Death Wish* series in which Charles Bronson, as yet another vigilante, kills muggers in random revenge for the murder of his wife. The same year produced *Taxi Driver*.

All these vigilante films produced hundreds of imitations; all came dealing sudden death in order to make the world a better place to live in ... *Robo-Cop*, *Predator*, *Die Hard*, *Scarface*, *Dillinger* ... and I was standing in the small market town of Hungerford looking at the grey ashes of a burned-out house with an army helmet and a VCR poking up out of it, undoubtedly the work of Rambo, the most violent man in the world.

Our piece on *Rambo* caused a satisfying uproar in which everybody wanted to get involved, and I wrote a few further features for the *Sunday Telegraph* in which I described the video industry as "rotten to the core" and inquired why it was so whole-heartedly engaged in this relentless pursuit of murder, violence and death.

Predictably, the British Videogram Association, as it was then called, under the directorship of Norman Abbott, responded vigorously. "All our videos are carefully certificated," Abbott wrote in a lengthy letter to the editor, Peregrine Worsthorne, "to ensure that they are not supplied to persons below the ages of fifteen or eighteen." They rented out nothing excessively horrific or violent and furthermore the video industry couldn't possibly be rotten to the core because it organised charity days and raised vast sums of money for children's homes. The most popular of their rentals was comedy followed by pop or rock music.

An outline of their charitable aims was cut from Mr Abbott's published letter, causing him to complain to the Press Council.

Then Prince Charles stepped into the fray in a speech at the opening of the Museum of the Moving Image in London. He condemned those responsible for "the excessive menu of gratuitous violence on television and video". Expressing concern on behalf of all those with children, he rejected as nonsense the argument of those who "defend their so-called art by claiming to portray the actuality of real life" and was equally dismissive of those who maintained that the viewer could always switch off the television.

"If you claim that a diet of violence is likely to have some effect on the way that some people behave then you are told that there is no proof that this has any effect. But this is palpable nonsense. It is a trick used by experts to confuse us and what we are seeing with our own eyes. It is high time someone told these experts that, like the emperor with his new clothes, they are wearing nothing at all."

These invigorating words led to a further chorus of pain and outrage from the television and video industries and Michael Winner was again wheeled in to serve up yet more of his self-serving claptrap: there's far more violence in Shakespeare etc. I had called Michael Winner a prat in one of my articles and, after a little thought, the *Telegraph* lawyer said it was all right because Winner so evidently *was* a prat.

While we waited for a date for the Press Council hearing and the British Videogram Association continued fuming because the *Telegraph* still wouldn't publish its lengthy letters about its widespread charitable activities there was another shooting at Higham Ferrers, a small village in Northamptonshire. This wasn't another Hungerford, but people were seriously injured and there was the same set of fingerprints all over the case, as I found when I went to investigate it, again for the *Sunday Telegraph*.

Darren Fowler, aged sixteen, had been expelled from the Higham Ferrers School the previous October. On an autumn morning in 1987, he walked to the school with his best friend, Simon Bates, as he had often before, leaving him at the school gates. Bates said that his mood had been normal and he could offer no explanation for what happened later in the day.

Fowler returned home and, during the morning, was interviewed by a worker from the support unit in nearby Rushden, which had helped him since his expulsion. At noon he still seemed normal, according to Bates, and they went back to watch a video. The film was *Critters*, a rather bloodthirsty and, at times, frightening story of a small group of monsters, a little like hedgehogs with huge teeth, who arrive in a spaceship and attack a family in their home. Amid the grisly carnage a young boy takes his father's shotgun and kills most of them.

By 3.15pm Fowler had changed and put on a donkey jacket with a wolf's tail hanging from it. He took out a single-barrel shotgun that belonged to his father, slung a cartridge belt bandolier-style across his shoulder and strapped a knife to his thigh. He also had a second hunting knife and a length of nylon rope. For trapping rabbits if he had to take to the forest, he later explained.

At 3.25pm he entered the schoolyard. Seconds later the first shot rang out – aimed at the window of the staff room where, just moments earlier, teacher Jane Cousins had been looking out. She ducked but the window glass imploded over her. Fowler started shooting wildly at the buildings, peppering the woodwork and brick-work before making for the science block. He searched the building, but it was not clear who or what he was looking for.

At 3.30pm, just after the bell rang for the end of the school day, deputy headmaster Michael Cousins and a mass of pupils were entering the quadrangle as Fowler came out of the science block. Seconds later Fowler fired again and hit Mr Cousins in the face, neck and chest. Two pupils, twelve-year-old Simon Druce and Ronald Sherratt, were also wounded in the face.

Meanwhile Paul Greenall, head of boys' PE at school, had begun stalking Fowler, waiting for the gun to be fired before rugby tackling him from behind and bringing him to the ground.

Following Fowler's trial at Oxford Crown Court and my own inquiries, I built a clearer picture of him. He was not a loner as he spent a lot of time with another youth, Cliff Phillips, and his best friend, Simon Bates, with whom he shared a common interest in weaponry, military and forest survival magazines like *Nam* and watching violent videos. I never traced the source of Fowler's videos but discovered Simon Bates was a registered member of the Video Box in nearby Rushden. "Simon only liked films with two stars," the manageress told me. "One was Sylvester Stallone and the other Arnold Schwarzenegger." In the window was a poster advertising the film *War Zone*: "It doesn't matter who you kill as long as you kill someone."

In school Fowler was a despised and rejected youth, weedy, with long mousy hair. He was often called "Smelly" or "the Gypsy". One pupil told me he would often walk around the playground on his own, muttering to himself, believing that everyone had it in for him. He knew almost every detail of the Hungerford massacre, it emerged at his trial, where he was ordered to be detained for life.

Fowler is so inarticulate we will probably never know what was on his mind that day. But we do know he watched all the Rambo films and that, in the manner of his dress and his interest in forest survival, he was trying to emulate his hero. There was the common element of revenge against those who had rejected him. We also know that there was a storm of violent imagery fresh in his mind on the day of the shooting after watching *Critters*. On Simon Bates' account Fowler became increasingly agitated as the film progressed, constantly turning and winking at him.

His parents refused to speak to me, as did the school. Fowler's solicitor did speak to me, but was not sure the Rambo films were an influence although she added that she had never seen one. This is important since, if you have not seen these films, the pictorial symbolism – as it has come to live and work in such immature imaginations – isn't significant.

In his *Film Guide* Leslie Halliwell described *First Blood* as: "socially irresponsible. There are enough nuts out there without giving them someone to cheer on."

Just days later, there was another shooting. On September 11, Anthony Haskett, aged eighteen, a former Territorial Army cadet, rampaged through the streets of Walsall after a nightclub drinking session. Armed with a 12-bore shotgun and wearing a bandolier of seventy-six cartridges Haskett returned and yelled racial abuse before shooting three black youths and threatening others. As the police moved in he put the gun to his chin and killed himself.

Senior police officers described the shooting as a "mini-Hungerford" and Superintendent Martin Burton of the West Midlands force said: "I think he was trying to be Rambo". The police revealed that the contents of his bedroom included a crossbow, airguns, knives, a machete, a balaclava, a starting pistol and camouflage paste. There was also a book, *Military Small Arms and Assault Weapons* and, on the walls, pictures of Rambo.

Other stories arising from mad dogs of the video age had already burst into the news. In 1984 James Huberty had walked into the McDonald's in San Ysidro, Southern California, wearing a Rambo kit of black T-shirt and camouflage gear and shot dead twenty people and wounded twenty more. Seven months before the massacre he had lost his job as a welder in Ohio and had moved to California where he lost another job as a condominium guard.

The day he was sacked he took his family to the zoo then went home, put on his Rambo kit and walked into the San Ysidro McDonald's with a semi-automatic rifle, a shotgun and a hand gun. When he was shot by a police marksman he still had a bag full of armour piercing bullets.

In August 1987 Julian Knight, a nineteen-year-old from Melbourne, Australia, had crouched beside the road in his suburban neighbourhood, picking off pedestrians and motorists as they passed. Six people were killed and eighteen injured before he ran out of ammunition and was arrested, dressed in full military gear and armed with a pump-action shotgun and two semi-automatic rifles.

Knight's life was characterised by failure. He was a dropout from the Royal Military College of Duntroon, the Australian equivalent of Sandhurst or West Point, where his army officer father had trained. At school Knight's nickname was Sof, for soldier of fortune. Slightly built he always wore military fatigues and was teased as a wimp.

Another dragon's tooth of violence sprang out of the ground in Stockton, California in January 1989. James Purdy, aged twenty-six, while wearing a bullet-proof jacket, a bandolier of ammunition, a camouflage vest and earplugs, attacked Cleveland Elementary School. He was carrying two handguns and a Russian AK47 automatic Kalashnikov complete with a banana clip of ammunition and a bayonet.

First he set fire to his car by shooting at three cans of petrol in it and then went to the school playground – where seventy per cent of the children were Vietnamese – killed five pupils and wounded thirty others before shooting himself in the head with his own handgun. (In *First Blood, Part Two* Rambo penetrates the jungles of Vietnam and slaughters hundreds of Vietnamese.)

Similar shootings have continued throughout the world to this day. After Hungerford I began keeping a record of them: now it has become the size of a small book and includes cuttings on Dunblane and the Columbine school massacre where the clear romantic outline of our modern man of lawlessness emerges again and again. Analyse these shootings long enough and you will see his outline every time and begin to understand his intention to destroy the world. We glimpse the same echoes of the same sturdy superman, given to introspection and outbursts of massive violence, seeing the world as sick and hoping it can be re-moulded – even cured – by his own intense criminality.

The world ubiquity of Rambo is vividly evoked by Brian Keenan in his *An Evil Cradling*, an account of his hostage years in Beirut. "The man unresolved in himself chooses, as men have done through history, to take up arms against his sea of troubles. He carries his Kalashnikov on his arm, his hand stuck in the waistband of his trousers, a belt of bullets around his shoulders. I had seen so many men in Beirut thus attired, their weapons hanging from them and glistening in the sun. The guns were symbols of potency. The men were dressed as caricatures of Rambo. Many of them wore a headband tied and knotted on the side above the ear, just as the character in the movies had done. It is a curious paradox that this Rambo figure, this all-American hero, was the stereotype which these young Arab revolutionaries had adopted. They had taken on the cult figure of the Great Satan they so despised and who they claimed was responsible for all the evil in the world and simultaneously rid themselves of an inadequacy they would never admit.

"I saw a war film once here and as each character pulled out a weapon and began firing furiously, the young Arabs around us would groan and moan in a kind of ecstasy, crying out the names of the weapons. All around is in the cinema we could hear the words 'Kalashnikov, Kalashnikov, Beretta, Beretta.' These young men knew the names of every type of gun, even the names of the mortars and rocket-launchers. The cinema rang with the chant of excited worship."

So is the link between the killings and the fiction anything more than anecdotal?

Yes, says Dr David Hill, a clinical psychologist with Mind, the mental health charity. It must be more than a coincidence that the men dressed exactly like Rambo and carried his kind of weapons. There was a copycat element in the link. The films give people the props and methods for their outrages.

Well no, say the creators. Sylvester Stallone was particularly miffed by any suggestion that these films might lead to real-life violence. Rambo does not exist, he said. He's only a mythical comic book character. This is just *movies*. They do not have a bad influence on people. They are made to entertain.

"It is so unfair when Rambo gets blamed for every lunatic who lets loose with a gun," Stallone cried. "It is the height of irresponsibility to link Rambo with real-life maniacs. If Rambo was a real person he could have a field day in court suing for libel. He has never gone on an unprovoked rampage against innocent citizens and he has never been shown to be mentally deranged. Sure he is isolated and depressed, but he is not psychotic. He is just an angry war veteran. Nothing more. There has never been any proven link between my films and these acts of violence."

The Press Council hearing on December 6, 1988, in their offices off Fleet Street, gave a salutary and even frightening insight into the kind of people who were running our video industry which, in Britain alone, turned over some £700 million a year in cassette rentals.

On my side I had Ian Watson, deputy editor of the *Sunday Telegraph*, and on the other the British Videogram Association represented by its director general Mr John Abbott; Mr John Gray, their chief fund-raiser for the National Children's Homes, and Mr Graham Bright MP whose Private Member's Bill became the Video Recordings Act 1984.

As we trooped into the chamber we found ourselves in front of a dozen people, including one woman, sitting behind a long bench, looking at us. We were invited to sit at separate tables at the far end from them.

Mr Abbott opened the proceedings by saying that he had been up all night reading a transcript of the Hungerford inquest and there had been nothing in it which implicated them or *First Blood* in the massacre as I had alleged. He had also brought along a cassette of *First Blood* to show them if they wanted. The main points of his opening remarks were that, far from being "corrupt" and "rotten" as I had claimed, they had developed a clean, well-regulated industry in which all their titles were certificated by the film censor with the clearest possible descriptions of the contents on the cassette. He also referred to our old friend "the catharsis theory" which, although stamped on by every side, continues to raise its deranged little head.

(On this theory Dr Wertham, a New York consultant psychiatrist, said, "This outlet theory is not only overdone: it is false. It is pseudo-scientific dogma. There is not a shred of clinical evidence for it. On the contrary the children are overexcited without being given an adequate release. Delinquent behaviour is not prevented, but promoted." Another survey of consultant psychiatrists by the Royal College of Psychiatry discovered that not a single psychiatrist believed that the viewing of scenes of extreme violence would enable a person to live out a horrific experience in fantasy or imagination and thus prevent them from carrying out such an act in reality.)

Furthermore, Mr Abbott continued, this "clean, well-regulated" industry gave vast sums each year to charity and happily complied with the 1984 Video Recordings Act which had set up a certification system for all videos for sale and hire which had also helped to clear out some thirty nine "nasties" which included *Driller Killer, Evil Dead* and *I Spit On Your Grave*. The best-selling video of all time, he said, was *Watch with Mother*. All this was hardly consonant with an industry which was "rotten to the core".

Mr Abbott called his two main witnesses. Mr John Gray of the National Children's Homes was fulsome in his support of the video industry, saying that in the years 1987 and 1988 the BVA had given them £600,000. In cross-examination he declared that he was quite happy with this amount which I had described in my own submission as being evidence of the most "staggering miserliness" particularly as the industry's total income for that period was well in excess of £700m. Mr Gray added that some of the officials from the video industry had even come down and run a stall at one of their charitable fêtes.

Mr Graham Bright MP said that what I had portrayed was wrong since the video industry was trying to bring in self-regulation and had shown nothing other than co-operation with his Bill. Since the Bill had become law the video "nasties" had disappeared from the shelves and now the industry did not put out anything illegal. "Any video containing gratuitous violence has been outlawed." He added that children had been doubly protected.

I was hardly able to believe we were speaking the same language. Were we talking about the same society even? Maybe we were all from different planets? *All gratuitous violence had been outlawed? The children had been doubly protected?* Was it possible I was going to a different video shop to everyone else? What about the NSPCC research that showed that even the youngest children had gained access to 18-certificated videos? What about the list of the current top sixty video rentals I had brought with me, borrowed from my local video shop? Was there no gratuitous violence in the number one that week, *Robocop*, the story of a mechanised Rambo who embarks on a relentless and non-stop orgy of violence? Was there no gratuitous violence in almost forty others featuring violence and sudden death in the top sixty? Who was kidding whom here?

At the start of my cross-examination of Mr Abbott I tried to clarify what his industry's view was on the effects of screen violence. In his original complaint about me to the Press Council he had said that the *Sunday Telegraph* had "published an unfair article about the effect of violent videos". Now in a second and more detailed submission their position seemed to have changed to a more Olympian stance. "The BVA does not claim that violence in films has no effect in real life. Nor have we ever argued to the contrary. We do note, however, that for every expert and every research project that supports one side of the argument, another can be found to support the other – all with equal-sounding authority and conviction."

So what was the BVA's position? That any form of art can promote any form of good or evil, I suppose. Was he aware that *every* research project both here and in America had found a link between televised and social violence? No, he was not. Could he name any of these experts who had denied there was a link? No, he hadn't come prepared for that kind of discussion. Just the name perhaps of *one* expert? No.

He had made much of the video certification system but did he know that, according to research done by the NSPCC, fifty per cent of all children between the ages of seven and seventeen had seen an 18-rated video? No. Did he know that forty-three per cent of these children had seen at least four? No. Did this seem like protection or, as Mr Bright put it, double protection? He wasn't sure. Did he have any children? He had two grown-up children and two young grandchildren. Would he want his grandchildren to see any of these films? No. Their parents would stop them from seeing those rated 15 and 18. Would all parents protect their children in this way? Responsible parents would. Are all parents responsible? He couldn't speak for them.

I then referred to their new releases and asked if he had seen *Killer Klowns from Outer Space?* No. *Scumbusters?* No. I then moved onto the top ten of video rentals for November 14 which he had supplied, with clear satisfaction, with his own submission. Had he seen *Lost Boys* which was number thirteen? No. He had listed it as a U when it was 15-rated. That was a mistake. Had he any idea what it was about? No. Would he believe me if I told him it was about dope-smoking vampires? No reply. Number four was *The Untouchables*. Had he seen it? No. Would he believe me if I told him it was about gangsters and that, in one scene, Al Capone smashes a man's head with a baseball bat and murders him on a dinner table? A shrug of the shoulders. Number five *Stakeout?* No. What about *Black Widow?* No. Did he know that it was about a woman who married a series of men and killed them for their money? Is it? It is. And did he know that his number ten, *Someone to Watch Over Me*, begins with a man being repeatedly stabbed in the chest and throat? Really?

It did not bode well then did it that, in your top ten, in a list supplied by yourself, you have films about witchcraft, vampirism, gangsterism, serial murder and psychopathic knifemen? No reply. It is also not encouraging, is it, that you haven't seen a single one of them yourself? Again no reply.

I moved on from the top ten that the BVA had supplied and produced a list of the current top sixty video rentals that my video shop had given me. I asked him if he had seen the number one, *Robocop*. He had not. Number three, *Predator?* No. *Flowers in the Attic?* No. *Death Wish 4 – The Crackdown?* No. Was he aware that Leslie Halliwell, in his film guide, had described *Death Wish 2* as a badly made exercise in the most repellent acts of violence? No he was not. Had he seen *Retribution?* No. Did he know it was one long splurge of horror? What about *Witchcraft?* No, he hadn't seen that either.

At this point Mr Abbott complained to the chairman who interrupted me saying I had made my point. I withdrew after telling them that, of the top sixty rentals that week, around thirty-five were exceedingly violent and a further eight were horror. (One in five rented videos are horror.)

Later in my summing-up I defined the word "rotten" as being decomposed, morally, socially and politically corrupt, disagreeable, impure. I further defined the core of any industry as being its product. On this evidence, I argued, it was both fair and right to describe the video industry as being "rotten to the core". Mr Abbott had come along to defend his industry but had brought no arguments with him. In all aspects of research into violence on our screens he had admitted he knew nothing. He could not name one expert who had denied there was a link between violence on the screen and real life. Furthermore we had established he had not even seen the films he had come to defend. These films represented a blizzard of violence blowing through our land. Their key themes were terror, vengeance, murder and death.

Mr Abbott declined to sum up and the hearing was over. His two main witnesses had left so, with Ian Watson, we went to a pub in Fleet Street where, after all the nasty things I had said about his industry, he bought us a pint. Soon the three of us were chatting on first name terms in the most cordial manner and he struck me as a decent, civilised man who would no more watch one of his violent videos than he would start a fight in that bar. Somehow he had got caught up in something which he knew little about and, inheriting the traditional time-worn arguments and ideas of the video industry and those who made those wretched films, just got on with defending them without thinking about or questioning them overmuch. He was, in short, just doing his job.

The Press Council rejected the complaint against me and the *Sunday Telegraph*. But, in the wake of Prince Charles's strictures and the Press Council adjudication, did that lead to any modification of the video industry's output? Did they make any attempt to prune their diseased list? Did it lead to the withdrawal of *Rambo 3* which was about to be released? Was *Critters* withdrawn? Nothing could be less likely. It was very much business as usual and the only conclusion we can draw from their unwillingness to do anything was because their overriding consideration was the overriding power of money. A £700m a year turnover was simply not enough.

Yet, apart from the quest for money, we can also witness here the falsity and lies that are at the very heart of our Man of Lawlessness' activities, particularly in the video industry which has clearly become one of his many homes. We see how he can overcome reason and deny the evidence of hard fact. On the issue of violence on our screens every body of research has come out against his activities but what does he do? Nothing. He ignores it and carries on as before, making violent sequel after violent sequel for the cinema and video industries while ensuring that in both Britain and America there is an act of violence every sixteen minutes on television screens with a murder every half an hour.

When Prince Charles attacked "this incessant menu of gratuitous violence" what happened? Precisely nothing. The following month produced another avalanche of violent videos.

FIFTY ONE

Around this time a few of my close friends had got into serious difficulties with their drinking. Their marriages had broken up and two of them found themselves homeless. I didn't think that I drank too much as it happened; I could take a few days off it now and again, albeit accompanied by the dull ache of withdrawal. I was firmly with Dylan Thomas, who defined an alcoholic as someone you didn't like who drank more than you. Alcoholism only happened to other people but one day, in absolute despair at what was happening to my friends – not myself! – I went to an AA meeting and to this day consider climbing those stairs at Llandaff Road Chapel in Cardiff my one and only truly intelligent act.

I had gone to this same chapel as a youth (I had even been baptised by total immersion there) and still had a stack of Bibles to verify my regular attendances at Sunday school (until about the age of thirteen when I became more preoccupied with girls). The smell in the side hallway was much the same as it always had been – floor polish, damp overcoats, hint of urine from the men's lavatory – and, upstairs, I sidled into a small, smoke-filled room with thirty people and took a chair at the back. The majority were elderly but there were a few middle-aged and young, some women and, at the main table, a beaming chairman who sat under a huge scroll which outlined the twelve steps of AA. The only qualification for membership was a desire to stop drinking, said one of them.

Most of those present seemed grateful to be sober and some talked of their sobriety as a precious possession they wouldn't give up for all the rugby balls in Wales. Sobriety had made them free and whole again, given them back their lives. These were new ideas in a new language for me and I listened intently, enthralled by their humour, candour and self-effacement. Most of them had no false pride: they had lost that in some gutter years ago. Many seemed happy just to be sitting there; this was their club, their meeting place.

It was indeed not unlike being in a good pub without the beer and at one stage a woman joined us and sat at the back knitting. When asked if she had anything to say she explained she was only there because she enjoyed the stories. We had a good laugh about that but the chairman pointed out this wasn't an entertainment and asked her to leave.

They were, however, clearly making up for their lack of alcohol by smoking themselves to an early death and you often had to peer through a deadly fug. "At least with the fags I'm only hurting *myself*," was the way they thought about it.

"When I was drinking I was hurting everyone."

Most were ordinary people who didn't understand what was happening to them until it was almost too late and they had found AA and pulled back. They had concealed their problem from their families, bosses and most crucially themselves, tippling consistently, often first thing in the morning in their locked bathrooms, knowing their health, marriages and families were under threat but never accepting that the booze was responsible for their multiplying woes.

In one routine meeting there might be the odd priest, a few doctors, a lot of businessmen, a journalist or three, a couple of poets and any number of actors. Half of Equity was in AA and anyone who watched television regularly or went to the cinema would recognise more than a few faces as soon as he walked in. Anthony Hopkins attended Llandaff Road Chapel in the early days of his recovery. You're not supposed to identify anyone in AA, or admit you're in it yourself – but Hopkins never attempted to conceal his membership. He believed it would help other sufferers if they knew what he had gone through.

Wholehearted acceptance of their alcoholism, said to affect one in thirteen of the population, was the first and vital step to recovery. The next step was to learn, one day at a time, not to pick up a drink. Don't pick up that first drink and you won't get drunk. Regular attendance at meetings was also urged, particularly during your first thirty days, and it was all as simple as that because what you heard in meetings changed the way you thought about drink and yourself.

It is worth repeating that I still didn't believe I had a drink problem and had only gone to those rooms in frustration that I couldn't get my mates to go. I was fine, thank you very much. Of course my hands shook like a pair of rogue butterflies unless I had a drink in me and the first thing I did every morning – even after my occasional day off the drink – was take a long puke into the lavatory pan. Drinking excessively was just one of the hazards of being a writer. Writers needed drink, lots of it, particularly Welsh writers: excessive drinking was central to their art and national heritage. But I still wasn't an alcoholic. I recognised drink as a part of my art and national heritage, that was all. I could deal with people in drink too, particularly those who got on my nerves. You can put up with a lot of crap when you've got enough alcohol inside you.

I attended meetings almost every night for two weeks, not saying much myself but listening to the "shares" and enjoying many of them. But the freshness of those early nights soon wore off because various members repeated themselves. Most were too polite to point this out so we were expected to suffer in stoic silence as someone droned on in the same monotone about his problems with his aunty who kept making jam tarts for him all the time. When was she going to understand that he didn't like her bloody jam tarts?

We put up with his woes, someone explained to me, because sitting through boring confessions was part of our recovery. We were learning tolerance, we who had been the very beacons of intolerance and for whom every other adjective was "touchy". We were shedding those old defects of character which had made us drunks in the first place, addressing the very roots of our alcoholism.

From time to time there were moments of almost intense religiosity in that room.

St Paul refers to the fellowship of suffering and sometimes I fancied there was the same feeling of healing excitement there as when the early Christians met to encourage one another and pray in hidden catacombs in Rome.

There were times when we sat in long silences on the edge of our seats reaching out to touch broken individuals who had fallen into our midst, sweating, hardly daring to breathe as we offered him a way of escaping the prison in which he had locked himself. These were silent times of Quaker prayer, listening to one another's breaking hearts as our own quickened with God's love. I experienced greater moments of holiness in that room than anything I had ever felt in any normal church.

Although I hadn't realised it yet, this healing process had begun happening to me. I would hear one speaker complaining that his real problem with drink was that he so often ended up in a strange bed with an even stranger woman who was often not even remotely attractive. That had happened to me often enough, but I had never seen it as a consequence of drink. I had always thought of it as inevitable in a super-virile Welsh writer, even if I did always wake up in the grip of a black hangover, depression and disgust.

Another speaker told how his health had failed almost completely and I sat bolt upright when he mentioned that he started every day with a long puke. Such remarks could set off a whizzing chain reaction in my own mind and memory. I recalled an earlier severe bout of illness which had almost seen me off; how my vision often went blurry even when I hadn't been drinking and the nagging stress of an ulcer which had once exploded into mouthfuls of blood and, after a few quiet years, was now back and throbbing as intensely as ever.

All these ailments, I now know, were the result of excessive drinking. How many more ailments did I want? How many more would I survive? How many more breakdowns in my health did I need before I accepted that I had a drink problem? Suddenly life was giving me an awful lot to think about and my mind began making new connections that only a few weeks earlier I would have blotted out with half a bottle of Scotch. Drunks don't think. They've nothing to think with. They just get ill and fall over.

But I still refused to admit my alcoholic condition. I could give it up any time, me. All I was doing in this room was trying to find a way to control my drinking. When I had it firmly under control, I could start again. I would get myself better so I could make myself ill again. The tissues of lies we manage to wrap ourselves in is staggering. "Stinking thinking", they call it in AA. But I *was* making progress and I *had* stopped drinking and I was *still* sitting in that smoke-filled room every night listening to the truths of others while continuing to tell lies to myself.

I don't know when AA finally broke me and I accepted my alcoholism. There was no searing epiphany and I hadn't kept any sort of diary. Yet I could feel something happening to me particularly when a speaker said something that chimed coldly with my experience.

It may have been prompted by the woman who one night said that she had become sick and tired of being sick and tired, another popular AA cliché. This one resonated deeply with me as I recalled those hopeless mornings when I had sat at the breakfast table, red-eyed after my early morning puke, staring down the long point-lessness of yet another day until it was time to pick up yet another drink and I would start feeling all right again. Oh yes, I was sick and tired of feeling sick and tired. I would give anything not to feel sick and tired any more, to sit at the breakfast table feeling fine and maybe even able to eat a little breakfast. It had been many years since I had done that.

Only then did the penny drop. All these suffering people had been telling *their* stories but they were really telling *mine*. The precise words and circumstances may have been different but we were telling the same story: our sorry addiction, our powerlessness to deal with it, our self-imprisonment. I couldn't escape because I wouldn't understand what it was that had imprisoned me. I hadn't seen it because I kept denying it was there. Other poor bastards might be locked in an alcoholic prison, but not me. I could give it up any time.

I had never hidden a bottle under a cushion and sat on it, refusing to answer the door whenever anyone called. But there had been serious deteriorations in my health and, of course, an ever-emptying pocket. My colleagues in AA kept holding up mirror images to me and it became impossible to deny that I was engaged in a destructive habit. I was as seriously alcoholic as them but still denying it more vig-orously than most.

I had gone to AA convinced that it was out of concern at the plights of my friends when subconsciously I was only concerned with myself. I couldn't even tell the truth to myself. Alcoholics always face up to any issue with a lie. The truth is too painful to handle.

Acceptance of your most basic failure is hard, almost the hardest thing under heaven. But I *was* recognising myself and I *was* getting there: I *was* seeing that for almost all my life drink had been taking me to places I should never have gone. After several months in AA and a few "slips", which didn't add up to more than a few beers, I began taking my first faltering steps on the road to recovery.

At every meeting we reminded one another of the truths we had dug up. Alcohol destroys all love and every relationship. We are always one drink away from being a drunk. Drink will reduce you to the rags on your back and pretty soon it will reach out and even take them. You do not say you have given up drink forever, merely that you are not going to pick up a drink *today*. Your alcoholism is something you will carry with you all your life: you may be sober today but you will never be relieved of your alcoholism: it will always be there at your shoulder encouraging you to pick up another glass.

There was an element of brainwashing in the meetings as we repeated these truths to one another like Buddhist mantras. But they worked. We *were* getting bet-ter. Some fell off their perches, but we were always ready to go to their homes to find them, often weeping and take them back to their "real home, their real family", to sit them back down on those little wooden Sunday School chairs, give them a fag and talk to them some more. Is this what you really want? Do you really want to go through all that again? Haven't you drunk enough?

I was becoming a new man. Almost the first thing that happened was my hands stopped shaking and I could hold a cup of tea without spilling it. Sleep was difficult for the first month or so, but I began getting a good eight hours and waking up fresh, no longer having to start the day with a long, hard puke. My eyes were clear and when I put my hand in my pocket I often found money in it.

I was getting calmer too, not so prone to blowing up over nothing as I had in the old hangover days. I began to think more before I spoke and, after I had thought, walk away. We react to all kinds of silly things when hungover, often stupidly and pointlessly.

The AA people were certainly good company and we often went to one another's homes for meals or spent a few hours rowing on Roath Park lake. I found their company fun and no longer cared to go to "normal" parties where everyone drank. It was all right for the first hour or so but then, almost always at the same time, everyone began talking rubbish very loudly and I had to practically run home with my hands clamped over my ears.

There was something of a strain on my own marriage however: Liz felt she was becoming isolated from my new pals and had no intention of giving up drinking. My body was also having strange long-term problems coming to terms with the lack of drink: parts of me would often go stiff when they should have been flabby, while others stayed flabby when they should have been stiff. My performance in bed had become well below par and when I complained about that in meetings, they said it would soon brighten up and get better than ever. But when? I didn't want to be the only man in AA whose marriage fell apart *after* he had got sober.

Liz never said as much, but she was finding my new persona boring. I even started entertaining the dark suspicion that she hadn't minded all that bad behaviour of my drinking days: that she had even in some strange way found it entertaining. "Who says sadomasochism doesn't work?" she had once written on a Valentine card to me. This theory helped to explain why she had stuck with me: there can't have been any other reason why she hadn't at least thrown something when I crawled in at the crack of dawn covered in dried blood after a cocaine session in a neighbour's house and claiming I had forgotten my own address. I'd long given up trying to understand my marriage anyway.

But now in my sobriety I was absolutely determined it was going to work and, besides, she made me happy. If I did have to start drinking again to keep it together that's exactly what I would do. But, just for today, I was sober.

St Paul told the Romans to free themselves from the world and let their minds be remade and their nature transformed. He saw how we are governed by our ideas and how, if we change them, we can change ourselves. The way in which we are controlled by ideas – often false ones which we have carelessly picked up without looking at them properly – has been a recurring theme of this memoir and, at a time when I really needed it and had started faltering badly, AA came along and changed mine. Not only did the fellowship undermine my old drunken personality and modify a lot of my character defects but it also began showing me new possibilities in a faith with which I had been struggling almost all my life but not actively embracing as I should. I always knew I had never been up to scratch as a Christian and here now surely was a real chance. You simply can't be a true disciple if you are a drunk: faith doesn't work that way.

For me it was particularly interesting and even exciting that, in the same chapel where I had taken my first steps into faith as a thirteen-year-old child full of fear, I was now making real strides into it as a fifty-year-old alcoholic full of regrets. But it wasn't a pulpit which was telling me how to turn my life around. It was a programme of recovery run by drunks.

The testimonies in that room had made me face myself. I had forgotten God if only because I was sure he had forgotten me. But here he was back in my life again, holding open the door to a new life, talking to me through others, warm, concerned, insistent that I start doing the right things. You can always do the right things when you get sober: it's one option you can always take. Drinkers seize on a dozen options, most of them wrong. Once you've seen what's wrong with you and accept it you put things right by doing the right things. I *think* that's how AA works anyway.

After years of dawdling along the Path of the Cross I was making some progress along it – and all because I chose the nightly company of a gang of chain-smoking, garrulous alcoholics who had allowed me to share the miracle of their recovery. And it *was* a miracle. I had no doubt about thatl. When I looked at the faces of the people in that room and when I considered the trouble they must have caused between them I knew that we had all been touched by God and that through his grace we had all been given another chance. In the face of all the odds we alcoholics had been born again.

My sobriety ramped up my work rate wonderfully: I soon submitted my completed manuscript of *Fire in the Bay* to Macdonald. I was still keen to work on Welsh themes and planned to set my next novel in New Quay in West Wales when I could tell of the time when Dylan Thomas had stayed there to escape the Second World War and how *Under Milk Wood* had begun coming together in his mind. It would be called *The Secret Sex Life of Polly Garter*.

I had been down to New Quay several times on scouting expeditions, staying at the Black Lion Hotel, one of Dylan's main haunts, and becoming friendly with its owner, Tom Hunter, who introduced me to many local characters including the landlord who had run the pub when Dylan had been there. There was also the balding, grumpy harbour master, who had attended many of Dylan's parties in the small asbestos hut, Majoda, which still sat there overlooking the wonderful sweep of Cardigan Bay and a woman who, it turned out, believed she was the prototype of Polly Garter.

I would live there while I was writing the novel, I decided, to see if I could do *Polly Garter* in the same way I'd done *Black Sunlight*, mooch around the place talking to everyone and letting the spirit of the place leech into my work. A lot of people had enjoyed the gritty atmosphere of *Black Sunlight*, which had pretty much gone missing in *Fire in the Bay*, and I wanted to repeat the performance.

Meanwhile I had been developing a bizarre sub-career as a media pundit, once appearing on Radio Four's *Moral Maze*, when most of the assembled hacks were on their hind legs screaming at me because I argued that the media had become the driving force behind the Troubles in Northern Ireland. They gave me a bruising about that but, yet again, my words later drew a huge and enthusiastic response in letters from the public.

I was becoming increasingly frustrated I couldn't get going in Northern Ireland, couldn't worm my way in there anywhere and explain to them how the media was destroying them. But then, in April 1990, right out of the blue, the Grand Orange Lodge of Northern Ireland asked me to speak to a symposium on the media that they had organised in Belfast. They even offered to print up my speech as a pamphlet, if I sent it in advance, and distribute it to their members.

It was one of those grey days in the city when the symposium's organiser took me and another speaker on a tour of some of the recently bombed buildings in much the same way as a tourist guide might take you around the local castles and museums. We then entered the conference hall packed with three hundred people, not only members of the Lodge but a lot of the local press. The Rev Ian Paisley was there with his son and I wondered nervously what they would *like* to hear me say. Was there any line of attack that would get my point over without causing offence to those present?

On the other hand they must have known what I was likely to say – or they wouldn't have invited me there in the first place – *and* they had already printed the pamphlet. So on February 13, 1993, in the Conference Hall of the Grand Orange Lodge, 61 Dublin Road, Belfast, I took in a deep breath and went for it:

"Hello Belfast. My name's Tom Davies and I'm from Cardiff. You may be upset by a few things I'm about to say, but come along with me just for an hour. Let's see if a few deadlocks can be broken and we can get beyond the clichés to a new form of understanding of ourselves. Just give me an hour."

I laid out my philosophy and beliefs that the Troubles in Northern Ireland were fuelled by the media's love of violence and that all parties in the fighting in Ulster, from the IRA to the UDV, understood that the more they rioted, killed and bombed, the greater the coverage they would generate in newspapers and on television. I explained the relationship that I – and surely everyone else? – could see between the violence and murder glorified in films such as *Rambo, Taxi Driver* and *Death Wish* and the murderous rampages of sick individuals in both the US and the UK.

I suggested that, in the case of Northern Ireland, if the media stopped reporting the violence, the killings would stop, starved of the oxygen of publicity. I asked them to join together to demand that the media stop giving blanket coverage to every outrage – even at the risk of being accused of advocating censorship and harming democracy. (The full text of this speech appears on the Berwyn Mountain Press website.)

"Ulster," I concluded, "is a small society with intimate communications. It is also a religious, compassionate society and it might even be the one society in the world which is so menaced by the mind which I have been talking about. If you found out how to deal with this violence in your media, this society would do nothing less than start healing immediately. Light a Pascal flame this Easter and put a candle in your window. Demand to be told more of whatsoever is beautiful, pure, honest and men of good report."

My Orange audience greeted my speech with a rousing cheer. It may be that they liked it because it was the first speech in the history of the Troubles that didn't blame them for anything (although I noticed that, when the Forum was open to questions, not one of them referred to my speech at all).

Ian Paisley Jr made quite a few interesting points about state-sponsored terrorism; another speaker complained that Ulster Protestants were always being portrayed as "sectarian, bowler-hatted bigots" in the media and yet another got everyone roaring when he referred to the way the Republic "down South" created and still supported the IRA. The very words "down south" kept eliciting the same reaction and they were none too thrilled by the "political bias" of the BBC either.

Between them the speakers gave an excellent insight into Ulster's real problems I thought: they hadn't listened to one word I'd said. Every speaker had a padlocked mind: all they wanted was to repeat the same old mantras and shibboleths, reiterating the long-standing grievances they would carry, fully polished on their chests, to their graves. They were always being portrayed as sectarian bowler-hatted bigots in the media because that's exactly what they were.

No new ideas wanted here. Or anywhere else. We will cling tenaciously to the same old ideas our fathers have clung to forever and this mess is nothing to do with us. No surrender!

After the meeting broke up, Andy Lockhart, commissioning editor of Ulster Television, suggested I should come back and make a film for them. "I'm not saying you're right, but we do need to be listening to what you are saying."

Was this one final chance to get through to the people of Northern Ireland? I told him about my film, *Visions of a Media Man*, and that it had been pulled in Ulster. He hadn't heard of it so I said I would send him a copy and maybe we could take it from there. I sent him a copy and after a few months he replied brusquely: "My colleagues in the current affairs department have looked at the programme but don't feel there is anything there for them at the moment."

I was outraged. Television cameras had been attendant on almost every terrorist atrocity in Ulster for the past twenty-five years. Terrorists put on spurious displays of military strength exclusively for television cameras and set off their bombs in time to catch the prime-time news. In everything they did and thought terrorists asked themselves how would it run in the media. Everyone knew there was a relationship between terrorism and the media. When would it ever be investigated?

Not just yet. The current affairs department in UTV felt there was nothing in there for them "at the moment". They wouldn't even put me up to knock me down. I wasn't being allowed into the Ulster wilderness, not even to cry in it. My ideas weren't worth discussing.

FIFTY TWO

By 1989 my literary career was down a deep, dark hole. Richard Evans at Macdonald returned *Fire in the Bay* for extensive revision. I had included some sword and sorcery sections which he didn't like and, if I was to pursue the Holy Grail theme, I should conceal it as I had with my allegory of the life of Christ in *Black Sunlight*.

I refused and within weeks, my new agent, David Grossman, placed *Fire in the Bay* with Collins who said they loved the story. We used the Collins advance to pay back the Macdonald advance but, although the book was published with real quality and my best cover to date, Collins gave it a nil promotion budget and seemed so uninterested in it I don't know why they bothered to publish it in the first place. They did briefly entertain my *Polly Garter* proposal but, after seeing a few chapters, lost interest in that.

I might have had a successful career as a Welsh novelist if only I had stayed with Richard and listened to what he had to say. Writers should do as they're told, no matter how important they think they are. But the real problem for us scribblers just then was that the economy was going haywire with interest rates peaking and businesses going bust by the minute. People had stopped buying books.

Liz left the *Sunday Telegraph* to work on *Wales on Sunday*, a new newspaper in Cardiff, so the family was together again although Julian and Steffan had just taken off for Australia. Liz took a huge pay cut to be in Cardiff but, as we had no mortgage, we just scraped by.

Then came a phone call.

I had written columns for the *Western Mail* on and off for many years, usually complaints about whoever had been upsetting me lately. After a couple of years I'd run out of steam and bile, give up for a year or so until, reinvigorated by a new gang of "enemies," I'd return to the fray. One of the assistant editors, Peter Jones, wondered if I fancied writing a weekly column and I did this for a year or so before running out of steam. Then Peter called asking if I fancied writing about religion.

The usual practice was that they found a retired vicar, who, for very little, if any, money, wrote this column, often about the meaning of some Biblical text. I certainly didn't want to do that but relished the challenge of writing about religion in a new way so, as I usually do when I'm looking for a new idea, I put myself to bed for a couple of days and lay there looking at the ceiling. In the end I came up with a new concept: a fictional character who lived in a moribund mining village in South

Wales, struggling to relate his faith to the dereliction around him. He would appear as a real character to the readers and sign the column as Caradoc, representing the traditional Welsh conscience and expressing fine ideals such as democracy, morality and the spirit of the Welsh people, the *gwerin*.

He would have the morning-dew passion of the old Welsh preachers, fearless in their attacks on the Devil and resolute in their defence of God and his kingdom. Nothing muzzled them. I picked the *nom-de-plume* Caradoc after the famous Welsh writer, Caradoc Evans, who repeatedly flayed his fellow countrymen. Caradoc would be a stern and powerful voice which, I guessed, the Welsh, particularly the elderly, would love to hear again.

He was going to be a retired warrior of the chapel and I was going to make him very old. This would cause him to be taken seriously by the Welsh who have never had much time for the young. He lived at the end of a terrace in a village where the pit had long closed and the Saturday night drunks urinated over his front door. There were going to be plenty of marauding sheep in Caradocland, kids vandalising everything in sight and, along every terrace, rows of satellite dishes which, in one column, all turned to face Caradoc and shot at him as he made his way home.

Caradoc would be trying to locate God in the real world. Each week, from his pulpit, he would struggle to understand how his community had fallen apart under the onslaught of drugs, crime and satellite television.

I nurtured him into a full-blown Christian warrior. He saw strange visions: of the spirits of his people materialising in the mists of the local cemetery: a bearded man walking into his allotment during a storm or a brilliant angel lighting the grey valley skies. These were but metaphors for my ideas and they were portents, Caradoc suggested, of a God who had not forgotten his people and was preparing the world for the return of the Son of Man.

Would his people be ready? Caradoc doubted it and persistently lacerated them for throwing in their spiritual hand, for falling asleep and giving up in the growing darkness. The Welsh, once the glory of all God's love and dreams, had become a nightmare from which he was trying to awake, but he was there forever raising his eyes to the hills of coal and beholding the coming of the Lord.

He wasn't all doom and gloom, however, and would often send himself up, complaining about his angina and dodgy knees or describing himself as Jurassic Caradoc. He would have some gentle fun at the expense of Mrs Caradoc – as he always referred to her – who was addicted to line-dancing and *EastEnders*.

To my surprise, Caradoc attracted a congregation of something like a quarter of a million every week. With his vivid, furious language and strange visions, he built up a strong following in the three years I wrote the column, particularly in the Bible belt of West Wales. Some of his more fiery sermons were performed by an actor on Radio Wales one Christmas and a website was set up for him which had an organ playing Bread of Heaven when you logged on. His sermons were also collected as a book with SPCK, *The Visions of Caradoc*.

We often believe we choose our careers but more often than not they choose us. It was certainly never even the vaguest ambition of mine to become a professional pilgrim but for the next five or six years, that's what happened.

I had been sober for eighteen months and had started working on a new novel inspired by my old sparring partner Jill Bennett who had killed herself recently after being rejected by her latest lover. But I could see from an early stage that the book was going to cause me almost as many problems as she had. When you came to take a closer look at her sulphurous personality she had scarcely any endearing qualities and, after a hard day's labour, she often emerged wilfully stupid or even downright deranged. There was no balance to almost anything she did and her suicide by taking her "sweeties" had a certain chilling predictability. Would I be able to make her even vaguely likeable? The chances didn't look good.

Then I had a letter from a new, young editor at the quaintly named Society for the Promotion of Christian Knowledge, the oldest religious publishing house in Britain, saying that she had enjoyed my work in the past and wondered if I'd like to write a book for them. We met and I was commissioned to write a book about a summer pilgrimage through England rather like my *Stained Glass Hours*. I would begin in Cornwall and end up on the island of Lindisfarne. It would be called *Landscapes of Glory*.

The fee was a not very charitable £2,000, but it gave me support and some solid work at a time when my literary career was going nowhere. I would attempt to answer such challenging questions as are we still people of faith? Do we still pray? Do we still believe that God has good things in store for us? I would do so exploring the everyday world, setting aside imaginative flights and treacherous passions, reporting on what I discovered.

I bought a small, old camper van, Nipper, which would get me from place to place economically, enabling me to pull into some pub yard at night and clear off early in the morning. The great advantage of a camper van is its mobility and flexibility: if anyone or anything gets on your nerves you can jump into the driving seat and be off in a blink. You don't even have to wave 'em goodbye.

Early in the long, hot summer of 1997 I found myself in a back lane in Cornwall where almost every foot of the hedgerows was bursting with wild flowers. Cabbage whites tumbled this way and that in the sunshine around an old water pump buried in brambles, I wrote in my notebook, clumps of foxgloves rose out of gorse and the outlying fields were strewn with ancient rocks. I found a rackety kissing-gate and picked up the exotic perfume of bluebells. Everywhere birds were whistling. Why did birds always seem so happy all the time? I asked my notebook. Why didn't they get depressed like everyone else?

Over the years I had developed a kind of internal computer which told me when I had harvested a couple of thousand of usable words during the course of a day. Only then would I relax and cook some food in Nipper before settling down for a good night's sleep. An early start followed, barrelling down more lanes, eagerly looking forward to whatever might crop up around the next bend. If it was a person he/she got interviewed; if it was a place, I snooped around it carefully for any revealing details before jumping back into Nipper. Anything complicated was quickly abandoned.

I liked the village of Zennor, particularly the Wayside Museum where I found a garden with spreading palms and gaudy tropical plants. The small church was a delight and, as soon as I stepped into it, I picked up the throb of long years of love and faithful prayer. I always dropped to my knees at the altar rails of such places and made my small contribution to the weave of prayer in the air, asking God to help me in my pilgrim endeavours, that he might show me something pleasing to him that day. Again and again that summer I travelled in the sure and certain belief my prayers were answered. Now that I was sober we had begun to get on well and I had finally started behaving myself.

Cornwall ravished my senses. As I trundled past extinct tin mine and golden estuary, I kept picking up echoes of the land's history, those derelict places where rebellious tin and silver miners were thrown into a pit to cool off; where children were shut inside kilns to cure them from whooping cough; where tin miners were blinded by crude blasting methods, tar was burned in streets to ward off cholera and dense fogs hung in the air as the land hummed in the flame and flood of an industrial revolution. In 1880 this area was producing enough arsenic to kill every man, woman and child in the world. Arsenic was being used to fight the boll weevil in the American cotton crop and, while it was being refined, the sulphur closed down the schools, polluted the surrounding land and even made cows roll over dead.

This huge poisonous industry has long gone, leaving a haunted landscape of strawberry field and plunging waterfall. There were ghost villages everywhere and, down a lane near Redruth, I discovered a genuine spiritual oddity: Gwennap Pit, an ancient mine transformed into a modern preaching arena. It was a small, grassed amphitheatre where John Wesley first formed the soul of Methodism to be followed by various other preachers who assailed "the pomp and vanities of this wicked world". See those crowds coming down those lanes again, in omnibuses and humble donkey carts, moving past blind men and beggars making dolorous appeals to the passing throngs, past the gingerbread and cake stalls, the ladies in their holiday dresses and carrying parasols, the men in their top coats and with their fob watches, all coming to hear a dying man preaching as to dying men. "I shall never see a larger congregation until we meet again in heaven," Wesley wrote in his journal.

And they've been coming here ever since: the Oddfellows, Foresters, Philanthropists and Rechabites, the Methodists, the Baptists, the Congregationalists, the Salvation Army, the Torbay Gospelaires – all of them gathering come rain or shine in this pit to listen to God's holy ordinance that his people be holy too.

I heard of a Lancashire couple nearby who had converted a derelict school into a bright and pretty chapel with its own baptistry. They told me over a meal how they believed God had called them to move down from the north to set up a "house of quiet and healing" here in Cornwall. They had done this completely by faith, first stumbling across this abandoned school and even bidding for it at auction without knowing how or if they were ever going to get the money since they had not sold their own house. "Don't give up," God kept telling them. "Put the fleece out again."

The money arrived within an hour of when it was needed and, during the long renovation, it remained so tight they often had to choose between buying a loaf or a lavatory roll. But they managed it after years of struggle and oh what a calm, uplifting place it was, used by local churches for meetings, retreats or quiet days. "The sun of righteousness shall rise with healing in its wings," it said on one wall.

After I left them I began wondering if their story might be a key to the understanding of the spiritual state of modern England. We had agreed over our meal that we were worried about our children and seemed to be moving towards end times of lawlessness and a demoralised Church. Might it even be that God was setting up such secret places of prayer throughout the land? Could it be that he was making preparatory moves for the end times? These were exciting questions and only the summer would tell if I could come close to answering them.

My next stop was Buckfast Abbey near Dartmoor where I found myself in the company of an odd bunch of retreatants: two beekeepers from Germany; a man who had been living in monasteries for two years trying to decide if he was going to become a Roman Catholic; a Dublin teacher licking his wounds after a collapsed marriage; a man who had been making a film about the abbey for years but didn't seem to have a camera and one who only put his teeth in when drinking but took them out again when he sat down to eat. We spent much of our free time in the Common Room arguing about anything and everything and it was surprising how quickly this anarchic bunch fell into a monastic routine with more rules than a council swimming pool: no talking here, no walking there, no running, do not open this door, keep off the grass.

On my second morning I tagged along with the German beekeepers because they had told me that this was a red-letter day in the bee calendar. The queen bees would fly out of their hives for the first time and mate with about half a dozen drones for two and half minutes each whereupon the drones would fall dead and the queens would return to the hive to begin the long process of reproducing little bees.

It sounded simple enough, but after a long conversation with Brother Daniel, who was in charge of the bees at Buckfast, it turned out that there was nothing simple about them. Bees are a bundle of inherited instincts handed down over fifty million years, Brother Daniel explained. A lot of these instincts (swarming, stinging children and dogs, burglarising weak neighbouring hives and making off with the honey) were anti-social so the Buckfast monks were now busy socialising them and putting them back on the straight and narrow.

Each year they engineered some five hundred virgin queens who were then carefully selected and bred so that they would be nicer, better-mannered and not hang around on street corners in threatening swarms. These bees would not attack children or dogs or go around thieving honey from neighbouring hives. The Buckfast bee would be an uncommonly well-mannered bee, a by-word in civilised behaviour. I loved the idea of a polite, devout Benedictine bee, holy and loving, who began the day with Gregorian chant and worked hard around the clock without thieving from its neighbours.

Exeter Cathedral was a gem, full of space and lacy stonework. A guide, Dr Richard Taverner, made the whole building come alive. The font is always near the door because it symbolises entry into the Christian life. Over there was the last

421

Devon man to die in a duel. This was the statue of a lady with two left feet. Most of the sculptures were puns and that was supposed to be an elephant with the back legs of a horse. Here was the tomb of the forgetful bishop who rode everywhere on a yellow bicycle and once sent a telegram to his wife: "Am in Ilfracombe. Why?"

The summer heat built up with extraordinary intensity and in the Parish Church of St Michael in East Coker I found the grave of Thomas Stearns Eliot, that inspirational Anglican with the pen of intellectual flame. "In my end is my beginning," his epitaph said. "Pray for the repose of the soul of Thomas Stearns Eliot."

A fly buzzed loudly in the cool shadows around the font as I prayed that the old poet's soul was getting on without too much difficulty; that he was at peace and would find time to come and watch over us less talented scribblers with the living example of his disciplined scholarship, the precision of his wordplay and the controlled passion that he brought to everything he wrote.

After I finished my prayer I read *East Coker*, which had been left there for passing pilgrims, almost feeling his soul move around inside me as he took me through "the electric heat" and "surly light" of those surrounding country lanes before he sailed on into a moving meditation on the cycles of life and the way in which we all go into the dark regardless of status or class. The poem is a celebration of English traditions which will survive the multiple betrayals of a modern world.

Heat wave after heat wave rolled over the countryside. Harvest was in full swing in the Cotswolds where huge bales of harvested straw lay on the shorn, stubbled fields. The rock-hard soil was cracked with jagged fissures silently crying out their thirst as butterflies tumbled in the heat hazes above them.

I was staying in Prinknash Abbey in Gloucestershire. The soupy air was difficult to breathe and the monks moved around the halls and corridors slowly like fish in an aquarium. The heat seemed to have taken its toll on everyone. Out in the grounds two men were sweating profusely as they dug a new grave in the clay. They hit a huge boulder which would have to come out no matter how big it was since Brother Giles, the man in charge of graves, insisted on the perfect shape and perpendicular walls. This grave was being prepared for Father Oswald who had died two days earlier, aged ninety-two. He had been a fine and much-loved monk, infirm in his later years and there had been a lot of prayer for his final release. The monks had looked after him with a faithful and tender diligence and he occasionally showed that he was still a fine piano player.

That night I went out to the monks' graves and sat there in the thickening, still stifling twilight. The cemetery was merely a row of simple wooden crosses, most pleasing, you could be sure, to the son of a carpenter who delighted in everything that was simple, modest and humble. Distant sounds of traffic carried in the darkness and bats came snatching insects out of the air.

Father Oswald's body was put in the chapel next day for the full service of the Receiving of the Body. The monks continued conducting their rites of love around the coffin on top of which they had laid Father Oswald's Greek breviary, his silver chalice, his stole and a rosary given him by Father Fabian.

At Compline that night God seemed to draw closer to everyone in the grieving, praying darkness and you sensed that the death of Oswald had brought these monks closer to the deep meanings and truths for which they craved and had given up everything to find. The Gregorian chants were exquisite; the melancholy voices gracefully beautiful. The life of the monastery had entered into the death of Oswald and made itself richer in the process. Like their Master's on the cross Oswald's death had given them more life so that they could live more abundantly.

The following morning Oswald was buried with a full Requiem Mass. Fifty mourners included twenty or so monks, estate workers, a visiting abbot and about six oblates: lay people associated with the order in prayer. The only members of Oswald's family were a nephew with his wife who, you could tell by the uncertainty of their movements, knew little about the rituals of Catholic worship.

The coffin looked as if it was already being burnished by the hands of busy angels in the coloured streams of light of the sun striking the stained-glass windows. At the end of the service he was taken out feet first (ordinary mortals go out head first). The coffin was lowered into the waiting grave beneath the oak and ash trees surrounded by the monks and sprinkled with holy water.

The two men then filled in the grave that had taken so long to dig in two hours flat. By the time they had finished, Prinknash monastery had settled back into its quiet, unvarying rhythm and the angels had long carried up Father Oswald in their arms over Jordan to receive his just and fitting reward.

After several weeks on the road I would run back home to Wales to write up my notes before returning to my journey, picking up the trail of William Tyndale in Gloucestershire or trying to hear again in the ruins of Tintern Abbey, the sounds of those old Cistercian monks.

You do not find God on journeys like this, but you do learn a little about his nature by taking pleasure from what gives him pleasure. You might feel the fullness of his smile as you travel across the Yorkshire Moors which, I was surprised to discover, were first cleared by monks who built their great abbeys there by draining the swamps and irrigating the land. They banished the wilderness forever, introducing sheep and selling the wool in Europe. Monks sculpted those lanes and track-ways; they built the stone bridges and rackety walls to settle disputes over land. They tilled the fields and even planted the millions of daffodil bulbs which explode into acres of shimmering yellow every spring.

In places like these you are reminded that the religious roots of England go far deeper than you imagine; that even the rain here has holy purpose, forever recycling itself through evaporation and cloud, bringing up crop after crop, year after year, in well-tuned cycles of resurrection and death. In the great abbeys themselves you are reminded that most of the inspirational art and architecture in the land has religious roots; that many great artists chose to worship God through their careful and intricate art.

In Hawes in Wensleydale, I met the eccentric Kit Calvert, a rough and ready Yorkshireman, who was spending his time translating the Bible into Yorkshire dialect: "Now it cam aboot; them days at Caesar A'gustus gav oot an order ..." He wore a battered trilby which he clamped on his head as soon as he got out of bed, his boots were unlaced, his clay pipe in his mouth upside down, his braces broken and his gritty face in need of a shave. He was seventy-six and his dog three-legged. On the wall, a good old Yorkshire adage: "Hear all, see all, say nowt."

Faith flourishes by meeting honest, if unusual, people like Kit Calvert; it becomes real when standing on lonely moors or musing through the shadows of an ancient abbey or when sitting on a stone wall early in the morning with a cup of coffee in your hands watching a river gurgling through the mists and noting the dew-jewelled cobwebs pegged out on the arthritic branches of the hawthorn trees.

Wordsworth saw God in the natural world and believed that this world was a vital, formative influence on us. Nature is a life and force in its own right, he said; every flower enjoys the air it breathes. Nature joins its power to the power of the human mind and feeling; nature helps us to see into the life of things.

I do not believe in pantheism but am convinced that we can see and understand many of the attributes of God in the natural world; that, with a sensitive openness, we can detect a lot about his character and personality by travelling through glorious landscapes.

You can no longer ignore the growing spirit of lawlessness in the modern world, of course, even if you are a monk. I was in a shrine, full of flickering candles and the smell of burning incense, when, near the door, I saw a newspaper, the *Daily Telegraph*, lying on the floor revealing a single, stark headline: BOYS, 10, HELD OVER DEATH OF WOMAN. The boys had dropped a lump of concrete off some high-rise flats on to this woman, the report said, and I looked back into the shrine short of breath. How do boys, aged ten, come to do something as barbaric as that? They had to have been indoctrinated by the violence, obscenity, perversion and cruelty that keeps seeping out of our media. Where else would they learn about the practice of such savagery?

Sometimes the nature and roots of this modern evil can reveal themselves unexpectedly, even while on a pilgrimage. I reached the coastal town of Whitby where, just below the Abbey, I had enjoyed St Mary's Church with its rectangular nave full of box pews and irregular galleries built nearly three hundred years ago from sections of ships. There is a three-decker pulpit in which the preacher would take up a level commensurate with the importance of what he had to say. Parish announcements were made from the bottom deck but sermons were always delivered from the crow's nest where the preacher could rake every corner and member of the congregation. No one nodded off when he got up there.

I sat on a bench at the end of the harbour, looking across the moored boats and mud flats at the stone stairs leading up to St Mary's Church among its higgledy-piggledy blackened tombstones. Way out on my left were the sands where Lewis Carroll is thought to have composed much of *Alice in Wonderland*. Captain Cook had lived in a terrace directly behind me. But the main focus of interest in Whitby now is on the bulky, red-haired writer, Bram Stoker, because it was here, in an apartment at number six Royal Crescent, that he began writing *Dracula*. Just along the sea road is a shop, The Dracula Experience, a small, dark museum full of various Dracula tableaux and memorabilia where an actor dressed in a black cape will sweep out of the shadows to put the wind up you, as he did me.

The heroines of the book, Mina and her friend, Lucy, were spending their summer holidays at East Crescent in Whitby and it was in number seven that a lawyer was engaged by Count Dracula to handle the import of a strange cargo, to wit, "fifty cases of common earth".

In that churchyard over there, Lucy, looking for her friend, saw a white figure "with what looked like something dark bending over her". In the setting sun reflected in the windows of St Mary's, Lucy also saw "his red eyes again".

One stormy night, the Russian schooner, *Demeter*, crashed against the Tate Hill pier directly across the harbour here with its dead captain lashed to the wheel and the ship deserted. A huge black dog leapt off the stricken ship and disappeared where the "the churchyard hangs over the laneway to the East Pier". Directly across the mudflats, Mina ran up the hundred and ninety-nine stone steps of the church stairs to find Lucy "sitting with something long and black beside her". In the cemetery itself Dracula, the dread count of the un-dead, took refuge in the unhallowed grave of a suicide buried as "an accidental death".

Thus, sitting here on a bench, it is possible to see, in one single view, the early framework of this influential book that has never been out of print since Stoker's death in 1912 and has been filmed more than eight times. Stoker might have been sitting on this very seat when he wrote those words.

Surely, then, this town with its narrow, cobbled alleyways, must have ominous implications for every single soul in this threatened world and there must be a strong argument that Whitby is not so much another English landscape of glory as a dried-up oasis in a desert of shame. For what else is *Dracula* – alongside Mary Shelley's *Frankenstein* – but another Gothic virus which went on to add further poison the bloodstream of the world's media?

I kept pushing on after Whitby, looking to celebrate stray and secretive beauties like the waterfall buried in a deep wood. It curved upwards slightly before tumbling down the face of a small cliff and splashing into a pool directly below. Every waterfall has its own music, from the merry tinklings of smaller cascades through to the loud chucklings of larger ones to the thrilling bass thunder of the great waterfalls, full of ancient defiance and determination as they trumpet the spectacular news of the marriage between water and gravity. This one had a light, tinkling voice with a background of percussive thunder. Deep within it was a vein of light laughter: the chortling happiness of a man telling a delightful story.

I am sure God displays some of his finest attributes in sculptures of light and movement like this. Every waterfall I've ever seen seems to sing its own pure song of renewal and you can see, by the way the pools below are surrounded by trees, birds and flourishing plants how water remains the source of all life.

The summer looked as if she was finally being lowered into the ground but just as the gravediggers were piling dead leaves on her coffin, something somewhere in the machinery of the planet threw everything into reverse and the sunshine and warmth of a simply gorgeous Indian summer arrived.

I was chugging out of the Northumberland town of Seahouses on a launch to visit the Farne Islands in search of St Cuthbert. The swell of the waves seemed to have imprisoned the sunshine as we approached the stained cliffs of these volcanic islands where grey seals began slipping off their ledges. We disembarked on to a wooden jetty and followed a rough stone path up to the tiny St Cuthbert's Chapel with its beheaded carvings of angels and oak choir stalls.

Somewhere near this spot – no one knows exactly where – Cuthbert built his beehive-shaped cell in 676AD, remaining here until his death in 684AD. He conducted his passionate hours of secret prayer amidst these birds and then there would have been the long, cold nights in his cell with the winds howling at its walls and the seals singing their love songs from their stained ledges in the distance.

But the overwhelming feature of this small island is not a peaceful silence in which we might imagine Cuthbert worshipped God, but the huge and terrifying noise of the thousands of nesting birds, not quite so raucous now that we were at the end of the mating season. The guillemots in particular staged fantastic displays of collective flight in season, taking off from the edges of Pinnacle Rock at the first sight of a boat and fluttering around in a huge black circle before coming back to land, the first bird arriving just as the last bird was taking off.

I stood on that bird-loud headland on that Indian summer afternoon, watching the waves wash over the rocks, trying to picture Cuthbert with his strange and saintly rapport with birds. All at once Cuthbert's shadow rose up out of the sunlight and I almost found myself falling backwards with my hands windmilling and eyes widening. "Better get a move on," this menacing shadow from the National Trust said. "The boat will be leaving in five minutes."

It was always a great thrill to see the splendid causeway stretching across to Lindisfarne, the flat sands massive with their own emptiness, odd pools catching the light as small crabs moved through them, black on silver. Nearby a line of rough poles marked the route of the Pilgrims' Way along which barefoot pilgrims carry a huge cross over to the island every Easter.

When Christ steps back on the stage of the world it will surely be somewhere like this; not to a fanfare of trumpets in a decorated coronation coach but on his own, with a staff and barefoot, following a line of rough wooden poles and to the welcoming fanfare of a couple of stray sandpipers.

The small island was quiet when I got there, licking its wounds and counting its money after an exceptionally busy summer and getting ready for the usual seasonal rites of the Harvest Festival with gladioli and fruit and vegetables in the spruce trim church. With a population of a hundred and fifty, the village is a small collection of stone cottages standing around a sort of square and the traditional priory ruin.

Even on such a small island there are secret places of prayer where you can sit alone, watching small boats in the bay or the strange geometric shapes of the fishing huts, or the reconstructed castle clinging to the rocky summit of a crag – the highest point in the island – or the huge wooden cross atop that steep bank.

There is a sense of deep spirituality here. It keeps throbbing up out of the ground as surely as if it was being created by some angelic generator. This power can enfold you as you sit in your secret place; it can give you a sense of hope and enormous possibilities; it can tell you that here indeed is a place to make a fresh start, where nothing, as yet, is wrong or about to go wrong. Here indeed is a place to dwell in the tides of men.

Blinding optimism is all factored straight into this thrumming spirituality. It's out there in the boats moored on the pebbles; in the outline of the clinging castle and hang-gliding on the drifting holiness of those sea breezes. All you need to do is sit here and let it wash over you. These feelings are so real that you know you can, if you want, reach out and take hold of St Cuthbert's hand, for it was when he lived here that he received the call to become a hermit on the Farnes.

If God does decide to send back the Son of Man, and if his whole army of angels is mobilising and if this return is to take place somewhere secret and holy like Lindisfarne then, yes, a huge part of the country would be prepared and ready. Yes, there are untold secret places of prayer and a large number of people who would not be taken by surprise: they are waiting faithfully in a state of preparedness, holding aloft the glittering candles of their living faith in the encroaching darkness.

That's about all I found out on my summer pilgrimage that year: the skies keep darkening but generally we hold onto our faith which will be our armour if we need it.

FIFTY THREE

Landscapes of Glory was reasonably successful as such books go when it was published in 1996 and the next year saw me set off on another pilgrimage for the same publisher, this time in search of what it meant to be a Celt.

Again I had no battle plan so I began my search by fetching up in Dingle, on the southwest tip of Ireland, where I parked Nipper on the quay. The many flags on the moored boats indicated some kind of carnival in the offing. A few questions revealed that Dingle is one long carnival: with a population of fifteen hundred it has forty-five pubs. That makes one pub for every thirty people. Some were chintzy bars with tasselled curtains and coloured lights but most were nicotine-stained, wood-panelled shebeens with gloomy corners and sawdust on the floorboards, populated by flat-capped old scoundrels ready to tell tall tales at the touch of a button.

The odd feature of these Dingle bars was that many of them doubled as shops. Thus you could get a drink at one counter and buy a pair of shoes or half a pound of margarine at the other. There were pubs that were also butchers' shops and one had a garden centre in the front, a bar inside, a room out the back for selling guns and another for coffins.

I had been teetotal for two years before my visit to Dingle and was enjoying the way my life had miraculously come together after so many years of falling apart. My health was good and, despite my religious adventures, my finances were sound. I was getting on well with Liz and Nathan, with whom I spent a lot of time, a sharp contrast to the way I had treated my other two sons when I was skirmishing around the wilds of Fleet Street. Many of my former newspaper colleagues were dead – often from failed livers – but I was chugging along quite well.

My sobriety had granted me the love and stability of a real marriage and I hoped I had left behind me the sorry days of all those drunken fumblings in strange beds. I had no idea why I had done it, but I did know that, after a few drinks, I was always ready to do it again. That's the nature of drink: it is the great peddler of easily-made – and genuinely meant at the time – promises which, in reality, are illusions; it purports to make you feel better while it keeps making matters worse. Yet everything became possible in sobriety. As long as I never turned to drink again, there was every chance of living a long, fruitful and happy life instead of sinking into a pit of despair like so many actors, journalists and writers I had known. Drink had done for most of our leading Welsh artists, cutting them down years too soon.

Surprisingly then, I ordered a glass of "the black stuff" in one Dingle bar and gained a sharp insight into the nature of Irish alcoholism. Here you drank because everyone else drank. You drank because you wanted to belong to the tribe and not be left out in the street. Drink was the entry fee to the club and its talk.

The lubricant on which half of Ireland is reared if not actually conceived is, of course, Guinness. Many of the men I met in Dingle seemed to live on a dozen or so pints of it a day. Poured with elaborate care, the drink had a thick head of cream atop a long black body with faint white tidal movements swirling around inside it. The bouquet had the aroma of old socks until you took your first sip (which always gave you a nice white moustache you either licked off or wiped away with the sleeve of your jacket). You worked your way down the glass, foaming ringlet by foaming ringlet. A night on the black stuff was like eating a dozen Mars bars and gave you the sleep of the dead. The men claimed it increased their sexual prowess; the women knew otherwise.

The next morning, most of the town turned out for eleven o'clock Mass and the church was packed. The priest spoke well, but I noticed another curious feature of Irish spiritual life: there were quite a few elderly men standing inside the vestry doors, a few visibly twitching with severe hangovers, unwilling to step inside the church but not quite capable of staying away. So they hung around the doors, neither in nor out, and, when the Mass was over, these holy ditherers dithered no more but hastened back to the pubs for another day on the black stuff.

This Sunday, the priest led a procession with a fife and drum band down to the quay where we took part in Dingle's annual Blessing of the Boats. The priest took a lifeboat out into the bay where he anchored and we packed into some sixty boats, sailed out in his wake and were duly blessed as we circled him. Fungie, the famous Dingle dolphin, came out too, leaping from boat to boat in supercharged arcs. He was on a long-term contract with the Irish Tourist Board and people came from all over the world to look at or swim with him if he was in a sociable mood.

That night there was the traditional barbecue for the Blessing of the Boats in the garden of Benner's Hotel where we all stuffed ourselves with steak, lobster and crab washed down with a lot more of the black stuff. Silver cups were presented to the skippers of the best-dressed boats and then everyone danced jigs and reels to a local band. After another misguided flirtation with the Guinness, I was dancing with a laughing, black-eyed woman, but there was no danger of the drink leading me astray again here. A huge hand rested on my shoulder and an even huger voice shouted in my ear: "You be careful, now. You're dancing with my mother."

It was only when I drove my hangover out of Dingle the next day that I realised I had already begun my investigation into the Celts, for surely what I had found in those lively bars was the famous *craic*, that pure and abiding quality of Irishness which had flourished for thousands of years. By this I mean the way they can be devastatingly frank in the face of what they perceive as weakness or softness; the way that, just like the ancient bards, their lips can come alight with scorching sarcasm towards someone who rouses their ire; the way they can dismantle whole theological systems with a string of cuss words and how they fully understand and already know all the secrets that the government is keeping from them.

These Celts knew all about raising hell and the Blessing of the Boats had a peculiarly Celtic flavour in so far as, in the Middle Ages, everything was blessed. The early Celts had a blessing for everything.

The SPCK was hardly going to be impressed, however, by an account of how I got drunk and danced with someone's mother in Dingle and I could see, even at this early stage in my journey, that this was going to be a particularly difficult book to write. The old Celtic values of purity and sustainability; of simplicity of worship and faith; of a return to the supreme values of nature had been undergoing a revival, particularly in America, but they wouldn't be easy to get at in any straight reportorial sense. I would be doing a lot of groping around in distant mists and ruined churches for this one.

My next trip was to the Skelligs, two ragged triangles of rock rising from the swelling seas three miles off the west coast. It was in lonely and inaccessible places like this that the early Celts learned the laws of God. Even to sign up for the original monastery a prospective monk had to know the psalms by heart and recite them, three times a day, out loud, to the winds and the birds.

In winter it was all but impossible to get to the Skelligs even on fine days. Now, in the early autumn, our boat was on its first trip for four days but our skipper, Joe Roddy, had not been happy about sailing. The winds picked up again as we lurched towards the smaller Skellig, disturbing thousands of gannets that rose up and wheeled around our heads in swirling, feathered clouds. With twenty-four thousand birds, this was the second largest gannetry in the world.

We headed for the larger Skellig Michael, named after the archangel. Its massive splintered outline towered over us as we approached. Joe jumped on to the small stone quay and steadied the boat as we scrambled ashore. The seas were deep, black, and some of those waves had travelled thousands of miles after being set loose in some distant depression. We said nothing as we climbed the steep slopes. Here, at last, was the authentic sound of silence broken only by the wash of black waves on the rocks below.

Joe, broad of girth and ruddy of complexion, struggled up the crumbling steps. "This climb never gets any easier," he puffed.

We took another set of steps and, high in the gently squalling winds, found an old stone oratory, a place of worship looking directly out over the heaving sea. We climbed higher and Joe was puffing a lot more when we got to the monastery itself with its six beehive huts, two oratories, lots of weather-pitted crosses and a graveyard where the monks had been buried. The weather had worn the tombstones down to bare stumps and from the smallness of the plot you would never guess how many monks had been buried there.

"We have no records of their daily lives so a lot of what we think we know is pure conjecture," said Michael Grimes, a student from the Office of Public Works on the island. "But we do know that the early Christians were always attracted to the seclusion of island and desert. They believed they should become exiles for Christ."

As he spoke you could sense the ghosts of those flinty, psalm-chanting monks slippering through the winds all around you. Their lives were exceptionally hard and, with an almost continual struggle to find fresh water, they had to barter from passing ships. They offered salted gannets or sacks of feathers. Guillemot eggs or a few puffins were sometimes enough for a barrel of water. None of those monks lasted long. Few reached the age of forty and, when they fell ill, death came quickly and they were buried on top of one another.

When they left in the thirteenth century, the island became a famous centre for pilgrimage and penitence. Pilgrims were expected to do the nerve-racking Stations of the Cross around the jutting rocks and then crawl out and kiss a stone slab overhanging the sea at Needle's Eye. Only one pilgrim fell off and died, but he was apparently an atheist so it didn't matter. Some later pilgrims got carried away and began partying here, said Joe. Offhand I couldn't think of a more inappropriate place for a party but apparently their singing and dancing became so enthusiastic the mainland police had to be called to clear them off.

My quest continued when, on a day of fine drizzle, I got to the Orkneys off the coast of Scotland where the history of the Celts may have begun. Rainbows came and disappeared in pockets of sunshine.

These islands are terrible, bleak places, lashed by rogue winds under weeping skies. At Kirkwall a man told me that they had three months of rain every year followed by nine months of bad weather. The voyage out had been lively, a bounce from one high wave to the next out of Scrabster and a drive along causeways built with huge concrete blocks around the smooth waters of Scapa Flow. The hulls of the scuttled German navy lie here still, many still visible, all rusty now, doubtless dreaming drowned dreams of the old glory days when they stalked the Atlantic and torpedoed our merchant shipping. A patch of stray sunshine marked the spot where a U-boat sank the battleship *Royal Oak*, with the loss of more than two hundred lives.

These wrecks apart, this area might be unchanged since the first day of creation. With three men walking over a mist-shrouded hill, black on grey, towards us, it didn't need too much imagination to see again the movements of the first settlers here, who built their crude Neolithic village on the shore at Skara Brae or put their dead to rest in the burial cairn at Maeshowe, or erected that huge and mysterious henge of free-standing stones in a dandelion meadow which we know as the Ring of Brodgar. The stones were still there, defiant in their preparedness to endure for all time, telling us something of men and women at their most primitive and yet most spiritual, as they set up their personal bridges to distant gods who, they believed, moved through the rainbows and mists around them.

The brilliant and fiery Norse colonised these islands and used them as a base to launch bloody attacks on the Welsh princes on Anglesey. Here we see the origins of Christianity in Britain. As the Norse were sacking Wales, a young nobleman, Magnus, refused to join in the pillaging, staying aboard the raiding ship and singing psalms, if you please. Magnus's head was chopped off: the times were not yet ripe for such revolutionary ideals of peace and love. With his death, these islands acquired their first Christian martyr and the fine red stone cathedral in Kirkwall is named after him.

Irish immigrants pitched up here as well as the odd Spanish sailor who might have survived one shipwreck but was pretty sure he wasn't going to survive another. The Picts fought their way in and, out of this heady Celtic brew, a common faith began emerging which led to the building of one of the first chapels in Europe at Deerness. I stood quietly in the ruin, listening to the ancient silence, under the sheer emptiness of those weeping Orkney skies.

This damp rubble had been one of the first places of Christian worship for the Celts; here they had rooted their lives in the pioneering notions of purity and innocence, making the first connections with a God who was the God of all things. "He lights the light of the sun," Patrick had told them. "He furnishes the light of the light. He has put springs in the dry land and has set stars to minister to the greater lights."

With the aid of such teachings the human, the natural and the divine were woven together in people's minds with a fresh intimacy and a sense of wonder. The river became a place of baptism and regeneration; the mountain a place of isolation and prayer and even the flapping wild geese became symbols of the Holy Spirit, the arm of the power with which God performed his mighty deeds.

The constant and changing revelations of light on these islands would have contained their own spiritual secrets. The Celts believed in the reality of personal angels or heavenly beings who, as emissaries of God, patrolled their assigned territories to watch over the fortunes of believers. You could all but see the wings of massing angels on those misty banks. Stare hard enough and you might spot Michael himself, putting his troops on red alert.

The simplicity of the structure of this chapel in Deerness also told us something of the way in which the early Celts had moved decisively away from the elaborate ceremonies and hierarchies of Rome where everything, even the bridges and triumphal arches in the streets, is about ten times bigger and fancier than anything you have ever seen before. You could fit a hundred of these chapels into St Peter's Church in Rome.

The Celtic faith was always more mystical and a good deal more anarchic than Rome's. On the matter of when Easter fell, for example, the Celts took the view that if the Pope wanted it on a certain date he could have it – they always respected Rome as a holy place – but *they* were going to take a date which better suited their own habits of fasting and sexual abstinence.

In the drifting Orkney mists, we could perhaps see something of the primary colours and ideas of the Celtic Church; not in any great structures but in this rubbled ruin and the seals out there, lolling with their pups on the tide-washed rocks and in the endless carolling of the skylark and the continual downpours which made the fields so lush and green. Faith seeped as deeply into the earth as the rain and we came a little closer to ourselves here; we sensed something of the mystery and wonder of God.

I journeyed on through Scottish pastures, uncovering the mysteries of the Celtic knot in the Great Wood of Culloden and picking up the trail of old Celtic warriors in a priory in Whithorn, Galloway.

St Ninian built this priory in 450AD and it became known as Candida Casa, a sort of early mission house to the Picts, that tribe of warrior Celts who were a constant thorn in the side of the Romans and who fought so hard the Romans called them *furor celticus*. They looked like fierce wood demons in their cloaks and long, shaggy, lime-hardened hair and, whenever their name was dropped in Roman circles, it caused apprehension. Before engaging in battle they sang songs and had a wide range of "horrible and diverse" yells, beating their shields with their swords and they were so determined in battle they would stand up to their necks in water for two days to conceal themselves. These wild men kept the heads of their enemies preserved in cedar oil in boxes and frequently staged raids to steal cattle. If that did not work out they would barter their wives or daughters for cattle. The more we learn about these early tribes who came from the lands north of the Alps, the more unlikely it seems that they were ever transformed into cultured early Christian knights.

I learned about the Celts in the most unexpected places. On Iona I met a man, Arrick, who was a pilgrim guide there. They even had a Celtic website which was maintained by an Anglican minister in Japan, he said, and the Abbey here, with its emphasis on whole salvation, had echoes in Celtic theology which has always united the spacious and small.

Arrick told me that the first Celtic Christians were adept at stirring people to faith, offering society a model of stability in times of spiritual collapse. They were inspired storytellers rather than dry theologians, borrowing the best of the old beliefs and putting their own stamp on them. Their one outstanding gift was the life of the imagination and, as it evolved, the Celtic faith was a means of connecting with God and every aspect of life that had spiritual significance. Their sympathy was always with the underdog.

The Celtic faith, he explained, does not have the ethereal spirituality of the New Agers with their stars, moons and ley lines. The Celtic belief is rooted in the senses, based in nature and all that is fine in that world.

A flock of geese, for example, one of the earliest Celtic symbols of the Holy Spirit, has a seventy per cent greater range than a lone goose. An arrowhead of geese, with each individual taking it in turn as leader, can fly seventy-five per cent faster. Any Church that celebrates such a co-operative effort by using geese as a symbol of the mighty arm of God has a nice eye for their functional practicality. Geese are faithful and pair for life; they look after their young diligently and grieve the loss of their mate.

It was the monasticism of the Celtic Church that provided the impetus to turn Christianity from the faith of an eccentric minority into a giant force that civilised the West.

Words are perhaps the primary Celtic tool and late that autumn, I went in search of our most famous Welsh wordsmith.

I had been to Laugharne many times, but it was a cold day just before Christmas when I called next. On the shore rooks were flapping around a ruined castle. Further up the shoreline was a house perched on stilts and, directly above the house, in a lane, a wooden shed, no more than a small garage, where a poet once sat at a table "in the singing light" and produced a glittering stream of words which charmed the world.

This had been the workplace of Dylan Thomas, the roaring boy on a runaway horse, whose life and work tells us much about the Celt, not all of it flattering. His failings were many and varied. A fat, rather ugly man, he had a Woodbine almost permanently stuck to his bee-stung lips and often a scarf curling around his neck like a long-deceased snake. He was a colossal liar who energetically fostered the myth of a great womanising drunk when most of his affairs were fantasy and, due to a diabetic condition, he could not down two or three pints of beer without falling into a coma. His definition of heaven was to be in a warm bath, sucking a boiled sweet and swigging a bottle of pop while his wife washed his back.

When not writing poetry in his "sea-shaken house on the breakneck of the rocks, high among the beaks and palavers of the birds", he perfected the art of the begging letter. He dispatched a series of agonised missives asking people to lend him money or settle a pressing debt. He often travelled to London broke and hoping to live off women. His one recognised masterpiece was *Under Milk Wood*, a play for voices in which he immortalised Laugharne and created some wonderfully comic characters like the schoolmaster who was always being nagged by his wife and was, in consequence, plotting to poison her; the girl who did it all the time because she liked babies and the woman who every morning shouted her name to the heavens.

On the day of my visit there were already signs of Christmas. The shops were announcing details of carol services, turkey darts shoots and Christmas raffles. Even at midday the light was thin as a Christmas afternoon and the river, swollen by recent rain, shaped and re-shaped the sand and mud banks. Herons stood in pools and, way out on the Pendine sands, gulls wheeled above the stooped shapes of cockle-pickers.

I met George Tremlett, writer and former member of the Greater London Council who, with his fat, genial smile, now runs the bookshop here. George finds the place relaxing; it gives him the peace to write his books. Yes, it is one of the loveliest places in Wales – almost too lovely – where you can still spot the magical dancing images of Dylan's work: the herons "priesting" the pools, the incessant gabbling of the gulls and the nearby St John's Hill. Dylan said he came one day, for the day, and never left. Got off the bus and forgot to get back on again. The insanity rate in the town was so high, he said, they had to lay on a special bus when it was visiting day in the local asylum. He had the usual Welsh penchant for exaggeration.

They buried him in the local cemetery after he died of "alcoholic insult to the brain" in New York on November 9, 1953, and he lies there still beneath a plain wooden cross. The paint on the cross was flaking when I found it and the flowers long dead with just a few plastic roses sticking defiantly up from the mess. It seemed shocking that this grave was so badly tended when his work, thanks largely to the United States, is on the verge of becoming one of the most successful and richest literary estates in the world. In his case death really does have a rich dominion.

Walking back through that Laugharne night and running many of his magical phrases through my mind, I thought I understood how Dylan, like St David before him, would live in the minds and hearts of people in the world for ever. Such men manage to touch our secret places with their visionary splendour; they have the ability to make their own hearts sing love songs to other hearts. Dylan's poetry always had the nature of music – he was incapable of writing a flat line – and you often found yourself moved by it, even when, as is often the case, neither he nor you could understand it.

Dylan once wrote: "These poems with all their crudities, doubts, and confusion, are written for the love of Man and in praise of God and I'd be a damned fool if they weren't." He found the roots of faith in every landscape in which he wandered and, like the old Celtic saints he understood the basic interconnectedness between everything that existed. But perhaps he displayed his full Celtic colours in his love of and use of words. The children playing in the park were "star-gestured" and "innocent as strawberries". The skies were "unminding" (skies always are) or else he was "singing in his chains in the sea". A meticulous craftsman, he worked and reworked his poems again and again, perhaps as many as a hundred times until they came together and, like the Psalmist, he had made a brilliant new song. Perhaps predictably his favourite line in the Bible was: "In the beginning was the Word ..."

The old drunk was still here in these slumbering, cold Laugharne streets, still here in those lace-curtained parlours where the Bible was left permanently open at Revelation; still here in the laughter in the bar of Brown's Hotel; still here in the lonely, brooding chapel and those night breezes rattling the bare branches of the trees.

Hush now and listen out for the pounding of his heart, beating in house after house and pub after pub, beating through the far reaches of this "Bible-black" night, beating steadily as it spins out those words of love and praise which have saved lives – and broken them too.

The Celt was a man of deep passion and multiple failings. The Celt brought his failings to the foot of the Cross and offered them up to a loving and forgiving God who understood them only too well. The Celt intuitively grasped the deep secrets of praise and how the act of worship was beneficial both to the worshipper and the worshipped, the root of a nation's spiritual life. Dylan was a Celt *par excellence*; his life and work will fascinate and torment us for all time.

The poet has always been venerated in Celtic societies, once enjoying an authority exceeding that of the wily old Druids. All Celts were the children of poets and, even in medieval times, the best were sent to schools of poetry where they had to work through the seven grades of the poets' curriculum. A poet could rework landscapes and tame the savage beast; a few well-delivered verses could even bring out blisters on the face of your enemy. At times these poets became such a tiresome rabble, with their rolling rhymes and satirical wordscapes, they had to be "voided from the realm".

So let's beg the Lord and make sure our Rimbaud of Cwmdonkin Drive is comfy in his cold cemetery. Let's further hope that one day they will pass around the collection plate for a nice tombstone on his grave. Or at least accord him fresh prayer and flowers daily, an honour he most richly deserves.

FIFTY FOUR

Caradoc stormed on in the *Western Mail,* in many ways the ghost writer of my unfolding spiritual biography. Faith, I believed, was the only way by which we could invest our lives with any sense or meaning. Faith gave meaning to my visions, with which I was continuing to battle, though not quite so intensely as in the days of old when, out and about as a journalist, I often saw them made flesh in real life, as in Hungerford or Northern Ireland.

Almost every aspect of the media continued to reinforce my isolation from my old work whether it was news footage of riotous soccer hooligans chanting racist abuse in the streets of Europe, or terrorist bombs blowing up buildings, or gangs attacking innocent people in town centres at night. All were presented as something the public needed to know about, but I saw that these images were actively feeding the violence of our times, dragging us into a future when everything would break down. That being so I needed faith to buffer my hardly rock-like sanity.

I'm still not sure why, but in 1994 I again tried to be accepted into the Church. Several years of study and regular prayer in some dusty theological college would screw down the loose bits, I reasoned. I'd already put together a sort of scaffolding of faith with the research I had put into Caradoc's weekly sermons and a theological college would help me brick it up and put some plaster over it.

The warden in charge of ordinands for the Church in Wales came to my home to assess my suitability. I clearly did nothing for him and I can't remember when I last took such an intense dislike to anyone the moment he opened his mouth. The interview lasted fifteen minutes and, having established that I wasn't a regular churchgoer and that I wasn't exactly sure what I wanted to do in the church, if accepted, he left and I never heard from him again. Not even a note telling me to buzz off. If this professional embalmer was in charge of new ordinands you knew why the Church wasn't coming up with any relevant answers to anything. I hadn't told him I was Caradoc although I did not think such an admission would have advanced my cause one iota.

No career in the church for me, then, but my career as a professional pilgrim continued. I was planning my next one, across France and Spain to Compostela, when my heart brought me up short.

At the time we were living temporarily in a flat next to Llandaff Cathedral, waiting to move to a house in nearby Penarth, and I was running a bath when what felt like a large, cold spring uncoiled inside my left shoulder and rolled straight across my chest. I became sweaty and breathless, unsure what was going on. Liz called a doctor and I was packed off to hospital where another doctor listened to my vagabond heart with a stethoscope. He tried a few speculative knocks on my chest and asked if that hurt. I was wired up to an electrocardiogram but not told the results before being put in a hospital bed opposite a white-faced man who sat up, complained he could never get a good night's sleep anymore and died.

They wired me up again the next morning and made me walk on a treadmill. The whole of my left side, from hip to shoulder, was suffused with pain. I saw another doctor, who told me I had suffered a minor heart attack which had left me with angina. It wasn't much to worry about. Everyone had angina these days. I wasn't going to fall off my perch today or tomorrow – how these doctors love their little jokes – and there were plenty of drugs to control the condition. Did he mean control – or cure? He meant control: the only real and certain cure for angina was radical surgery.

I don't think I've ever been as lost or scared as I struggled along the heartless corridors of the NHS for the next year or so trying to get myself fixed. I suffered almost hourly pain down my left side and was unable to climb stairs or hills without stopping frequently to catch my breath. When I did see a doctor, I was always referred to another. The only thing that would sort me out was a bypass operation, I kept being told, but there was a long waiting list for them in Wales and I wasn't nearly ill enough to be shunted to the top. But don't worry too much. A few more heart attacks and you might qualify. You haven't got £12,000 by any chance, have you? Pity. You could be done privately for that: it's what everyone who is anyone is doing these days. The consultants haven't got the time for the poor. That's why our waiting lists keep growing. They're full of poor people. We're not really much bothered about them: they haven't got any money.

My own general practitioner prescribed various pills that gave me headaches of various intensities, and, far from controlling my condition, seemed to make it worse. After a while I managed to badger my local hospital into giving me an angiogram which sent a probe up my groin to take a look around my heart. One of my coronary veins was completely shot and two others on the blink. Only one seemed to be working properly. A bypass operation would re-plumb my heart with veins taken from other parts of the body, usually the legs. But for that I had to whistle up £12,000 which I couldn't. "Don't worry: you've still got that good one, it'll keep you going until we find a way of sorting you out."

Every time I went to the hospital I saw a different doctor, hardly out of medical school, some of them, and I had to explain everything from the beginning yet again since my notes would have gone missing in their prehistoric filing system. I'd seen maybe twenty different doctors before I stopped counting and none of them seemed able or prepared to do anything other than to prescribe more pills. My libido was posted missing, presumed dead, and when I did mention this to one doctor he said that was only to be expected with all the pills I was taking. They were supposed to control your blood pressure and could put a damper on your sex drive. Oh thanks a bunch. You'd think that at least one of my growing list of doctors might have mentioned this rather crucial fact. My sex life was one of the few activities that ever calmed me down.

"You'd be far better off abroad or if you lived in Belfast or Glasgow," one Cardiff specialist told me. "Heart disease in Wales is the big killer but we do almost nothing about it. For poor people, anyway. No other country treats its heart victims like us. We treat our heart victims little better than dogs."

A few years later, my brother, Alan, ended up in the care of this same specialist who gave him much the same speech one morning, explaining that he would have to wait anything up to a year before he could be sorted out and then he might have to travel to England to be seen to. That afternoon Alan discovered that he had private health care through his work and that evening the same consultant rang him at his home offering to perform the operation immediately.

As a journalist for most of my working life I had written many times about the way people suffered from tangled bureaucracy and money-grabbing consultants. Even so, it came as something of a shock to find myself treated like this. I wouldn't have minded so much had I met a doctor who appeared concerned, but they always gave the impression that everything was so hopeless there was no point. There was nothing they could do unless I had private health care. I wrote letters of complaint to whoever I could think of but almost always received no reply.

In the end I gave up, stopped going to see the doctors, stopped taking their rotten pills and only held on to my small puffer to spray the underside of my tongue if my angina caught me short of breath while trying to get up a hill. We had moved to a coastguard tower in Penarth and I was happy there, or at least as happy as anyone could be in my state.

After about six months, sitting in my study one day, looking out over the sea and listening to the seagulls dancing on the roof, I decided that I'd had enough and, rather than sit here waiting for my remaining coronary vein to conk out, I would go ahead with my pilgrimage to Compostela. Liz was absolutely opposed to this but I said that I couldn't stand sitting around here any more and I'd be far happier out on The Road. I might even pick up a cure while I was at it. After all this had often been the point of a pilgrimage. It might even make an interesting theme for the book I had been commissioned to write about the journey.

Thus it was that I got on my way in my new VW campervan and began feeling better as I made my way down through France, pulling over to the side of the road for a nap if I got tired. I drove into Lourdes, a town set apart by its profusion of advertisement hoardings, hotels and tacky shops. The thronging streets spoke of commercial crookedness, headaches without end and I gazed up longingly at the wild freedom of the outlying Pyrenees, huge, dark hump-backed whales frozen there for all time. Down here was a traffic jam and shops piled high with glittering tat.

A closer look at the shops revealed their true horror: the T-shirts, the gilt crucifixes, the plastic holy water bottles, the pious bracelets, the bum-bags, the stamps, the postcards, the medallions, the pots, the pens, the Lourdes dolls, the perfumes, the coloured pebbles and a Holy Mother with a halo of winking lights (batteries not included).

Four million pilgrims a year come here. It is the largest pilgrim centre in the world, bigger even than Mecca. They were milling around me now: a screeching mob of boys and girls in national costume from Zagreb; Breton pastors dangling their rosaries; wrinkled French peasant women dressed in black; shouting Scots from Glasgow; ruddy-faced priests with a weakness for hard drink (Irish presumably); young women from Spain with armfuls of babies; fat Italian mammas with flabby muscles and dancing Catalans from Barcelona ... wave after wave of them, the whole shuffling army of God, come by road, rail or air to pay their respects to a famous place of healing where, in the famine year of 1858, a frail young girl, Bernadette Soubirous, had seen a heavenly vision.

She was out gathering firewood, the story goes, when she saw an apparition of the Virgin Mary in the mist, high above a rock in a grotto. The Lady spoke to the child saying: "Please come here every day for a fortnight. Tell the priests to build a chapel on this spot. Prayer and penitence! Go and drink in the spring and wash in it. I am the Immaculate Conception."

A four-year commission of investigation by the Catholic Church vindicated Bernadette's story and, in 1862, the Bishop of Tarbes and Lourdes issued a decree saying that the apparition had been real and the faithful were justified in believing it. Bernadette died at Nevers in 1879 and was canonised in 1933. Soon this strange place of candles and prayer became unofficially incorporated into the pilgrimage to Compostela.

I made my way down towards the Lourdes basilica where thousands were crushing together around the outskirts of the empty forecourt and the amplified tenor voice of a priest bellowed through the trees. This area around the basilica, the Domaine, was like some huge spiritual fair with different activities going on in almost every part of its thirty acres. Everywhere you looked there was something beautiful – from the trout rising to take insects in the clear river to tray after tray of guttering candles in the grotto where Bernadette had seen her vision.

Somehow the Church authorities had managed to maintain the integrity of the Domaine. There were no shops or advertisements in sight. Green lawns, on which you could not lie or even sit, spread out between high trees with statues of the Archangel Raphael, protector of travellers, Gabriel opening his book and Michael crushing Satan under his heel.

The Procession of the Blessed Sacrament was about to start and the first of a great crocodile of wheelchairs began rolling into the forecourt of the basilica, accompanied by a peal of bells. That tenor voice rose up again and a white drift of nurses swept through the crowd. By now there were some three thousand sufferers in wheelchairs lined up in front of the basilica. They had been struck down and torn apart by some of the deadliest diseases known to man. Faces were deformed, tongues lolled. Backs were hunched and legs but twisted stumps. Some were blind. Others wore hearing aids. Vacant faces stared blankly. But this was Lourdes, this was the last port of them all, and these invalids were in the market for a miracle. *Lord, they whom thou lovest are sick.*

The Sacred Host was held up and another huge prayer rolled up to the gates of heaven. Rosaries rose high in the air. Then a silence fell as the pilgrims' eyes widened with a hope – a terrifying hope – that they be made whole again.

But no miracles were on offer today. The sick and dying were wheeled away to the accompaniment of a sweetly sorrowful gypsy violin. In more than a hundred years of business some five thousand cures have been recorded by the Lourdes Medical Bureau, sixty-four having been pronounced miracles. Most of the cures have taken place during these services and, behind the officiating priest, a small group of doctors waited and observed. *Lord, that I may hear.*

As I stood there in the rapidly thinning crowds I had to consider that I too was a *malade* – maybe not as *malade* as most of them but pretty *malade* anyway – yet, perhaps because of my lack of faith and a history of my own unanswered prayers, I hadn't petitioned God on my own behalf. You'd have thought it worth a five-minute prayer, here in a place of healing, but I hadn't bothered. I didn't know what was the matter with me. Every time I looked at my faith it seemed to get more threadbare, like a garment bought in a charity shop only to fall apart on the first wash. Maybe that warden in charge of ordinands had got it right.

So I just stood there looking up at the Pyrenees, wondering what to do next, when my unformed prayers were answered and I received what I still consider a miracle cure, even if the Lourdes Medical Bureau might have a few problems with it.

I spotted a small figure being wheeled towards me in one of the official blue invalid carriages with a hood and big wheels. I had seen plenty of illness since I arrived but the sight of this small figure hit me across the face like a wet towel. The boy was a wraith with a thin, pointed face and shrunken head, barely any hair, cold dead eyes and blotched skin. There was a dreadful absence of animation about every part of him to the degree that he barely seemed alive. His lower forearms and hands were parchment skin on bone, his fingers tiny and skeletal. Not so much a boy as a disease in a human shape and you knew that this terrible illness, perhaps AIDS, was going to kill him.

After I had recovered from the shock I was left with only one question: why am I feeling so sorry for myself? I've had a full and exciting life, three sons, a good marriage and written a few decent books even if the world hasn't quite caught up with what I was trying to tell it. I had even planted a tree in Israel, fulfilling the ancient injunction that every man should father a son, write a book and plant a tree. And I had almost constantly roamed the world and tasted many of its greatest sights and pleasures.

Yet this boy had never been offered anything but a handful of spit and a bucket of broken glass. He probably couldn't even read a book, let alone write one. He would never know the exquisite joys of holding a woman, never journey much beyond his sick bed. That boy was a vegetable with no future, no present and not much of a past. I had no right to feel sorry for myself?

That boy cured my health problems. My coronary veins remained occluded but, for the rest of my pilgrimage to Compostela, I forgot about them and spent every remaining day of my journey in a sunny good humour, even when the pain in my side was severe and I ran short of breath. I concluded that when I died, I died, end of story. I also decided never again to ask God for anything, but be content to receive whatever he might be gracious enough to offer me in the sunset of my years.

That moment in Lourdes was my greatest breakthrough ever in matters of faith. I had simply handed over my life to the care of God and since then have never had so much as one moment of spiritual difficulty or doubt while God also has faithfully looked after me.

The candlelight procession and evening service that night in the Domaine began in the twilight with invalid youngsters again wheeled up in lines in the quadrangle in front of the basilica which, with the statue of Notre Dame de Lourdes, had been floodlit. The young invalids were pushed by their mothers who, heartbreakingly, knelt behind their carriages when they got to their positions, mutely pleading with the Holy Mother to heal the fruit of their wombs.

A bell rang dolefully. The sun sank behind the Pyrenees. Thousands gathered at the entrance to the Domaine before moving in slow and careful procession down through the trees and thickening darkness, everyone holding up a candle and singing the *Canticle of Bernadette* with the stanzas ending with an *Ave Maria*.

A distant jet speared a vapour trail across the sunset. A few swallows bulleted overhead and, when the night had really settled in, the Domaine looked magnificent surrounded by a moving river of candles which caught everything in a flickering warmth. Occasionally a charred and smoky smell wafted towards you where a candle had burned its holder and been dropped on the ground.

As the procession progressed, the candles seemed to be held ever higher and for a moment it was as if the universe would burst into a spectacular cry of triumph. The purity of those candle flames spoke of the heart of the Christian Mystery, a massed call on the Lord that they whom thou lovest are indeed sick. Now the candles were turning around and around on themselves in huge wheels of fire and as many as sixty thousand people gathered in front of the Basilica to chant the Credo.

At the end of the service I lingered near the grotto after the crowds had gone, feeding off the undoubted power of a century of massed prayer. Many of the huge candles, lit by various pilgrim groups, still glowed over the jagged rocks, making the discarded crutches seem to float in the darkness. The river murmured gently behind me.

This place of candles and prayer was invaluable. As well as brightening up wayward travellers like myself and offering solace to the suffering, it brought the maimed and the sick out into the open when our instincts are to lock them away. We are judged by the way we tend our sick. It reveals whether we are civilised or not.

There in the cold darkness I felt some of the warm pleasure of God that so many of the old and broken of his flock had made their way here in an act of faith. These invalids, with their multiple and horrific injuries, were close to him. They were especially close to his son who knew everything there was to know about pain, the cruelty of rejection and the illnesses that destroy hope itself.

I crossed the Pyrenees in furious rainstorms and continued across Northern Spain, enjoying the Cathedral de Santa Maria la Redonda in Logrono where many storks lived in huge ragged nests amongst its ornamental spires. They made clicking noises like hollow bamboo sticks being knocked together or went off for a spot of angling in the nearby river Ebro.

The somewhat dilapidated condition of the cathedral, which had huge cracks down its walls, was not much helped by the droppings of these storks, whole smelly pizzas of the stuff, full of fish bones and suspicious black lumps. The storks used to leave for the sunnier climes of Africa every November but for the last three years they hadn't bothered to go anywhere at all, preferring to stay put here in good old Logrono.

I happened across an English teacher, Simon Ryan, who told me that the priests had once argued that the storks were ruining the cathedral, dropping their messes on people on their way to confession and generally clogging up the gutters and fouling the roof. When the storks flew off for their winter break they at least had a chance to push the nests off the roof with poles, but now the birds were staying put, the problem with the storks and their young was getting worse. The priests were calling for a full cull which caused an almighty row with radicals calling for a full cull of priests. Storks were rare, but there had always been too many priests, said the radicals.

The radical argument did not prevail and the priests remained unculled. They did occasionally shoot the storks when they thought no one was looking but, for the most part, the birds remained unmolested, snootily gazing down on us from their great nests.

After Burgos I threaded across the *meseta*, one of the main breadbaskets of Spain. Other pilgrims to Compostela wandered across distant horizons in the *meseta* singly and in groups, rather like wildebeest making their way across the savannah. They seemed to be trooping towards the dawn of time with their staves and floppy hats as the pillars of sunlight propped up the edges of heady black clouds. These plains were famous for their shadows of things that were not there. Swarms of locusts had once eaten everything in sight. Villages had been hit by the plague and the many who had died had been buried in still-visible mass graves.

I met a wide variety of pilgrims on the *camino:* a woman with a two-stroke engine attached to the back wheel of her bike to help her up hills; a Spanish family taking it in turns to lead their blind father to Compostela, and a Belgian doing the whole journey by taxi. He had twisted his ankle while walking out of Roncevalles and, as he didn't want to return home, he went ahead of his mates in a taxi, booking hotels or hostels for them and welcoming them with a stiff drink when they came limping in. Dutch courts even ordered delinquents to make the pilgrimage on foot accompanied by a policeman instead of being imprisoned. Only when they returned with their pilgrim passport, the *compostelle,* fully stamped, would the magistrate consider the sentence completed.

Galicia was mountainous, wet and cold and more lines of pilgrims were making their ways along boulder-strewn paths lined with nettles and slithery with cow pats, scratching their heads as they studied their maps or put yet more plasters on blistered and torn feet or merely sat on a damp rock, with mountain mists swirling all around them, enjoying a fag.

The grass was lush, with purple patches of clover telling that same story of lots of rain. Heather mingled with gorse and broom. Chestnut trees surrounded pine forests. You could often pick up the taste of eucalyptus and wild horses roamed distant slopes. Shellfish were on sale in a market and a man was boiling squid in a bucket, the small tentacles flailing in pink bubbles.

I had never been this way before, yet everything about it seemed familiar. The wildness of the place stirred something in my ancestral memory; a sensation impossibly vague and difficult to describe. I couldn't get it into perspective until I got to the refuge at Cebrero, a group of sanctuary buildings high on the top of a mountain, set around a small church, a museum and a huge building with a high, conical thatched roof.

I was back in the land of the Celts. These were the homes favoured by the early Celts and this tiny hamlet, with its marauding chickens and stone church, was like almost any Welsh village stuck in the middle of a rainy nowhere with no visible means of support. Galicia had long been known as the home of Celtic mysticism and perhaps what I had been sniffing in the air were the smells of my own Welsh homeland – the damp, cold chapels; the cockerels strutting along the ash paths; the packs of dogs wandering the streets; the sporadic stuttering of cold rain on a lonely, insecure people who had grown up beneath empty skies and preferred to worship in the open air because it brought them closer to God.

Road signs had even been crossed out and replaced with what looked like Gallego – just as our own Welsh nationalists like to do with English signs when they find themselves with a pot of paint, some spare energy and a free hour.

The huge cathedral in the Playa de Espana in Santiago de Compostela was an eccentric collection of ornamental arches and spires, each one improbably balanced on top of the other and soaring up into the skies of Northern Spain with all the flamboyant panache of a champion flamenco dancer.

The blackened stonework was delicately patterned with orange splashes of lichen and a variety of weeds that grew abundantly in the cracks and crevices. A lot of the exuberant towers also seemed out of true and such was the profusion of balcony, pyramid and sculptured head the whole façade seemed to vibrate like a field of flowers in a light wind. The architectural word for all this is churrigueresque, a word with a wonderful Dixieland strut to it which means an extremely ornate fashion of Spanish baroque architecture.

More pilgrims were crowding in through the Romanesque doorway – the *Portico de la Gloria* – whose roof and walls were amok with many forms of carving depicting everything from the details of the Crucifixion to the Last Judgement. St James himself, looking more than a little fed up, stood on the top of a pillar where there was an impression of four fingers and a thumb left in the stone by the hands of millions of pilgrims over the years. I put my hand in there too, connecting briefly in the smooth touch of warm stone, with all those who had gone before me on the long road of St James. Inside I found the pews full, hundreds crowding the aisles and abandoned backpacks. The Sunday morning Mass for pilgrims was about to begin.

A strange mood of aggravation was in the air. Something to do with frustration between the visiting pilgrims, tetchy and tired after walking for so long to get there, and the local Galicians who regarded the cathedral as their own. One elderly Galician woman told me to beat it with a few sharp jerks of her thumb when I tried to sit in an empty space next to her and, a few rows back, there was an almighty row going on between four Galicians who had taken a pew which had been booked by some young Spanish pilgrims with their backpacks before they went off to have a look around the cathedral. The backpacks had been dumped in the aisle. You can't book a pew with a backpack, the Galicians seemed to be shouting, and the row sucked in other members of the congregation who were shouting at the Galicians for taking the seats of the *peregrinos*. At that crucial moment, a procession of white-robed priests entered the church following a processional cross and the shouting reached new heights although one of the Galicians, who had earlier seemed at the epicentre of the storm, fell to his knees – presumably to thank God for keeping these foreign pilgrim bastards off his pew.

I managed to squeeze in next to a man who, not at all happy about having to move his own backpack and giant staff with his water bottle and scallop shells hanging off it, muttered to himself in deep irritation. I don't think I had ever known such ill temper in a holy place *and* just prior to a religious service. Everyone seemed to be annoyed about something or other and, to make matters worse, the body odour was horrific. This was surely the smelliest, most ragged, most irritable congregation ever to come together to praise the Lord.

Then, in a further bizarre twist, one of the tourists with a video camera followed the procession of priests right up to the High Altar, where he filmed each of the priests as they took up their positions until he was shooed away. This Mass was going to end up as pantomime unless everyone calmed down.

Everyone did calm down when the officiating priest began singing a song of welcome to the pilgrims with sections of the congregation joining in uncertainly. A further speech of welcome was followed by another hymn and a meandering sermon in Spanish about the meaning of the pilgrimage to Compostela. I think.

Next came communion and we trooped up to the altar in a more or less orderly fashion to take our wafer except for, surprise, surprise, that elderly Spanish woman who had given me the heave-ho from the seat next to her, who came barging past the lot of us to get her wafer first before holding up her hands slowly and with exaggerated reverence as if the whole of the service and indeed the cathedral were solely for her.

The tourist with the video camera joined the line of communicants and there was a brief stand-off as the priest held out the wafer and he stood there videoing the priest's outstretched hand. The priest waggled the wafer around and lifted his eyebrows into one question: "Are you going to take this from me or are you going to stand there filming me all morning?"

Moments of confusion followed as we tried to get back into our seats, climbing over backpacks and staves. Then the whole building shook with a heart-stopping burst of organ music. Everyone surged forward as the *botafumeiro* – or giant silver censer — was carried in on a pole on the shoulders of two men. About the size of a Sumo wrestler, it was opened and the incense inside it lit.

Eight men in red robes began hauling the giant silver mass up into the air on an intricate system of ropes. The higher they pulled it the greater its swing back and forth across the transept until, at the peak of its swing, it practically touched the walls on either side. The priests at the altar had moved closer to the arc of the swing, some ascending the pulpits for a better view. The rush of air fanned the burning incense into furious flames. Despite its size, the *botafumeiro* made little sound swishing up into the high shafts of sunshine with long wisps of smoke trailing behind it like a crash-landing Spitfire. Children cried out and covered their eyes. Mouths dropped open. The priests, who had seen it all a thousand times before, smiled.

Traditionally the *botafumeiro* symbolically fumigated the pilgrims after their long, sweaty walk. Somewhat amazingly no one had ever been seriously injured by it, despite the medieval air of those ropes.

The men on the ropes broke its swing and it started getting slower and slower as it was lowered. There was a loud burst of applause when it was finally unclipped and shouldered out by the same two men. The Mass broke up into such an unruly crowd that not even the priests on the High Altar could get out.

You could see, though, that the priests were used to it. They didn't pull faces or mutter about indignities. They knew all about the way this pilgrim Mass attracted the strangest mixture of proprietorial locals, the worn-out and the smelly, the fractious and the merely rude. Priests knew all there was to know about the failings of people especially when at the end of their tether. Priests understood that, for all our fine words and ideals, we are first and last human and perhaps we shouldn't be too hard on ourselves. None of us is a saint even if, in our dreams and fantasies, we may believe we ought to be. We're just pilgrims on the road, more broken than whole.

FIFTY FIVE

$\mathbf{M}$y account of the Compostela pilgrimage was duly written and delivered to my publishers and despite my continuing heart problems I remained cheerful as I tapped away. Then, quite unexpectedly in April 1997, I was asked to report to the new cardiac unit at Swansea's Morriston Hospital where they sliced open my chest, cut out the occluded arteries and knitted in a few veins from my legs. My heart was completely re-plumbed. But if I had felt like death before the operation, it was nothing to how I felt when I came round in intensive care, my chest a mass of bloody stitches. Claustrophobia oppressed every part of me.

Some of the other coronary artery bypass patients (or Cabbages as they are perhaps revealingly called in NHS circles) in my ward told appalling stories about their own delays in being treated. One had suffered a heart attack every week since the previous Christmas. Another had been rushed into his local hospital twelve times and they still couldn't find time to operate. This Morriston cardiac unit, opened only three months earlier, already had a six-month waiting list.

Discharged after five days I returned to my coastguard tower chewing painkillers as I gazed out at the sea, my poor chest looking like something which had been stitched up by Frankenstein's aunty. But within two weeks I was walking freely. The pain in my left side had left and, after five weeks, I started going to a gymnasium, running on a treadmill and pumping iron. I had lost two stone with a low-fat, high-fibre diet and my sex life returned again with a whoosh (or something). I was up to snuff again. There was indeed life after a triple by-pass. Apparently this was one operation that really did work.

My novel-writing career continued in the doldrums right up to the millennium and it didn't look like getting moving again. I put my novel about Jill aside and returned to a similarly complex problem, Dylan Thomas. I intended to present the book as a sort of Welsh *Shakespeare in Love*, hoping to produce a commercial book with film prospects. Dylan's literary estate had become the third biggest in the world after endorsements from Presidents Carter and Clinton; the poet was increasingly popular on American campuses and the fiftieth anniversary of his death was approaching. But no London publisher seemed to be interested in *The Secret Sex Life of Polly Garter* or, indeed, anything else from Wales.

But there did seem to remain a career for me as a pilgrim and the next year I was off again working my way from Berlin to Rome.

My eyes opened on a meadow of golden mist. The dew on the newly mown grass

446

was so heavy you could wash your face in it and, as the rising sun broke through, my mouth picked up the clear taste of autumn. The morning air gave the leaf mould an unusually fresh edge and the fanned leaves on a chestnut tree were wrinkled and brown.

I stepped out of my campervan into a resurrection dawn. There were glittering teardrops of dew in the cobwebs' gossamer tightropes. A gang of blackbirds flew up, all fluttering one way and then suddenly wheeling about. How they managed to avoid collisions only a blackbird could know for sure.

A path took me down to the bank of a broad river, flowing silently among the pockets of ghostly mist. A man was fishing on the opposite bank and I saw the tail of a field mouse twitch in the damp grass. Directly behind me a church spire rose, black on gold, over the trees. That spire might not be the most famous in all Christendom but the church certainly had the most famous door.

A bell rang out over the meadow. This was a quiet and intimate moment with God; a time when our heartbeats became as one. A hot-air balloon floated above the trees: a dusky globe on a sea of gold. At such moments we can twist one of Martin Luther's brilliant metaphors and say that our wickedness is clothed in the merits of Christ, our sins are forgiven as we stand in an autumnal field glorying in the truth of our faith. My pilgrimage to Rome was going well.

People, mostly students, awaited the train at Wittenberg station as I pressed a button on the level crossing to get back into town. A sea captain had told me about the meadow the night before but it had taken me ages to find that level-crossing button in the dark. A medieval calm pervaded the town square that, with its cobblestones and old houses, was as you might have expected it to have been in Martin Luther's time. This calm was at odds with the grey geometry of the smelly fertiliser and rubber factories that you see as you drive in. Nasty whiffs from these industries rode the winds. Before the fall of the Berlin Wall, Wittenberg had been but another arthritic outpost of the old German Democratic Republic.

Many of the shops and offices in the square were already open – Salamander, Commerzbank, Kaufhaus – and another church bell rang out as an old lady on failing legs stumbled past the open-air stalls selling flowers and fruit. You wondered what those old legs had stumbled through in their time, what outrages those shrewd eyes had witnessed. But there would be nothing to upset her on this resurrection morning.

He joined me as I walked down towards the castle church: a bulky, squat figure with a bull-neck, short grey hair and a pugnacious face, not handsome in any formal sense. He had been putting on a lot of weight, largely through drinking too much beer. His wife had been nagging him about it. He had angina, dropsy, piles, a kidney stone and a mysterious swelling of the muscles. Beer helped him live with it, he told his wife, but she wasn't convinced.

We walked past an antiquarian bookshop and a ladies' clothes shop with frilly French underwear in the window. Students, their satchels bulging with books, rode past on bicycles. The streets were largely litter-free but there were the usual drifts of fag ends everywhere. If nothing else the communists managed to teach everyone to smoke.

He was humming to himself when we came to the door of the castle church to which he had once so defiantly nailed his ninety-five theses attacking the sale of indulgences and serving notice on the Pope that the days of ecclesiastical corruption were over. The primacy of scriptural authority over church tradition was a key principle for him which he promoted through a sort of popular journalism. He spoke directly to the people and fully understood the power of publicity. He used crude cartoons to show the difference between papal and primitive Christianity, but his main method of evangelism was through pamphlets and books. He was the first media celebrity, the first to bask in mass appeal and his thoughts became the talk of Germany. The nailing of his theses to the door here was the first great publicity stunt.

We entered the church through the other door and I was pleased I had met him at last. This was a man with a great mind which created important new insights; he was street-wise and could punch his weight and was always prepared to listen to ordinary people; someone who believed in the value of music, beer and laughter; someone who did not advocate literacy merely that people could read the Bible but because he wanted them to read *everything*.

"Avoid sorrow however you are," he wrote. "Except for manifest sins I hereby absolve you of all merriments wherein you may seek comfort, be it eating, dancing, gaming, whatever."

He was one of the first to support the emancipation of women, not only encouraging a group to flee a nunnery but marrying a nun himself. "No sweeter thing than the love of a woman," he wrote. "May a man be so fortunate." Fatherhood was the supreme earthly joy and this most human of men even recommended sexual fantasy as a way of overcoming melancholy. Children were not the sole object of making love, he went on, a great truth which again didn't fill the Pope with much delight when he heard it.

Luther insisted on the inscrutable mystery of the mind of God. Rationality was not one of God's special qualities, he believed, although he admired it in man, saying that it was what made us different from animals. God did "proper" and "strange" works: you never really knew what was on his mind; you could never guess his motives.

It all began in this town, a strange, intense journey to God, at first through books, vigils and prayers, then through intense soul-searching until he finally discovered that the real path to God lay through the heart, ordered by intuition and based on faith. In medieval times the heart was always seen as the key to understanding. I feel therefore I know.

An organist was playing in the castle church as we walked down the aisle and a youth was polishing the pews. Sunshine smashed against the stained glass as sculptures of other Protestant reformers like Knox and Wycliffe looked on. Luther's grave was on the right of the altar with a single white rose in a brown earthenware jug directly in front of it. The grave was quiet this morning but you could still sense the tempestuous fury which had exploded out of that pulpit: a fury of hot passion and diamond-hard words which had swarmed up out of this small German town and blown everywhere, changing the thoughts of the world for ever.

No fury was erupting from the pulpit these days. We stood there looking down on his grave where he lay in a pauper's coffin with the calm of a life fulfilled. I was about to hug him and murmur: "Well done," but a group of chattering schoolchildren arrived and the Great Reformer disappeared in a splash of stained glass light.

I had come to enjoy my pilgrimages for the SPCK. You often lose sight of God in the clamour of society and these journeys (this was my fifth) were always a chance to get close to him again, listen to his voice and sometimes bear witness to his heartbreak.

My days on The Road often brought radiant joys but there was painful darkness too – there often is when God is present – when I struggled with his intractable unknowability. This happened after I left Worms and followed another sunshine autumnal road to the *Konzentrationslager* at Dachau where I pulled up in the car park and the attendant told me the time of the "English" film in the cinema. I walked into the camp across a railway line and passed a high watchtower. The electrified fence was intact and a large blockhouse stood on my left. The main square was the size of ten football pitches and built around a central avenue of poplars. There were no flowers, no colour anywhere and, yes, no birdsong.

They had taken down most of the blockhouses but had reconstructed one with the original lavatories, mess halls and wooden bunks. Four hundred men would have lived in these rooms designed for fifty. Cutlery had to be kept spotlessly clean, a sign said. No mark or spot could be left on the tables or a penalty was immediate and harsh. If anyone tried to escape everyone had to attend a roll-call, a full night and half a day of standing in the square, often in the snow.

"Tolerance means weakness," the Camp Code began with simplistic savagery. "Beware of being caught lest you be grabbed by the neck and silenced by your own methods."

Dachau was the first concentration camp and the prototype for the others. Around two hundred thousand prisoners were incarcerated here, of whom thirty-one thousand died. This former munitions factory became the first training-ground for murder for the SS. Prisoners perished through work and malnutrition. The inmates were mostly Communists, Jews and priests, the latter confined to the *Priesterblock*. The Nazis treated the priests with special venom, forcing them to clear the snow in winter, making them sing German love songs, using them as medical guinea pigs and putting them on roll-calls lasting up to seven hours. Twenty died on one such roll-call as the camp leader preached bizarre sermons to them. "You dunderheads, you sluts, you motorised wild boars. Your Peter and Paul rock will be blown up but our rock will remain as hard as steel."

Martin Neimoller, the Lutheran theologian, was locked up here after he began denouncing the pagan tendencies of Nazism and supporting the Confessing Church. A strong, picturesque personality, he was several times offered release if he would renounce his faith, but turned them down every time.

In the museum was a series of huge black and white photographs with blistering impact. There was a machine-gunner in his watch tower, a suicide tangled in barbed wire, a man hanged from a tree by the wrists, the solitary confinements and the beatings to death. Medical experiments – including infecting them with malaria – were conducted on twelve hundred prisoners. A flogging table with a whip was on display and descriptions of various stages of the "final solution of the Jewish question".

The other visitors to Dachau that day were all silent, far more silent than they would have been inside a cathedral. They too could make no sense of it or find the words which would enable them to talk about it sensibly.

At 11.30am we filed into the theatre where, on wooden seats, we saw a film that portrayed the history of the camp created by the Nazis who called such places "protective custody camps" and used them largely to deal with their political enemies. The inmates, especially Jews who were given the hardest and dirtiest work, were tortured and murdered. When the camp was liberated on 29 April 1945, the Americans had already found a freight train piled with corpses. In the camp itself they found thirty thousand survivors from thirty-one nationalities.

I left the theatre by the rear door and walked the length of the camp compound. I needed fresh, clean air. There was no one in sight and a breeze on the gravel seemed to keen with its own ancient sorrow. I headed for distant church spires in a wood, hoping for spiritual comfort there, but the first building I came across was the crematorium with its high chimney. Fresh flowers sat in the gaping iron mouths of the ovens. You could reach out and touch their coldness. They had once been red-hot day and night.

Across the small yard were the gas chambers disguised as shower rooms. These had never been used and those who were to be gassed – usually the Jews, the chronically sick and the insane – were transported to Hartheim Castle near Linz which had its own murderous facilities.

I retreated in confusion and dismay to the wood. Sun broke through the overhanging pine boughs and I found a large wooden cross with the inscription "For The Thousands Who Have Died". My fragile balance toppled at that point: I crashed to my knees and asked God why? Why did you let it happen? Why didn't you do something about it? Many of these men were your private soldiers and you let them down. You chose to show yourself on earth in the shape of your son – *A Jew!* – the very embodiment of gentleness and love. So what was this Old Testament obscenity about? You could have stopped this in its tracks but there are sides to you we are never going to understand, aren't there? Turning women into salt, flooding the world, levelling cities, destroying armies and then regretting it. Sometimes you don't even seem to understand yourself. How can we be expected to have any sort of love for you when you don't even understand yourself?

We have had two world wars in which millions died and children were murdered in places like this. Why? Where were you hiding your face? You made the world, so surely you could have done *something*. Haven't you heard the news that so many turned against you, emptying the churches and giving up their faith, because of obscenities like this?

I waited for a few answers to my angry questions but none came. A few birds fluttered in the waiting silence. I sniffed, a plane flew overhead, and I turned and looked back into the wood where sunshine suddenly brightened a shadowy clearing. That was all. That cold indifference again; that unwillingness to explain anything.

I awoke on a former lake floor they called the Vale of Spoleto, peering out at a ruined landscape silent under thick mists. Sometimes these mists parted to reveal a glimpse of a ruined building or a line of cedars. A chorus of birds was already singing the psalms of autumn.

This flat vale stretched for miles in every direction and occasionally a jumble of red-tiled roofs or a basilica floated up out of the mists. Over there was the hill town of Assisi which seemed to sit on top of the mists in the same improbable way Venice sits on water. Dark mountains brooded in the distance. My obscured view was made mistier by fires in a nearby field. Farmers were burning stubble and black and grey smoke billowed as if from minor volcanoes. At times I could see barely anything although I once glimpsed the backsides of a few animals clearly on the run from the fires.

All at once, five figures in corded habits moved joyfully along the road on their way towards Assisi where, unless I was very much mistaken, they would beg from door to door before moving on to the next place as pilgrims and strangers, defending the truth of their words with the simple beauty of their lives. You can always recognise these Franciscan fools for God: they are just a rabble of happiness, come to taunt the emptiness of our lives and briefly warm the coldness of our hearts.

They disappeared and I made myself a cup of coffee, knowing that today was going to be fine, perhaps even finer than the fine day I'd had the day before and the day before that.

The sun shone strongly, vanquishing the mists, and a lizard came out on a rock. I shaved in my wing mirror and, just as I was working my way under my chin, I caught a glimpse of someone threading through a nearby vineyard. He might have been a farm labourer except he not so much walked as danced, a little like a butterfly collector leaping about in a meadow in hot pursuit of something rare. I fell in love with him at first sight. Here was ecstatic joy on two legs, someone not only attractive to people in general, but women in particular, someone whom even the animals found irresistible. He cared deeply for all animals and birds, feeding the bees with honey and wine in the winter, making nests for the doves. The only things he found it hard to love were ants whom he thought too frantic, always hurrying around the place and using up too much valuable energy getting nowhere.

I was blowing a bit as I struggled up the steep hills of Assisi. Sullen vendors of useless plastic memorabilia had opened their souvenir shops and were sitting in their doorways. It was in the tiny church of St Damian here that Francis prostrated himself before a painting of Christ and the image spoke to him: "Go, Francis and repair my house, for it has fallen into ruin."

From that moment he was possessed by the fire and certainty of his vision. He never let it go in a life which was profoundly radical and dynamically creative. There *must* have been times when he roundly cursed that vision and wanted to lay it down, but you can never lay a vision down because you have tired of it. Visions are tenacious; they possess all your waking hours. Once seen, they nag and torment and refuse to let you be.

Enslaved by his vision, Francis stripped himself of his possessions and gave them to the poor, though he did keep spending his father's money to build churches and was duly taken to court. Outside the courtroom his father vented his anger at his profligate son in a loud and irate voice. Francis replied with one of the theatrical gestures for which he was later to become famous: he took off all his clothes and flung them at his father's feet. He then had nothing whatsoever and remained in that blessed state all his life.

Later that morning, in the basilica in Assisi, I found a museum full of his relics. His habit was set out in one glass case and made me laugh out loud for it was a scabby old thing which wouldn't have got through an Oxfam door on a slow week, patched with this and that, moth-eaten and full of holes. His sandals were also on view looking as if they had been given to him by a beggar, though in contrast there was a nice, white tunic, his pyjamas.

I explored the golden streets of Rome for three or four days, working through almost every inch of St Peter's and the Vatican museum. Then, early one evening, the air turned chilly and a huge black cloud, swollen with rain, came rolling in over the hills.

Torrential rain brought the traffic to a standstill and forced the moped riders to take shelter under the bridges where they smoked or stood around chatting to one another. Men were walking along the pavements with plastic carrier bags on their heads. Giant puddles swelled up out of the gutters, already blocked by the fallen leaves, and spilled out over the road. A big, bright flower stall with no customers swam into view.

Another roll of thunder, another crack of lightning and buckets of rain sluiced down on everyone and everything. Lightning flashed over the Tiber, briefly illuminating the ornate stone bridges and moored houseboats. There are six million trees in Rome and everywhere leaves rode the racing river like speedy brown coracles. It might have been the setting for another sack of Rome as when the angry Lutherans poured down into the city from the North in 1527, killing half the population. A young man ran down the pavement with his head low and shoulders hunched. A businessman was frantically trying to wave down a taxi with his briefcase.

Down near the Trevi fountain the rain caused so much diffusion you were never sure whether the lights were on or off. Light kept pushing down into darkness and being repelled. Occasionally the very skies seemed to be affected when an iridescent crown of bright gold briefly capped the towers before slipping back into the dripping darkness.

More by luck than design my pluvial travels that night finally brought me to St Peter's Square where earlier in the week I had sat among the crowds at the Pope's weekly audience. Now it was fully rinsed of pilgrims and pigeons. Nothing moved in the pouring rain except an occasional African who materialised from nowhere to offer me an umbrella or a bunch of flowers and disappeared again. It was a fine moment, nevertheless, as I gazed up at the dark silhouettes of the apostles lined up on the church roof like a stone army poised to go on some new crusade. It was curious that the Reformation had been started in Germany by Luther because he objected to the sale of indulgences which had actually financed the building of this great Italian church.

A low-flying plane droned overhead, lights flickering, a stuttering angel wanting to get home to its wife and warm bed. I wanted to get home to my wife and warm bed too and, waiting for the storm to abate a little, finally got on my way.

FIFTY SIX

By 2005 my literary career was dead on its feet. My pilgrimage books were only for sale in religious or cathedral bookshops, meaning they barely sold in double figures, and my payments from the libraries had shrunk to nothing. The big Welsh novels always made me money in Public Lending Right – in the year of its publication *Black Sunlight* made £1,400 in PLR alone – but by now most of my novels had clearly fallen apart on the shelves and were registering few loans anywhere.

I had no luck in interesting any publisher with *The Secret Sex Life of Polly Garter,* my novel about Dylan Thomas – or *The Tyranny of Ghosts,* the novel inspired by Jill which I had finally finished – and I feared my career was going to implode into a life of frustration like that of practically every other writer I had ever met or known. Even writers who have had big successes can find it impossible to maintain them and, despite my eighteen books, I'd hardly had what you might call a successful career. Few outside Wales knew of my work and – even in Wales – fewer had read it. Nevertheless I had started this memoir with no great hope of seeing it published. But I was determined to finish it. This would be my last and final word on everything: I would get it all down and find something else to occupy my time.

My career did briefly wave a hand out of its grave when Carreg Gwalch, a North Wales publisher, agreed to take *The Secret Sex Life of Polly Garter*. It was a well-produced paperback with a scantily-clad Polly Garter astride a German torpedo on the cover and attracted no reviews except the predictable attacks in the Welsh literary magazines. It sold a hundred and fifty copies.

Carreg Gwalch also offered to re-publish *One Winter of the Holy Spirit*, my love story set in the 1904 chapel revival, which they again produced well, with the help of a Welsh Books Council grant, but in its first year, it sold sixty five. I only kept working on this memoir because I had nothing else to do and I could not conceive of life without writing. After writing for three or four hours a day for seven days a week for twenty-five years I *needed* to write and got even nuttier than normal when I didn't. Writing was about the only activity that stopped me worrying about myself.

Then, with my literary career back in its coffin with its eyes closed, yet another publisher came along and nailed down the lid. After several more re-workings and some editorial advice from a friend, Kate Jones, and further work by Don Dale-Jones, I submitted *The Tyranny of Ghosts* to Accent, a new publisher in West Wales of whom I had heard good reports. Somewhat to my amazement, they accepted it within a week of receiving the manuscript.

They said they'd get a reader's report on it which turned out to be overwhelmingly enthusiastic despite saying it needed some severe editing. Would I fix this? I most certainly would and Liz and I went to Tenerife for two weeks where we went through every word carefully on a hotel balcony in the sun.

The manuscript was re-submitted and there followed a silence of two months which was more like the publishing practice I'd been familiar with. Then Bob Cushion, who ran Accent with his wife Hazel, said he'd been looking at my book again and felt that I should cut out the making of the violent film in which the two lovers had become involved. The scenes of street violence should go too. It amounted to the excision of my main theme – a bit like telling Graham Greene his novels were all right but he should take out all references to Catholicism – and, if I felt I couldn't do the cutting myself, as I might be too close to it, he could get someone to do it for me at a cost of £1,600. In the long list of publishing atrocities this was a new one: £1,600 to get someone to slash your book.

I withdrew the book and had now run out of options. I had been fully and finally silenced.

Yet while this was going on, other events which would have a keen relevance to me, were unfolding in the rural wilds of North Wales. Liz's Aunt Dorothy had fallen ill and been hospitalised. She'd asked Liz to look after her affairs so we drove up there to sort them out at her home in Llandrillo, a small village which lies in the folds of the beautiful Dee Valley.

I had never been close to Dorothy, an eccentric recluse and former teacher who would never answer the door unless she could find her wig, which she often couldn't, and whose house was falling apart at the joints because she didn't believe in spending any money repairing it. We visited her in hospital where she was unusually cheerful and positive and went back to Llandrillo to find her house in an even worse mess than I had remembered. Every room was dirty and smelly with all her papers piled up on her writing desk. Cobwebs and dust decorated everything and it looked as if someone had just died there which, in a sense, had almost happened.

Dorothy had recently collapsed on the landing and lain there for a day or so until found by neighbours. Stubbornly, she had refused to go into any sort of care and had practically been dragged to hospital moaning and weeping because she would have to rely on someone else. She valued her independence even more than money or the air she breathed.

As Liz tidied up the house I began flicking though the papers on the writing desk. There were bank statements going back to the Fifties, bonds, National Savings books, stamps, insurance policies, coins, old pound notes, Embassy cigarette coupons…I had always believed Dorothy was eking out her days on the thin gruel of a teacher's pension but these papers were telling a different story. There might have been well over £100,000 in that desk. The house had to be worth the same again.

Within a few months we arranged for Dorothy to be moved to a residential home in Penarth, where Liz could keep an eye on her. We tried, but failed, to sell the house in the state it was in, so we spent a lot of Dorothy's money renovating it.

Running dangerously low on money ourselves, we sold our coastguard tower in Penarth and rented a house in Windsor Esplanade in Cardiff Bay, a few doors from where I had once written *Fire in the Bay*. Dorothy's condition continued to deteriorate and she became blackly pessimistic and upset. Eventually, one morning, we got the call from the care home saying she had died, leaving her estate to us. I looked out at the sun rising on the full waters of Cardiff Bay and knew our lives were about to change completely. It wasn't so much that what was left of her money would affect us as the fact that, if we went to live in Llandrillo, we wouldn't have to spend the money we had made from the sale of our coastguard tower.

We had long been unhappy on the Esplanade where there was clearly a growing rift between the rich incomers, attracted by the redevelopment of the Bay with their expensive but poky flats, and the longstanding docks people who broke into spots of hatred at the sight of every BMW. Our youngest, Nathan, was mugged one night outside the house and that one act made the peaceful calm of Llandrillo very enticing indeed. So we moved up to Dorothy's house while Nathan, following in his older brothers' footsteps, went off to travel around the world.

I also decided to solve my literary problems once and for all by starting my own publishing house with the help of a few friends from my Fleet Street days. *The Tyranny of Ghosts* and this memoir would be given the highest production values with strong promotion. It didn't much matter if the books didn't sell: what did matter was that I could finally tie up my career in a proper, if unprofitable, end.

I felt an enormous sense of relief that I was free from publishers at last. There can't be a writer anywhere who hasn't bitterly cursed publishers and their often weird decisions, usually to do with saving money. Almost all my books had been published unsatisfactorily in one way or another. The paper for the books was often the cheapest, the covers crude and, with a few exceptions, publicity non-existent. But now it was all going to be different: *The Tyranny of Ghosts* was going to get the best of everything.

Luckily I was friendly with Harry Holland, the Welsh Rembrandt, who paints exquisite – and costly – portraits in his studio in the Bay. It is said that he is one of the foremost painters of skin in the world and his work hangs in many major collections including Tate Britain in London, the Metropolitan Museum of Art in New York and the National Museum of Wales, Cardiff. He had been one of the first to encourage me to set up my own publishing house when I had first talked about it over our regular Friday lunches and he had taken a photograph of a young Jill Bennett and painted her portrait from it. In a masterstroke he put a small tear in the corner of one of her eyes which told of the terrifying sadness which finally overwhelmed her and drove her to suicide. What's more, Harry did the portrait and cover as a favour: even with my money I might well have found it hard paying Harry Holland prices.

My main hope was to sell the books from home through the internet by setting up and advertising our own website. At first, we were going to concentrate on Wales and learn from our mistakes before tackling London: some two-thirds of British book buyers live in London.

We knew we were finally on our way when Liz took a call one morning asking to be put through to the Goods Inward department. She said they must have the wrong number but, after the caller explained it was a consignment of books from the printer we had chosen in Dubai, she agreed that it was indeed the right number and he asked if she had a fork lift truck. Two days later, a truck came down our lane, breaking down trees on either side, and unloaded two huge palettes of books into our garage. I couldn't believe how much space fifteen hundred books took up; they sat there like a paper Everest.

A few small but valuable reviews came in – and there was a useful interview on BBC Radio Wales – but I did notice that within a few weeks of our sending out review copies to the national newspapers and magazines at least seven had popped up on Amazon at half price.

Yet even though we weren't selling in any significant quantities we were learning something new and interesting almost every day. With the hit counter from Google Analytics we had a map of the world and every hit put a little red dot on it somewhere. Most of Britain already looked as if it had suffered from an outbreak of measles and we began showing up in America, France, Australia and Hong Kong. Then we had an even stranger run from Florida, Kuwait and the Russian Federation. Thailand and Brussels followed. They weren't buying the book but they were looking at the website and we even knew how long they were taking reading each page. It was a big thrill one morning to see that the *New York Times* had been taking a long look at it. But even after advertising in the Welsh press, with some quotes acclaiming it as the greatest book since *War and Peace*, the Welsh didn't show the slightest interest.

It was a struggle all the way: in the first few months we only managed to move three hundred copies, often at a discount and many for promotional reasons. But it was a start and a year later I had managed to move 600.

In another twist we bought a former butcher's shop, with an apartment above, next to the old town hall in the centre of nearby Bala, a market town eight miles from Llandrillo set on the edge of a lake in the Snowdonia National Park. We opened an art gallery in the shop and turn the apartment into the head office of the Berwyn Mountain Press. I loved Welsh-speaking Bala the first time I walked through it. The farmers auction their sheep there every Thursday and the wide, tree-lined main street is an unlikely collection of pubs, hotels and shops where everyone you come across has a friendly word or smile. I was particularly pleased that our new premises were but a few doors away from the home of the great Thomas Charles, one of those famous Welsh pulpit-shakers who created the British and Foreign Bible Society which first distributed Bibles to the most remote corners of the world.

For a while Thomas Charles made Bala the spiritual capital of Wales and he worked with the other Methodist leader, Daniel Rowland, for more than half a century. When Charles died, twenty thousand people came to his funeral at Talgarth in 1773 and six ministers preached nine sermons.

Early in 2006, we discovered cruising and took a five-week voyage across the Atlantic to the Bahamas and up the eastern seaboard of the United Sates. I found the way America changed throughout our journey up the coast most absorbing, from the high modernism of Miami through to the tangled, sultry drowsiness of Savannah and Wilmington and then to the wide spaces of Philadelphia and on to the bustling dynamism of New York, a city which in many ways had always been the very beat of my heart.

I had returned several times since that golden summer of 1962 when I had caught my first inklings of the power of redemptive love with those ragged-arsed children of the Lower East Side. Here I had also been first signed up for an honours degree in joyous sex with my Swedish girlfriend and been introduced to the world of fizzy ideas in those Greenwich Village parties where we stood around for hours, drink in hands, lips flapping without pause for thought, as we tried to pull apart the existentialist pie in the books of Jack Kerouac or figure out the inherent mysticism of dreams in the films of Ingmar Bergman.

I had come back as a newspaperman interviewing such as Norman Mailer and Henry Kissinger and I was now here again with my wife of forty years, looking up, still goggle-eyed and in awe of all those skyscrapers vibrating above us.

There was one essential difference in the city for this visit, of course, Ground Zero, the result of 9/11 when two hijacked planes had brought down the twin towers of the World Trade Center. Ground Zero was now a big hole in the ground with no activity anywhere when we looked down into it, any development shackled in a welter of municipal argument.

We walked on through Greenwich Village — you always walk in Manhattan, barely noticing the pain in your aching legs — to the Lower East Side where I looked in vain for traces of the old neighbourhood I had once known.

The first time I had come here I had encountered a vibrant slum of high brownstone tenements linked by hundreds of fire escapes; bustling shops with stalls set out on the sidewalks and shoeshine boys busily pumping their elbows on the corners. Kids of all shapes and ages came bundling through the alleyways and sometimes a fire hydrant was set off so that they could all play in the water and cool down in the ferocious summer heat. Most of the stoops hosted daylong parties of music and chatter by the Puerto Ricans, Poles and Africans.

Every doorway was full of life and love but now it was clear from the moment we began walking down Henry Street that all that had changed — the street was full of dead and doomed music with doors locked and triple-locked, windows and washing protected by thick grilles and graffiti aerosolled over every wall space like some new rampant dead weed. The ragged bums with defeated shoulders were still around but whole buildings had been burned and gutted, blocks bulldozed and the sidewalks were so full of holes they might have been recently land-mined.

There *were* people in the park enjoying the fresh spring sunshine with their kids, mostly poor and black, and the one thing we noticed about *all* of them was that they were suffering from extreme obesity; this generation had eaten nothing but junk food and they had all paid for it with their bodies. No one spoke to us as we walked around either, unusual in most parts of America but almost unheard of here in New York.

I would like to say that I again heard the joyful music of my children in that street; that they somehow resurfaced in my consciousness and contrived to greet me as they had every morning on those wild days of love when we took them up through Chinatown or over to the Bronx Zoo or for a trip to Jones Beach.

But I had tracked down Ora Dorsey, my former supervisor at La Guardia project. Ora was one of the great unsung heroines of our time, a woman who had devoted her life to working among the most appalling social casualties. She looked old with grey hair and fingers twisted with arthritis but she had lost none of the necessary mental toughness to work in these parts. The neighbourhood had broken down over the years, she said, and, one by one, I went through the names of my group – even after all these years I remembered all their names – asking what had happened to them. One by one she said that they had either gone missing, overdosed, been imprisoned or – in two cases – murdered. None of them had made it. Not one!

I left her with tears in my eyes. I guess it shouldn't have been too much of a shock had I thought about it, but I'd just assumed they'd all grown up and lived an unhappy life in some dank tenement like everyone else.

Michael Moncrease. Raul Ramos. John Casciani. Harry Dinzes. John Burns. Mandy Westlake. Bruce Pasadov. Michael Jay. Caesar Bell. Gary Harmon. You poor little bastards. You just didn't have a chance.

I'd first learned about love in these baking streets but now I had come back and learned about the death of it. God does indeed give a lot but someone, somewhere, takes a lot away too.

FIFTY SEVEN

In January 2007, with the sounds of New Year celebrations still ringing in our ears, Liz and I flew to Hong Kong to begin a tour of south east Asia, looking for a proper end to these memoirs.

Memoirs don't have a proper end, of course, any more than they can have a proper middle or beginning, but in a strange and positive way, parts of south east Asia had overshadowed and even changed me at key moments of my life. This might seem an odd claim for a Welshman who lives in North Wales but I often had the feeling that I'd been there before, that parts of me had been buried in a few obscure paddy fields; that I belonged there and might even die there.

I had visited various parts of the region for various reasons over the years – and it was in Alor Star in Malaya, after all, that my youth had been ripped apart and left in bits. All my subsequent ideas had begun in that strange Malayan town. What might I find out about myself if I went back?

I began my search in Hong Kong, a city that had taken up an odd position in my life. First built by opium ghosts the city remains the world's biggest exporter of plastic flowers and you could never work out what went on in those teeming back alleyways if you lived to be a million. Even before China took back the city, half the underworld of Shanghai was running everything in those back alleys.

Still as mysterious as mahjong and as complex as the Stock Exchange, the city remains bloody but unbowed by the Reds: this supremely beautiful hussy who'll still give you a rollicking good time as long as she can get her hands on your rapidly slimming wallet. Money has always been the name of the game in Hong Kong: if a bomb took out the middle of Central Road, it would take a dozen billionaires with it.

And they were still at it as wave after wave of workers hurried about their business, gorgeous women in revealing cheongsams, severe-looking policemen with guns and Armani-suited businessmen plotting how to make their second million of the morning. "You can never make enough money," one told me. It was all a million miles from the enduring images of the Boat People which I had carried in my mind all these years.

Liz and I took the cruise ship out of Hong Kong and, as we slipped out of the harbour into the dusk, the myriad coloured lights of the city were flickering on as we stood together on the aft deck. Behind us the stewards were busying themselves in the dining room preparing for dinner and I'd already studied the menu and worked out what I was going to have: smoked salmon and crayfish tails with a caviare dressing, the Gressingham duck with a blackberry compôte and a caramel dessert. But as I anticipated what they would taste like, my memory took me again back to that day in 1980 when I had been out with the Navy welcoming the Vietnamese Boat People on these very waters.

At midday our police boat had pounded out past hundreds of boats huddled in the typhoon shelter of Aberdeen Harbour. Our radio crackled and we spotted a boat on the horizon, no bigger than a small dot in the glittering sea just off Lantau Island. As we approached the long, thin craft it was a shattering sight. There were a dozen on board beneath a patchwork sail. Two were feverishly bailing water out of the hold while a mother sat under a tarpaulin holding two naked babies – one with a terrible rash. The boat bobbed crazily as we cruised up to them and their eyes widened with fear. Our boat was heavily and visibly armed and their heads jerked around worriedly as one of our crew read out the statutory warning in Cantonese that they were trespassing on foreign territory. Two women with full, beautiful mouths were stretched out on the deck, backs of wrists against foreheads, too tired to even be frightened. Two boys were asleep under a sack. The man on the tiller had a lampshade for a hat and all wore ragged clothes.

I gave them beer and cigars that I had brought out with me while our crew provided vegetables and rice. Their surprise and joy at receiving these were unconfined, particularly as they had clearly been half-expecting to be shot. They had done it, they had made it and their throats erupted with laughter. I could only cry as they took the tops off the beer bottles with their teeth and thoughtfully shared them amongst themselves, including the women and boys. It was this spirit of self-help that had got them through one of the most fearful journeys known to man. The men carried their cigars and beer down to the man in the lampshade who remained at the tiller, clearly the boss man. He took the cigar and puffed on it smiling radiantly.

We told them where to go and set off to meet the next boat which had about twenty jammed in it, all in a far worse condition than the previous lot.

On the next boat a woman in great pain was lying in the arms of a man. Her face was white and her hands kept pressing down on her belly while her legs splayed out unevenly. The man fanned her with his cap and every now and then a breeze picked up her thin groans of anguish. A woman poked her head out from beneath a canopy and, on seeing us, patted her hair to make sure it was tidy. They had been at sea for five weeks and had lost their way a few times. They would have been driven out of their homes at gunpoint, stripped of all their possessions and made to take any boat that was available. On the journey they would have been menaced by pirates, lack of water, heat exposure and sea-sickness. Cholera raged on these small vessels and many of the old had died of starvation. Naked toddlers were covered with sores and baked by the heat of the steel decks.

I handed out more beer and cigars while our crew again provided vegetables and rice. One of the deckhands passed over a packet of biscuits which they seemed unsure about until he showed them how to open it. The man holding the sick woman kept imploring me to do something and I kept indicating with my hands that he should stay calm.

We decided to escort this one in ourselves but the captain didn't dare tow it in case we ripped the tiny craft apart. So we pounded on for a couple of hundred yards at a time and sat there waiting for them to catch up. The little boat had two big eyes painted on either side of its prow and, as the sun dipped over the mountain, silent lightning glimmered beneath a low-slung canopy of thick cloud. Other boats darted around us including a hydrofoil taking fat cats for a night of gambling in Macau.

Our engines stopped in the harbour. Night had fallen and the captain switched on a searchlight to reveal row after row of boats tied up to a large pontoon. It was a vision of hell. There were hundreds of people trapped on these boats and our searchlight picked up images each more horrific than the last. One was a floating chicken shed with small brown faces peering out through metal bars. A man was urinating over the side and babies were crawling over sleeping bodies. Dogs sniffed around the decks looking for food.

We pulled away from the boat we had escorted in and our searchlight picked up the man with his sick wife. He was standing up and holding her in his arms, ready to get off straight away. He looked up at me with his tragic, illuminated mouth as if to say "What now?" and I told him they would get off tomorrow, which was almost certainly a lie. He carefully lowered his wife to the deck and smoothed her face reassuringly.

After dinner on the cruise ship we were entertained by a small band before returning to our cabin with fresh cotton sheets on our bed, a fridge full of free beer and Cokes, almost a dozen bottles of various beauty treatments in the bathroom, a lounge chair and a writing desk. The large window peered out on the empty South China Sea where we had been warned to expect monsoons.

Our sheets had been turned down with a chocolate on the pillow and our night things arranged in elaborate floral patterns on the bed. The television had six channels if you didn't feel too sleepy: one giving a continual view of what the captain could see from the bridge and another repeating the lectures if you couldn't quite be bothered to walk the hundred or so yards to the main lounge where they were delivered twice a day. We were looked after by a Filipino butler whose job it was to make sure we never wanted for anything.

I tried to sleep but the Boat People came sailing into the dark waters of my dream in a small craft with big white eyes painted on either side of the prow. I awoke feeling so *ashamed*.

We did sail into a monsoon and a lot of us took to our beds with seasickness. At such times I liked to take to the aft deck and watch the wild waves. I had done a lot of watching such waves in my life, particularly on my early voyages as a young merchant seaman when, fag in mouth, I would spend hours leaning on the deck rail constructing elaborate fantasies about the times when I would become a famous writer wandering the world being chased by an ever-growing series of hopeful, exotic women.

Not that such a blessed situation ever came close to working out and as a writer I seemed to become *less* famous with every passing year, even if I'd always kept at it with the persistence of those waves swelling up before me with a menacing roar before subsiding again like cowardly wimps. That was the thing about waves: their sheer, bloody pointlessness; the way they so often mirrored the patterns of life.

It was odd for me to finally be on the other side of the fence. Where once I was a useless steward who was either getting beaten up or sniffing around brothels wondering if he was ever going to lose my virginity, I was now a fully pampered passenger. Liz reckoned I tipped so well because I was feeling guilty about making it to the other side. Even so I still liked to think that I had a natural affinity with the gutter and was slightly amazed that I had made much progress out of it. I remained convinced I might still end up in some Salvation Army hostel one day, hiding my face away in some meths corner where God couldn't find me.

Yet my greatest pleasure in wave watching was that, in their hugeness and unknowability, they reminded me of God, someone who was there but not there, strong but weak, ready to give you a lift up or even drop you down if the mood took him. Christmas Evans, one of the great old Welsh pulpit bashers, always liked to conjure with storms in his sermons: "The godless must turn out on a dark night full of fear, in winds and storms and raging tempests ..."

There were times when my very soul seemed drenched in this Biblical rhetoric and I still feared God, still believed he might be moved to stretch out a hand and strike me down for being so feckless and stupid.

Seven children are reported to have died worldwide after seeing video footage of the execution of former Iraqi dictator Saddam Hussein, many in "play" hangings that ended in tragedy, it said in the *Borneo Bulletin*, (January 10, 2007).

Television pictures of Saddam's hanging in Baghdad were broadcast globally and a more graphic and grisly bootleg of his execution, shot using a mobile phone, spread like wildfire on the Internet. The latest victim was a twelve-year-old boy who hanged himself in Saudi Arabia. After seeing Saddam's execution he stood on a chair, wrapped a wire around his neck and attached it to a door at the family home.

In Yemen police said two thirteen-year-old boys hanged themselves from a tree in Sanaa. Three days later, two hundred kilometres south of Sanaa, Mohammed al-Razami died when he also attached himself to a rope and found he could not free himself.

In Pakistan police said a boy who tried to copy scenes from the execution video died in a similar manner. Mubasha Ali, nine, hanged himself while re-enacting Saddam's hanging with the help of his elder sister, aged ten. He tied a rope to the ceiling. His father said the children had been watching the video on television and his son tried to imitate the hanging while other family members thought they were playing in another room.

A fifteen-year-old girl from eastern India hanged herself from a ceiling fan after watching the execution. "She said they had hung a patriot," her father said. "She said she wanted to feel the pain Saddam had felt in his execution. She kept watching the scene again and again and didn't take any food on Saturday or Sunday to protest at the hanging."

In America a ten-year-old accidentally killed himself after seeing the video clip on television, the *Houston Chronicle* reported. He tied a slipknot around his neck while on a bunk bed on New Year's Eve. He had watched Saddam's death on the Spanish language *Telemundo* news broadcast, his mother said.

Two days earlier, in Algeria, a group of schoolchildren had hanged a twelve-year-old classmate in a "game" imitating the execution.

Our first port of call was Guanzhou. I had been looking forward to this visit: I had been here before, when it was called Canton, riding around the great city on a bicycle researching *Merlyn the Magician and the Pacific Coast Highway.*

My ride that day had been a great hymn to peace and freedom, pedalling along these crowded roads with the loudest sound being that of thousands of axles stirring millions of ball bearings and the tinkling of bells. At night hundreds of bikes rolled out of the thickening darkness in unwinding circles with white shirt tails fluttering in the breeze behind the cyclists as they sailed past. There was the odd bus or lorry but mostly, in that magical, ball-bearing evening, there were bikes, bikes and yet more bikes.

I stopped at a huge crossroads where a policeman was standing on a dais, alone and distant like one of those tiny mounted ballerinas on a music box. He was busy directing the bikes and, as far as I could see, no one was taking the slightest bit of notice of him. Next to his dais was his own bike, a speedy racing job, presumably for chasing traffic violators.

I turned down a side street where the unmistakable smell of night soil hung in the air. A man with buckets on the end of a long pole came running out of a house to empty the waste into a cart. A girl pushed past with a barrow piled high with char-coal briquettes and on the pavement a man was repairing some shoes while a woman knitted. *Everyone* was busy; they seemed to adore work and I don't think I ever saw anyone sitting down and staring into space.

Those were the days when, on my sacred bicycle, I had rescued myself and what was left of my faith from a deep, dark pit down which I was falling fast. No matter what I did as the diarist on the *Observer* – and there are a few things I'm still not owning up to – I knew I couldn't come to any real harm as long as I stayed on that saddle.

My bike kept me fit, insisted I ate regularly and, after one damaging and bloody collision with railings, made sure I was usually soberish when I was pedalling. There were times when I felt a real intimacy with God too, as when I coasted down the baking hills of Jerusalem or made it through the hell of a Los Angeles dusk.

But the day I returned to Guanzhou I found horror on four wheels. Everything had changed. Where the bike had once ruled, the car had taken over and our small tour bus moved out of one traffic jam only to get locked in the next. The exhaust pipes of lorries belched with black fumes and people sat, expressionless, in the crowded buses. Everywhere you moved you felt you were going sideways – or even backwards – and it seemed unbelievable that the Chinese, so clever in so many ways, had totally succumbed to the rule of the car. They even proudly told us that they were taking positive steps to ease the congestion by banning motorbikes. About thirteen bikes can be parked in the space needed by one car and up to thirty can move in the space taken up by one.

The Chinese had lost none of their enthusiasm for controlling tourists though and, while we were keen to meet the people and perhaps look at the shops or department stores, they were having none of that. Tourists were here to look at temples and, failing that, *tombs*. When in doubt show them a tomb seemed to be the motto of the China Travel Service and, no matter how much you complained, that's what you got. Once I was marched down a tunnel almost a mile long and invited to look reverentially at a brick wall behind which lay someone or other famous in the Ming dynasty.

We had to flog up a high hill to a pagoda that had a good view of the high-rise apartments and traffic-thronged streets of the city. Then it was a memorial tomb to Sun Yat-sen and yet another tomb that had been discovered when the Marriott chain wanted to build the China Hotel. It was like a long tour through Tombs R Us, although we were allowed to visit an orchid garden where the orchids were not in bloom. Lunch was the bland mish-mash you taste when you go to a Chinese restaurant and settle for the four-person set menu, a sure invitation to the kitchen to serve up all the leftover rubbish no Chinese wants to eat.

Nothing had quite prepared us for Saigon with the open crookedness of its taxi drivers, the persistent aggression of the trishaw drivers and the scooters ridden by a people in a raging hurry. Our first taxi driver in Saigon managed to rip us off three times in two currencies for a short trip around a corner; it was almost impossible to shake off pursuing trishaw drivers in the streets, even by running down side alleyways, although that was nothing compared to the city centre traffic where every changing traffic lights signalled a mass charge of motorbikes, the odd car and even odder bicycle, a charge which never seemed to slow up or thin out, whether it be early in the day or late at night. There were supposed to be a maximum of two people on these motorbikes but we often saw three or four or even whole families, many clutching their babies. None wore crash helmets.

The only way you could cross any road was by stepping straight out into the traffic and trusting that they would somehow find their way around you. Such crossings required a good deal of Buddhist optimism. There were apparently men in green uniforms whose function – to escort tourists through the traffic – we only learned after we had left.

We came across a street of art galleries which, on closer inspection, turned out to be places where masterpieces were churned out by the hour, with lines of young people copying Munch's *Scream* or Van Gogh's *Sunflowers* with much the same vivid colours, if not skill, as the originals. Other shops sold the normal profusion of tourist rubbish from Saigon T-shirts to bottled scorpions, butterfly bracelets and wooden carvings, all sold for whatever price you could settle on after loud argument. The only way to win was to start to walk away as if you really meant it.

A drive out of the city to the Mekong Delta the next morning revealed that the

Vietnamese countryside can't have changed much since the war. Thousands were moving along the potholed roads in lorries, pedicabs, bicycles and motorbikes, many with huge loads that looked as if they might topple over at any moment. Handcarts were piled high with items like cages stuffed with outraged chickens but no one seemed in the slightest concerned, not even when they pranged one another. I never saw anyone give a hand signal: it was every man for himself.

The buildings under construction were scaffolded by bamboo, no matter how high they were, and single lengths were often sold by the roadside. Few painted their houses and most of the shops were utilitarian, offering piles of wire, wheels, batteries and spare parts for engines. Every other garden featured a lorry with its insides pulled out waiting to be fixed.

The raw countryside comprised endless square fields of maize and fish farms, every available corner intensely cultivated by peasants in conical straw hats wielding their hoes. Yet this picture of serene rural beauty was destroyed by the piles of rubbish scattered everywhere, on street corners, in gardens and on riverbanks.

At My Tho, we took a motorised sampan across the Mekong and transferred to a smaller boat which took us up a channel in the delta where we were surrounded by the big roots of the mangrove. Large butterflies fluttered through dark spaces.

We were chugging through the mangrove when I felt parts of my old life nagging me again, that I had been here and suffered before. Such feelings made no sense particularly as I had never visited Vietnam although, there again, thanks to the American cinema, I had probably been here a hundred, if not a thousand times, shooting up the natives in Apache attack helicopters to the sound of Wagner, sailing up the river into huge golden burst of napalm with Martin Sheen and even sitting in some backstreet gaming bar in Saigon playing Russian roulette with Christopher Walken. Our imaginations had been assaulted by that war again and again, making us suffer almost as much as the troops who were fighting here.

But there was no gunfire today in the Mekong Delta nor a Rambo killing hundreds of Vietnamese. We took a raised walkway to a farmer's house where we were given a cup of tea and fresh fruit. A little boy took a python out of a box and draped it around his neck: this was offered to us as a photo-opportunity at a dollar a go. He was pulling in quite a few dollars until his big brother came along and took the python off him. A brisk row followed when big brother hit little brother and the boy ran away crying to his mother.

That's the trouble with reality, I suppose. There's never any bloody drama in it.

Liz and I were quite exhausted when we reached Singapore, the Lion City, at the end of the cruise. I found it depressing that this city had changed hardly a jot since I'd last been here. Welcome to Lee Kuan Yew's transistorised, deodorised, air-conditioned state where it was as if some giant had taken a big rubber and carefully erased all colour, shade and interest out of the city's personality.

This was an Orwellian new world which turned up a new campaign or fresh slogan every week. Floss your teeth for dental health. Give drugs the boot. Put your heart into sports. Eat wisely. Exercise regularly and then relax. Give a child a book. Stop at two babies. Save water. For fun and relaxation everyone should have a hobby. Speak more Mandarin and less dialects. In government offices and departments those with long hair will be served last. Those with short hair will be served first. If you ring up for the time you are told it's later than you think.

Infractions bring big fines. Smoking in a prohibited place would cost 500 Singapore dollars; littering another 500 dollars. Jaywalking cost 50 dollars and everyone without exception waited for the little green man on the traffic lights before crossing the road. You could also be fined for shouting loudly in the street, spitting and allowing mosquitoes to breed. One persistent malingerer was asked what he thought of life in Singapore and he said: "Fine, fine, fine."

Possession of more than fifteen grams of heroin, however, would cost you your life.

But there was some accidental humour. In Maxwell Road police station there was a room called "The Excuses Room".

Even as we walked these busy, scrubbed streets I kept catching glimpses of myself as I was when fresh out of university: a youth who'd read too much Jack Kerouac and Henry Miller, unsure about anything privately and sure of everything publicly. And there I was again wandering past the palms and manicured lawns of Collyer Quay, having just been thrown out of Djakarta in Indonesia after President Sukarno's anti-Malaysian confrontation in 1963.

The one characteristic of that whole period with Voluntary Service Overseas, I now know, was an almost savage loneliness. In one bar I had grabbed hold of a taxi girl, who was only there to chat to the punters and keep them drinking, merely because I had *needed* to hold someone, anyone. After I'd been thrown out I'd gone to a brothel where, according to Henry Miller, I could perform a sacred function and achieve the ultimate orgasm with an exalted purity of its own.

In fact it was a joyless screw with an elderly whore. Lovemaking didn't get any more loveless than that and, after I'd finished, I went outside and sat on a wall and, unable to understand anything that was happening to me since my brain was so packed with other people's stupid ideas, those guerrillas forever hiding in the darkness of my mind, always poised to start some kind of trouble. I was unaware of the way my internal passengers were causing me so much grief at the time, of course, and merely cried into my hands, wondering if I could take this for much longer.

I'd no more go with a whore these days than I would play a trumpet in a Chinese funeral band and it seemed strange and even miraculous that I was now in Singapore all these years later with a beautiful wife whom I loved and relied on more and more every day. "There is no more lovely, friendly and charming relationship, communion or company than a good marriage," said Martin Luther.

We didn't hang around long in Singapore — why would anyone ever want to hang around there? — and began making our way up through Malaysia, first on a bus to Kuala Lumpur. So I was finally on the road to Alor Star where perhaps I could take a crack at the one question which had been playing on my mind almost daily for forty years. Had I been touched by God there and told about a coming tide of evil or had it been a nervous breakdown all along?

There was not much to detain us in Kuala Lumpur — the famed Petronas Twin

Towers were, well, high and even up there on Skyway on the 41st floor the view was not spectacular although it gave you a good overview of the city, showing how the brazen modern was clearly fenced off from the decrepit old.

Then it was the night train to Alor Star where, early the next morning, with a great deal of nervousness fluttering in my belly, we got off at the small railway station with a clock on top of the ticket office and a single platform, hardly changed in forty years. I asked our taxi driver to give us a quick tour noting that the town had grown a lot, with many new buildings, although you could plainly make out the old buildings and shops with their archways and monsoon gutters. They didn't knock down the old here but merely built on top of them. The huge bus terminus had been moved out of the main street to the outskirts; the Milk Bar, where I had spent many evenings, removed altogether and many of the local characters gone too: the blind man singing the Koran for one and Ahmad the fag-maker who scavenged the gutters for dibby ends before making big new ones which he sold on. The cinema had closed but, in a nod to the 21st century, Yamaha were staging a loud jamboree in the street, complete with rip-roaring, colourful new motorbikes and loud pop music, trying to interest the local young in their new models.

We signed into the new hotel there and took a stroll over to the imposing Sultan Abdul Hamed College which sat in its large impressive grounds with a sports field at the front, a new sports pavilion and the classrooms themselves set out in a single storey, deserted today because it was half-term. We walked down the main drive and I peered up towards the room in the hostel where I had once lived, writing a book which had exploded on me. The hostel was locked, I discovered with some relief. I noticed as we walked that I had developed a quite noticeable ache all over, a little like flu, but I couldn't quite work out what it was.

We met a few teachers who lived in the school grounds and suggested we came back the following morning when there would probably be other teachers who could fill us in on what had happened since I'd last been here. Later that night Mr Ken Ho, a history teacher, turned up at our hotel showing us some of the school magazines from 1962 onwards. There were school photographs in which I found myself: skinny, wan, looking as if I was about to throw up at any moment, pretty much how I always was. Ken stayed for an hour and offered to give us a proper tour of the school the next morning.

Later that night Liz and I walked around the town and you could make out almost all the old buildings sitting there under the new. The river was smelly and deep, as were the monsoon gutters which had always been full of rats. In essence the place hadn't changed much at all and I was able to work out what that ache was which had got hold of me ever since we got off the train. Even all these years later, and even with my wife, that fearful sense of loneliness and isolation had got to me again, that quiet sadness which had taken hold of me for almost all of my later months here.

I had seen visions here which, in a sense, had gone on to frame my whole life and thoughts; everything had blown up when, as I later realised, I had been forcibly ejected from the fog of romanticism. But might it have been, I wondered yet again as I walked through that Alor Star night, that I had been suffering from extreme loneliness and stress? Had I merely suffered a thumping great breakdown?

There were elements of that period which I had buried: I'd had three separate bits of bad news prior to my mental explosion which hadn't helped. I'd had a letter from home telling me that I had fathered a baby in drunken circumstances in Glasgow, the details of which I could barely recall. The baby had been born in Belfast and taken in by nuns who had arranged her adoption. Only a few days later I'd had a letter from the sociology department of Cardiff University – where I had hoped to return – telling me they didn't want me there. Then the headmaster here had scrapped a play I had long been working on with the sixth formers as being too dirty and subversive – which it was. Some of my "actors" hadn't liked it and complained to him about it.

On top of that I'd been brought up decidedly short by the essays on romanticism which my pupils had produced. What with all the romantic fictional characters I had been creating in my novel, straining on the leash to escape, I was being pressured both from outside and within. Perhaps an explosion of some kind or other was simply inevitable. Too much had been happening to me and none of it desirable.

I am now fairly sure there was no fungus growing out of my manuscript at the start of my visionary sequence and that I had probably merely chosen that as a metaphor for a corrupt system of thought. I couldn't be certain that the ideas of the book had attacked me like a swarm of bees either although I had seen a clear vision of a world under attack by people like me and there was a real moment when I felt a metaphysical force which kept whipping me around like a spinning top.

The Welsh are natural romantics, it is often said: they just can't help it and I suppose I'm no different. Even when I was describing a break from romanticism, I was still romanticising the event, still busy gilding the lily as if the truth wasn't dramatic enough. Yes, that was true.

We went back to the school the following morning where we met Ken Ho and I was relieved when he said that they still couldn't trace a key to the hostel so I wouldn't be able to see my old room. He also gave me a bit of news which convinced me I really didn't want to go in again: when the Japanese had occupied Alor Star they had used the school as a military HQ and many British soldiers had been tortured and killed right there, in my old room.

Instead we were shown around the various new developments in the school, which would be celebrating its hundredth anniversary the next year, and I was presented with an honorary school badge, a school tie and small satchel. Only when we were about to leave did the school caretaker turn up and announce that he could open up my room in the hostel. I still wasn't keen but, after travelling so far and hearing about it all for so many years, Liz insisted we went inside.

It was eerie, almost sickening, as I stepped inside the room where I had once experienced the execution of my youth. I kept swallowing and my brain was bubbling as I looked around the bare, musty walls of the room, empty except for a few metal bunks with no mattresses. The geckos had long gone, I noticed inanely, wondering how long geckos lived. The truth, I guess, is that I don't really have a clue what happened to me in there. I could probably write six different accounts of those wild few weeks and all six of them would have some truth in them.

Ken Ho took us for a tour in the surrounding countryside and that night in our hotel I would have loved to have put down several bottles of wine, if only to calm my brain, only to learn that the hotel didn't serve wine. We could have two bottles of Tiger Beer but would have to sit at the back of the restaurant where we couldn't be seen. It confirmed my worst fears about the place. This was a Muslim society where I would always be an outsider no matter how many doors I knocked on asking to be allowed in. I remembered how everyone had been friendly enough to me here but never, once, had anyone ever invited me into their home.

I was feeling pretty blue, almost desolate, the next morning when Ken Ho took us to the bus station where we caught a coach to Butterworth, which was the mainland stop for Penang. Indeed as I looked out at the surrounding palm trees and rice paddy I was almost, for the first time in my life, convinced that it was not the hand of God which had caught hold of me in Alor Star but probably one big breakdown when my fragile system couldn't keep me together any longer. I was both saddened and purged, realising also that Liz, who always saw everything clearly and had never once knowingly told a lie, had helped me through this here and enabled me to see it for perhaps what it was, rather than what I had always thought it was.

Could it be that all my life's ideas about everything from Northern Ireland to Hungerford were plain wrong? Had all the premises on which I had based my subsequent ideas merely have been drawn from one shattering nervous breakdown? Such conclusions would be very hard to take and live with, particularly as they had inspired almost all my books. I wouldn't be writing anything else after finishing this memoir, I knew. This would be it.

We caught the ferry from Butterworth and were soon on the lovely island of Penang, signing into the Traders, the most luxurious hotel in Georgetown. It was time to relax and I wasn't even worried about the bill which turned out to be almost nothing.

We hung out by the pool for a quiet few days and I thought about my visions, trying to see them with clarity and honesty. When I had calmed down a bit in Alor Star after those weeks when I was bashed from pillar to post, I had caught a bus down here to Penang, needing to speak to the British Council man, Malcolm Dalziel. Penang had always had a soothing effect on me and it was while strolling around these streets that I saw what has always seemed to me a real vision.

As I have already described it, the vision was as if someone was tearing a hole in the selfsame sky above me and luminous cylinders began forming in the ripped patch. These cylinders seemed to be interconnected, revolving slowly at first but then accelerating. Black marks appeared on the cylinders which disappeared and a trickle of fat black drops began falling out of the blue sky, a few at first but then in a quickening torrent. The black rain.

Now, whatever doubts I may harbour about what did happen to me in Alor Star,

I have no doubt at all that this vision in Penang was from God and I described it exactly as it happened. What's more, I have come to admire and even worship that single vision since it seems to me such an exact and brilliant metaphor for a world in violent change; a vision which even manages to subvert all our conventional under-standing of why the world is in such a mess. That vision of the black rain says very clearly, to me at least, that we live in a world where most of our artists, writers and communicators are obsessed with perversion, crime and violence and this obsession is, in itself, leading the world into a growing disorder.

Once we have grasped the simple insight, enshrined in the black rain, we do indeed start seeing the world anew, seeing the world perhaps as God sees it. We can make sense of, say, the recent outbreak of European violence which started in the *banlieue* of Paris after two boys had died when being pursued by the police. This violence burst across France and broke through almost every European border. It was only found to die down again when television ramped down its coverage - not that they have ever openly admitted that. That this violence grew out of television is the one simple answer to its growth when you think about it clearly. Nothing else makes any sense.

Soccer hooliganism remains a growing threat too, cropping up in European sta-dia with a vicious and fearsome regularity, undoubtedly fertilised by the black rain. You can understand the spread of soccer hooliganism once you understand the black rain. But it might take a long time before you can convince our newspapers and tel-evision companies of that, even if some are getting there. They keep insisting they are reporting the world as it is, that they are merely relating the truth which some-how excuses them from any possible consequences attendant on their actions.

The growing knife crime and violence in our inner cities is causing widespread fear and that, too, becomes understandable when you consider the black rain which is pouring relentlessly out of cinemas and television dramas which young kids watch almost all their waking hours. In Bala, where I now live and work, the kids regularly beat the hell out of one another, particularly after having too much to drink on Saturday nights. The chapel under Thomas Charles once reigned supreme here so what has got into them? More than a hundred were at it one recent Saturday night. These young kids – some not even in their teens – were ripping up our history and culture and many of those watching them felt they were watching the end of their way of life. Barely anyone could give a reason for the violent behaviour they were witness-ing. But I could and I was further sure that the spirit of Thomas Charles still haunts these streets with tears in his eyes watching nothing less than the fall of his nation.

I have never set foot in Iraq but would bet my last penny that television is squarely in the middle of the civil war there, seizing on every stray act of violence and feeding all those violent images into every home, motivating an intense and serious people to rush out and take revenge on their neighbours. This is what hap-pened for more than thirty years in Northern Ireland when television news set neighbour against neighbour and, such was the power of the evil involved in the whole process, no one could ever quite figure out what was happening – particular-ly those who were perpetrating it. But everything falls into place within the frame-work of the black rain.

Our Man of Lawlessness, then, firmly straddles the world through these processes although his most triumphant creation must be the Internet which has made all these processes more vicious and intense. On the Net even the mild control on television and print news is non-existent: you don't even have to be in a small group of thugs like the IRA to send out your message. All you need is a camcorder, a gun and a computer and you can engage the whole world in your congregation, telling them of your latest murders and beheadings. On the Net even the all time super-crazies like those who shoot up the campuses get encouragement and a platform. They all get on prime time news in America, a great reward indeed for some twisted nerd who would never achieve anything useful or worthwhile.

When we scrabble around in the dark motives of all these new brand of killers we keep coming up with the same clues: their naked lust for celebrity in their appearances on YouTube even prior to their terrible acts, their conviction that they are expressing new ideas when they are merely mirror men expressing the old, their belief that they are the new supermen punishing the world for not conforming to their sad ideals. One killer in Finland called himself Sturmgeist after the Nordic god who cleansed everywhere with thunder and lightning.

But most of all we find the same clips of the same old films on their personal videos: the excerpts from gangster epics like *The Untouchables*, Michael Douglas shooting his way home in *Falling Down* or Woody Harrelson and Juliet Lewis gunning everyone down in *Natural Born Killers*. Those who shot up Columbine wore trench coats like Keanu Reeves in *The Matrix*. The boy who shot up Virginia Tech filmed himself brandishing a claw hammer like the Korean gangster in *Oldboy* who despatched hundreds with the same weapon. Everywhere the same clues point to the same guilty party, a man of intense and global criminality whose aim is simply to get us all in the end, to leave not one of us unscathed, to drive all our kids rotten with no one ever landing a punch on him *because he is not there*. Except that he is and the rough beast has finally taken over Bethlehem.

Yet if you want to understand his real *modus operandi* perhaps all you need do is understand my story; the way my mind was taken over by the wrong artists when young and, but for the literal intervention of God, would have certainly proceeded not only to make a mess of my life but damage everyone close to me. We are all children of the black rain and only some make their way to shelter from the storm; only a few receive a life-changing revelation even if it didn't seem like that at the time.

The youngsters in Bala are today merely beating each other's heads in: tomorrow they will be killing one another just as happened to my charges on the Lower East Side of New York. And all we will do is stand here wringing our hands wondering what's going on.

This global monsoon of evil is attacking and destroying almost every corner of the world and it can only mean that the terms of St Paul's prophecy on a coming Man of Lawlessness are being fulfilled, that our betrayal is complete and that God is finally preparing the stage for the return of the Son of Man.

The last forty years of my life, I now see, have been a stumbling, often drunken; failing and sometimes successful, search to define and expose the meaning of what I once saw in that clear blue Penang sky. I have often tried to abandon this self-imposed search, but then something will happen to remind me that our Man of Lawlessness is still around and extremely active. I saw him in full swing in Northern Ireland and his fingerprints were all over the Hungerford massacre and the shootings of President Reagan and John Lennon. He remains at his most active and destructive in Hollywood, made all the more evil by the way he is still constantly garlanded with Oscars by a people blind to his very presence. After he was clearly seen in *Rambo: First Blood* in 1982, he was allowed to run out again in *Rambo 4* over quarter of a century later!

But invisibility and elusiveness have remained his key features: he has often made a last minute escape as when the scum of the world's paparazzi, dizzy with the scent of sexual betrayal, tracked down and killed Princess Diana in that Paris tunnel, as well as hindered her rescue, only to then be let off the hook by the drunkenness of the chauffeur Henri Paul. "Without the motorcyclists there would have been no accident," her bodyguard, Trevor Rhys-Jones, who survived the crash said bluntly.

We now live an age of suicide bombers. Their murderous work is perfect for our violence-loving media in every way: bloody carnage spread throughout the world to promote the message of a few extremists. On a more intimate level, up to March 2008, there have been a series of seventeen suicides of young men and women in just over a year in and around the small town of Bridgend in South Wales where I come from. All his features are present in these suicides: the copycat ways of death (all hanged themselves); the desire for celebrity in the "reward" of front-page headlines in national newspapers, lead items on the television news and the transformation of their profiles on internet network sites into virtual shrines. Even many of the parents and the police chief in charge of the investigations have blamed the media which, of course, has shown no sign of culpability, remorse or even change. "We are just reporting the events which have nothing to do with us," they cry as it all happens again and again.

But the most insidious factor in this suicide cluster is the presence of Bebo, the social networking site on the net whose language, "having a laugh up there", and "see you later", together with colourful pictorial tributes, can only - there is no other word for it - romanticise suicide, making it seem an attractive, even desirable release from all problems. Our Man of Lawlessness is alive and well on the net for sure; he has merely changed his abode yet again, leaving everyone blaming everyone else and no one knowing what he looks like. And who could ever really track him down as he makes a further escape on the roads of Grand Theft Auto?

So, in those apocalyptic moments forty years ago, God said it all and left me to work out the full implications of the black rain. I hope I have finally done so with honour and credibility. As a vision with a message it would be impossible to improve. It says everything. It is whole and complete. That's all I know and this is my testament.

END

THE TYRANNY OF GHOSTS
by Tom Davies

A most intense and heartfelt book by our most intense and heartfelt writer. Apart from the lovers, London is the third main character in the book and the story is simply terrific. – Phil Rickman, BBC Radio Wales

A triumphant book which has heart-rending moments as well as splendidly comic touches. What a vivid picture Davies paints of the media in all its excesses and daftness. The cover portrait by Harry Holland is achingly beautiful and, with a bit of luck and a fair wind, this book will be turned into a film which will shake the world. – Herbert Williams

Wales, in Tom Davies, has found a novelist whose books are wonderfully passionate, gripping and red-blooded. The same raw power permeates the whole story. – BBC Radio 4

This novel leaves little to the imagination, though the sometimes provocative narrative is easily digested, as we delve into the minds of two deeply disturbed souls. Though based in the London of the 1980s, it has a highly contemporary feel to it. Tom Davies is an adventurous writer and certainly The Tyranny of Ghosts is a most original work of what we trust is fiction. – Norma Penfold, www.gwales.com

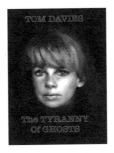

A relentless earthquake of a love story from Tom Davies. Lisa Moran is one of the most famous and unhappy actresses in London who spends most of her time plotting how to acquire yet more money, fame and sex. She meets an odd Welsh writer, Daniel Jenkins, and together they embark on a global love story via Paris, Israel and New York, a journey which slowly becomes a nightmare. The doomed lovers are remorselessly drawn to their own hells in an unfolding tragedy with will live long in the mind of the reader. – Western Mail

Price £15.99 (inc p&p) from:
www.berwynmountainpress.com